Contents

P9-DCJ-922

Acknowledgements & Advisements

Acknowledgments

The 2010 edition of AHA Hospital Statistics is published by Health Forum an affiliate of the American Hospital Association, Richard J. Umbdenstock, President and CEO.

Advisements

The data published here should be used with the following advisements: The data are based on replies to an annual survey that seeks a variety of information, not all of which is published in this book. The information gathered by the survey includes specific services, but not all of each hospital's services. Therefore, the data do not reflect an exhaustive list of all services offered by all hospitals. For information on the availability of additional data, please contact Health Forum, (800) 821-2039.

Health Forum does not assume responsibility for the accuracy of information voluntarily reported by the individual institutions surveyed. The purpose of this publication is to provide basic data reflecting the delivery of health care in the United States and associated areas, and is not to serve an official and all-inclusive list of services offered by individual hospitals.

T R E N D S :

Even as Health Reform Takes Center Stage, Economic Challenges Remain

Hospital Statistics is a comprehensive compilation of data on trends in the hospital field through 2008 based on the results of the American Hospital Association's (AHA) Annual Survey of Hospitals. Overall, Hospital Statistics identifies both long-standing and emerging trends and offers insights into what the future may hold for hospitals.

Caroline Rossi Steinberg
Vice President, Trends Analysis
American Hospital Association

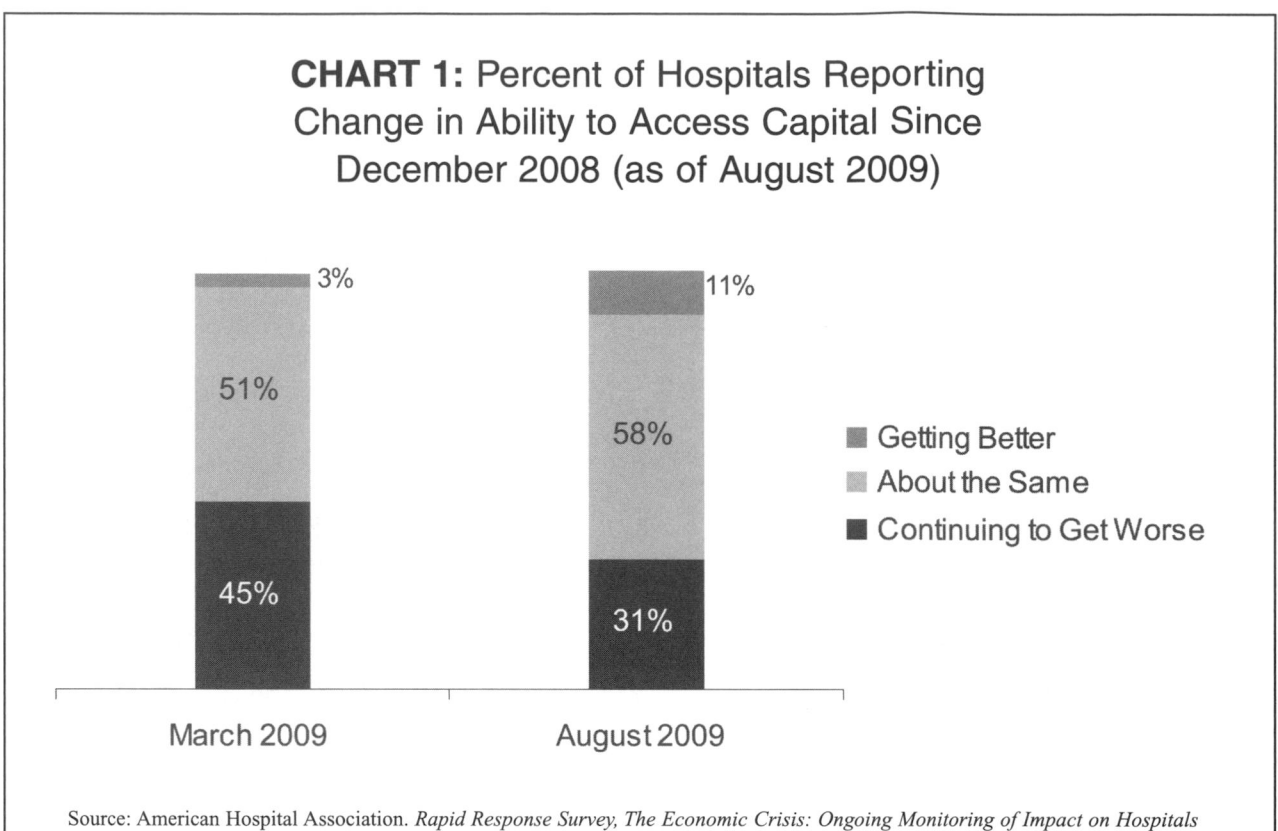

CHART 1: Percent of Hospitals Reporting Change in Ability to Access Capital Since December 2008 (as of August 2009)

March 2009: 3% / 51% / 45%

August 2009: 11% / 58% / 31%

- Getting Better
- About the Same
- Continuing to Get Worse

Source: American Hospital Association. *Rapid Response Survey, The Economic Crisis: Ongoing Monitoring of Impact on Hospitals* (Surveys conducted in March 2009 and August 2009).

With the national spotlight squarely focused on health care reform, the impact of the economy on the country's health care system has moved into the background but still bears watching closely. While economists point to signs of recovery, most still believe that improvement will be slow especially with respect to employment and state budget deficits; some expect setbacks along the way. Data from the 2008 AHA Annual Survey – which would have only picked up the very beginnings of the economic crisis – show a marked deterioration in the financial health of hospitals. Data from subsequent AHA surveys in 2009 indicate challenges continue.

Access to Capital Constrained

The collapse of the housing market had ramifications for hospitals in the early part of 2008 as capital markets were rattled. Hospitals saw variable interest rates skyrocket and sources of borrowing evaporate. By December, nine out of 10 hospitals reported that their ability to access tax-exempt bonds – the most important source of external capital for most hospitals – was severely constrained or non-existent.[1] Hospitals also rely on borrowing to meet day-to-day obligations because payment often lags care delivery. This type of capital became more expensive and more difficult to obtain as well.

By December 2008, nearly half of all hospitals surveyed had delayed capital improvements or even stopped some projects already in progress.[2] While the 2009 *American Recovery and Reinvestment Act* had some provisions beneficial to hospitals, few hospitals reported

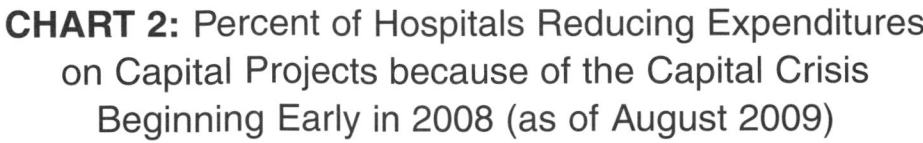

CHART 2: Percent of Hospitals Reducing Expenditures on Capital Projects because of the Capital Crisis Beginning Early in 2008 (as of August 2009)

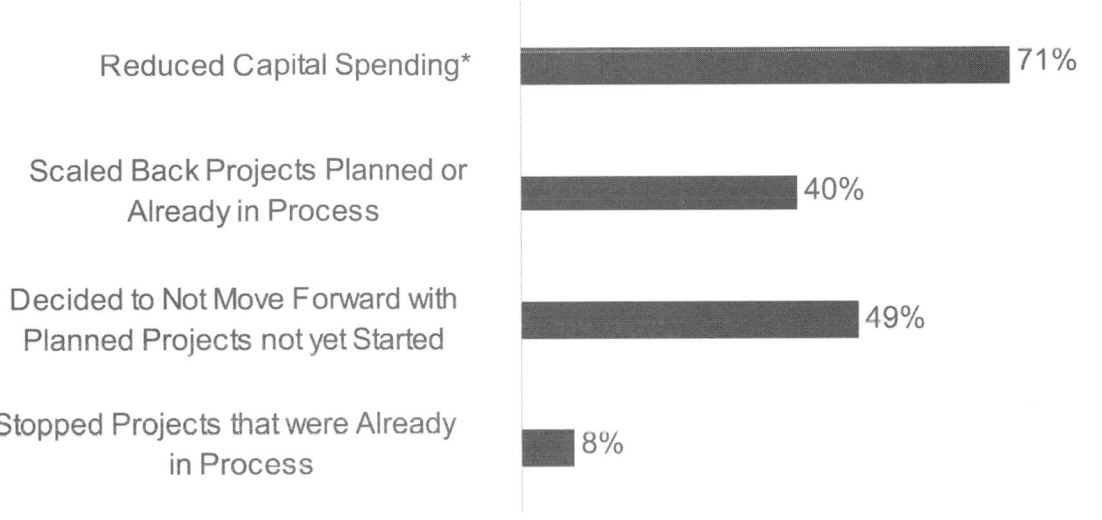

Source: American Hospital Association. *Rapid Response Survey, The Economic Crisis: Ongoing Monitoring of Impact on Hospitals* (Survey conducted in August 2009).
*Includes any hospital reporting that it had scaled back, decided not to move forward with or stopped projects planned or already in process.

an improvement in the capital situation by the end of the first quarter of 2009 and only slightly more reported improvement as of August (Chart 1).

In response, the majority of hospitals cut capital spending for facility upgrades, clinical technology and/or information technology (Chart 2). These projects include renovating and updating aging facilities, expanding clinical technology available to the communities served or expanding access to existing services. The continued difficulties in borrowing are particularly worrisome as hospitals scramble to invest in information technology to qualify as "meaningful users" to obtain the add-on Medicare and Medicaid payments for

information technology authorized under the *American Recovery and Reinvestment Act*.

Hospitals Face Loss of Non-operating Income and Shrunken Reserves

Access to outside capital was only part of the reason hospitals were reluctant to make investments. The precipitous decline in the stock market drove down the value of reserves and turned non-operating gains to losses for the year. Also, many hospitals saw a drop in charitable donations. The 2008 aggregate total margin for community hospitals plummeted to its lowest level in more than 25 years (Chart 3). Hospitals tradition-ally rely on reserves to fund capital projects and income from investments to help cover underfunding from

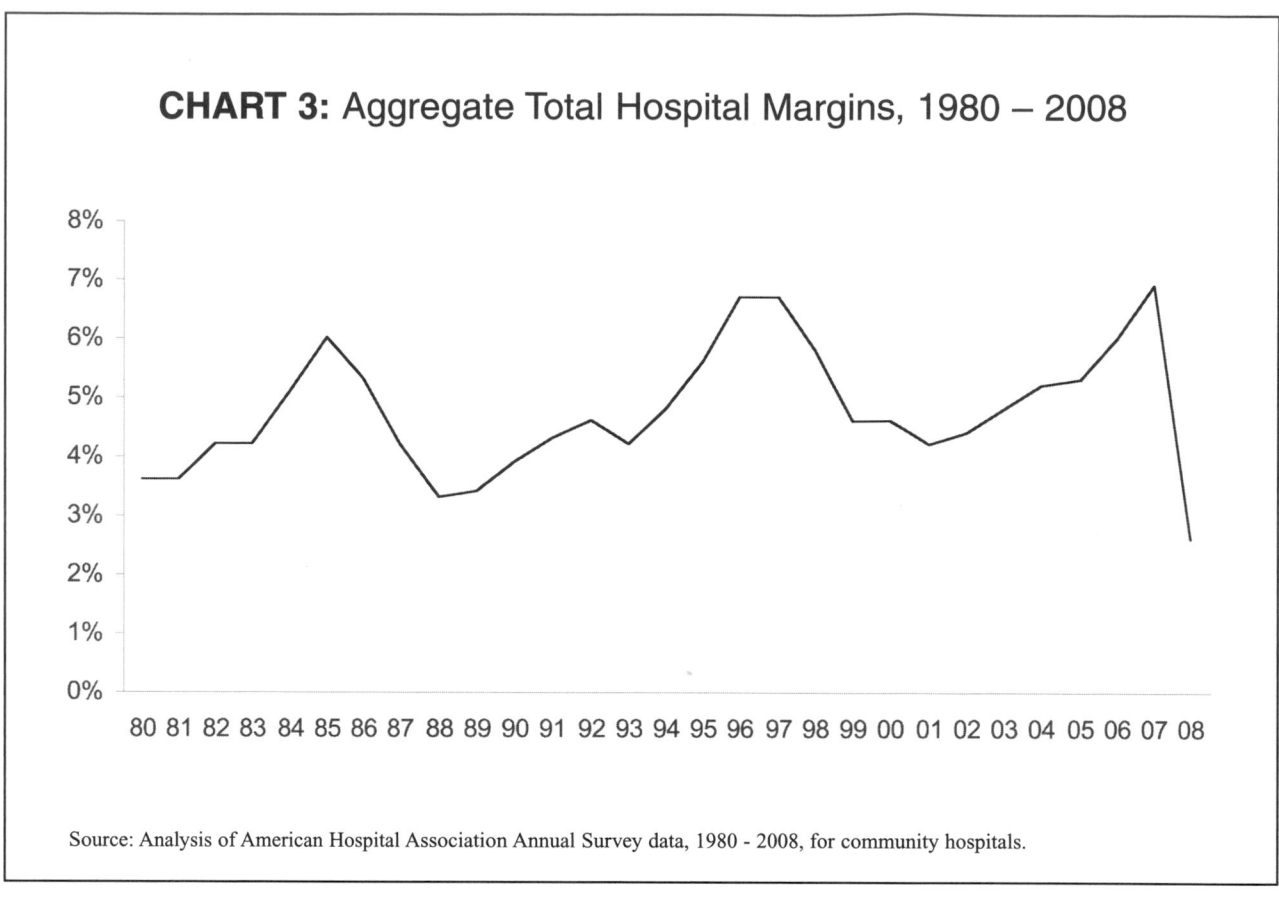

CHART 3: Aggregate Total Hospital Margins, 1980 – 2008

Source: Analysis of American Hospital Association Annual Survey data, 1980 - 2008, for community hospitals.

Medicare, Medicaid and the uninsured. Historically, non-operating income represents a third or more of overall margin.

Broader Economic Woes Put Pressure on Operations

The broader economic woes also have taken a toll on hospitals and the communities they serve. From January to December 2008, the unemployment rate rose by 47 percent (Chart 4). Research indicates that for every one percentage point increase in unemployment, 2.5 million people lose their employer-sponsored insurance.[3] By late 2008 many hospitals were seeing moderate or significant declines in elective procedures while a greater proportion of patients seeking care were unable to pay. Hospitals also were reporting an increase in the need for

subsidized services such as clinics, screening and outreach.[4] These trends were evident in operating margins for 2008, which were down nearly 25 percent from 2007.[5]

Going into 2009, unemployment continued to rise sharply. As of August, unemployment was at 9.7 percent (Chart 4). Not surprisingly, for the first half of 2009, nearly half of all hospitals reported a moderate to significant increase in the percentage of patients covered by Medicaid, Children's Health Insurance Program and/or other programs for low-income populations, and uncompensated care continues to increase (Chart 5).

The stimulus package provided necessary relief to state Medicaid programs, forestalling what could have translated into significant

CHART 4: Unemployment Rate (Non-Farm), 2007-2009

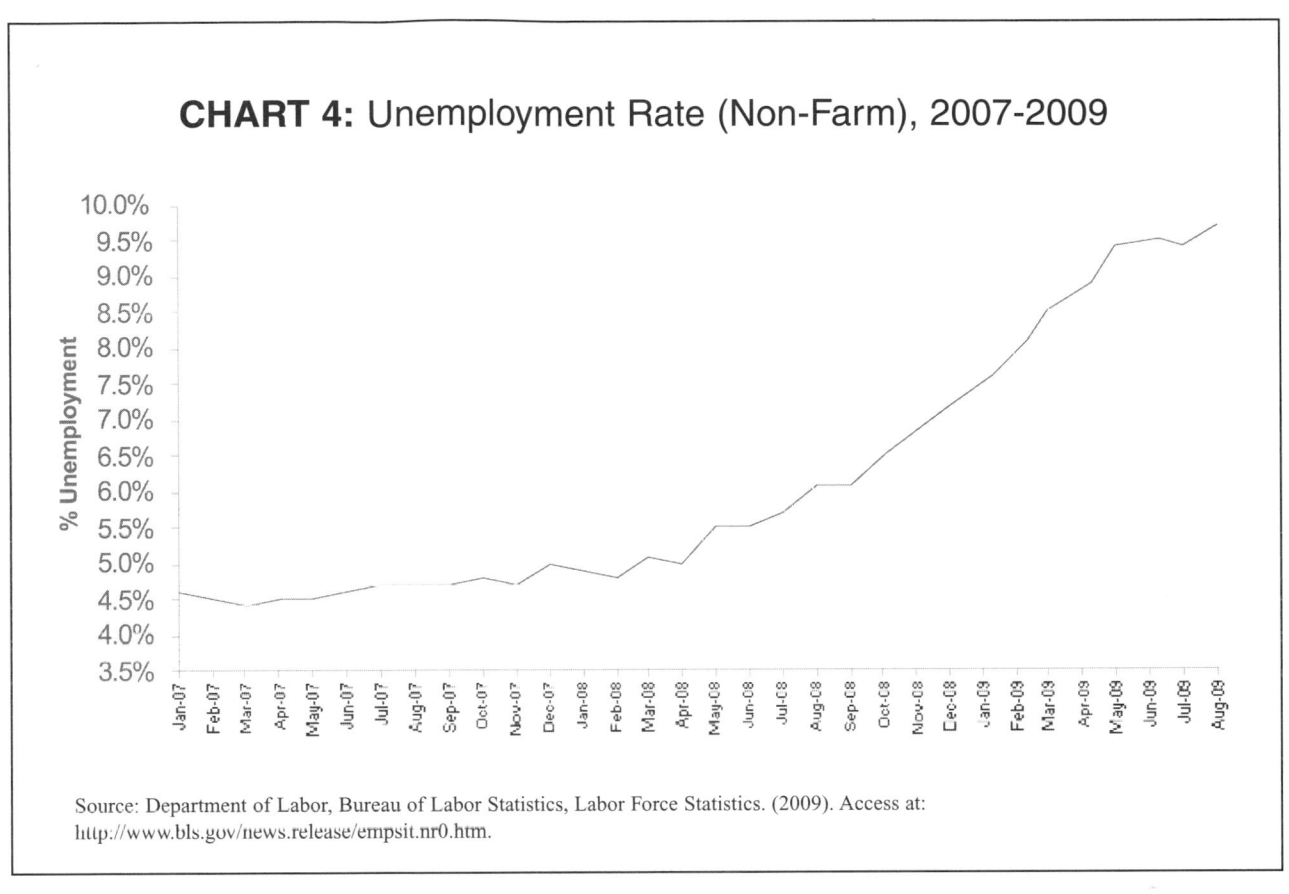

Source: Department of Labor, Bureau of Labor Statistics, Labor Force Statistics. (2009). Access at:
http://www.bls.gov/news.release/empsit.nr0.htm.

CHART 5: Change in Uncompensated Care and Patients Covered by Medicaid and Other Programs for Low Income Populations, YTD June 2009 versus Same Period Last Year

Source: American Hospital Association. *Rapid Response Survey, The Economic Crisis: Ongoing Monitoring of Impact on Hospitals* (Survey conducted in August 2009).

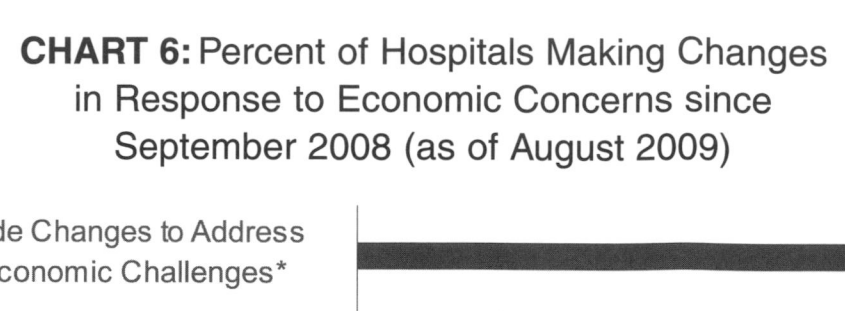

CHART 6: Percent of Hospitals Making Changes in Response to Economic Concerns since September 2008 (as of August 2009)

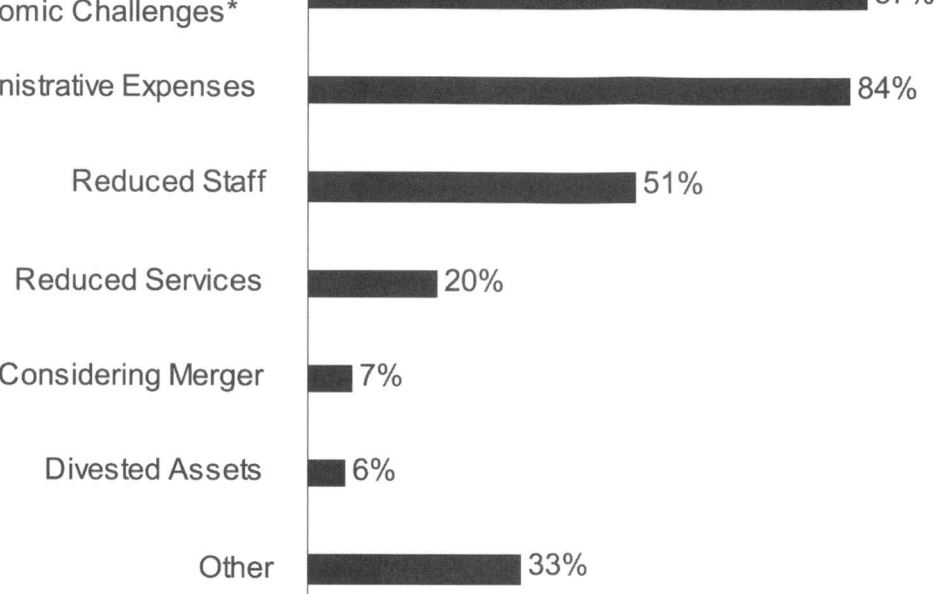

Made Changes to Address Economic Challenges* — 87%

Cut Administrative Expenses — 84%

Reduced Staff — 51%

Reduced Services — 20%

Considering Merger — 7%

Divested Assets — 6%

Other — 33%

Source: American Hospital Association. *Rapid Response Survey, The Economic Crisis: Ongoing Monitoring of Impact on Hospitals* (Survey conducted in August 2009).

*Percent of hospitals making at least one of changes below to weather the economic storm.

cuts to provider payments. However, fiscal recovery at the state level is slow – property, sales and income taxes have not yet begun to rebound. The majority of states still face large future budget deficits and future cuts to provider payments are likely.

Cutbacks in Expenses Help Stabilize Financial Performance

Nearly nine in 10 hospitals report making changes in response to economic concerns since the fall of 2008. More than 80 percent of hospitals have cut administrative expenses and just over half have reduced staff. A smaller but still significant percentage (20 percent) of

hospitals have reduced services that their communities depend on (Chart 6). Services most often targeted include those that tend to be poorly reimbursed such as behavioral health, post-acute care, clinics and patient education.

The combination of challenges to hospitals' financial performance – increased borrowing costs, sharp drops in investment income and the value of reserves, and pressures on operations – has caused financial indicators important to creditors to slip. In addition to declining margins, many hospitals saw their days cash on hand and debt service coverage ratios decline. Nearly one in 10 hospitals was

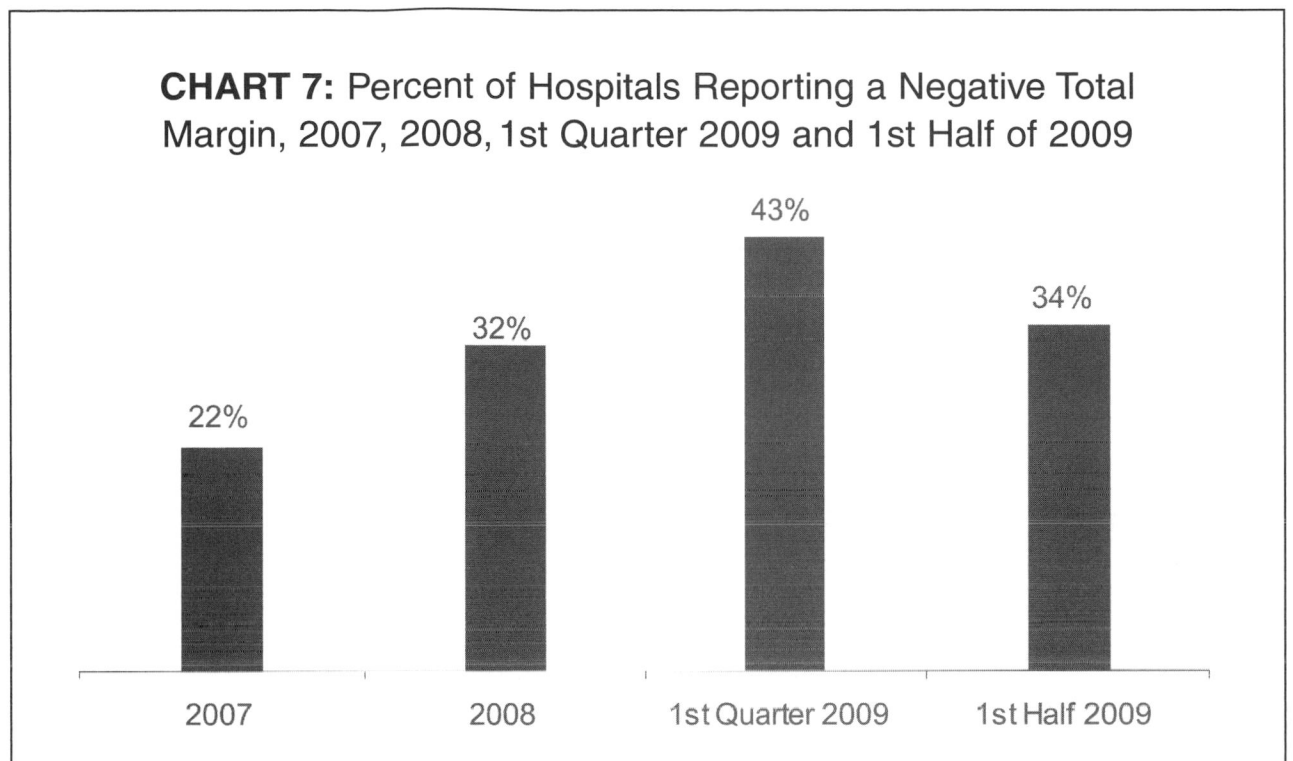

CHART 7: Percent of Hospitals Reporting a Negative Total Margin, 2007, 2008, 1st Quarter 2009 and 1st Half of 2009

22% — 2007

32% — 2008

43% — 1st Quarter 2009

34% — 1st Half 2009

Source: American Hospital Association. Analysis of AHA Annual Survey data 2007 and 2008; *Rapid Response Survey, The Economic Crisis: Ongoing Monitoring of Impact on Hospitals* (Surveys conducted in March 2009 and August 2009).

in technical default on a bond covenant at some point between September 2008 and August 2009.[6]

In 2008, 32 percent of hospitals reported losing money overall, up from 22 percent in 2007.[7] In surveys conducted in 2009, 43 percent of hospitals reported expected losses for the first quarter and 34 percent reported losses for the first half of 2009 (Chart 7). The rebound since the first quarter indicates that the actions hospitals have taken to bolster financial performance have helped, but it may be years before hospitals rebound to 2007 levels.

Physicians Turn to Hospitals for Financial Support

Hospitals have seen a marked increase in the number of physicians seeking the financial support of hospitals since the fall of 2008. Eight in 10 hospitals have seen an increase in the number of physicians seeking compensation for services such as on-call coverage. Nearly three-quarters of hospitals report an increase in physicians seeking hospital employment and over one-third report an increase in the number of physicians seeking to sell their practices to the hospital (Chart 8).

Hospitals Remain Critical to Economic Health of Communities

Traditionally, hospitals are the economic mainstays of their communities, offering a steady source of employment even during times of economic stress. In 2008, hospitals employed more than 5.3 million people.[8] Though many hospitals made cutbacks, the hospital field as a whole added jobs through

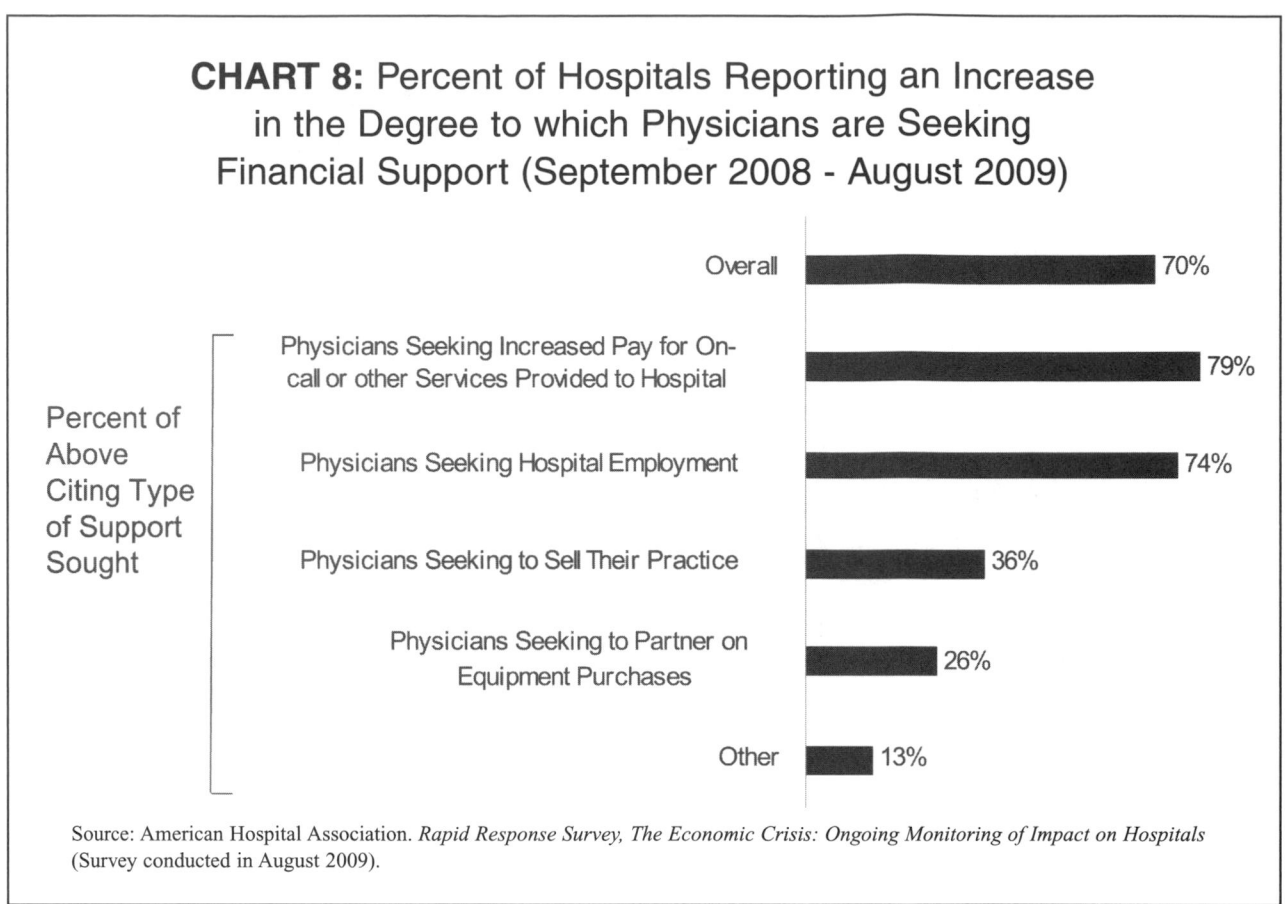

CHART 8: Percent of Hospitals Reporting an Increase in the Degree to which Physicians are Seeking Financial Support (September 2008 - August 2009)

Overall — 70%

Percent of Above Citing Type of Support Sought

- Physicians Seeking Increased Pay for On-call or other Services Provided to Hospital — 79%
- Physicians Seeking Hospital Employment — 74%
- Physicians Seeking to Sell Their Practice — 36%
- Physicians Seeking to Partner on Equipment Purchases — 26%
- Other — 13%

Source: American Hospital Association. *Rapid Response Survey, The Economic Crisis: Ongoing Monitoring of Impact on Hospitals* (Survey conducted in August 2009).

August 2009, despite declining employment in the economy as a whole (Chart 9). In 2008, hospitals spent approximately $322 billion on employee compensation and $268 billion on other goods and services.[9] Hospital wages, purchases from other businesses and taxes support jobs and other economic activity throughout the community.

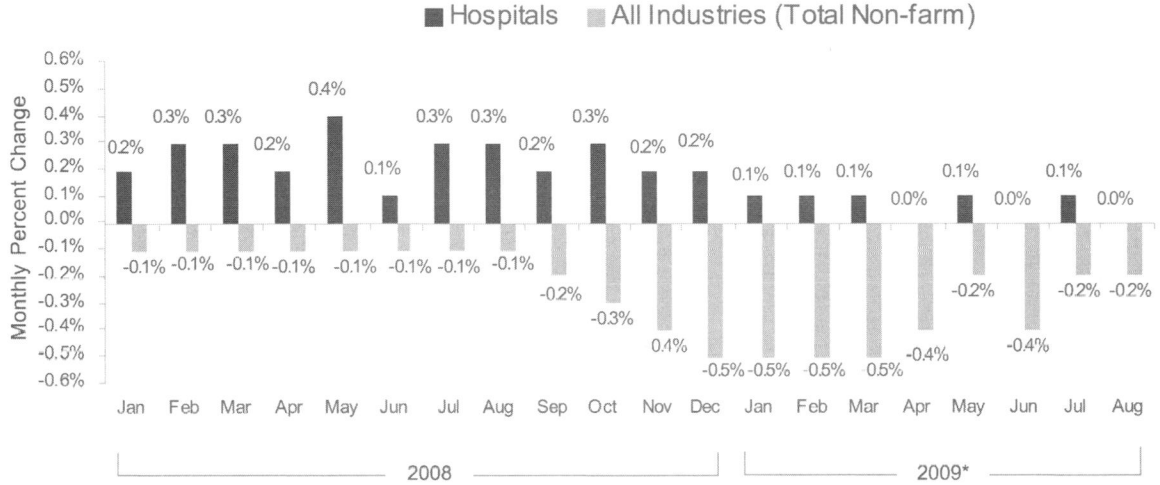

CHART 9: Percent Change in Employment, Seasonally Adjusted: Hospital vs. All Industries (Total Non-farm), 2008 - 2009

Source: Department of Labor, Bureau of Labor Statistics. (2009). Link: http://www.bls.gov/bls/employment.htm.
*July and August 2009 data are preliminary.

References

1 American Hospital Association. *Report on the Capital Crisis: Impact on Hospitals.* (January 2009).

2 Ibid.

3 Dorn, S., et al. *Medicaid, SCHIP and the Economic Downturn: Policy Challenges and Policy Responses.* Washington, DC: Kaiser Commission on Medicaid and the Uninsured. (April 2008).

4 American Hospital Association. *Report on the Economic Crisis: Initial Impact on Hospitals.* (November 2008).

5 Analysis of AHA Annual Survey data for 2007 and 2008.

6 American Hospital Association. *Rapid Response Survey, The Economic Crisis: Ongoing Monitoring of Impact on Hospitals.* (Survey Conducted in August 2009).

7 Analysis of AHA Annual Survey data for 2007 and 2008.

8 Analysis of AHA Annual Survey data for 2008.

9 Ibid.

For six decades, *AHA Hospital Statistics*™ has reported aggregate hospital data derived from the AHA Annual Survey and is the definitive source when doing trend analysis with data by bed size category, U.S. Census Divisions, States, and Metropolitan Statistical Areas (MSAs). As the health care delivery system changes, so have the data tracked by the survey and presented in this report. Recent additions include:

- **Community health indicators** that offer readers a connection to the community for their analysis and planning: the data are broken down into beds, admissions, inpatient days, ER outpatient visits, and other indicators per 1000 population, as well as expense per capita.

- **Utilization, personnel and finance** by all MSAs in the United States.

- **Five-year trend data** on physician models, insurance products, and managed care contracts enable you to identify changes in relationships between hospitals and other health care systems and providers.

- **Tables 3 through 6 have been organized** to show breakdowns between inpatient and outpatient care to better reflect market shifts toward outpatient-centered care. Additional clarity is gained by the breakdown between total facility data (which includes nursing home type units under the control of the hospital) and hospital units (which exclude the nursing home data).

TABLE 6 Sample State

U.S. Registered Community Hospitals
(Nonfederal, short-term general and other special hospitals)

Overview 2004-2008

	2008	2007	2006	2005	2004
Physician Models					
Independent Practice Association	14	17	17	17	14
Group Practice without Walls	4	5	5	8	4
Open Physician-Hospital Organization	20	21	24	23	18
Closed Physician-Hospital Organization	21	17	18	17	11
Management Service Organization	14	18	20	14	9
Integrated Salary Model	35	29	30	26	24
Equity Model	4	3	4	6	3
Foundation	9	8	23	21	19
Insurance Products					
Health Maintenance Organization	20	22	23	24	19
Preferred Provider Organization	39	47	52	53	37
Indemnity Fee for Service	7	12	14	12	6
Managed Care Contracts					
Health Maintenance Organization	64	67	62	49	42
Preferred Provider Organization	97	93	92	87	72

Example of five-year trend data

- **Facilities and Services information** on more than 100 categories of hospital facilities and services in Table 7. At a glance, you can determine the number and percentage of hospitals offering a specific service such as Oncology, Angioplasty, Palliative Care Program, Complementary Medicine, Women's Health Services and Tobacco Cessation.

- **Plus, System and Network involvement along with Group Purchasing Organizations** that demonstrate ways in which organizations are linked.

The survey instrument and the glossary

A good place to begin your analysis is the AHA Annual Survey instrument. Found on page 217, it includes the instructions, questions, and terms that were used to gather the data for fiscal year 2008. This can be extremely valuable for a clearer understanding of the data we collect and the tables presented in *AHA Hospital Statistics*.

Please also review the glossary in the back of the book. The glossary contains complete definitions for specific terms used in the tables and text of *AHA Hospital Statistics*. These definitions will clarify how terminology is being used.

As mentioned above, it is important to note that the primary focus of the most detailed data contained in *AHA Hospital Statistics* is community hospitals. As defined, community hospitals are all non-federal, short-term general and special hospitals whose facilities and services are available to the public. If the majority of a hospital's patients are admitted to units where the average length of stay is 30 days or less, a hospital may still be classified as short-term even if it includes a nursing- home-type unit. (For a more complete definition of community hospitals, please see the glossary definition, located on page 201.)

Getting the most out of *AHA Hospital Statistics*

This section of the book provides an introduction for getting the most out of your *AHA Hospital Statistics* 2010 edition. Here, you'll find a guide to the book, with insights into each table.

Equity model: An arrangement that allows established practitioners to become shareholders in a professional corporation in exchange for tangible and intangible assets of their existing practices.

Expenses: Includes all expenses for the reporting period including payroll, non-payroll, bad debt, and all nonoperating expenses. *Payroll expenses* include all salaries and wages. *Non-payroll expenses* are all professional fees and those salary expenditures excluded from payroll. *Labor related expenses* are defined as payroll expenses plus employee benefits. *Non-labor related expenses* are all other non-payroll expenses. *Bad debt* has been reclassified from a "reduction in revenue" to an expense in accordance with the revised AICPA Audit Guide. However, for purposes of historical consistency, the expense total that appears throughout *AHA Hospital Statistics does not include "bad debt" as an expense item.* Note: Financial data may not add due to rounding.

Extracorporeal shock wave lithotripter (ESWL): A medical device used for treating stones in the kidney or urethra. The device disintegrates kidney stones noninvasively through the transmission of acoustic shock waves directed at the stones.

Fitness center: Provides exercise, testing, or evaluation programs and fitness activities to the community and hospital employees.

Example of Glossary definitions.

CLASSIFICATION	YEAR	HOSPITALS	BEDS (in thousands)	ADMISSIONS (in thousands)	AVERAGE DAILY CENSUS (in thousands)	ADJUSTED AVERAGE DAILY CENSUS (in thousands)
Total United States	1946	6,125	1,436	15,675	1,142	—
	1950	6,788	1,456	18,483	1,253	—
	1955	6,956	1,604	21,073	1,363	—
	1960	6,876	1,658	25,027	1,402	—
	1965	7,123	1,704	28,812	1,403	—
	1970	7,123	1,616	31,759	1,298	—
	1971	7,097	1,556	32,664	1,237	—
	1972	7,061	1,550	33,265	1,209	—
	1973	7,123	1,535	34,352	1,189	—
	1974	7,174	1,513	35,506	1,167	—
	1975	7,156	1,466	36,157	1,125	—
	1976	7,082	1,434	36,776	1,090	—
	1977	7,099	1,407	37,060	1,066	—
	1978	7,015	1,381	37,243	1,042	—
	1979	6,988	1,372	37,802	1,043	—
	1980	6,965	1,365	38,892	1,060	—
	1981	6,933	1,362	39,169	1,061	—
	1982	6,915	1,360	39,095	1,053	—
	1983	6,888	1,350	38,887	1,028	—
	1984	6,872	1,339	37,938	970	—
	1985	6,872	1,318	36,304	910	—
	1986	6,841	1,290	35,219	883	—
	1987	6,821	1,267	34,439	873	—
	1988	6,780	1,248	34,107	863	—
	1989	6,720	1,220	33,742	853	—
	1990	6,649	1,213	33,774	844	—
	1991	6,634	1,202	33,567	827	—
	1992	6,539	1,178	33,536	807	—
	1993	6,467	1,163	33,201	783	—
	1994	6,374	1,128	33,125	745	—
	1995	6,291	1,081	33,282	710	—
	1996	6,201	1,062	33,307	685	—
	1997	6,097	1,035	33,624	673	—
	1998	6,021	1,013	33,766	662	—
	1999	5,890	994	34,181	657	—
	2000	5,810	984	34,891	650	—
	2001	5,801	987	35,644	658	—
	2002	5,794	976	36,326	662	—
	2003	5,764	965	36,611	657	—
	2004	5,759	956	36,942	658	—
	2005	5,756	947	37,006	656	—

Example of Table 1

Table 1 at a Glance

This table is used to evaluate historical data and allows you to examine long-term trends in health care with data dating back more than fifty years. Table 1 reports on all AHA registered hospitals in the United States. One important note: To be considered an AHA-registered hospital, a hospital does not need to be an AHA member. Rather, the hospital must meet particular certification or satisfy a number of requirements. These Registration Requirements immediately follow this section and begin on page (xxvii.)

This table segments the data into various organizational structure categories. Here's a brief look at these different classifications:

- Total United States Hospitals.
- Total Non-Federal Short-term and other special hospitals.
- Community hospitals
- Non-government not-for-profit community hospitals
- Investor-owned (for-profit) community hospitals
- State and local government community hospitals

Table 1 also provides input on nationwide utilization, personnel and finance trends. You'll find answers to questions such as: *Over the past 25 years, what trends do I see comparing the average length of stay at government and non-government not-for-profit community hospitals and investor-owned for-profit community hospitals?* or *What has been the trend in outpatient visits?*

Table 2 — 2008 U.S. Registered Hospitals: Utilization, Personnel and Finances

Table 2 at a Glance

This table takes a closer look at U.S. Registered Hospitals for 2008. It offers a snapshot of utilization, personnel and finance statistics, and breaks down this information for specialty hospitals. In addition, this is the only table that outlines data on federal hospitals. You'll be able to use this table to better understand the number of beds set-up and staffed, how many personnel and trainees are on the payroll, and what the financial implications of these may be.

TABLE 3

TOTAL UNITED STATES

U.S. Registered Community Hospitals
(Nonfederal, short-term general and other special hospitals)

Utilization, Personnel, Revenue and Expenses, Community Health Indicators 2004-2008

	2008	2007	2006	2005	2004
TOTAL FACILITY (Includes Hospital and Nursing Home Units)					
Utilization - Inpatient					
Beds	839,988	853,287	862,352	872,736	902,061
Admissions	31,811,673	31,576,960	31,098,959	30,945,357	30,718,136
Inpatient Days	191,430,450	192,504,015	193,747,004	199,876,367	207,180,278
Average Length of Stay	6.0	6.1	6.2	6.5	6.7
Inpatient Surgeries	9,735,705	9,509,081	9,545,612	9,700,613	9,833,938
Births	3,726,233	3,742,191	3,723,871	3,764,698	3,809,367
HOSPITAL UNIT (Excludes Separate Nursing Home Units)					
Utilization - Inpatient					
Beds	758,186	769,505	782,504	794,502	824,969
Admissions	31,265,867	31,047,930	30,652,820	30,577,564	30,403,766
Inpatient Days	165,644,176	165,605,620	168,189,130	174,898,504	182,702,882
Average Length of Stay	5.3	5.3	5.5	5.7	6.0
Personnel					
Total Full Time	3,235,153	3,183,730	3,154,603	3,166,729	3,147,922
Total Part Time	1,213,426	1,214,232	1,153,790	1,146,082	1,122,957
Revenue and Expenses - Totals					
(Includes Inpatient and Outpatient)					
Total Net Revenue	$333,054,828,642	$322,459,942,930	$310,513,291,998	$298,519,717,355	$285,858,018,951
Total Expenses	314,709,758,455	301,905,101,393	290,128,641,153	282,372,557,487	272,840,121,437

Example of Table 3. Helps contrast acute and long-term care

Table 3 — Total United States

Table 3 at a Glance

This table provides a look at all U .S. Registered Community Hospitals, in terms of general overview with utilization by inpatient and outpatient, personnel, revenue, expenses and community health indicators. It provides a snapshot of the past five years, allowing you to track emerging trends.

This national information can be compared to local or regional trends, for benchmarking

- Both inpatient and outpatient information is included, for better evaluation of data.

- Reporting by total facility *Includes hospital and Nursing Home Units* and hospital unit only *Excludes Separate Nursing Home Units* helps contrast acute and long-term care.

- Community health indicators can help uncover trends and help determine future facility needs

Example of Table 4. Compares facilities with peers.

Table 4 — Bed Size Categories

Table 4 at a Glance

This table provides a look at all U.S. Registered Community Hospitals, broken down by bed size. The table includes general overview, utilization, personnel, and revenue and expense information. These categories of bed sizes were developed by the AHA, and have become an industry standard. By categorizing each facility into a peer group, this table provides a snapshot of the past five years allowing you to compare facilities with their peers.

TABLE 5

U.S. CENSUS DIVISION 2: MIDDLE ATLANTIC

U.S. Registered Community Hospitals
(Nonfederal, short-term general and other special hospitals)

Utilization, Personnel, Revenue and Expenses, Community Health Indicators 2004-2008

	2008	2007	2006	2005	2004
COMMUNITY HEALTH INDICATORS PER 1000 POPULATION					
Total Population (in thousands) . . .	38,292	38,216	38,184	38,147	38,108
Inpatient					
Beds	3.6	3.8	3.9	4.0	4.1
Admissions	135.8	136.7	136.2	138.3	137.4
Inpatient Days	963.5	988.8	1,019.0	1,093.8	1,145.0
Inpatient Surgeries	42.2	41.4	41.2	42.7	43.6
Births	13.0	13.2	13.6	13.7	14.3
Outpatient					
Emergency Outpatient Visits	367.7	362.0	363.4	379.5	360.1
Other Outpatient Visits	1,970.9	1,802.3	1,767.7	1,680.3	1,573.9
Total Outpatient Visits	2,338.6	2,164.3	2,131.1	2,059.8	1,934.0
Outpatient Surgeries	67.8	62.4	59.9	55.4	53.5
Expense per Capita (per person)	$1,494.9	$1,462.7	$1,428.6	$1,429.8	$1,369.2

Example of Table 5. Uncovers trends to determine future facility needs.

Table 5 — U.S. Census Divisions

Table 5 at a Glance
This table provides a look at all U.S. Registered Community Hospitals, broken down by Census Division. The table includes general overview, utilization, personnel, and expenses, and community health indicator information. It provides a snapshot of the past five years, allowing you to track trends on a regional level. In addition, this allows you to compare this data to other population based health indicators, offering a more comprehensive look than the survey data alone. Community health indicators can help uncover trends and help determine future facility needs.

Table 6 — States

Table 6 at a Glance
This table provides a look at all U.S. Registered Community Hospitals, broken down by State. The table includes general overview, utilization, personnel, revenue and expenses, and community health indicator information. It provides a snapshot of the past five years, allowing you to track trends on a state level.

Note:
You can use the information in tables 3, 4, 5 and 6 to make accurate comparisons across Total U.S., Bed Size Category, Census Division and State.

Table 7 — 2008 Facilities and Services in the U.S. Census Divisions and States

Table 7 at a Glance

This table examines facilities and services by both Census Division and State. A comprehensive alphabetical guide helps make each facility or service easy to find. This table will allow you to better understand what service lines are emerging and how many facilities offer a particular service in a discrete state or region.

This collection of facilities and services information data is unique to *AHA Hospital Statistics* and the list is continually growing. Recent additions include:

- Blood Donor Center
- Cardiac Rehabilitation
- Computer assisted orthopedic surgery (CAOS)
- Freestanding/Satellite Emergency Department
- Full-field digital mammography (FFDM)
- Full time equivalent employees (FTE):
- Image-guided radiation therapy (IGRT)
- Mobile health services
- Positron emission tomography/CT (PET/CT)
- Robotic surgery
- Stereotactic radiosurgery
- Virtual colonoscopy

Example of Table 7.

These new categories reflect the trends as hospitals expand their service lines to mirror the needs of their patients. For example, services such as acupuncture or massage therapy are now accounted for in the Complementary Medicine service item.

This table can answer questions such as: *What percentage of hospitals in the United States offer complementary medicine or wound management?* or *How are these new services distributed by state?*

Table 8 — Utilization, Personnel and Finances in Community Hospitals by MSAs for 2008.

Table 8 at a Glance

This table provides a look at all U.S. Registered Community Hospitals, broken down by Metropolitan Statistical Area (MSA). The table includes general overview, utilization, personnel, and finance information. It provides a snapshot of the past year.

Additional Resources

Again, in the back of the book you will find the comprehensive glossary and the 2008 annual survey questionnaire. The survey itself can be a valuable resource to understanding what was asked in order to gather the data in the book. This survey is also used to produce the *AHA Guide®* and AHA Annual Survey Database™.

AHA-Registered Hospitals

Any institution that can be classified as a hospital according to the requirements may be registered if it so desires. Membership in the American Hospital Association is not a prerequisite.

The American Hospital Association may, at the sole discretion of the Executive Committee of the Board of Trustees, grant, deny, or withdraw the registration of an institution.

An institution may be registered by the American Hospital Association as a hospital if it is accredited as a hospital by The Joint Commission or is certified as a provider of acute services under Title 18 of the Social Security Act and has provided the Association with documents verifying the accreditation or certification.

In lieu of the preceding accreditation or certification, an institution licensed as a hospital by the appropriate state agency may be registered by AHA as a hospital by meeting the following alternative requirements:

Function: The primary function of the institution is to provide patient services, diagnostic and therapeutic, for particular or general medical conditions.

1. The institution shall maintain at least six inpatient beds, which shall be continuously available for the care of patients who are nonrelated and who stay on the average in excess of 24 hours per admission.

2. The institution shall be constructed, equipped, and maintained to ensure the health and safety of patients and to provide uncrowded, sanitary facilities for the treatment of patients.

3. There shall be an identifiable governing authority legally and morally responsible for the conduct of the hospital.

4. There shall be a chief executive to whom the governing authority delegates the continuous responsibility for the operation of the hospital in accordance with establish policy.

5. There shall be an organized medical staff of fully licensed physicians* that may include other licensed individuals permitted by law and by the hospital to provide patient care services independently in the hospital. The medical staff shall be accountable to the governing authority for maintaining proper standards of medical care, and it shall be governed by bylaws adopted by said staff and approved by the governing authority.

6. Each patient shall be admitted on the authority of a member of the medical staff who has been granted the privilege to admit patients to inpatient services in accordance with state law and criteria for standards of medical care established by the individual medical staff. Each patient's general medical condition is the responsibility of a qualified physician member of the medical staff. When nonphysician members of the medical staff are granted privileges to admit patients, provision is made for prompt medical evaluation of these patients by a qualified physician. Any graduate of a foreign medical school who is permitted to assume responsibilities for patient care shall possess a valid license to practice medicine, or shall be certified by the Educational Commission for Foreign Medical Graduates, or shall have qualified for and have successfully completed an academic year of supervised clinical training under the direction of a medical school approved by the Liaison Committee on GAT Medical Education.

7. Registered nurse supervision and other nursing services are continuous.

8. A current and complete‡ medical record shall be maintained by the institution for each patient and shall be available for reference.

9. Pharmacy service shall be maintained in the institution and shall be supervised by a registered pharmacist.

10. The institution shall provide patients with food service that meets their nutritional and therapeutic requirements; special diets shall also be available.

Types of Hospitals

In addition to meeting these 10 general registration requirements, hospitals are registered as one of four types of hospitals: general, special, rehabilitation and chronic disease, or psychiatric. The following type of hospital and special requirements for registration are employed:

General

The primary function of the institution is to provide patient services, diagnostic and therapeutic, for a variety of medical conditions. A general hospital also shall provide:

- diagnostic x-ray services with facilities and staff for a variety of procedures
- clinical laboratory service with facilities and staff for a variety of procedures and with anatomical pathology services regularly and conveniently available
- operating room service with facilities and staff.

Special

The primary function of the institution is to provide diagnostic and treatment services for patients who have specified medical conditions, both surgical and nonsurgical. A special hospital also shall provide:

- such diagnostic and treatment services as may be determined by the Executive Committee of the Board of Trustees of the American Hospital Association to be appropriate for the specified medical conditions for which medical services are provided shall be maintained in the institution with suitable facilities and staff. If such conditions do not normally require diagnostic x-ray service, laboratory service, or operating room service, and if any such services are therefore not maintained in the institution, there shall be written arrangements to make them available to patients requiring them.
- clinical laboratory services capable of providing tissue diagnosis when offering pregnancy termination services.

Rehabilitation and Chronic Disease

The primary function of the institution is to provide diagnostic and treatment services to handicapped or disabled individuals requiring restorative and adjustive services. A rehabilitation and chronic disease hospital also shall provide:

- arrangements for diagnostic x-ray services, as required, on a regular and conveniently available basis
- arrangements for clinical laboratory service, as required on a regular and conveniently available basis
- arrangements for operating room service, as required, on a regular and conveniently available basis
- a physical therapy service with suitable facilities and staff in the institution
- an occupational therapy service with suitable facilities and staff in the institution
- arrangements for psychological and social work services on a regular and conveniently available basis

---

* Physician–Term used to describe an individual with an M.D. or D.O. degree who is fully licensed to practice medicine in all its phases.

‡ The completed records in general shall contain at least the following: the patient's identifying data and consent forms, medical history, record of physical examination, physicians' progress notes, operative notes, nurses' notes, routine x-ray and laboratory reports, doctors' orders, and final diagnosis.

- arrangements for educational and vocational services on a regular and conveniently available basis
- written arrangements with a general hospital for the transfer of patients who require medical, obstetrical, or surgical services not available in the institution.

Psychiatric

The primary function of the institution is to provide diagnostic and treatment services for patients who have psychiatric-related illnesses. A psychiatric hospital also shall provide:

- arrangements for clinical laboratory service, as required, on a regular and conveniently available basis
- arrangements for diagnostic x-ray services, as required on a regular and conveniently available basis
- psychiatric, psychological, and social work service with facilities and staff in the institution
- arrangements for electroencephalograph services, as required, on a regular and conveniently available basis.
- written arrangements with a general hospital for the transfer of patients who require medical, obstetrical, or surgical services not available in the institution.

The American Hospital Association may, at the sole discretion of the Executive Committee of the Board of Trustees, grant, deny, or withdraw the registration of an institution.

Data Comparability

The economic climate, demographic characteristics, personnel issues, and health care financing and payment policies differ by region, state, and city across the country. *Differences in these factors must be taken into account when using the data.* In addition, the profiles of hospitals across comparison groups vary. For example, states will differ in terms of the number and percentage of hospitals by size, ownership, services provided, types of patients treated, and so forth. *Differences in these variables must also be taken into consideration when doing a comparative analysis.*

Notes on the Survey

The 2010 edition of *AHA Hospital Statistics*™ draws its data from the 2008 AHA Annual Survey of Hospitals. It is the statistical complement to the 2010 edition of the *AHA Guide*®, which contains selected data about individual hospitals.

The AHA Survey was mailed to all hospitals, both AHA-registered and nonregistered, in the U.S. and its associated areas: American Samoa, Guam, the Marshall Islands, Puerto Rico, and the Virgin Islands. U.S. government hospitals located outside the U.S. were not included. Overall, the average response rate over the past five years has been approximately 83 percent.

Reporting Period

In completing the survey, hospitals were requested to report data for a full year, in accord with their fiscal year, ending in 2008. The statistical table present data reported or estimated for a 12-month period, except for data on personnel, which represent situations as they existed at the end of the reporting period.

Respondents

Data for Tables 1 and 2 include 5,815 AHA-registered hospitals in the U.S. Data on community hospitals (nonfederal, short-term general and other special hospitals) only are presented in Tables 3-6, and Table 8.

It is important to note that the AHA-registered hospitals included in *AHA Hospital Statistics* are not necessarily identical to those included in *AHA Guide*. The institutions listed in the 2010 edition of AHA Guide include all of those institutions CMS certified, Joint Commission accredited, or AHA registered as of September 2008. Tables 1-6 in *AHA Hospital Statistics* present data for AHA-registered hospitals that were in operation during the 12-month reporting period ending 2008.

Estimates

Estimates were made of data for nonreporting hospitals and for reporting hospitals that submitted incomplete AHA Annual Survey questionnaires. Estimates were not made for beds, bassinets and facilities and services. Data for beds and bassinets of nonreporting hospitals were based on the most recent information from those hospitals. (Note that in all statistical tables, whenever bed-size categories are listed, all eight categories appear, whether or not there are hospitals in every category.)

Missing revenue, expenses, admissions, births, inpatient days, surgical operations, outpatient visits, and full-time-equivalent personnel values are estimates from regression models. For all other variables the estimates were based on ratios such as per bed averages derived from data reported by hospitals similar in size, control, major service provided, length of stay, and geographical characteristics to the hospitals that did not report this information.

Tables 1–2

Table

1

Historical Trends in Utilization, Personnel, and Finances for Selected Years from 1946 through 2008

Data are for all AHA-registered hospitals in the United States. Data are estimated for nonreporting hospitals with the exception of newborn and outpatient data before 1972. Personnel data exclude residents, interns, and students from 1952 on; personnel data include full-time personnel and full-time equivalents for part-time personnel from 1954 on. As a result of the AHA Annual Survey validation process, the New York state expense data from 1976 were revised after the 1977 edition was published. The revised figures are included below. In order to provide trend data on a consistent basis, the 1970 and 1971 psychiatric and long-term data have been slightly modified. The 1982 FTE figures have updated to provide the most accurate data possible.

CLASSIFICATION								NEWBORNS		FTE PERSONNEL		TOTAL EXPENSES		
YEAR	HOSPITALS	BEDS (in thousands)	ADMISSIONS (in thousands)	AVERAGE DAILY CENSUS (in thousands)	ADJUSTED AVERAGE DAILY CENSUS (in thousands)	AVERAGE STAY (days)	OUTPATIENT VISITS (in thousands)	Bassinets	Births	Number (in thousands)	Per 100 Adjusted Census	Amount (In Millions of dollars)	Adjusted per Inpatient Stay (dollars)	Adjusted per Inpatient Day (dollars)
Total United States														
1946	6,125	1,436	15,675	1,142	—	—	—	85,585	2,135,327	830	—	$1,963	—	—
1950	6,788	1,456	18,483	1,253	—	—	—	90,101	2,742,780	1,058	—	$3,651	—	—
1955	6,956	1,604	21,073	1,363	—	—	—	98,823	3,476,753	1,301	—	$5,594	—	—
1960	6,876	1,658	25,027	1,402	—	—	—	102,764	3,835,735	1,598	—	$8,421	—	—
1965	7,123	1,704	28,812	1,403	—	—	125,793	101,287	3,565,344	1,952	—	$12,948	—	—
1970	7,123	1,616	31,759	1,298	—	—	181,370	97,128	3,537,000	2,537	—	$25,556	—	—
1971	7,097	1,556	32,664	1,237	—	—	199,725	94,344	3,464,513	2,589	—	$28,812	—	—
1972	7,061	1,550	33,265	1,209	—	—	219,182	92,960	3,231,875	2,671	—	$32,667	—	—
1973	7,123	1,535	34,352	1,189	—	—	233,555	90,071	3,087,210	2,769	—	$36,290	—	—
1974	7,174	1,513	35,506	1,167	—	—	250,481	88,269	3,043,386	2,919	—	$41,406	—	—
1975	7,156	1,466	36,157	1,125	—	—	254,844	86,875	3,091,629	3,023	—	$48,706	—	—
1976	7,082	1,434	36,776	1,090	—	—	270,951	85,284	3,067,063	3,108	—	$56,005	—	—
1977	7,099	1,407	37,060	1,066	—	—	263,775	83,193	3,223,699	3,213	—	$63,630	—	—
1978	7,015	1,381	37,243	1,042	—	—	263,606	80,650	3,250,373	3,280	—	$70,927	—	—
1979	6,988	1,372	37,802	1,043	—	—	262,009	79,720	3,376,467	3,382	—	$79,796	—	—
1980	6,965	1,365	38,892	1,060	—	—	262,951	79,842	3,500,043	3,492	—	$91,886	—	—
1981	6,933	1,362	39,169	1,061	—	—	265,332	78,823	3,558,274	3,661	—	$107,146	—	—
1982	6,915	1,360	39,095	1,053	—	—	313,667	77,998	3,615,751	3,746	—	$123,219	—	—
1983	6,888	1,350	38,887	1,028	—	—	273,168	77,837	3,596,146	3,707	—	$136,315	—	—
1984	6,872	1,339	37,938	970	—	—	276,566	77,845	3,563,106	3,630	—	$144,114	—	—
1985	6,872	1,318	36,304	910	—	—	282,140	77,202	3,630,961	3,625	—	$153,327	—	—
1986	6,841	1,290	35,219	883	—	—	294,634	76,002	3,680,178	3,647	—	$165,194	—	—
1987	6,821	1,267	34,439	873	—	—	310,707	74,770	3,698,294	3,742	—	$178,662	—	—
1988	6,780	1,248	34,107	863	—	—	336,208	72,568	3,794,369	3,839	—	$196,704	—	—
1989	6,720	1,226	33,742	853	—	—	352,248	71,491	3,920,384	3,937	—	$214,886	—	—
1990	6,649	1,213	33,774	844	—	—	368,184	70,539	4,046,704	4,063	—	$234,870	—	—
1991	6,634	1,202	33,567	827	—	—	387,675	69,464	4,047,504	4,165	—	$258,508	—	—
1992	6,539	1,178	33,536	807	—	—	417,874	69,052	4,007,179	4,236	—	$282,531	—	—
1993	6,467	1,163	33,201	783	—	—	435,619	67,911	3,949,788	4,289	—	$301,538	—	—
1994	6,374	1,128	33,125	745	—	—	453,584	67,311	3,886,667	4,270	—	$310,834	—	—
1995	6,291	1,081	33,282	710	—	—	483,195	66,256	3,833,132	4,273	—	$320,252	—	—
1996	6,201	1,062	33,307	685	—	—	505,455	65,138	3,790,678	4,276	—	$330,531	—	—
1997	6,097	1,035	33,624	673	—	—	520,600	64,649	3,811,522	4,333	—	$342,334	—	—
1998	6,021	1,013	33,766	662	—	—	545,481	63,485	3,795,212	4,407	—	$355,450	—	—
1999	5,890	994	34,181	657	—	—	573,461	62,714	3,829,881	4,369	—	$372,933	—	—
2000	5,810	984	34,891	650	—	—	592,673	61,915	3,940,017	4,454	—	$395,391	—	—
2001	5,801	987	35,644	658	—	—	612,276	61,527	3,929,733	4,535	—	$426,849	—	—
2002	5,794	976	36,326	662	—	—	640,515	62,151	3,934,421	4,610	—	$462,222	—	—
2003	5,764	965	36,611	657	—	—	648,560	60,699	3,976,886	4,651	—	$498,104	—	—
2004	5,759	956	36,942	658	—	—	662,131	59,660	3,965,906	4,696	—	$533,853	—	—
2005	5,756	947	37,006	656	—	—	673,689	59,073	4,048,442	4,791	—	$570,534	—	—
2006	5,747	947	37,189	653	—	—	690,425	58,670	4,126,598	4,907	—	$607,355	—	—
2007	5,708	945	37,120	645	—	—	693,510	58,429	4,128,796	5,024	—	$641,124	—	—
2008	5,815	951	37,529	649	—	—	709,960	58,133	4,109,081	5,116	—	$690,074	—	—

Table 1 (Continued)

CLASSIFICATION: Total nonfederal short-term general and other special

YEAR	HOSPITALS	BEDS (in thousands)	ADMISSIONS (in thousands)	AVERAGE DAILY CENSUS (in thousands)	ADJUSTED AVERAGE DAILY CENSUS (in thousands)	AVERAGE LENGTH OF STAY (days)	OUTPATIENT VISITS (in thousands)	NEWBORNS Bassinets	NEWBORNS Births	FTE PERSONNEL Number (in thousands)	FTE PERSONNEL Per 100 Adjusted Census	EXPENSES Amount (In Millions of dollars)	EXPENSES Adjusted per Inpatient Stay (dollars)	EXPENSES Adjusted per Inpatient Day (dollars)
1946	4,444	473	13,655	341	—	9.1	—	80,987	2,087,503	505	—	$1,169	—	—
1950	5,031	505	16,663	372	—	8.1	—	86,019	2,660,982	662	—	$2,120	—	—
1955	5,237	568	19,100	407	—	7.8	—	93,868	3,304,451	826	—	$3,434	—	—
1960	5,407	639	22,970	477	—	7.6	—	98,127	3,678,051	1,080	—	$5,617	—	—
1965	5,736	741	26,463	563	620	7.8	92,651	96,782	3,413,370	1,386	224	$9,147	$316.37	$40.56
1970	5,859	848	29,252	662	727	8.2	133,545	93,079	3,403,064	1,929	265	$19,560	$604.59	$73.73
1971	5,865	867	30,142	665	736	8.0	148,423	90,444	3,337,605	1,999	272	$22,400	$667.44	$83.43
1972	5,843	884	30,777	664	739	7.9	166,983	89,315	3,119,446	2,056	278	$25,549	$747.42	$94.61
1973	5,891	903	31,761	681	768	7.8	178,939	86,851	2,987,089	2,149	280	$28,496	$793.88	$101.78
1974	5,977	931	32,943	701	793	7.8	194,858	85,208	2,947,342	2,289	289	$32,751	$883.04	$113.21
1975	5,979	947	33,519	708	806	7.7	196,311	83,834	2,998,590	2,399	298	$39,110	$1,024.72	$133.08
1976	5,956	961	34,068	715	816	7.7	207,725	82,307	2,962,305	2,483	304	$45,402	$1,172.25	$152.24
1977	5,973	974	34,353	717	820	7.6	204,238	80,228	3,117,756	2,581	315	$51,832	$1,316.70	$173.25
1978	5,935	980	34,575	720	841	7.6	204,461	78,090	3,156,570	2,662	323	$58,348	$1,470.13	$193.81
1979	5,923	988	35,160	729	841	7.6	203,873	77,277	3,287,157	2,762	328	$66,184	$1,631.16	$215.75
1980	5,904	992	36,198	748	861	7.6	206,752	77,539	3,408,699	2,879	334	$76,970	$1,844.19	$244.44
1981	5,879	1,007	36,494	764	876	7.6	206,729	76,557	3,465,683	3,039	347	$90,739	$2,167.70	$283.94
1982	5,863	1,015	36,429	763	882	7.6	250,888	75,739	3,514,761	3,110	353	$105,094	$2,493.09	$326.68
1983	5,843	1,021	36,201	750	869	7.6	213,995	75,471	3,490,629	3,102	357	$116,632	$2,775.55	$368.01
1984	5,814	1,020	35,202	703	824	7.3	216,474	75,537	3,456,467	3,023	367	$123,550	$2,984.00	$409.85
1985	5,784	1,003	33,501	650	780	7.1	222,773	74,899	3,521,296	3,003	385	$130,700	$3,238.94	$459.57
1986	5,728	982	32,410	631	774	7.1	234,270	73,688	3,584,530	3,032	392	$140,907	$3,529.60	$499.19
1987	5,659	961	31,633	624	780	7.2	247,704	72,516	3,602,416	3,120	400	$152,909	$3,848.79	$536.96
1988	5,579	949	31,480	622	795	7.2	271,436	70,361	3,706,748	3,209	404	$168,941	$4,194.39	$581.08
1989	5,497	936	31,141	619	805	7.3	287,909	69,436	3,831,051	3,307	411	$185,204	$4,572.23	$630.59
1990	5,420	929	31,203	620	820	7.3	302,691	68,443	3,958,646	3,423	417	$203,927	$4,929.93	$681.52
1991	5,370	926	31,084	612	828	7.2	323,202	67,440	3,965,489	3,539	427	$225,230	$5,345.63	$745.37
1992	5,321	923	31,053	606	832	7.1	349,397	67,095	3,925,024	3,624	436	$248,318	$5,788.52	$815.99
1993	5,289	921	30,770	535	834	7.0	368,558	66,060	3,870,392	3,681	441	$266,382	$6,120.94	$874.98
1994	5,256	904	30,739	539	814	6.8	384,680	65,728	3,809,367	3,697	454	$276,148	$6,230.33	$929.65
1995	5,220	874	30,966	549	811	6.5	415,710	64,742	3,764,756	3,718	458	$286,073	$6,220.54	$966.79
1996	5,160	864	31,116	531	800	6.2	440,645	63,646	3,723,907	3,728	466	$293,920	$6,225.95	$1,005.45
1997	5,082	855	31,595	529	813	6.1	450,907	63,247	3,742,240	3,794	467	$306,088	$6,266.24	$1,031.68
1998	5,039	842	31,830	527	821	6.0	474,365	62,162	3,726,234	3,835	467	$319,035	$6,387.53	$1,064.93
1999	4,977	831	32,377	527	835	5.9	495,650	61,534	3,760,295	3,840	460	$335,405	$6,512.44	$1,101.47
2000	4,934	825	33,102	527	850	5.8	522,970	60,845	3,880,166	3,916	461	$356,757	$6,650.68	$1,147.99
2001	4,927	828	33,834	534	866	5.8	539,316	60,454	3,873,395	3,990	461	$383,911	$6,979.29	$1,216.04
2002	4,949	823	34,501	541	887	5.7	557,336	59,974	3,870,191	4,072	459	$416,791	$7,353.17	$1,288.63
2003	4,918	815	34,800	540	895	5.7	563,804	59,662	3,915,842	4,112	459	$450,403	$7,798.19	$1,378.78
2004	4,942	810	35,098	542	910	5.6	573,126	58,710	3,931,508	4,151	456	$481,517	$8,168.06	$1,449.90
2005	4,956	804	35,265	542	930	5.6	587,296	58,195	3,987,766	4,260	458	$516,172	$8,538.30	$1,521.58
2006	4,947	805	35,403	540	940	5.6	599,397	57,832	4,075,193	4,347	462	$552,276	$8,972.85	$1,610.76
2007	4,915	803	35,370	535	944	5.5	603,411	57,546	4,077,962	4,468	473	$583,550	$9,377.82	$1,694.38
2008	5,026	810	35,776	538	963	5.5	624,185	57,301	4,073,724	4,552	473	$626,823	$9,789.69	$1,780.45

Table 1 (Continued)

CLASSIFICATION: Total community hospitals

YEAR	HOSPITALS	BEDS (in thousands)	ADMISSIONS (in thousands)	AVERAGE DAILY CENSUS (in thousands)	ADJUSTED AVERAGE DAILY CENSUS (in thousands)	AVERAGE LENGTH OF STAY (days)	OUTPATIENT VISITS (in thousands)	NEWBORNS Bassinets	NEWBORNS Births	FTE PERSONNEL Number (in thousands)	FTE PERSONNEL Per 100 Adjusted Census	EXPENSES Amount (In Millions of dollars)	EXPENSES Adjusted per Inpatient Stay (dollars)	EXPENSES Adjusted per Inpatient Day (dollars)
1975	5,875	942	33,435	706	798	7.7	190,672	83,829	2,998,552	2,392	300	$38,962	$1,030.34	$133.81
1976	5,857	956	33,979	713	810	7.7	201,247	82,296	2,962,216	2,475	306	$45,240	$1,176.25	$152.76
1979	5,842	984	35,099	727	833	7.6	198,778	77,266	3,287,012	2,756	331	$66,004	$1,641.67	$217.34
1980	5,830	988	36,143	747	857	7.6	202,310	77,522	3,408,482	2,873	335	$76,851	$1,851.04	$245.12
1981	5,813	1,003	36,438	763	873	7.6	202,768	76,561	3,465,401	3,033	347	$90,572	$2,171.20	$284.33
1982	5,801	1,012	36,379	762	878	7.6	248,124	75,733	3,514,457	3,103	353	$104,876	$2,500.52	$327.37
1983	5,783	1,018	36,152	749	864	7.6	210,044	75,465	3,490,254	3,096	358	$116,438	$2,789.18	$369.49
1984	5,759	1,017	35,155	702	820	7.3	211,961	75,581	3,456,308	3,017	368	$123,336	$2,995.38	$411.10
1985	5,732	1,001	33,449	649	777	7.1	218,716	74,893	3,521,135	2,997	386	$130,499	$3,244.74	$460.19
1986	5,678	978	32,379	629	770	7.1	231,912	73,682	3,584,408	3,025	393	$140,654	$3,532.51	$500.81
1987	5,611	958	31,601	622	776	7.2	245,524	72,510	3,602,296	3,114	401	$152,585	$3,850.16	$538.96
1988	5,533	947	31,453	620	787	7.2	269,129	70,325	3,706,402	3,205	407	$168,722	$4,206.73	$586.33
1989	5,455	933	31,116	618	796	7.2	285,712	69,405	3,830,615	3,303	415	$184,898	$4,587.87	$636.96
1990	5,384	927	31,181	619	813	7.2	301,329	68,412	3,958,263	3,420	421	$203,693	$4,946.68	$686.83
1991	5,342	924	31,064	611	820	7.2	322,048	67,434	3,965,396	3,535	431	$225,023	$5,359.56	$752.10
1992	5,292	921	31,034	604	827	7.1	348,522	67,089	3,924,944	3,620	437	$248,095	$5,794.43	$819.83
1993	5,261	919	30,748	592	828	7.0	366,885	66,054	3,870,376	3,677	444	$266,089	$6,132.06	$880.52
1994	5,229	902	30,718	568	812	6.7	382,924	65,722	3,809,367	3,692	455	$275,779	$6,229.83	$930.71
1995	5,194	873	30,945	548	809	6.5	414,345	64,736	3,764,698	3,714	459	$285,588	$6,215.51	$967.69
1996	5,134	862	31,099	531	799	6.2	439,863	63,640	3,723,871	3,725	466	$293,755	$6,224.94	$1,006.14
1997	5,057	853	31,577	528	811	6.1	450,140	63,241	3,742,191	3,790	467	$305,763	$6,261.93	$1,032.70
1998	5,015	840	31,812	525	819	6.0	474,193	62,156	3,726,233	3,831	468	$318,834	$6,385.99	$1,066.96
1999	4,956	830	32,359	526	833	5.9	495,346	61,528	3,760,295	3,838	461	$335,246	$6,511.72	$1,102.61
2000	4,915	824	33,089	526	849	5.8	521,404	60,839	3,880,166	3,911	461	$356,564	$6,648.82	$1,149.40
2001	4,908	826	33,814	533	865	5.7	538,480	60,448	3,873,395	3,987	461	$383,735	$6,979.53	$1,217.27
2002	4,927	821	34,478	540	886	5.7	556,404	59,974	3,870,191	4,069	459	$416,591	$7,354.60	$1,289.87
2003	4,895	813	34,783	539	894	5.7	563,186	59,662	3,915,842	4,109	460	$450,124	$7,796.41	$1,379.48
2004	4,919	808	35,086	541	909	5.6	571,569	58,710	3,931,508	4,148	456	$481,247	$8,165.55	$1,450.35
2005	4,936	802	35,239	540	929	5.6	584,429	58,195	3,987,766	4,257	458	$515,740	$8,534.90	$1,522.42
2006	4,927	803	35,378	538	939	5.6	599,553	57,832	4,075,193	4,343	463	$551,835	$8,970.31	$1,612.23
2007	4,897	801	35,346	533	943	5.5	603,300	57,546	4,077,962	4,465	474	$583,252	$9,377.17	$1,696.10
2008	5,010	808	35,761	536	962	5.5	624,098	57,301	4,073,724	4,550	473	$626,577	$9,788.25	$1,782.28

Table 1 (Continued)

CLASSIFICATION: Nongovernment not-for-profit community hospitals

YEAR	HOSPITALS	BEDS (in thousands)	ADMISSIONS (in thousands)	AVERAGE DAILY CENSUS (in thousands)	ADJUSTED AVERAGE DAILY CENSUS (in thousands)	AVERAGE LENGTH OF STAY (days)	OUTPATIENT VISITS (in thousands)	NEWBORNS Bassinets	NEWBORNS Births	FTE PERSONNEL Number (in thousands)	FTE PERSONNEL Per 100 Adjusted Census	EXPENSES Amount (In Millions of dollars)	EXPENSES Adjusted per Inpatient Stay (dollars)	EXPENSES Adjusted per Inpatient Day (dollars)
1975	3,339	658	23,722	510	574	7.8	131,435	57,496	2,131,057	1,712	298	$27,938	$1,040.21	$133.36
1976	3,345	670	24,082	517	586	7.9	140,914	56,442	2,100,917	1,791	306	$32,764	$1,208.23	$152.94
1979	3,330	690	24,874	528	603	7.7	139,565	52,859	2,308,548	1,999	332	$47,937	$1,684.40	$218.06
1980	3,322	692	25,566	542	621	7.7	142,156	52,659	2,389,478	2,086	336	$55,780	$1,901.64	$245.74
1981	3,340	706	25,945	555	636	7.8	143,380	52,302	2,455,033	2,213	399	$66,267	$2,225.17	$285.64
1982	3,338	712	25,898	553	637	7.8	176,245	51,566	2,483,345	2,265	355	$76,806	$2,572.93	$330.41
1983	3,347	718	25,827	544	629	7.7	150,839	51,649	2,465,604	2,270	362	$85,637	$2,868.80	$373.78
1984	3,351	716	25,236	512	598	7.4	153,281	51,491	2,446,540	2,222	372	$90,814	$3,072.51	$415.04
1985	3,349	707	24,179	476	569	7.2	158,953	51,424	2,507,288	2,216	389	$96,150	$3,307.41	$462.69
1986	3,323	689	23,483	460	563	7.2	167,653	50,885	2,547,170	2,241	398	$103,524	$3,589.64	$503.64
1987	3,274	673	22,937	455	566	7.2	177,413	50,133	2,557,294	2,298	406	$112,325	$3,914.23	$543.67
1988	3,242	668	22,939	456	577	7.3	195,363	48,828	2,653,794	2,373	412	$124,703	$4,272.95	$591.13
1989	3,220	661	22,792	455	584	7.3	209,191	48,305	2,751,426	2,454	420	$136,889	$4,649.22	$642.45
1990	3,191	657	22,878	455	596	7.3	221,073	47,441	2,833,204	2,533	424	$150,673	$5,001.24	$692.36
1991	3,175	656	22,964	451	603	7.2	238,204	47,229	2,845,995	2,624	435	$166,806	$5,393.30	$758.21
1992	3,173	656	23,056	445	606	7.1	257,887	47,185	2,846,386	2,692	443	$183,793	$5,808.80	$828.44
1993	3,154	651	22,749	432	602	6.9	270,138	46,214	2,802,164	2,711	451	$197,187	$6,177.69	$897.70
1994	3,139	637	22,704	413	589	6.6	282,653	46,381	2,792,116	2,719	462	$204,219	$6,256.72	$950.31
1995	3,092	610	22,557	393	578	6.4	303,851	45,198	2,725,641	2,702	468	$209,614	$6,279.17	$994.39
1996	3,045	598	22,542	379	567	6.1	320,746	44,650	2,683,750	2,711	478	$215,950	$6,344.05	$1,042.04
1997	3,000	591	22,905	376	575	6.0	330,215	44,434	2,698,086	2,765	481	$225,287	$6,392.74	$1,074.26
1998	3,026	588	23,282	377	587	5.9	352,114	44,037	2,715,958	2,834	483	$237,978	$6,525.68	$1,110.50
1999	3,012	587	23,871	381	605	5.8	370,784	44,172	2,746,453	2,862	473	$251,534	$6,607.51	$1,139.89
2000	3,003	583	24,452	382	618	5.7	393,168	43,655	2,833,615	2,919	472	$267,051	$6,717.48	$1,182.32
2001	2,998	585	24,983	385	628	5.6	404,901	43,640	2,829,691	2,971	473	$287,250	$7,051.76	$1,255.25
2002	3,025	582	25,425	391	646	5.6	416,910	43,241	2,820,159	3,039	471	$312,726	$7,457.84	$1,328.81
2003	2,984	575	25,668	389	647	5.5	424,215	42,965	2,854,764	3,059	473	$337,696	$7,904.93	$1,429.62
2004	2,967	568	25,757	388	655	5.5	430,262	41,968	2,844,617	3,077	470	$359,414	$8,266.64	$1,501.09
2005	2,958	561	25,881	388	667	5.5	441,653	41,585	2,876,677	3,155	473	$385,993	$8,670.83	$1,585.34
2006	2,919	559	25,798	385	671	5.4	453,501	40,888	2,905,275	3,207	478	$412,868	$9,189.58	$1,685.62
2007	2,913	554	25,752	380	673	5.4	455,825	40,681	2,907,002	3,286	488	$436,319	$9,592.93	$1,776.06
2008	2,923	557	25,899	380	683	5.4	469,804	40,567	2,901,854	3,340	489	$468,080	$10,080.50	$1,875.78

Table 1 (Continued)

Investor-owned (for-profit) community hospitals

CLASSIFICATION YEAR	HOSPITALS	BEDS (in thousands)	ADMISSIONS (in thousands)	AVERAGE DAILY CENSUS (in thousands)	ADJUSTED AVERAGE DAILY CENSUS (in thousands)	AVERAGE LENGTH OF STAY (days)	OUTPATIENT VISITS (in thousands)	NEWBORNS Bassinets	NEWBORNS Births	FTE PERSONNEL Number (in thousands)	FTE PERSONNEL Per 100 Adjusted Census	Amount (in Millions of dollars)	EXPENSES Adjusted per Inpatient Stay (dollars)	EXPENSES Adjusted per Inpatient Day (dollars)
1975	775	73	2,646	48	53	6.6	7,713	4,062	141,392	139	263	$2,561	$876.48	$132.80
1976	752	76	2,734	50	54	6.6	8,048	4,044	144,751	147	272	$3,085	$1,031.91	$156.35
1979	727	83	2,963	53	59	6.6	9,289	4,110	174,843	174	300	$4,820	$1,476.42	$225.87
1980	730	87	3,165	57	62	6.5	9,696	4,439	199,722	189	304	$5,847	$1,675.85	$257.12
1981	729	88	3,239	58	63	6.5	9,961	4,523	207,405	203	322	$6,856	$1,952.56	$299.02
1982	748	91	3,316	60	66	6.6	13,193	4,736	219,675	212	320	$8,177	$2,224.75	$340.03
1983	757	94	3,299	59	66	6.5	10,389	5,039	228,883	213	323	$9,208	$2,517.53	$385.42
1984	786	100	3,314	57	64	6.3	11,090	5,807	242,088	214	335	$10,251	$2,748.51	$438.30
1985	805	104	3,242	54	63	6.1	12,378	6,117	266,839	221	350	$11,486	$3,033.06	$500.48
1986	834	107	3,231	54	65	6.1	14,896	6,305	291,112	229	354	$12,987	$3,341.79	$552.40
1987	828	106	3,157	54	66	6.2	16,566	6,391	306,492	242	367	$14,067	$3,617.19	$585.01
1988	790	104	3,090	53	66	6.2	17,926	6,254	308,828	249	379	$15,545	$4,022.77	$649.33
1989	769	102	3,071	53	67	6.3	19,341	6,354	325,711	261	390	$17,240	$4,406.20	$707.90
1990	749	101	3,066	54	69	6.4	20,110	6,261	340,555	273	396	$18,822	$4,727.27	$751.55
1991	738	100	3,016	52	69	6.3	21,174	6,358	359,115	281	409	$20,516	$5,133.53	$820.19
1992	723	99	2,969	51	69	6.3	22,900	6,519	357,776	285	412	$22,496	$5,548.24	$888.73
1993	717	99	2,946	51	69	6.2	24,936	6,395	363,358	289	417	$23,077	$5,643.21	$914.39
1994	719	101	3,035	50	70	6.1	26,443	6,329	354,477	302	434	$23,445	$5,528.91	$923.90
1995	752	106	3,428	55	77	5.8	31,940	7,164	408,339	343	443	$26,653	$5,425.20	$946.99
1996	759	109	3,684	56	82	5.6	37,347	7,441	444,697	359	437	$28,385	$5,207.44	$945.49
1997	797	115	3,953	60	89	5.5	40,919	8,026	465,919	385	433	$31,179	$5,218.69	$961.96
1998	771	113	3,971	60	90	5.5	42,072	7,895	466,025	383	425	$31,732	$5,262.44	$968.00
1999	747	107	3,905	58	86	5.5	39,896	7,486	467,585	362	422	$31,179	$5,350.07	$999.03
2000	749	110	4,141	61	90	5.4	43,378	7,792	503,497	378	418	$34,969	$5,642.18	$1,057.32
2001	754	109	4,197	63	92	5.4	44,706	7,413	494,669	379	413	$37,348	$5,971.81	$1,121.31
2002	766	108	4,365	64	93	5.3	45,215	7,467	496,988	380	407	$40,082	$6,161.44	$1,180.83
2003	790	110	4,481	65	95	5.3	44,246	7,491	515,693	391	411	$43,953	$6,589.91	$1,264.50
2004	835	113	4,599	68	100	5.4	44,962	7,763	534,503	406	406	$48,971	$7,139.13	$1,362.42
2005	868	114	4,618	68	101	5.3	46,016	7,714	546,307	421	418	$51,833	$7,351.96	$1,412.74
2006	890	115	4,735	68	103	5.2	44,237	8,012	574,113	423	413	$55,030	$7,422.08	$1,471.53
2007	873	116	4,626	66	101	5.2	43,943	7,760	555,670	432	429	$56,405	$7,823.44	$1,535.98
2008	982	121	4,839	70	109	5.3	44,897	7,791	562,711	450	414	$61,762	$7,984.62	$1,555.55

Table 1 (Continued)

CLASSIFICATION	YEAR	HOSPITALS	BEDS (in thousands)	ADMISSIONS (in thousands)	AVERAGE DAILY CENSUS (in thousands)	ADJUSTED AVERAGE DAILY CENSUS (in thousands)	AVERAGE LENGTH OF STAY (days)	OUTPATIENT VISITS (in thousands)	NEWBORNS Bassinets	NEWBORNS Births	FTE PERSONNEL Number (in thousands)	FTE PERSONNEL Per 100 Adjusted Census	EXPENSES Amount (In Millions of dollars)	EXPENSES Adjusted per Inpatient Stay (dollars)	Adjusted per Inpatient Day (dollars)
State and local government community hospitals	1975	1,761	210	7,067	148	171	7.6	51,525	22,271	726,103	540	316	$8,463	$1,030.86	$135.64
	1976	1,760	210	7,163	146	170	7.5	52,286	21,810	716,548	537	315	$9,391	$1,132.50	$151.00
	1979	1,785	211	7,262	146	171	7.4	49,924	20,297	803,621	583	341	$13,247	$1,561.04	$211.89
	1980	1,778	209	7,413	149	174	7.3	50,459	20,424	819,282	598	343	$15,204	$1,750.13	$238.63
	1981	1,744	210	7,255	150	174	7.6	49,427	19,736	802,963	618	354	$17,449	$2,071.57	$274.25
	1982	1,715	210	7,165	149	175	7.6	58,685	19,431	811,437	627	320	$19,893	$2,364.09	$311.56
	1983	1,679	207	7,025	145	170	7.6	48,816	18,777	795,767	613	360	$21,593	$2,621.28	$347.56
	1984	1,622	201	6,606	133	158	7.3	47,590	18,283	767,680	581	368	$22,271	$2,823.13	$385.17
	1985	1,578	189	6,028	119	145	7.2	47,386	17,352	747,008	561	387	$22,863	$3,106.14	$432.84
	1986	1,521	182	5,665	114	142	7.4	49,383	16,492	746,126	555	391	$24,143	$3,404.69	$466.17
	1987	1,509	180	5,507	113	144	7.5	51,544	15,986	738,510	573	399	$26,192	$3,717.77	$499.33
	1988	1,501	175	5,424	112	145	7.6	55,340	15,243	743,780	583	403	$28,474	$4,033.67	$538.63
	1989	1,466	170	5,253	110	145	7.7	57,179	14,746	753,478	589	406	$30,769	$4,430.12	$582.15
	1990	1,444	169	5,236	111	148	7.7	60,146	14,710	784,504	614	415	$34,198	$4,837.76	$634.45
	1991	1,429	168	5,084	108	143	7.8	62,670	13,847	760,286	630	424	$37,701	$5,339.75	$695.89
	1992	1,396	166	5,008	108	152	7.9	67,734	13,385	720,782	643	424	$41,806	$5,870.76	$753.92
	1993	1,390	169	5,054	109	157	7.8	71,311	13,445	704,854	676	430	$45,825	$6,205.52	$799.73
	1994	1,371	164	4,979	104	154	7.6	73,828	13,012	662,774	672	438	$48,115	$6,513.39	$858.62
	1995	1,350	157	4,961	100	154	7.4	78,554	12,374	630,718	670	435	$49,322	$6,445.18	$877.85
	1996	1,330	155	4,873	96	150	7.2	81,770	11,549	595,424	654	437	$49,420	$6,418.65	$903.41
	1997	1,260	148	4,720	92	148	7.1	79,007	10,731	578,186	640	433	$49,298	$6,475.07	$913.62
	1998	1,218	139	4,559	87	142	7.0	80,008	10,174	544,250	614	433	$49,123	$6,612.23	$949.36
	1999	1,197	136	4,583	86	143	6.9	84,667	9,870	546,257	614	430	$52,534	$6,923.35	$1,006.91
	2000	1,163	131	4,496	83	140	6.7	84,858	9,392	543,054	614	438	$54,544	$7,106.05	$1,063.75
	2001	1,156	132	4,634	85	145	6.7	88,873	9,395	549,035	637	438	$59,137	$7,400.01	$1,113.79
	2002	1,136	130	4,688	84	147	6.6	94,260	9,266	553,044	651	442	$63,783	$7,772.93	$1,188.12
	2003	1,121	129	4,634	84	152	6.6	94,725	9,206	545,385	658	434	$68,475	$8,205.10	$1,237.64
	2004	1,117	128	4,730	85	154	6.5	96,245	8,979	552,388	666	431	$72,861	$8,473.18	$1,291.06
	2005	1,110	128	4,740	85	161	6.5	96,760	8,896	564,782	681	424	$77,914	$8,793.26	$1,329.64
	2006	1,119	128	4,848	86	165	6.5	101,845	8,932	595,805	713	433	$83,974	$9,147.40	$1,400.09
	2007	1,111	131	4,967	87	169	6.4	103,552	9,105	615,290	747	443	$90,528	$9,523.22	$1,472.26
	2008	1,105	131	5,023	86	170	6.3	109,358	8,943	609,159	760	446	$96,735	$9,826.94	$1,552.32

Table 2

2008 U.S. Registered Hospitals: Utilization, Personnel, and Finances

Excludes U.S.-Associated Areas, Puerto Rico, and nonregistered hospitals.

CLASSIFICATION	HOSPITALS	BEDS	ADMISSIONS	INPATIENT DAYS	ADJUSTED PATIENT DAYS	AVERAGE DAILY CENSUS	ADJUSTED AVERAGE DAILY CENSUS	AVERAGE STAY (days)	SURGICAL OPERATIONS	OUTPATIENT VISITS Emergency	OUTPATIENT VISITS Total	NEWBORNS Bassinets	NEWBORNS Births
UNITED STATES	5,815	951,045	37,529,270	237,155,375	—	648,599	—	—	28,149,852	126,716,715	709,960,064	58,133	4,109,081
6-24 Beds	437	7,537	220,835	1,010,324	—	2,754	—	—	290,141	1,693,539	9,968,041	472	14,798
25-49	1,249	40,618	1,303,398	7,184,359	—	19,660	—	—	1,312,578	8,286,714	49,830,393	2,976	116,142
50-99	1,245	89,648	2,706,686	19,634,558	—	53,711	—	—	2,330,880	12,388,502	70,341,253	5,619	266,292
100-199	1,254	179,603	6,769,072	42,032,760	—	115,018	—	—	5,494,849	27,456,497	138,768,117	12,621	776,644
200-299	692	168,432	7,139,639	42,083,094	—	115,090	—	—	5,288,774	24,557,406	117,003,466	11,619	794,470
300-399	402	138,397	6,036,433	35,525,408	—	97,034	—	—	4,058,041	17,940,376	99,233,493	8,391	678,865
400-499	214	94,398	4,002,014	24,780,766	—	67,744	—	—	2,923,063	11,041,226	65,294,537	5,309	435,954
500 or more	322	232,412	9,351,193	64,904,106	—	177,588	—	—	6,451,526	23,352,455	159,520,764	11,126	1,025,916
Psychiatric	456	81,781	757,060	25,129,814	—	68,743	—	—	7,902	197,041	8,458,700	0	0
Hospitals	448	77,858	756,583	23,992,864	—	65,634	—	—	7,902	197,041	8,455,387	0	0
Institutions for mentally retarded	8	3,923	477	1,136,950	—	3,109	—	—	0	0	3,313	0	0
General	4,758	819,065	35,885,373	199,081,159	—	544,427	—	—	27,538,663	125,635,125	683,800,605	57,383	4,047,188
Hospitals	4,739	816,808	35,868,366	198,404,735	—	542,575	—	—	27,538,190	125,531,590	683,532,503	57,383	4,047,188
Hospital units of institutions	19	2,257	17,007	676,424	—	1,852	—	—	473	103,535	268,102	0	0
TB and other respiratory diseases	1	72	78	12,775	—	35	—	—	0	0	1,024	0	0
Obstetrics and gynecology	13	1,756	102,958	453,991	—	1,241	—	—	81,026	105,524	1,053,336	572	56,706
Eye, ear, nose and throat	6	190	4,094	15,278	—	42	—	—	72,389	52,553	734,662	0	0
Rehabilitation	203	16,600	287,659	4,200,215	—	11,479	—	—	15,648	0	6,382,219	40	1,253
Orthopedic	25	1,331	53,453	242,157	—	677	—	—	91,796	62,989	927,872	0	0
Chronic Disease	4	290	2,097	81,139	—	222	—	—	323	6,379	76,134	0	0
Surgical	8	166	9,205	21,294	—	58	—	—	38,443	6,970	68,114	0	0
Cancer	9	1,731	76,949	539,724	—	1,477	—	—	66,488	28,505	3,168,276	0	0
Heart	8	888	51,328	226,375	—	618	—	—	40,910	34,346	177,355	0	0
Acute long-term care hospital	274	20,890	207,203	5,512,579	—	15,097	—	—	132,694	372,892	1,800,416	16	894
All other	50	6,285	91,813	1,638,875	—	4,483	—	—	63,570	214,391	3,311,351	122	3,040
Federal	213	45,992	955,899	11,406,234	—	31,216	—	—	675,084	3,345,486	78,639,942	790	35,216
Psychiatric	9	3,085	26,202	914,960	—	2,501	—	—	6,340	27,194	2,465,874	0	0
General and other special	204	42,907	929,697	10,491,274	—	28,715	—	—	668,744	3,318,292	76,174,068	790	35,216
Nonfederal	5,602	905,053	36,573,371	225,749,141	—	617,383	—	—	27,474,768	123,371,229	631,320,122	57,343	4,073,865
Psychiatric	447	78,696	730,858	24,214,854	—	66,242	—	—	1,562	169,847	5,992,826	0	0
Hospitals	439	74,773	730,381	23,077,904	—	63,133	—	—	1,562	169,847	5,989,513	0	0
Institutions for mentally retarded	8	3,923	477	1,136,950	—	3,109	—	—	0	0	3,313	0	0
TB and other respiratory diseases	1	72	78	12,775	12,775	35	35	164.0	0	0	1,024	0	0
Long-term general and other special	128	16,479	65,969	4,943,678	5,164,632	13,524	14,128	75.0	13,768	93,474	1,141,098	42	141
Short-term general and other special	5,026	809,806	35,776,466	196,577,834	352,059,202	537,582	962,987	5.5	27,459,438	123,107,908	624,185,174	57,301	4,073,724
Hospital units of institutions	16	1,737	15,716	499,366	499,366	1,367	1,367	32.0	0	83,884	86,878	0	0
Community Hospitals	5,010	808,069	35,760,750	196,078,468	351,559,836	536,215	961,620	5.5	27,459,438	123,024,024	624,098,296	57,301	4,073,724
6-24 Beds	389	6,726	204,522	835,702	3,297,586	2,276	9,021	4.1	286,047	1,505,235	8,383,154	424	13,938
25-49	1,151	37,142	1,218,123	6,342,577	18,257,560	17,353	49,932	5.2	1,264,176	7,781,578	40,729,016	2,813	106,334
50-99	995	71,477	2,318,730	14,775,775	34,278,619	40,422	93,802	6.4	2,182,498	11,523,593	56,743,285	5,313	252,752
100-199	1,070	153,488	6,304,036	34,742,992	69,165,909	95,081	189,227	5.5	5,324,353	26,601,799	119,780,484	12,513	765,495
200-299	596	144,895	6,866,533	35,165,769	60,668,557	96,163	165,936	5.1	5,169,808	24,185,692	107,976,773	11,440	794,470
300-399	355	122,363	5,894,366	31,089,796	50,480,316	84,901	138,081	5.3	4,019,681	17,724,755	90,619,742	8,391	678,865
400-499	184	80,815	3,895,152	20,830,426	33,554,730	56,932	91,708	5.3	2,873,559	10,828,538	57,642,828	5,281	435,954
500 or more	270	191,163	9,059,288	52,295,431	81,856,559	143,087	223,913	5.8	6,339,316	22,872,834	142,223,014	11,126	1,025,916
Nongovernment not-for-profit	2,923	556,651	25,898,803	138,989,998	249,539,308	380,048	682,502	5.4	20,049,476	86,473,441	469,803,768	40,567	2,901,854
Investor-owned (for profit)	982	120,887	4,839,306	25,553,070	39,704,497	69,912	108,622	5.3	3,692,908	16,188,125	44,896,646	7,791	562,711
State and Local Government	1,105	130,531	5,022,641	31,535,400	62,316,031	86,255	170,496	6.3	3,717,054	20,362,458	109,397,882	8,943	609,159

Table 2 (Continued)

CLASSIFICATION	FULL-TIME EQUIVALENT PERSONNEL — Physicians and Dentists	Registered Nurses	Licensed Practical Nurses	Other Salaried Personnel	Total Personnel	FULL-TIME EQUIVALENT TRAINEES — Medical and Dental Residents	Other Trainees	Total Trainees	EXPENSES / LABOR — Payroll (in thousands)	Employee Benefits (in thousands)	Total (in thousands)	Percent of Total	EXPENSES / TOTAL — Amount (in thousands)	Adjusted per Admission	Adjusted per Inpatient Day
UNITED STATES	125,940	1,323,913	129,596	3,536,823	5,116,272	98,249	14,269	112,518	$287,383,598	$74,571,908	$361,955,506	52.5	$690,073,646	—	—
6-24 Beds	971	9,234	2,547	31,173	43,925	19	15	34	$2,216,294	$546,276	$2,762,570	52.1	$5,306,681	—	—
25-49	6,163	49,158	12,058	177,343	244,722	502	770	1,272	$10,690,743	$2,679,640	$13,370,383	51.7	$25,877,640	—	—
50-99	10,047	90,274	16,791	292,559	409,671	1,032	1,188	2,220	$20,427,049	$5,201,494	$25,628,543	54.2	$47,266,608	—	—
100-199	18,548	218,710	27,139	605,260	869,657	6,112	1,274	7,386	$46,416,347	$11,957,612	$58,373,959	53.0	$110,237,171	—	—
200-299	16,962	232,942	21,613	600,781	872,298	9,209	1,383	10,592	$46,993,886	$12,944,229	$61,938,115	51.9	$119,332,889	—	—
300-399	15,561	197,697	15,469	501,240	729,967	11,866	1,122	12,988	$42,315,707	$10,878,677	$53,194,384	51.7	$102,897,773	—	—
400-499	12,419	148,613	11,031	374,443	546,506	14,246	2,026	16,272	$32,557,013	$8,432,844	$40,989,857	53.9	$75,982,253	—	—
500 or more	45,269	377,285	22,948	954,024	1,399,526	55,263	6,491	61,754	$82,766,559	$21,931,137	$104,697,695	52.0	$203,172,631	—	—
Psychiatric	4,932	25,488	8,239	155,322	193,961	476	484	960	$8,666,601	$3,023,227	$11,689,828	72.3	$16,168,612	—	—
Hospitals	4,903	25,278	7,982	148,240	186,403	476	484	960	$8,394,661	$2,937,649	$11,332,310	72.0	$15,739,121	—	—
Institutions for mentally retarded	29	210	257	7,082	7,578	0	0	0	$271,940	$85,578	$357,518	83.2	$429,491	—	—
General	115,256	1,254,348	112,917	3,223,907	4,706,428	95,734	12,298	108,032	$266,575,894	$66,551,935	$335,127,830	51.9	$645,911,698	—	—
Hospitals	115,207	1,253,564	112,391	3,221,276	4,702,438	95,734	12,297	108,031	$266,397,961	$66,477,216	$334,875,177	51.9	$645,515,055	—	—
Hospital units of institutions	49	784	526	2,631	3,960	0	1	1	$177,934	$74,719	$252,652	63.7	$396,643	—	—
TB and other respiratory diseases	0	19	16	109	144	0	0	0	$5,521	$1,546	$7,067	58.7	$12,032	—	—
Obstetrics and gynecology	158	3,487	159	6,569	10,373	77	9	86	$624,886	$151,922	$776,807	54.9	$1,414,521	—	—
Eye, ear, nose and throat	154	449	26	2,515	3,144	106	52	158	$153,954	$41,893	$195,847	46.9	$418,000	—	—
Rehabilitation	536	11,504	2,786	45,975	60,801	160	29	189	$2,823,761	$655,652	$3,479,413	58.1	$5,990,664	—	—
Orthopedic	425	2,145	165	7,541	10,276	59	8	67	$717,592	$182,030	$899,622	49.5	$1,818,523	—	—
Chronic Disease	9	189	49	945	1,132	0	24	24	$57,354	$14,692	$72,046	59.3	$121,405	—	—
Surgical	2	316	28	711	1,057	2	0	2	$47,939	$10,771	$58,710	29.6	$198,324	—	—
Cancer	2,702	6,950	132	31,000	40,734	1,323	1,161	2,484	$2,727,577	$727,171	$3,454,748	50.8	$6,804,717	—	—
Heart	47	1,577	72	3,103	4,799	8	2	10	$223,455	$75,518	$398,973	47.0	$847,989	—	—
Acute long-term care hospital	531	11,898	3,895	39,712	56,036	70	21	91	$3,014,344	$718,392	$3,732,735	54.0	$6,906,736	—	—
All other	1,188	5,543	1,112	19,414	27,257	234	181	415	$1,644,721	$417,159	$2,061,880	59.6	$3,460,424	—	—
Federal	25,692	64,544	14,711	236,126	341,073	7,301	4,248	11,549	$20,585,152	$5,710,857	$26,296,009	59.7	$44,021,087	—	—
Psychiatric	594	1,879	799	8,547	11,819	75	85	160	$781,272	$193,567	$974,840	66.3	$1,470,649	—	—
General and other special	25,098	62,665	13,912	227,579	329,254	7,226	4,163	11,389	$19,803,879	$5,517,289	$25,321,169	59.5	$42,550,438	—	—
Nonfederal	100,248	1,259,369	114,885	3,300,697	4,775,199	90,948	10,021	100,969	$266,798,446	$68,861,051	$335,659,497	52.0	$646,052,559	—	—
Psychiatric	4,338	23,609	7,440	146,775	182,162	401	399	800	$7,885,329	$2,829,659	$10,714,988	72.9	$14,697,963	—	—
Hospitals	4,309	23,399	7,183	139,693	174,584	401	399	800	$7,613,389	$2,744,081	$10,357,470	72.6	$14,268,472	—	—
Institutions for mentally retarded	29	210	257	7,082	7,573	0	0	0	$271,940	$85,578	$357,518	83.2	$429,491	—	—
TB and other respiratory diseases	0	19	16	109	144	0	0	0	$5,521	$1,546	$7,067	58.7	$12,032	$154,257.31	$941.85
Long-term general and other special	502	6,689	2,425	31,433	41,049	4	49	53	$2,252,801	$603,184	$2,855,984	63.2	$4,519,601	$64,163.33	$875.11
Short-term general and other special	95,408	1,229,052	105,004	3,122,380	4,551,844	90,543	9,573	100,116	$256,654,795	$65,426,663	$322,081,453	51.4	$626,822,964	$9,789.69	$1,780.45
Hospital units of institutions	8	669	442	1,165	2,284	0	0	0	$95,309	$50,176	$145,485	59.1	$246,006	$15,653.20	$492.64
Community Hospitals	95,400	1,228,383	104,562	3,121,215	4,549,560	90,543	9,573	100,116	$256,559,486	$65,376,486	$321,935,972	51.4	$626,576,958	$9,788.25	$1,782.28
6-24 Beds	654	8,347	2,423	28,126	39,550	19	9	28	$1,846,397	$452,484	$2,298,882	51.0	$4,510,451	$5,254.22	$1,367.80
25-49	4,214	44,936	11,069	155,396	215,615	236	528	764	$10,092,290	$2,509,764	$12,602,055	52.3	$24,074,709	$6,426.20	$1,318.62
50-99	5,205	75,258	13,190	230,431	324,084	266	221	487	$16,092,844	$4,106,792	$20,199,637	52.7	$38,332,175	$7,084.60	$1,118.25
100-199	12,916	199,142	21,729	521,541	755,328	4,931	581	5,512	$40,232,773	$10,242,675	$50,475,449	52.1	$96,955,948	$7,936.73	$1,401.79
200-299	11,726	215,814	17,317	531,456	776,373	7,349	975	8,324	$43,515,782	$11,230,009	$54,745,791	50.7	$108,021,530	$9,197.38	$1,780.52
300-399	12,276	188,713	12,931	458,524	672,444	10,185	754	10,939	$39,298,025	$9,912,435	$49,210,459	50.9	$96,680,861	$10,091.05	$1,915.22
400-499	9,798	140,103	8,490	338,522	496,913	13,645	1,418	15,063	$29,630,849	$7,627,646	$37,258,495	52.8	$70,515,262	$11,236.78	$2,101.50
500 or more	38,611	356,070	17,413	857,219	1,269,313	53,912	5,087	58,959	$75,850,524	$19,294,680	$95,145,205	50.7	$187,486,021	$13,221.31	$2,290.42
Nongovernment not-for-profit	78,073	895,442	62,776	2,303,673	3,339,964	63,966	6,501	70,467	$190,847,369	$48,383,523	$239,230,891	51.1	$468,079,866	$10,080.50	$1,875.78
Investor-owned (for profit)	2,077	142,530	18,241	287,062	449,910	1,878	377	2,255	$23,708,088	$5,285,146	$28,993,234	46.9	$61,762,475	$7,984.62	$1,555.55
State and Local Government	15,250	190,411	23,545	530,480	759,686	24,699	2,695	27,354	$42,004,029	$11,707,817	$53,711,847	55.5	$96,734,616	$9,826.94	$1,552.32

Tables 3–6

Total U.S.

TABLE 3

TOTAL UNITED STATES

U.S. Registered Community Hospitals
(Nonfederal, short-term general and other special hospitals)

Overview 2004–2008

	2008	2007	2006	2005	2004
TOTAL U.S. Community Hospitals	5,010	4,897	4,927	4,936	4,919
Bed Size Category					
6-24	389	360	375	370	352
25-49	1,151	1,076	1,066	1,032	988
50-99	995	971	969	1,001	1,028
100-199	1,070	1,083	1,117	1,129	1,141
200-299	596	613	607	619	621
300-399	355	343	354	368	351
400-499	184	191	180	173	185
500 +	270	260	259	244	253
Location					
Hospitals Urban	3,012	2,900	2,926	2,927	2,744
Hospitals Rural	1,998	1,997	2,001	2,009	2,175
Control					
State and Local Government	1,105	1,111	1,119	1,110	1,117
Not for Profit	2,923	2,913	2,919	2,958	2,967
Investor owned	982	873	889	868	835
Physician Models					
Independent Practice Association	597	654	683	700	726
Group Practice without Walls	160	166	166	174	170
Open Physician-Hospital Organization	672	691	715	751	739
Closed Physician-Hospital Organization	213	240	237	249	229
Management Service Organization	436	453	445	438	443
Integrated Salary Model	1,583	1,534	1,486	1,390	1,312
Equity Model	97	75	72	72	59
Foundation	248	236	230	236	191
Insurance Products					
Health Maintenance Organization	597	632	663	670	682
Preferred Provider Organization	685	842	887	931	883
Indemnity Fee for Service	250	292	289	298	280
Managed Care Contracts					
Health Maintenance Organization	2,670	2,655	2,667	2,682	2,681
Preferred Provider Organization	3,125	3,099	3,163	3,187	3,173
Affiliations					
Hospitals in a System	2,868	2,730	2,755	2,716	2,668
Hospitals in a Network	1,490	1,472	1,508	1,455	1,464
Hospitals in a Group Purchasing Organization	3,677	3,591	3,666	3,612	3,492

TABLE 3

TOTAL UNITED STATES

U.S. Registered Community Hospitals
(Nonfederal, short-term general and other special hospitals)

Utilization, Personnel, Revenue and Expenses, Community Health Indicators 2004–2008

	2008	2007	2006	2005	2004
TOTAL FACILITY (Includes Hospital and Nursing Home Units)					
Utilization - Inpatient					
Beds	808,069	800,892	802,658	802,311	808,127
Admissions	35,760,750	35,345,986	35,377,659	35,238,673	35,086,061
Inpatient Days	196,078,468	194,549,348	196,366,512	197,073,770	197,564,172
Average Length of Stay	5.5	5.5	5.6	5.6	5.6
Inpatient Surgeries	10,105,156	10,189,630	10,095,683	10,097,271	10,050,346
Births	4,073,724	4,077,962	4,075,193	3,987,766	3,931,508
Utilization - Outpatient					
Emergency Outpatient Visits	123,024,024	120,811,299	118,374,029	114,750,874	112,603,969
Other Outpatient Visits	501,074,272	482,489,075	481,178,996	469,677,862	458,965,365
Total Outpatient Visits	624,098,296	603,300,374	599,553,025	584,428,736	571,569,334
Outpatient Surgeries	17,354,282	17,146,334	17,235,141	17,445,587	17,351,490
Personnel					
Full Time RNs	984,649	950,064	900,326	861,789	826,658
Full Time LPNs	86,750	89,577	93,038	97,400	99,883
Part Time RNs	487,480	482,239	476,549	464,926	452,882
Part Time LPNs	35,602	38,213	39,712	41,488	42,945
Total Full Time	3,919,415	3,846,287	3,720,405	3,647,422	3,555,422
Total Part Time	1,460,487	1,441,216	1,431,738	1,399,672	1,367,507
Revenue - Inpatient					
Gross Inpatient Revenue	$1,090,598,012,951	$1,013,168,556,764	$939,459,919,425	$868,755,031,289	$792,898,585,941
Revenue - Outpatient					
Gross Outpatient Revenue	$711,918,761,681	$632,728,034,944	$570,420,556,680	$510,148,795,934	$446,498,117,963
Revenue and Expenses - Totals					
(Includes Inpatient and Outpatient)					
Total Gross Revenue	$1,802,516,774,632	$1,645,896,591,708	$1,509,880,476,105	$1,378,903,827,223	$1,239,396,703,904
Deductions from Revenue	1,191,615,889,365	1,072,315,472,850	969,154,780,687	873,105,390,216	768,932,980,774
Net Patient Revenue	610,900,885,267	573,581,118,858	540,725,695,418	505,798,437,007	470,463,723,130
Other Operating Revenue	37,136,577,114	35,765,948,073	34,170,257,365	29,888,418,352	28,649,264,451
Other Nonoperating Revenue	(4,453,107,631)	17,000,138,209	12,172,041,974	8,992,031,048	8,399,457,952
Total Net Revenue	643,584,354,750	626,347,205,140	587,050,913,892	544,678,886,407	507,512,445,533
Total Expenses	626,576,957,912	583,252,287,933	551,835,328,219	515,740,325,861	481,246,587,226
HOSPITAL UNIT (Excludes Separate Nursing Home Units)					
Utilization - Inpatient					
Beds	753,905	743,401	742,652	743,022	746,479
Admissions	35,522,351	35,087,765	35,095,084	34,948,319	34,784,253
Inpatient Days	179,043,949	176,068,211	177,215,236	178,203,116	177,782,767
Average Length of Stay	5.0	5.0	5.0	5.1	5.1
Personnel					
Total Full Time	3,875,073	3,795,278	3,671,780	3,603,648	3,447,200
Total Part Time	1,436,850	1,416,918	1,406,083	1,374,027	1,326,749
Revenue and Expenses - Totals					
(Includes Inpatient and Outpatient)					
Total Net Revenue	$639,389,781,304	$621,836,200,340	$580,082,238,834	$540,528,381,448	$503,219,788,467
Total Expenses	622,828,801,705	579,272,589,469	547,742,177,612	511,928,599,756	477,428,333,001
COMMUNITY HEALTH INDICATORS PER 1000 POPULATION					
Total Population (in thousands)	304,060	301,290	298,363	295,561	292,892
Inpatient					
Beds	2.7	2.7	2.7	2.7	2.8
Admissions	117.6	117.3	118.6	119.2	119.8
Inpatient Days	644.9	645.7	658.1	666.8	674.5
Inpatient Surgeries	33.2	33.8	33.8	34.2	34.3
Births	13.4	13.5	13.7	13.5	13.4
Outpatient					
Emergency Outpatient Visits	404.6	401.0	396.7	388.2	384.5
Other Outpatient Visits	1,647.9	1,601.4	1,612.7	1,589.1	1,567.0
Total Outpatient Visits	2,052.6	2,002.4	2,009.5	1,977.4	1,951.5
Outpatient Surgeries	57.1	56.9	57.8	59.0	59.2
Expense per Capita (per person)	$2,060.7	$1,935.8	$1,849.5	$1,745.0	$1,643.1

TABLE 4

BED SIZE CATEGORY 6-24

U.S. Registered Community Hospitals
(Nonfederal, short-term general and other special hospitals)

Overview 2004–2008

	2008	2007	2006	2005	2004
Total Community Hospitals in					
Bed Size Category 6-24...................	**389**	**360**	**375**	**370**	**352**
Location					
Hospitals Urban..........................	103	97	95	101	81
Hospitals Rural	286	263	280	269	271
Control					
State and Local Government...............	148	138	150	144	148
Not for Profit	186	177	174	179	165
Investor owned	55	45	51	47	39
Physician Models					
Independent Practice Association	49	51	54	49	34
Group Practice without Walls...............	11	11	14	14	17
Open Physician-Hospital Organization	34	33	33	27	18
Closed Physician-Hospital Organization	9	6	8	11	7
Management Service Organization	18	15	16	13	12
Integrated Salary Model....................	110	99	101	106	89
Equity Model............................	6	5	2	5	2
Foundation..............................	7	7	10	9	5
Insurance Products					
Health Maintenance Organization	34	35	32	33	32
Preferred Provider Organization..............	39	52	48	47	39
Indemnity Fee for Service	15	16	13	11	9
Managed Care Contracts					
Health Maintenance Organization	137	120	128	138	124
Preferred Provider Organization..............	203	190	186	189	182
Affiliations					
Hospitals in a System.....................	158	141	145	145	132
Hospitals in a Network	116	103	113	117	105
Hospitals in a Group Purchasing Organization..	263	242	263	256	233

TABLE 4

BED SIZE CATEGORY 6-24

U.S. Registered Community Hospitals
(Nonfederal, short-term general and other special hospitals)

Utilization, Personnel, Revenue and Expenses, Community Health Indicators 2004–2008

	2008	2007	2006	2005	2004
TOTAL FACILITY (Includes Hospital and Nursing Home Units)					
Utilization - Inpatient					
Beds	6,726	6,238	6,446	6,316	6,030
Admissions	204,522	199,900	191,951	185,689	181,662
Inpatient Days	835,702	792,847	772,553	772,972	745,115
Average Length of Stay	4.1	4.0	4.0	4.2	4.1
Inpatient Surgeries	36,519	39,047	37,527	36,766	36,110
Births	13,938	13,267	12,310	12,004	10,695
Utilization - Outpatient					
Emergency Outpatient Visits	1,505,235	1,399,997	1,269,428	1,312,747	1,223,838
Other Outpatient Visits	6,877,919	6,297,926	6,533,512	6,657,699	6,018,718
Total Outpatient Visits	8,383,154	7,697,923	7,802,940	7,970,446	7,242,556
Outpatient Surgeries	249,528	215,459	212,620	209,196	194,560
Personnel					
Full Time RNs	6,382	5,763	5,759	5,438	5,058
Full Time LPNs	1,996	1,633	1,632	1,633	1,794
Part Time RNs	3,931	3,232	3,354	3,374	3,064
Part Time LPNs	859	769	800	782	783
Total Full Time	32,101	29,240	29,489	28,924	26,579
Total Part Time	14,933	12,801	13,707	13,649	12,320
Revenue - Inpatient					
Gross Inpatient Revenue	$2,459,057,974	$2,173,593,992	$1,828,399,829	$1,794,653,960	$1,722,861,214
Revenue - Outpatient					
Gross Outpatient Revenue	$6,343,851,906	$5,307,718,755	$4,642,506,692	$4,326,712,250	$3,677,188,569
Revenue and Expenses - Totals					
(Includes Inpatient and Outpatient)					
Total Gross Revenue	$8,802,909,880	$7,481,312,747	$6,470,906,521	$6,121,366,210	$5,400,049,783
Deductions from Revenue	4,391,015,802	3,707,878,289	3,001,843,000	2,937,005,012	2,539,972,888
Net Patient Revenue	4,411,894,078	3,773,434,458	3,469,063,521	3,184,361,198	2,860,076,895
Other Operating Revenue	343,522,682	346,123,111	323,188,226	299,545,114	192,978,846
Other Nonoperating Revenue	69,707,381	85,878,584	86,665,700	61,973,855	41,904,855
Total Net Revenue	4,825,124,141	4,205,436,153	3,891,511,549	3,545,880,167	3,094,960,596
Total Expenses	4,510,451,244	3,898,795,232	3,644,293,348	3,494,293,653	2,922,377,161
HOSPITAL UNIT (Excludes Separate Nursing Home Units)					
Utilization - Inpatient					
Beds	6,693	6,214	6,355	6,210	5,902
Admissions	204,445	199,884	191,730	185,287	181,141
Inpatient Days	823,878	781,994	740,244	741,578	710,462
Average Length of Stay	4.0	3.9	3.9	4.0	3.9
Personnel					
Total Full Time	31,993	29,116	29,285	28,752	26,475
Total Part Time	14,902	12,723	13,619	13,519	12,211
Revenue and Expenses - Totals					
(Includes Inpatient and Outpatient)					
Total Net Revenue	$4,821,483,710	$4,200,890,155	$3,882,018,849	$3,535,620,933	$3,082,667,170
Total Expenses	4,508,680,031	3,896,171,176	3,636,207,924	3,486,754,501	2,914,954,576

TABLE 4

BED SIZE CATEGORY 25-49

U.S. Registered Community Hospitals
(Nonfederal, short-term general and other special hospitals)

Overview 2004–2008

	2008	2007	2006	2005	2004
Total Community Hospitals in Bed Size Category 25-49..................	**1,151**	**1,076**	**1,066**	**1,032**	**988**
Location					
Hospitals Urban...........................	411	334	341	319	237
Hospitals Rural	740	742	725	713	751
Control					
State and Local Government................	397	399	395	388	375
Not for Profit	527	515	506	492	479
Investor owned	227	162	165	152	134
Physician Models					
Independent Practice Association	104	115	134	120	132
Group Practice without Walls...............	27	35	32	35	27
Open Physician-Hospital Organization	92	97	95	96	88
Closed Physician-Hospital Organization	24	28	32	28	24
Management Service Organization	54	54	54	48	54
Integrated Salary Model....................	309	298	292	257	250
Equity Model	14	9	13	6	6
Foundation...............................	42	37	36	29	24
Insurance Products					
Health Maintenance Organization	83	81	84	87	94
Preferred Provider Organization..............	112	140	154	171	172
Indemnity Fee for Service	39	43	48	53	48
Managed Care Contracts					
Health Maintenance Organization	474	451	433	422	415
Preferred Provider Organization..............	649	622	633	618	597
Affiliations					
Hospitals in a System......................	580	499	507	485	451
Hospitals in a Network.....................	296	297	301	277	278
Hospitals in a Group Purchasing Organization..	795	775	768	739	669

TABLE 4

BED SIZE CATEGORY 25-49

U.S. Registered Community Hospitals
(Nonfederal, short-term general and other special hospitals)

Utilization, Personnel, Revenue and Expenses, Community Health Indicators 2004–2008

	2008	2007	2006	2005	2004
TOTAL FACILITY (Includes Hospital and Nursing Home Units)					
Utilization - Inpatient					
Beds	37,142	34,350	34,217	33,726	33,206
Admissions	1,218,123	1,169,941	1,187,667	1,173,390	1,091,908
Inpatient Days	6,342,577	5,786,668	5,837,190	5,791,292	5,510,912
Average Length of Stay	5.2	4.9	4.9	4.9	5.0
Inpatient Surgeries	242,142	227,059	234,999	258,110	219,300
Births	106,334	109,618	108,279	106,210	94,683
Utilization - Outpatient					
Emergency Outpatient Visits	7,781,578	7,409,466	7,198,343	6,782,800	6,238,224
Other Outpatient Visits	32,947,438	31,766,431	29,855,259	28,388,737	26,207,757
Total Outpatient Visits	40,729,016	39,175,897	37,053,602	35,171,537	32,445,981
Outpatient Surgeries	1,022,034	927,021	977,191	942,109	850,150
Personnel					
Full Time RNs	34,935	32,045	31,047	28,674	26,124
Full Time LPNs	9,165	8,382	8,551	8,527	8,165
Part Time RNs	20,005	18,171	18,793	17,223	15,644
Part Time LPNs	3,809	3,590	3,803	3,635	3,503
Total Full Time	178,257	165,913	160,152	148,276	136,279
Total Part Time	76,222	69,915	70,714	67,690	60,886
Revenue - Inpatient					
Gross Inpatient Revenue	$18,764,220,947	$15,192,815,130	$15,288,298,943	$13,434,987,001	$11,427,214,492
Revenue - Outpatient					
Gross Outpatient Revenue	$31,292,050,672	$26,532,671,728	$24,089,062,315	$20,788,166,751	$16,679,591,250
Revenue and Expenses - Totals					
(Includes Inpatient and Outpatient)					
Total Gross Revenue	$50,056,271,619	$41,725,486,858	$39,377,361,258	$34,223,153,752	$28,106,805,742
Deductions from Revenue	26,923,199,398	21,510,609,136	20,293,853,524	17,235,829,652	13,961,648,475
Net Patient Revenue	23,133,072,221	20,214,877,722	19,083,507,734	16,987,324,100	14,145,157,267
Other Operating Revenue	1,982,012,610	1,814,575,058	1,642,531,689	1,145,047,951	1,062,738,662
Other Nonoperating Revenue	142,977,449	580,543,731	402,345,248	260,606,802	208,685,047
Total Net Revenue	25,258,062,280	22,609,996,511	21,128,384,671	18,392,978,853	15,416,580,976
Total Expenses	24,074,708,651	21,232,861,615	20,009,399,050	17,448,779,323	15,091,393,418
HOSPITAL UNIT (Excludes Separate Nursing Home Units)					
Utilization - Inpatient					
Beds	35,230	32,433	32,229	31,830	31,238
Admissions	1,215,522	1,166,976	1,184,151	1,170,103	1,087,816
Inpatient Days	5,747,460	5,198,062	5,222,566	5,223,816	4,884,727
Average Length of Stay	4.7	4.5	4.4	4.5	4.5
Personnel					
Total Full Time	176,408	164,033	158,542	146,955	133,972
Total Part Time	75,100	68,994	69,755	66,864	59,790
Revenue and Expenses - Totals					
(Includes Inpatient and Outpatient)					
Total Net Revenue	$25,153,457,365	$22,466,173,311	$20,973,029,022	$18,294,311,809	$15,314,682,454
Total Expenses	23,996,899,302	21,157,891,227	19,924,029,677	17,371,613,986	15,011,416,072

Bed Size Categories

TABLE **4**

BED SIZE CATEGORY 50-99

U.S. Registered Community Hospitals
(Nonfederal, short-term general and other special hospitals)

Overview 2004–2008

	2008	2007	2006	2005	2004
Total Community Hospitals in					
Bed Size Category 50-99.................	**995**	**971**	**969**	**1,001**	**1,028**
Location					
Hospitals Urban..........................	480	449	449	459	419
Hospitals Rural	515	522	520	542	609
Control					
State and Local Government...............	215	227	219	230	241
Not for Profit	508	506	514	539	558
Investor owned	272	238	236	232	229
Physician Models					
Independent Practice Association	97	112	114	125	149
Group Practice without Walls...............	25	28	27	30	33
Open Physician-Hospital Organization	112	123	119	126	128
Closed Physician-Hospital Organization	34	36	30	41	33
Management Service Organization	61	68	61	62	58
Integrated Salary Model...................	277	268	247	246	235
Equity Model...........................	14	8	7	13	10
Foundation.............................	45	41	44	44	37
Insurance Products					
Health Maintenance Organization	94	99	83	102	92
Preferred Provider Organization..............	135	171	167	189	165
Indemnity Fee for Service	56	56	51	57	50
Managed Care Contracts					
Health Maintenance Organization	456	447	439	464	493
Preferred Provider Organization..............	564	566	559	606	634
Affiliations					
Hospitals in a System.....................	559	536	537	537	539
Hospitals in a Network....................	271	278	278	270	277
Hospitals in a Group Purchasing Organization..	682	674	689	699	715

TABLE 4

BED SIZE CATEGORY 50-99

U.S. Registered Community Hospitals
(Nonfederal, short-term general and other special hospitals)

Utilization, Personnel, Revenue and Expenses, Community Health Indicators 2004–2008

	2008	2007	2006	2005	2004
TOTAL FACILITY (Includes Hospital and Nursing Home Units)					
Utilization - Inpatient					
Beds	71,477	69,974	69,408	71,737	73,606
Admissions	2,318,730	2,295,002	2,300,638	2,412,206	2,451,031
Inpatient Days	14,775,775	14,354,674	14,534,929	15,431,019	15,572,044
Average Length of Stay	6.4	6.3	6.3	6.4	6.4
Inpatient Surgeries	573,876	593,650	576,043	596,930	606,300
Births	252,752	257,346	249,458	258,665	252,082
Utilization - Outpatient					
Emergency Outpatient Visits	11,523,593	11,373,584	11,175,926	11,476,375	11,206,355
Other Outpatient Visits	45,219,692	42,938,775	41,798,859	41,905,407	41,845,036
Total Outpatient Visits	56,743,285	54,312,359	52,974,785	53,381,782	53,051,391
Outpatient Surgeries	1,608,622	1,564,443	1,604,168	1,644,342	1,630,682
Personnel					
Full Time RNs	58,276	56,028	54,130	53,824	51,988
Full Time LPNs	10,739	10,921	11,263	11,785	12,185
Part Time RNs	33,996	34,128	32,746	33,928	33,136
Part Time LPNs	4,911	5,415	5,475	5,635	5,897
Total Full Time	264,056	255,144	248,689	249,926	247,735
Total Part Time	121,026	120,860	118,080	121,285	117,694
Revenue - Inpatient					
Gross Inpatient Revenue	$46,010,068,854	$42,120,063,662	$38,928,521,152	$38,525,318,701	$35,220,714,707
Revenue - Outpatient					
Gross Outpatient Revenue	$51,849,631,924	$45,947,957,640	$40,228,937,486	$38,120,374,172	$33,860,048,014
Revenue and Expenses - Totals					
(Includes Inpatient and Outpatient)					
Total Gross Revenue	$97,859,700,778	$88,068,021,302	$79,157,458,638	$76,645,692,873	$69,080,762,721
Deductions from Revenue	59,144,961,432	52,387,575,211	46,042,196,389	44,596,328,790	38,954,281,643
Net Patient Revenue	38,714,739,346	35,680,446,091	33,115,262,249	32,049,364,083	30,126,481,078
Other Operating Revenue	1,598,169,545	1,434,537,429	1,534,330,530	1,256,387,458	1,245,302,991
Other Nonoperating Revenue	248,970,994	970,524,605	523,502,772	404,735,044	510,398,426
Total Net Revenue	40,561,879,885	38,085,508,125	35,173,095,551	33,710,486,585	31,882,182,495
Total Expenses	38,332,175,201	35,148,034,292	32,959,605,126	31,942,729,820	30,179,868,109
HOSPITAL UNIT (Excludes Separate Nursing Home Units)					
Utilization - Inpatient					
Beds	60,983	58,916	58,329	60,198	62,179
Admissions	2,293,835	2,271,564	2,273,677	2,383,963	2,419,973
Inpatient Days	11,528,634	10,951,518	11,041,775	11,737,614	11,952,581
Average Length of Stay	5.0	4.8	4.9	4.9	4.9
Personnel					
Total Full Time	257,784	248,223	241,410	242,719	238,740
Total Part Time	116,770	115,925	113,258	110,400	112,515
Revenue and Expenses - Totals					
(Includes Inpatient and Outpatient)					
Total Net Revenue	$39,967,178,977	$37,463,316,808	$34,506,004,025	$33,135,268,164	$31,314,330,042
Total Expenses	37,833,276,129	34,678,598,342	32,492,030,193	31,462,084,219	29,711,563,327

TABLE 4

BED SIZE CATEGORY 100-199

U.S. Registered Community Hospitals
(Nonfederal, short-term general and other special hospitals)

Overview 2004–2008

	2008	2007	2006	2005	2004
Total Community Hospitals in Bed Size Category 100-199...............	**1,070**	**1,083**	**1,117**	**1,129**	**1,141**
Location					
Hospitals Urban...........................	726	729	753	752	731
Hospitals Rural	344	354	364	377	410
Control					
State and Local Government...............	162	166	176	171	179
Not for Profit............................	660	670	681	699	702
Investor owned	248	247	260	259	260
Physician Models					
Independent Practice Association	124	144	161	173	169
Group Practice without Walls................	33	33	34	34	31
Open Physician-Hospital Organization	167	176	181	203	188
Closed Physician-Hospital Organization	53	63	61	47	57
Management Service Organization	91	97	96	96	96
Integrated Salary Model....................	308	302	301	276	255
Equity Model.............................	26	20	21	17	17
Foundation...............................	43	43	41	51	37
Insurance Products					
Health Maintenance Organization	108	126	154	140	137
Preferred Provider Organization..............	122	169	182	183	173
Indemnity Fee for Service	44	60	68	56	53
Managed Care Contracts					
Health Maintenance Organization	591	620	642	648	629
Preferred Provider Organization..............	668	677	722	729	711
Affiliations					
Hospitals in a System......................	661	652	668	663	662
Hospitals in a Network.....................	296	302	314	304	312
Hospitals in a Group Purchasing Organization..	792	800	830	826	802

TABLE 4

BED SIZE CATEGORY 100-199

U.S. Registered Community Hospitals
(Nonfederal, short-term general and other special hospitals)

Utilization, Personnel, Revenue and Expenses, Community Health Indicators 2004–2008

	2008	2007	2006	2005	2004
TOTAL FACILITY (Includes Hospital and Nursing Home Units)					
Utilization - Inpatient					
Beds	153,488	155,291	160,426	161,593	162,914
Admissions	6,304,036	6,341,170	6,661,921	6,678,452	6,663,344
Inpatient Days	34,742,992	35,016,507	36,835,335	37,214,649	37,569,329
Average Length of Stay	5.5	5.5	5.5	5.6	5.6
Inpatient Surgeries	1,670,856	1,728,464	1,830,464	1,808,340	1,837,353
Births	765,495	777,562	806,893	772,895	754,512
Utilization - Outpatient					
Emergency Outpatient Visits	26,601,799	26,879,730	27,389,126	26,060,878	25,358,603
Other Outpatient Visits	93,178,685	92,574,821	97,037,200	94,992,257	92,252,521
Total Outpatient Visits	119,780,484	119,454,551	124,426,326	121,053,135	117,611,124
Outpatient Surgeries	3,653,497	3,645,361	3,799,265	3,921,007	3,874,762
Personnel					
Full Time RNs	154,376	150,102	149,572	142,820	138,151
Full Time LPNs	17,825	19,168	20,951	21,913	22,476
Part Time RNs	89,500	89,687	92,656	89,373	85,408
Part Time LPNs	7,788	8,822	9,517	9,944	10,310
Total Full Time	623,645	625,608	633,024	622,155	606,675
Total Part Time	274,371	277,630	285,739	281,251	272,342
Revenue - Inpatient					
Gross Inpatient Revenue	$161,279,571,502	$149,688,308,624	$146,940,017,410	$134,365,113,034	$121,866,612,680
Revenue - Outpatient					
Gross Outpatient Revenue	$131,980,398,456	$119,230,252,656	$112,299,803,462	$98,340,565,270	$85,044,607,819
Revenue and Expenses - Totals					
(Includes Inpatient and Outpatient)					
Total Gross Revenue	$293,259,969,958	$268,918,561,280	$259,239,820,872	$232,705,678,304	$206,911,220,499
Deductions from Revenue	195,921,601,786	175,628,976,504	167,765,995,762	147,503,617,409	127,911,802,621
Net Patient Revenue	97,338,368,172	93,289,584,776	91,473,825,110	85,202,060,895	78,999,417,878
Other Operating Revenue	3,635,678,864	3,559,652,278	3,276,140,856	3,351,223,953	3,146,466,524
Other Nonoperating Revenue	(86,795,995)	2,031,003,137	1,781,503,506	1,499,749,837	1,373,761,522
Total Net Revenue	100,887,251,041	98,880,240,191	96,531,469,472	90,053,034,685	83,519,645,924
Total Expenses	96,955,948,353	92,365,463,660	90,741,587,854	84,781,005,927	79,652,478,305
HOSPITAL UNIT (Excludes Separate Nursing Home Units)					
Utilization - Inpatient					
Beds	137,233	137,797	141,656	143,005	144,365
Admissions	6,247,190	6,276,370	6,591,271	6,603,803	6,585,615
Inpatient Days	29,546,134	29,443,800	30,891,705	31,274,777	31,546,138
Average Length of Stay	4.7	4.7	4.7	4.7	4.8
Personnel					
Total Full Time	612,571	613,811	620,505	609,840	589,026
Total Part Time	267,530	270,208	278,049	273,478	262,598
Revenue and Expenses - Totals					
(Includes Inpatient and Outpatient)					
Total Net Revenue	$99,832,442,896	$97,743,593,245	$94,798,499,907	$89,030,821,502	$82,451,392,352
Total Expenses	95,982,012,829	91,367,396,890	89,519,669,886	83,837,219,377	78,698,091,507

TABLE 4

BED SIZE CATEGORY 200-299

U.S. Registered Community Hospitals
(Nonfederal, short-term general and other special hospitals)

Overview 2004–2008

	2008	2007	2006	2005	2004
Total Community Hospitals in Bed Size Category 200-299...............	**596**	**613**	**607**	**619**	**621**
Location					
Hospitals Urban...........................	515	526	525	540	521
Hospitals Rural	81	87	82	79	100
Control					
State and Local Government...............	62	61	63	66	64
Not for Profit	435	448	440	444	457
Investor owned	99	104	104	109	100
Physician Models					
Independent Practice Association	72	78	81	86	94
Group Practice without Walls................	26	21	26	24	29
Open Physician-Hospital Organization	110	102	122	132	129
Closed Physician-Hospital Organization	27	37	39	46	40
Management Service Organization	84	85	84	87	83
Integrated Salary Model....................	206	200	198	181	175
Equity Model	14	13	13	12	8
Foundation...............................	35	32	33	30	26
Insurance Products					
Health Maintenance Organization	93	96	107	107	116
Preferred Provider Organization..............	95	114	123	125	124
Indemnity Fee for Service	33	46	47	53	46
Managed Care Contracts					
Health Maintenance Organization	400	410	426	428	426
Preferred Provider Organization..............	421	425	447	454	449
Affiliations					
Hospitals in a System......................	377	378	382	379	381
Hospitals in a Network.....................	195	192	204	209	207
Hospitals in a Group Purchasing Organization..	475	460	475	471	459

TABLE 4

BED SIZE CATEGORY 200-299

U.S. Registered Community Hospitals
(Nonfederal, short-term general and other special hospitals)

Utilization, Personnel, Revenue and Expenses, Community Health Indicators 2004–2008

	2008	2007	2006	2005	2004
TOTAL FACILITY (Includes Hospital and Nursing Home Units)					
Utilization - Inpatient					
Beds	144,895	149,546	148,541	151,290	151,197
Admissions	6,866,533	7,009,011	7,007,798	7,075,077	6,928,872
Inpatient Days	35,165,769	36,324,208	36,681,087	37,345,741	37,128,574
Average Length of Stay	5.1	5.2	5.2	5.3	5.4
Inpatient Surgeries	1,945,775	2,006,491	1,981,815	2,052,544	1,976,550
Births	794,470	806,019	803,495	807,357	783,857
Utilization - Outpatient					
Emergency Outpatient Visits	24,185,692	23,913,978	23,583,282	22,775,575	21,997,288
Other Outpatient Visits	83,791,081	82,621,482	79,848,179	84,556,147	77,828,723
Total Outpatient Visits	107,976,773	106,535,460	103,431,461	107,331,722	99,826,011
Outpatient Surgeries	3,224,033	3,281,300	3,255,244	3,456,049	3,507,669
Personnel					
Full Time RNs	171,515	167,333	161,572	159,272	150,192
Full Time LPNs	14,215	15,105	15,865	17,210	16,612
Part Time RNs	88,610	92,245	92,421	93,256	90,059
Part Time LPNs	6,221	6,952	6,919	7,525	8,246
Total Full Time	651,645	656,376	641,525	647,445	618,528
Total Part Time	265,981	271,077	271,052	276,003	268,734
Revenue - Inpatient					
Gross Inpatient Revenue	$197,533,594,288	$192,707,619,825	$180,028,152,728	$170,616,345,762	$155,294,785,296
Revenue - Outpatient					
Gross Outpatient Revenue	$124,669,613,502	$116,124,524,652	$103,386,338,141	$94,794,997,798	$82,164,264,391
Revenue and Expenses - Totals					
(Includes Inpatient and Outpatient)					
Total Gross Revenue	$322,203,207,790	$308,832,144,477	$283,414,490,869	$265,411,343,560	$237,459,049,687
Deductions from Revenue	215,803,795,922	205,589,245,758	186,023,673,013	172,106,934,465	151,887,190,782
Net Patient Revenue	106,399,411,868	103,242,898,719	97,390,817,856	93,304,409,095	85,571,858,905
Other Operating Revenue	5,082,400,440	4,909,405,746	5,003,781,859	4,083,925,703	3,962,288,724
Other Nonoperating Revenue	(782,268,587)	2,859,845,478	2,257,123,002	1,672,783,382	1,510,698,932
Total Net Revenue	110,699,543,721	111,012,149,943	104,622,047,660	99,061,118,180	91,044,846,561
Total Expenses	108,021,530,166	103,273,675,370	98,273,430,973	93,355,766,103	86,077,421,150
HOSPITAL UNIT (Excludes Separate Nursing Home Units)					
Utilization - Inpatient					
Beds	136,050	140,265	138,521	141,761	140,504
Admissions	6,806,537	6,944,618	6,933,995	7,003,676	6,857,430
Inpatient Days	32,384,629	33,356,376	33,409,499	34,317,326	33,667,207
Average Length of Stay	4.8	4.8	4.8	4.9	4.9
Personnel					
Total Full Time	642,916	649,221	633,780	640,026	602,684
Total Part Time	261,723	267,280	267,116	272,208	261,307
Revenue and Expenses - Totals					
(Includes Inpatient and Outpatient)					
Total Net Revenue	$109,893,167,266	$110,282,485,903	$103,386,452,224	$98,249,103,654	$90,313,938,352
Total Expenses	107,333,326,624	102,575,812,740	97,628,510,565	92,716,630,522	85,489,134,699

TABLE 4

BED SIZE CATEGORY 300-399

U.S. Registered Community Hospitals
(Nonfederal, short-term general and other special hospitals)

Overview 2004–2008

	2008	2007	2006	2005	2004
Total Community Hospitals in Bed Size Category 300-399...............	**355**	**343**	**354**	**368**	**351**
Location					
Hospitals Urban...........................	331	321	332	345	327
Hospitals Rural	24	22	22	23	24
Control					
State and Local Government...............	47	45	50	48	47
Not for Profit............................	259	253	259	277	258
Investor owned	49	45	45	43	46
Physician Models					
Independent Practice Association	65	63	59	73	58
Group Practice without Walls................	11	13	13	12	10
Open Physician-Hospital Organization	61	64	65	71	76
Closed Physician-Hospital Organization	29	23	21	33	34
Management Service Organization	50	52	53	58	55
Integrated Salary Model....................	140	133	132	131	118
Equity Model............................	8	6	3	5	4
Foundation..............................	25	24	23	33	25
Insurance Products					
Health Maintenance Organization	69	70	78	76	82
Preferred Provider Organization..............	67	65	78	84	84
Indemnity Fee for Service	22	27	23	24	28
Managed Care Contracts					
Health Maintenance Organization	250	242	254	262	253
Preferred Provider Organization..............	260	256	263	270	255
Affiliations					
Hospitals in a System.....................	227	217	220	233	218
Hospitals in a Network.....................	141	124	129	120	117
Hospitals in a Group Purchasing Organization..	287	272	283	291	274

TABLE 4

BED SIZE CATEGORY 300-399

U.S. Registered Community Hospitals
(Nonfederal, short-term general and other special hospitals)

Utilization, Personnel, Revenue and Expenses, Community Health Indicators 2004–2008

	2008	2007	2006	2005	2004
TOTAL FACILITY (Includes Hospital and Nursing Home Units)					
Utilization - Inpatient					
Beds	122,363	118,160	121,747	126,899	120,509
Admissions	5,894,366	5,637,441	5,720,821	6,025,261	5,764,742
Inpatient Days	31,089,796	30,016,302	30,853,206	32,448,452	30,711,591
Average Length of Stay.	5.3	5.3	5.4	5.4	5.3
Inpatient Surgeries.	1,679,276	1,626,862	1,634,694	1,725,447	1,659,042
Births.	678,865	676,761	682,838	710,328	681,445
Utilization - Outpatient					
Emergency Outpatient Visits	17,724,755	17,121,428	17,144,271	17,521,842	16,519,917
Other Outpatient Visits.	72,894,987	64,549,780	65,772,041	67,844,183	67,812,543
Total Outpatient Visits	90,619,742	81,671,208	82,916,312	85,366,025	84,332,460
Outpatient Surgeries	2,340,405	2,279,223	2,345,497	2,470,707	2,414,313
Personnel					
Full Time RNs	151,208	143,484	139,473	141,847	130,202
Full Time LPNs	10,864	11,311	12,244	13,443	14,178
Part Time RNs.	75,014	69,901	69,952	74,727	70,366
Part Time LPNs	4,125	4,365	4,932	5,408	5,510
Total Full Time.	575,521	554,813	554,388	568,290	536,011
Total Part Time	215,729	204,796	212,170	219,278	212,832
Revenue - Inpatient					
Gross Inpatient Revenue.	$188,790,420,618	$169,713,323,276	$159,727,014,412	$159,263,214,837	$139,637,421,386
Revenue - Outpatient					
Gross Outpatient Revenue	$107,500,249,231	$91,813,591,084	$85,030,303,818	$82,354,123,219	$69,588,216,914
Revenue and Expenses - Totals					
(Includes Inpatient and Outpatient)					
Total Gross Revenue.	$296,290,669,849	$261,526,914,360	$244,757,318,230	$241,617,338,056	$209,225,638,300
Deductions from Revenue	201,399,629,121	176,791,285,927	161,994,484,185	158,773,214,706	134,268,491,890
Net Patient Revenue	94,891,040,728	84,735,628,433	82,762,834,045	82,844,123,350	74,957,146,410
Other Operating Revenue	5,496,095,330	4,775,900,317	4,311,575,332	4,584,684,323	4,238,436,521
Other Nonoperating Revenue	(735,779,905)	2,352,647,862	1,820,794,415	1,454,600,821	1,504,494,878
Total Net Revenue.	99,651,356,153	91,864,176,612	88,895,203,792	88,883,408,494	80,700,077,809
Total Expenses.	96,680,861,169	85,991,812,527	83,742,334,417	83,960,197,153	76,000,965,751
HOSPITAL UNIT (Excludes Separate Nursing Home Units)					
Utilization - Inpatient					
Beds	115,956	111,008	114,872	120,190	114,080
Admissions	5,852,894	5,593,182	5,673,915	5,973,783	5,713,580
Inpatient Days	29,131,108	27,762,180	28,602,063	30,289,334	28,646,372
Average Length of Stay.	5.0	5.0	5.0	5.1	5.0
Personnel					
Total Full Time.	570,294	548,396	548,927	562,625	522,514
Total Part Time	212,975	201,430	209,541	216,580	207,159
Revenue and Expenses - Totals					
(Includes Inpatient and Outpatient)					
Total Net Revenue.	$98,992,882,329	$91,064,513,405	$87,874,129,969	$88,248,210,144	$80,124,386,205
Total Expenses.	96,149,983,308	85,383,983,393	83,178,661,808	83,379,302,567	75,569,639,844

TABLE 4

BED SIZE CATEGORY 400-499

U.S. Registered Community Hospitals
(Nonfederal, short-term general and other special hospitals)

Overview 2004–2008

	2008	2007	2006	2005	2004
Total Community Hospitals in Bed Size Category 400-499...............	**184**	**191**	**180**	**173**	**185**
Location					
Hospitals Urban...........................	180	188	176	169	177
Hospitals Rural	4	3	4	4	8
Control					
State and Local Government................	24	26	24	24	23
Not for Profit	142	149	141	138	150
Investor owned	18	16	15	11	12
Physician Models					
Independent Practice Association	34	35	27	22	31
Group Practice without Walls................	15	11	8	8	9
Open Physician-Hospital Organization	39	45	45	35	47
Closed Physician-Hospital Organization	15	17	21	17	14
Management Service Organization	29	33	31	25	36
Integrated Salary Model....................	79	89	81	72	73
Equity Model.............................	4	3	2	4	4
Foundation...............................	23	25	17	16	17
Insurance Products					
Health Maintenance Organization	36	41	42	36	43
Preferred Provider Organization..............	40	54	64	56	51
Indemnity Fee for Service	12	17	14	15	15
Managed Care Contracts					
Health Maintenance Organization	134	148	137	122	144
Preferred Provider Organization..............	135	149	147	127	145
Affiliations					
Hospitals in a System......................	122	131	121	108	113
Hospitals in a Network.....................	65	72	74	62	74
Hospitals in a Group Purchasing Organization..	154	154	155	138	150

TABLE 4

BED SIZE CATEGORY 400-499

U.S. Registered Community Hospitals
(Nonfederal, short-term general and other special hospitals)

Utilization, Personnel, Revenue and Expenses, Community Health Indicators 2004–2008

	2008	2007	2006	2005	2004
TOTAL FACILITY (Includes Hospital and Nursing Home Units)					
Utilization - Inpatient					
Beds	80,815	84,136	79,732	76,894	82,071
Admissions	3,895,152	4,043,595	3,871,574	3,634,451	3,820,781
Inpatient Days	20,830,426	21,561,191	20,851,846	19,933,190	21,145,667
Average Length of Stay	5.3	5.3	5.4	5.5	5.5
Inpatient Surgeries	1,133,598	1,241,437	1,158,386	1,130,395	1,170,577
Births	435,954	436,346	450,952	411,625	433,687
Utilization - Outpatient					
Emergency Outpatient Visits	10,828,538	11,467,478	10,442,303	9,399,341	10,225,226
Other Outpatient Visits	46,814,290	49,136,174	49,997,574	46,623,633	45,897,248
Total Outpatient Visits	57,642,828	60,603,652	60,439,877	56,022,974	56,122,474
Outpatient Surgeries	1,739,961	1,764,315	1,679,079	1,693,003	1,694,814
Personnel					
Full Time RNs	113,628	115,451	105,572	96,959	96,101
Full Time LPNs	7,035	7,749	7,645	7,669	8,170
Part Time RNs	52,946	57,353	55,876	49,155	52,895
Part Time LPNs	2,903	3,355	2,893	3,125	3,273
Total Full Time	435,911	450,198	423,369	408,463	411,149
Total Part Time	152,140	157,418	150,778	134,140	144,493
Revenue - Inpatient					
Gross Inpatient Revenue	$134,562,622,630	$133,204,086,152	$117,571,183,567	$98,929,690,803	$95,969,587,663
Revenue - Outpatient					
Gross Outpatient Revenue	$77,496,854,013	$72,665,010,884	$63,147,077,256	$53,733,717,952	$49,070,741,153
Revenue and Expenses - Totals (Includes Inpatient and Outpatient)					
Total Gross Revenue	$212,059,476,643	$205,869,097,036	$180,718,260,823	$152,663,408,755	$145,040,328,816
Deductions from Revenue	144,218,038,992	137,448,298,436	117,343,128,467	94,649,595,109	89,747,898,869
Net Patient Revenue	67,841,437,651	68,420,798,600	63,375,132,356	58,013,813,646	55,292,429,947
Other Operating Revenue	4,570,160,760	4,690,966,723	3,949,229,017	4,147,981,291	3,934,017,927
Other Nonoperating Revenue	(823,396,082)	2,572,380,989	1,734,466,487	1,160,095,364	1,014,920,075
Total Net Revenue	71,588,202,329	75,684,146,312	69,058,827,860	63,321,890,301	60,241,367,949
Total Expenses	70,515,262,080	70,823,523,589	65,100,973,378	60,199,912,859	57,371,278,700
HOSPITAL UNIT (Excludes Separate Nursing Home Units)					
Utilization - Inpatient					
Beds	77,661	80,693	76,731	73,987	77,692
Admissions	3,878,278	4,023,773	3,850,518	3,615,936	3,796,311
Inpatient Days	19,817,710	20,501,012	19,955,104	19,053,667	19,824,492
Average Length of Stay	5.1	5.1	5.2	5.3	5.2
Personnel					
Total Full Time	431,434	446,149	419,376	405,812	396,476
Total Part Time	150,412	156,426	149,020	133,265	140,291
Revenue and Expenses - Totals (Includes Inpatient and Outpatient)					
Total Net Revenue	$71,316,876,706	$75,352,413,590	$68,387,154,288	$63,079,537,305	$59,659,362,844
Total Expenses	70,261,647,760	70,461,579,770	64,709,737,350	59,906,565,277	56,740,100,143

TABLE 4

BED SIZE CATEGORY 500 +

U.S. Registered Community Hospitals
(Nonfederal, short-term general and other special hospitals)

Overview 2004–2008

	2008	2007	2006	2005	2004
Total Community Hospitals in Bed Size Category 500 +..................	270	260	259	244	253
Location					
Hospitals Urban...........................	266	256	255	242	251
Hospitals Rural	4	4	4	2	2
Control					
State and Local Government................	50	49	42	39	40
Not for Profit.............................	206	195	204	190	198
Investor owned	14	16	13	15	15
Physician Models					
Independent Practice Association	52	56	53	52	59
Group Practice without Walls................	12	14	12	17	14
Open Physician-Hospital Organization	57	51	55	61	65
Closed Physician-Hospital Organization	22	30	25	26	20
Management Service Organization	49	49	50	49	49
Integrated Salary Model....................	154	145	134	121	117
Equity Model.............................	11	11	11	10	8
Foundation...............................	28	27	26	24	20
Insurance Products					
Health Maintenance Organization	80	84	83	89	86
Preferred Provider Organization..............	75	77	71	76	75
Indemnity Fee for Service	29	27	25	29	31
Managed Care Contracts					
Health Maintenance Organization	228	217	208	198	197
Preferred Provider Organization..............	225	214	206	194	200
Affiliations					
Hospitals in a System......................	184	176	175	166	172
Hospitals in a Network.....................	110	104	95	96	94
Hospitals in a Group Purchasing Organization..	229	214	203	192	190

TABLE 4

BED SIZE CATEGORY 500 +

U.S. Registered Community Hospitals
(Nonfederal, short-term general and other special hospitals)

Utilization, Personnel, Revenue and Expenses, Community Health Indicators 2004–2008

	2008	2007	2006	2005	2004
TOTAL FACILITY (Includes Hospital and Nursing Home Units)					
Utilization - Inpatient					
Beds	191,163	183,197	182,141	173,856	178,504
Admissions	9,059,288	8,649,926	8,435,289	8,054,147	8,183,721
Inpatient Days	52,295,431	50,696,951	50,000,366	48,136,455	49,180,940
Average Length of Stay	5.8	5.9	5.9	6.0	6.0
Inpatient Surgeries	2,823,114	2,726,620	2,641,755	2,488,739	2,545,114
Births	1,025,916	1,001,043	960,968	908,682	920,547
Utilization - Outpatient					
Emergency Outpatient Visits	22,872,834	21,245,638	20,171,350	19,421,316	19,834,518
Other Outpatient Visits	119,350,180	112,603,686	110,336,372	98,709,799	101,102,819
Total Outpatient Visits	142,223,014	133,849,324	130,507,722	118,131,115	120,937,337
Outpatient Surgeries	3,516,202	3,469,212	3,362,077	3,109,174	3,184,540
Personnel					
Full Time RNs	294,329	279,858	253,201	232,955	228,842
Full Time LPNs	14,911	15,308	14,887	15,220	16,303
Part Time RNs	123,478	117,522	110,751	103,890	102,310
Part Time LPNs	4,986	4,945	5,373	5,434	5,423
Total Full Time	1,158,279	1,108,995	1,029,769	973,943	972,466
Total Part Time	340,085	326,719	309,498	286,376	278,206
Revenue - Inpatient					
Gross Inpatient Revenue	$341,198,456,138	$308,368,746,103	$279,148,331,384	$251,825,707,191	$231,759,388,503
Revenue - Outpatient					
Gross Outpatient Revenue	$180,786,111,977	$155,106,307,545	$137,596,527,510	$117,690,138,522	$106,413,459,853
Revenue and Expenses - Totals					
(Includes Inpatient and Outpatient)					
Total Gross Revenue	$521,984,568,115	$463,475,053,648	$416,744,858,894	$369,515,845,713	$338,172,848,356
Deductions from Revenue	343,813,646,912	299,251,603,589	266,689,606,347	235,302,865,073	209,661,693,606
Net Patient Revenue	178,170,921,203	164,223,450,059	150,055,252,547	134,212,980,640	128,511,154,750
Other Operating Revenue	14,428,536,883	14,234,787,411	14,129,479,856	11,019,622,559	10,867,034,256
Other Nonoperating Revenue	(2,486,522,886)	5,547,313,823	3,565,640,844	2,477,485,943	2,234,594,217
Total Net Revenue	190,112,935,200	184,005,551,293	167,750,373,337	147,710,089,142	141,612,783,223
Total Expenses	187,486,021,048	170,518,121,648	157,363,704,073	140,557,641,023	133,950,804,632
HOSPITAL UNIT (Excludes Separate Nursing Home Units)					
Utilization - Inpatient					
Beds	184,099	176,075	173,959	165,841	170,519
Admissions	9,023,650	8,611,398	8,395,827	8,011,768	8,142,387
Inpatient Days	50,064,396	48,073,269	47,352,280	45,565,004	46,550,788
Average Length of Stay	5.5	5.6	5.6	5.7	5.7
Personnel					
Total Full Time	1,151,673	1,096,329	1,019,955	966,919	937,313
Total Part Time	337,438	323,932	305,725	281,713	270,878
Revenue and Expenses - Totals					
(Includes Inpatient and Outpatient)					
Total Net Revenue	$189,412,292,055	$183,262,813,923	$166,274,950,550	$146,955,507,937	$140,959,028,248
Total Expenses	186,762,975,722	169,751,155,931	156,653,330,209	139,768,429,307	133,293,432,833

Census Divisions

Census Division 1

New England
Connecticut, Maine, Massachusetts, New Hampshire, Rhode Island, Vermont

Census Division 2

Middle Atlantic
New Jersey, New York, Pennsylvania

Census Division 3

South Atlantic
Delaware, District of Columbia, Florida, Georgia, Maryland, North Carolina, South Carolina, Virginia, West Virginia

Census Division 4

East North Central
Illinois, Indiana, Michigan, Ohio, Wisconsin

Census Division 5

East South Central
Alabama, Kentucky, Mississippi, Tennessee

Census Division 6

West North Central
Iowa, Kansas, Minnesota, Missouri, Nebraska, North Dakota, South Dakota

Census Division 7

West South Central
Arkansas, Louisiana, Oklahoma, Texas

Census Division 8

Mountain
Arizona, Colorado, Idaho, Montana, Nevada, New Mexico, Utah, Wyoming

Census Division 9

Pacific
Alaska, California, Hawaii, Oregon, Washington

U.S. Census Divisions

TABLE 5

U.S. CENSUS DIVISION 1: NEW ENGLAND

U.S. Registered Community Hospitals
(Nonfederal, short-term general and other special hospitals)

Overview 2004–2008

	2008	2007	2006	2005	2004
Total Community Hospitals					
in Census Division 1, New England	200	202	205	206	203
Bed Size Category					
6-24	10	8	9	8	4
25-49	38	39	38	42	43
50-99	42	45	44	44	43
100-199	54	54	56	54	56
200-299	22	23	26	29	25
300-399	17	16	16	13	16
400-499	5	5	3	3	2
500 + ...	12	12	13	13	14
Location					
Hospitals Urban...........................	142	144	147	148	126
Hospitals Rural	58	58	58	58	77
Control					
State and Local Government................	5	6	6	6	6
Not for Profit	180	182	183	184	182
Investor owned	15	14	16	16	15
Physician Models					
Independent Practice Association	40	46	50	56	54
Group Practice without Walls...............	7	7	8	11	10
Open Physician-Hospital Organization	50	51	58	60	61
Closed Physician-Hospital Organization	11	16	17	14	12
Management Service Organization	20	23	21	23	25
Integrated Salary Model....................	98	92	101	96	90
Equity Model	6	5	5	5	3
Foundation...............................	8	12	11	12	9
Insurance Products					
Health Maintenance Organization	19	22	20	21	25
Preferred Provider Organization..............	9	21	21	25	27
Indemnity Fee for Service	4	12	9	11	11
Managed Care Contracts					
Health Maintenance Organization	132	139	149	155	152
Preferred Provider Organization..............	127	131	142	151	147
Affiliations					
Hospitals in a System......................	74	75	79	74	71
Hospitals in a Network.....................	69	74	77	79	70
Hospitals in a Group Purchasing Organization..	164	171	174	168	160

TABLE 5

U.S. CENSUS DIVISION 1: NEW ENGLAND

U.S. Registered Community Hospitals
(Nonfederal, short-term general and other special hospitals)

Utilization, Personnel, Revenue and Expenses, Community Health Indicators 2004–2008

	2008	2007	2006	2005	2004
TOTAL FACILITY (Includes Hospital and Nursing Home Units)					
Utilization - Inpatient					
Beds	33,743	34,140	34,353	34,207	34,267
Admissions	1,660,654	1,691,347	1,688,920	1,651,462	1,637,291
Inpatient Days	8,992,337	9,029,013	9,240,145	9,213,139	9,158,050
Average Length of Stay.	5.4	5.3	5.5	5.6	5.6
Inpatient Surgeries	457,144	469,330	444,881	463,184	455,130
Births	163,857	165,858	182,170	188,628	168,615
Utilization - Outpatient					
Emergency Outpatient Visits	6,848,347	6,732,398	6,691,531	6,379,473	6,262,078
Other Outpatient Visits.	37,188,267	34,540,452	33,649,121	32,672,509	31,283,835
Total Outpatient Visits	44,036,614	41,272,850	40,340,652	39,051,982	37,545,913
Outpatient Surgeries	996,495	1,010,447	1,056,911	1,067,889	1,104,291
Personnel					
Full Time RNs	43,571	42,761	39,126	37,724	36,852
Full Time LPNs	1,972	2,052	2,069	2,067	2,185
Part Time RNs	39,421	39,108	37,918	35,874	35,790
Part Time LPNs	1,768	1,863	1,706	2,199	2,040
Total Full Time	217,995	212,334	198,629	192,138	187,759
Total Part Time	121,345	120,603	116,013	110,168	109,769
Revenue - Inpatient					
Gross Inpatient Revenue.	$44,041,639,373	$41,786,910,589	$37,170,857,983	$33,302,111,863	$31,824,799,153
Revenue - Outpatient					
Gross Outpatient Revenue	$43,645,548,924	$38,945,410,783	$35,925,073,139	$31,378,420,843	$27,637,479,556
Revenue and Expenses - Totals					
(Includes Inpatient and Outpatient)					
Total Gross Revenue.	$87,687,188,297	$80,732,321,372	$73,095,931,122	$64,680,532,706	$59,462,278,709
Deductions from Revenue	50,488,459,964	45,898,543,565	40,515,901,458	35,025,138,133	32,160,783,569
Net Patient Revenue	37,198,728,333	34,833,777,807	32,580,029,664	29,655,394,573	27,301,495,140
Other Operating Revenue	3,637,620,235	3,373,305,081	3,113,979,625	2,601,207,927	2,606,545,163
Other Nonoperating Revenue	(272,745,680)	1,107,269,692	748,697,662	523,042,046	473,318,177
Total Net Revenue.	40,563,602,888	39,314,352,580	36,442,706,951	32,779,644,546	30,381,358,480
Total Expenses.	39,734,569,287	36,994,342,737	34,779,690,838	31,439,056,968	29,161,999,714
HOSPITAL UNIT (Excludes Separate Nursing Home Units)					
Utilization - Inpatient					
Beds	32,109	32,789	32,825	32,330	32,598
Admissions	1,654,586	1,682,524	1,675,178	1,636,168	1,623,243
Inpatient Days	8,442,410	8,577,083	8,728,611	8,586,567	8,590,889
Average Length of Stay.	5.1	5.1	5.2	5.2	5.3
Personnel					
Total Full Time	215,906	210,754	197,029	190,898	183,892
Total Part Time	119,472	119,412	114,872	108,937	106,988
Revenue and Expenses - Totals					
(Includes Inpatient and Outpatient)					
Total Net Revenue.	$40,395,735,597	$39,176,727,876	$36,238,128,346	$32,614,381,638	$30,237,644,809
Total Expenses.	39,589,865,862	36,879,337,539	34,618,507,186	31,303,107,618	29,026,346,841
COMMUNITY HEALTH INDICATORS PER 1000 POPULATION					
Total Population (in thousands)	14,304	14,259	14,233	14,208	14,202
Inpatient					
Beds	2.4	2.4	2.4	2.4	2.4
Admissions	116.1	118.6	118.7	116.2	115.3
Inpatient Days	628.7	633.2	649.2	648.4	644.8
Inpatient Surgeries	32.0	32.9	31.3	32.6	32.0
Births	11.5	11.6	12.8	13.3	11.9
Outpatient					
Emergency Outpatient Visits	478.8	472.1	470.2	449.0	440.9
Other Outpatient Visits.	2,599.9	2,422.3	2,364.2	2,299.5	2,202.7
Total Outpatient Visits	3,078.7	2,894.4	2,834.4	2,748.5	2,643.7
Outpatient Surgeries	69.7	70.9	74.3	75.2	77.8
Expense per Capita (per person).	$2,778.0	$2,594.4	$2,443.6	$2,212.7	$2,053.3

U.S. Census Divisions

TABLE 5

U.S. CENSUS DIVISION 2: MIDDLE ATLANTIC

U.S. Registered Community Hospitals
(Nonfederal, short-term general and other special hospitals)

Overview 2004–2008

	2008	2007	2006	2005	2004
Total Community Hospitals					
in Census Division 2, Middle Atlantic.......	468	462	470	474	483
Bed Size Category					
6-24	7	8	8	8	9
25-49	41	29	30	26	23
50-99	65	60	59	64	65
100-199	115	119	130	131	137
200-299	95	98	96	98	107
300-399	56	57	58	61	49
400-499	34	38	32	35	41
500 + ...	55	53	57	51	52
Location					
Hospitals Urban..........................	379	374	382	386	403
Hospitals Rural	89	88	88	88	80
Control					
State and Local Government................	33	31	26	26	25
Not for Profit	388	397	412	418	427
Investor owned	47	34	32	30	31
Physician Models					
Independent Practice Association	63	69	64	66	75
Group Practice without Walls................	20	19	19	19	23
Open Physician-Hospital Organization	55	55	55	55	63
Closed Physician-Hospital Organization	15	18	15	18	15
Management Service Organization	52	51	55	47	54
Integrated Salary Model....................	142	150	143	134	130
Equity Model	6	6	7	8	8
Foundation...............................	11	12	8	9	10
Insurance Products					
Health Maintenance Organization	83	78	74	70	79
Preferred Provider Organization..............	80	76	70	74	84
Indemnity Fee for Service	33	31	27	25	32
Managed Care Contracts					
Health Maintenance Organization	283	289	290	277	302
Preferred Provider Organization..............	270	271	276	265	286
Affiliations					
Hospitals in a System.....................	231	218	231	224	222
Hospitals in a Network....................	154	152	151	134	146
Hospitals in a Group Purchasing Organization..	308	315	324	303	314

TABLE 5

U.S. CENSUS DIVISION 2: MIDDLE ATLANTIC

U.S. Registered Community Hospitals
(Nonfederal, short-term general and other special hospitals)

Utilization, Personnel, Revenue and Expenses, Community Health Indicators 2004–2008

	2008	2007	2006	2005	2004
TOTAL FACILITY (Includes Hospital and Nursing Home Units)					
Utilization - Inpatient					
Beds	122,511	123,639	125,252	124,760	126,236
Admissions	5,516,053	5,505,319	5,548,934	5,510,766	5,476,222
Inpatient Days	33,922,806	34,215,129	34,456,727	34,373,589	34,653,619
Average Length of Stay	6.1	6.2	6.2	6.2	6.3
Inpatient Surgeries	1,475,219	1,495,234	1,535,961	1,501,811	1,500,367
Births	493,580	498,628	500,614	499,733	493,349
Utilization - Outpatient					
Emergency Outpatient Visits	17,471,705	17,141,299	16,764,369	16,096,919	15,916,707
Other Outpatient Visits	91,694,245	89,970,276	89,966,865	87,179,404	84,948,606
Total Outpatient Visits	109,165,950	107,111,575	106,731,234	103,276,323	100,865,313
Outpatient Surgeries	2,667,312	2,673,530	2,759,965	2,677,026	2,704,979
Personnel					
Full Time RNs	154,609	153,296	145,453	139,183	134,422
Full Time LPNs	11,135	11,648	11,916	12,778	13,194
Part Time RNs	59,586	61,316	59,512	61,470	60,870
Part Time LPNs	3,915	4,192	4,433	4,916	5,143
Total Full Time	652,192	645,979	623,974	610,899	601,947
Total Part Time	187,630	190,730	186,861	188,090	187,381
Revenue - Inpatient					
Gross Inpatient Revenue	$204,106,922,337	$191,802,352,802	$177,688,048,241	$167,127,975,929	$151,115,513,963
Revenue - Outpatient					
Gross Outpatient Revenue	$108,338,945,283	$97,230,945,480	$90,009,081,885	$80,559,995,861	$72,056,564,602
Revenue and Expenses - Totals					
(Includes Inpatient and Outpatient)					
Total Gross Revenue	$312,445,867,620	$289,033,298,282	$267,697,130,126	$247,687,971,790	$223,172,078,565
Deductions from Revenue	217,335,551,911	198,289,740,098	181,556,755,763	166,798,862,867	147,628,349,961
Net Patient Revenue	95,110,315,709	90,743,558,184	86,140,374,363	80,889,108,923	75,543,728,604
Other Operating Revenue	5,905,669,784	6,338,357,464	6,577,538,742	5,939,476,131	5,615,764,568
Other Nonoperating Revenue	(522,530,088)	2,136,486,090	1,764,422,561	1,205,293,393	1,280,876,485
Total Net Revenue	100,493,455,405	99,218,401,738	94,482,335,756	88,033,878,447	82,440,369,657
Total Expenses	101,341,325,573	94,889,661,651	91,387,151,168	85,358,448,159	80,203,606,103
HOSPITAL UNIT (Excludes Separate Nursing Home Units)					
Utilization - Inpatient					
Beds	114,721	115,326	117,117	117,843	117,937
Admissions	5,477,486	5,465,485	5,508,450	5,472,172	5,433,347
Inpatient Days	31,398,678	31,360,166	31,721,535	32,104,839	31,812,952
Average Length of Stay	5.7	5.7	5.8	5.9	5.9
Personnel					
Total Full Time	644,394	638,846	617,422	605,638	574,772
Total Part Time	184,048	187,399	183,604	183,613	181,686
Revenue and Expenses - Totals					
(Includes Inpatient and Outpatient)					
Total Net Revenue	$99,744,284,282	$98,469,053,061	$93,800,512,716	$87,491,509,142	$81,836,025,189
Total Expenses	100,633,830,609	94,212,728,480	90,738,596,774	84,900,083,379	79,677,850,994
COMMUNITY HEALTH INDICATORS PER 1000 POPULATION					
Total Population (in thousands)	40,621	40,502	40,395	40,323	40,258
Inpatient					
Beds	3.0	3.1	3.1	3.1	3.1
Admissions	135.8	135.9	137.4	136.7	136.0
Inpatient Days	835.1	844.8	853.0	852.5	860.8
Inpatient Surgeries	36.3	36.9	38.0	37.2	37.3
Births	12.2	12.3	12.4	12.4	12.3
Outpatient					
Emergency Outpatient Visits	430.1	423.2	415.0	399.2	395.4
Other Outpatient Visits	2,257.3	2,221.4	2,227.2	2,162.0	2,110.1
Total Outpatient Visits	2,687.4	2,644.6	2,642.2	2,561.2	2,505.5
Outpatient Surgeries	65.7	66.0	68.3	66.4	67.2
Expense per Capita (per person)	$2,494.8	$2,342.8	$2,262.3	$2,116.9	$1,992.3

TABLE **5**

U.S. CENSUS DIVISION 3: SOUTH ATLANTIC

U.S. Registered Community Hospitals
(Nonfederal, short-term general and other special hospitals)

Overview 2004–2008

	2008	2007	2006	2005	2004
Total Community Hospitals					
in Census Division 3, South Atlantic	**762**	**735**	**741**	**743**	**738**
Bed Size Category					
6-24	18	17	17	20	21
25-49	129	112	111	106	99
50-99	128	120	128	127	141
100-199	209	203	203	207	205
200-299	116	122	118	126	113
300-399	67	66	72	66	64
400-499	30	33	33	34	38
500 + ...	65	62	59	57	57
Location					
Hospitals Urban...........................	516	489	496	495	447
Hospitals Rural	246	246	245	248	291
Control					
State and Local Government................	147	148	145	142	139
Not for Profit	406	394	396	402	405
Investor owned	209	193	200	199	194
Physician Models					
Independent Practice Association	52	51	57	62	65
Group Practice without Walls...............	24	24	24	25	18
Open Physician-Hospital Organization	80	81	89	107	110
Closed Physician-Hospital Organization	39	40	40	45	34
Management Service Organization	51	50	53	47	49
Integrated Salary Model....................	255	249	228	193	196
Equity Model	20	18	17	14	17
Foundation...............................	21	20	18	14	13
Insurance Products					
Health Maintenance Organization	62	64	83	83	85
Preferred Provider Organization..............	75	97	124	126	129
Indemnity Fee for Service	24	37	46	46	45
Managed Care Contracts					
Health Maintenance Organization	402	407	406	404	396
Preferred Provider Organization..............	435	446	463	468	468
Affiliations					
Hospitals in a System......................	479	443	451	449	443
Hospitals in a Network.....................	211	219	219	215	225
Hospitals in a Group Purchasing Organization..	542	490	497	488	465

TABLE 5

U.S. CENSUS DIVISION 3: SOUTH ATLANTIC

U.S. Registered Community Hospitals
(Nonfederal, short-term general and other special hospitals)

Utilization, Personnel, Revenue and Expenses, Community Health Indicators 2004–2008

	2008	2007	2006	2005	2004
TOTAL FACILITY (Includes Hospital and Nursing Home Units)					
Utilization - Inpatient					
Beds	156,622	154,101	153,115	152,564	151,039
Admissions	6,958,360	6,913,804	6,862,970	6,870,008	6,758,902
Inpatient Days	38,331,279	38,540,724	38,694,981	38,714,804	38,218,282
Average Length of Stay	5.5	5.6	5.6	5.6	5.7
Inpatient Surgeries	2,003,768	1,998,114	2,008,456	2,047,968	1,995,331
Births	764,298	771,074	754,948	734,589	717,018
Utilization - Outpatient					
Emergency Outpatient Visits	24,482,937	24,095,446	23,813,876	23,007,000	22,360,452
Other Outpatient Visits	69,838,160	67,864,346	66,355,974	65,404,860	64,181,107
Total Outpatient Visits	94,321,097	91,959,792	90,169,850	88,411,860	86,541,559
Outpatient Surgeries	3,346,983	3,262,710	3,294,862	3,440,867	3,392,029
Personnel					
Full Time RNs	195,655	191,207	182,267	173,865	165,119
Full Time LPNs	16,133	17,055	17,858	18,560	18,343
Part Time RNs	79,445	77,184	75,586	74,252	70,779
Part Time LPNs	5,177	5,470	5,540	5,857	6,154
Total Full Time	731,835	716,204	697,654	690,209	661,078
Total Part Time	219,295	214,064	211,258	209,300	201,834
Revenue - Inpatient					
Gross Inpatient Revenue	$190,255,383,250	$179,774,493,773	$165,578,390,457	$150,510,815,327	$134,169,078,228
Revenue - Outpatient					
Gross Outpatient Revenue	$123,592,865,886	$110,871,408,881	$97,769,350,198	$88,755,991,497	$75,463,034,619
Revenue and Expenses - Totals (Includes Inpatient and Outpatient)					
Total Gross Revenue	$313,848,249,136	$290,645,902,654	$263,347,740,655	$239,266,806,824	$209,632,112,847
Deductions from Revenue	204,204,305,242	186,436,266,133	165,215,098,511	147,502,610,445	124,405,790,632
Net Patient Revenue	109,643,943,894	104,209,636,521	98,132,642,144	91,764,196,379	85,226,322,215
Other Operating Revenue	5,395,566,187	4,847,826,689	4,785,098,906	4,231,278,257	4,044,693,679
Other Nonoperating Revenue	(1,072,116,225)	2,512,438,728	1,821,994,128	1,434,272,025	1,236,278,942
Total Net Revenue	113,967,393,856	111,569,901,938	104,739,735,178	97,429,746,661	90,507,294,836
Total Expenses	109,762,268,873	103,137,798,170	97,065,907,476	91,569,165,057	85,733,852,845
HOSPITAL UNIT (Excludes Separate Nursing Home Units)					
Utilization - Inpatient					
Beds	145,784	142,648	140,818	141,696	139,285
Admissions	6,913,674	6,864,373	6,814,310	6,825,392	6,710,353
Inpatient Days	34,834,753	34,608,173	34,675,520	35,145,534	34,248,832
Average Length of Stay	5.0	5.0	5.1	5.1	5.1
Personnel					
Total Full Time	723,355	706,613	686,079	680,932	646,868
Total Part Time	216,083	210,620	207,340	205,902	197,758
Revenue and Expenses - Totals (Includes Inpatient and Outpatient)					
Total Net Revenue	$113,171,813,994	$110,708,005,981	$101,638,027,688	$96,693,647,230	$89,524,617,660
Total Expenses	109,002,752,761	102,312,602,232	96,238,962,477	90,855,608,011	84,825,439,412
COMMUNITY HEALTH INDICATORS PER 1000 POPULATION					
Total Population (in thousands)	58,398	57,747	56,981	56,054	55,147
Inpatient					
Beds	2.7	2.7	2.7	2.7	2.7
Admissions	119.2	119.7	120.4	122.6	122.6
Inpatient Days	656.4	667.4	679.1	690.7	693.0
Inpatient Surgeries	34.3	34.6	35.2	36.5	36.2
Births	13.1	13.4	13.2	13.1	13.0
Outpatient					
Emergency Outpatient Visits	419.2	417.3	417.9	410.4	405.5
Other Outpatient Visits	1,195.9	1,175.2	1,164.5	1,166.8	1,163.8
Total Outpatient Visits	1,615.1	1,592.5	1,582.5	1,577.3	1,569.3
Outpatient Surgeries	57.3	56.5	57.8	61.4	61.5
Expense per Capita (per person)	$1,879.5	$1,786.0	$1,703.5	$1,633.6	$1,554.6

TABLE 5

U.S. CENSUS DIVISION 4: EAST NORTH CENTRAL

U.S. Registered Community Hospitals
(Nonfederal, short-term general and other special hospitals)

Overview 2004–2008

	2008	2007	2006	2005	2004
Total Community Hospitals					
in Census Division 4, East North Central....	774	742	741	744	735
Bed Size Category					
6-24	37	31	33	36	32
25-49	193	171	161	147	134
50-99	162	150	148	160	165
100-199	159	169	178	177	178
200-299	99	101	100	95	94
300-399	56	50	51	63	63
400-499	29	33	30	29	29
500 + ...	39	37	40	37	40
Location					
Hospitals Urban............................	499	469	468	469	446
Hospitals Rural	275	273	273	275	289
Control					
State and Local Government................	103	107	108	108	109
Not for Profit	589	583	580	591	587
Investor owned	82	52	53	45	39
Physician Models					
Independent Practice Association	88	88	90	81	85
Group Practice without Walls...............	28	27	28	29	24
Open Physician-Hospital Organization	151	156	152	171	169
Closed Physician-Hospital Organization	47	67	69	62	67
Management Service Organization	96	94	94	105	102
Integrated Salary Model....................	295	281	257	249	242
Equity Model	30	15	16	13	9
Foundation...............................	49	44	49	46	47
Insurance Products					
Health Maintenance Organization	140	154	157	138	142
Preferred Provider Organization.............	155	197	197	172	180
Indemnity Fee for Service	57	71	58	54	54
Managed Care Contracts					
Health Maintenance Organization	529	491	518	509	511
Preferred Provider Organization.............	576	535	564	572	563
Affiliations					
Hospitals in a System......................	452	421	405	405	393
Hospitals in a Network	271	252	264	253	254
Hospitals in a Group Purchasing Organization..	643	598	634	631	603

TABLE 5

U.S. CENSUS DIVISION 4: EAST NORTH CENTRAL

U.S. Registered Community Hospitals
(Nonfederal, short-term general and other special hospitals)

Utilization, Personnel, Revenue and Expenses, Community Health Indicators 2004–2008

	2008	2007	2006	2005	2004
TOTAL FACILITY (Includes Hospital and Nursing Home Units)					
Utilization - Inpatient					
Beds	124,957	123,858	125,144	126,170	127,568
Admissions	5,730,456	5,656,902	5,666,562	5,621,734	5,580,722
Inpatient Days	29,237,134	28,818,795	29,071,025	29,539,423	29,798,462
Average Length of Stay	5.1	5.1	5.1	5.3	5.3
Inpatient Surgeries	1,641,475	1,611,589	1,570,026	1,564,638	1,582,194
Births	590,869	595,181	596,871	591,825	601,542
Utilization - Outpatient					
Emergency Outpatient Visits	20,682,680	20,641,691	20,042,357	19,351,860	18,990,202
Other Outpatient Visits	102,419,976	100,771,454	99,366,389	96,055,128	94,959,549
Total Outpatient Visits	123,102,656	121,413,145	119,408,746	115,406,988	113,949,751
Outpatient Surgeries	3,147,665	3,131,378	3,160,980	3,243,949	3,136,209
Personnel					
Full Time RNs	154,002	148,084	141,688	136,639	129,203
Full Time LPNs	10,480	10,888	11,206	11,896	11,799
Part Time RNs	96,817	94,856	98,318	96,025	95,914
Part Time LPNs	6,489	6,726	7,058	7,595	7,806
Total Full Time	647,246	631,125	616,060	608,538	587,245
Total Part Time	306,273	296,396	307,330	299,308	296,832
Revenue - Inpatient					
Gross Inpatient Revenue	$149,698,495,809	$138,385,536,623	$128,438,375,170	$118,813,927,360	$108,311,909,673
Revenue - Outpatient					
Gross Outpatient Revenue	$125,559,569,848	$112,453,910,765	$101,789,022,674	$89,993,491,249	$78,870,661,671
Revenue and Expenses - Totals					
(Includes Inpatient and Outpatient)					
Total Gross Revenue	$275,258,065,657	$250,839,447,388	$230,227,397,844	$208,807,418,609	$187,182,571,344
Deductions from Revenue	169,876,753,425	151,738,136,454	137,355,334,545	121,595,959,764	106,120,808,063
Net Patient Revenue	105,381,312,232	99,101,310,934	92,872,063,299	87,211,458,845	81,061,763,281
Other Operating Revenue	6,300,528,903	5,973,060,158	5,159,399,104	4,846,875,073	4,398,960,733
Other Nonoperating Revenue	(2,457,450,887)	3,688,479,320	2,568,302,789	1,839,512,478	1,580,505,955
Total Net Revenue	109,224,390,248	108,762,850,412	100,599,765,192	93,897,846,396	87,041,229,969
Total Expenses	108,029,056,637	100,228,770,592	94,345,981,361	87,901,348,738	81,708,366,236
HOSPITAL UNIT (Excludes Separate Nursing Home Units)					
Utilization - Inpatient					
Beds	118,085	116,254	116,691	116,938	118,362
Admissions	5,687,064	5,612,602	5,612,044	5,565,439	5,524,664
Inpatient Days	27,072,122	26,485,828	26,473,334	26,735,473	27,024,447
Average Length of Stay	4.8	4.7	4.7	4.8	4.9
Personnel					
Total Full Time	642,131	620,539	610,220	602,139	569,647
Total Part Time	302,441	292,478	302,984	295,315	286,298
Revenue and Expenses - Totals					
(Includes Inpatient and Outpatient)					
Total Net Revenue	$108,726,765,462	$108,179,483,196	$99,932,380,489	$93,191,654,589	$86,457,086,696
Total Expenses	107,600,938,852	99,700,838,980	93,726,813,114	87,189,659,740	81,171,474,485
COMMUNITY HEALTH INDICATORS PER 1000 POPULATION					
Total Population (in thousands)	46,396	46,288	46,165	46,036	45,921
Inpatient					
Beds	2.7	2.7	2.7	2.7	2.8
Admissions	123.5	122.2	122.7	122.1	121.5
Inpatient Days	630.2	622.6	629.7	641.7	648.9
Inpatient Surgeries	35.4	34.8	34.0	34.0	34.5
Births	12.7	12.9	12.9	12.9	13.1
Outpatient					
Emergency Outpatient Visits	445.8	445.9	434.2	420.4	413.5
Other Outpatient Visits	2,207.5	2,177.1	2,152.4	2,086.5	2,067.9
Total Outpatient Visits	2,653.3	2,623.0	2,586.6	2,506.9	2,481.4
Outpatient Surgeries	67.8	67.6	68.5	70.5	68.3
Expense per Capita (per person)	$2,328.4	$2,165.3	$2,043.7	$1,909.4	$1,779.3

TABLE 5

U.S. CENSUS DIVISION 5: EAST SOUTH CENTRAL

U.S. Registered Community Hospitals
(Nonfederal, short-term general and other special hospitals)

Overview 2004–2008

	2008	2007	2006	2005	2004
Total Community Hospitals					
in Census Division 5, East South Central ...	449	441	437	438	433
Bed Size Category					
6-24	18	16	15	14	13
25-49	126	115	109	108	101
50-99	107	109	107	111	111
100-199	99	103	112	109	110
200-299	39	41	36	39	44
300-399	26	23	26	26	21
400-499	14	14	14	13	14
500 + ...	20	20	18	18	19
Location					
Hospitals Urban...........................	211	203	201	202	173
Hospitals Rural	238	238	236	236	260
Control					
State and Local Government.................	119	118	119	117	116
Not for Profit	188	190	186	194	196
Investor owned	142	133	132	127	121
Physician Models					
Independent Practice Association	35	36	34	35	37
Group Practice without Walls...............	10	12	9	8	7
Open Physician-Hospital Organization	49	55	51	58	45
Closed Physician-Hospital Organization	17	14	10	9	5
Management Service Organization	34	39	37	38	32
Integrated Salary Model....................	94	84	76	74	59
Equity Model	2	1	1	2	—
Foundation...............................	22	21	16	22	12
Insurance Products					
Health Maintenance Organization	39	44	50	54	39
Preferred Provider Organization..............	83	90	100	113	65
Indemnity Fee for Service	28	27	30	32	16
Managed Care Contracts					
Health Maintenance Organization	176	160	153	159	163
Preferred Provider Organization..............	233	211	212	217	207
Affiliations					
Hospitals in a System......................	286	275	276	276	264
Hospitals in a Network	111	108	109	108	111
Hospitals in a Group Purchasing Organization..	240	242	244	254	241

TABLE 5

U.S. CENSUS DIVISION 5: EAST SOUTH CENTRAL

U.S. Registered Community Hospitals
(Nonfederal, short-term general and other special hospitals)

Utilization, Personnel, Revenue and Expenses, Community Health Indicators 2004–2008

	2008	2007	2006	2005	2004
TOTAL FACILITY (Includes Hospital and Nursing Home Units)					
Utilization - Inpatient					
Beds	63,626	64,505	63,514	63,708	64,110
Admissions	2,587,919	2,695,512	2,565,449	2,568,031	2,574,086
Inpatient Days	14,460,015	14,787,799	14,300,824	14,461,395	14,494,590
Average Length of Stay	5.6	5.5	5.6	5.6	5.6
Inpatient Surgeries	736,745	773,623	755,751	757,883	731,898
Births	245,061	253,405	237,866	238,061	232,379
Utilization - Outpatient					
Emergency Outpatient Visits	9,557,382	9,547,437	8,840,824	9,051,997	8,843,497
Other Outpatient Visits	25,382,539	24,408,334	23,078,091	23,114,077	22,776,351
Total Outpatient Visits	34,939,921	33,955,771	31,918,915	32,166,074	31,619,848
Outpatient Surgeries	1,309,219	1,361,522	1,289,816	1,264,386	1,233,939
Personnel					
Full Time RNs	70,022	71,100	65,926	62,979	59,783
Full Time LPNs	8,614	9,593	9,818	10,148	10,484
Part Time RNs	25,507	28,291	24,318	23,762	23,045
Part Time LPNs	2,568	2,954	2,901	2,902	3,056
Total Full Time	263,757	275,742	260,548	248,959	244,738
Total Part Time	74,148	81,297	72,460	69,677	67,555
Revenue - Inpatient					
Gross Inpatient Revenue	$67,429,348,071	$64,100,535,279	$57,208,623,237	$51,625,768,080	$47,935,661,161
Revenue - Outpatient					
Gross Outpatient Revenue	$46,662,139,027	$43,516,710,261	$37,377,336,043	$32,822,416,403	$28,945,624,483
Revenue and Expenses - Totals					
(Includes Inpatient and Outpatient)					
Total Gross Revenue	$114,091,487,098	$107,617,245,540	$94,585,959,280	$84,448,184,483	$76,881,285,644
Deductions from Revenue	79,115,671,773	72,599,542,258	62,204,265,707	54,555,698,031	48,750,345,308
Net Patient Revenue	34,975,815,325	35,017,703,282	32,381,693,573	29,892,486,452	28,130,940,336
Other Operating Revenue	1,625,010,586	1,664,289,342	1,346,242,721	1,218,309,114	1,278,446,046
Other Nonoperating Revenue	(19,706,728)	964,949,462	658,282,487	520,488,052	480,174,247
Total Net Revenue	36,581,119,183	37,646,942,086	34,386,218,781	31,631,283,618	29,889,560,629
Total Expenses	34,933,934,594	35,466,530,096	32,228,480,833	29,947,795,643	27,999,718,544
HOSPITAL UNIT (Excludes Separate Nursing Home Units)					
Utilization - Inpatient					
Beds	59,075	59,580	58,500	58,491	58,988
Admissions	2,569,243	2,673,641	2,543,509	2,541,254	2,548,390
Inpatient Days	12,982,972	13,211,639	12,688,369	12,722,810	12,853,927
Average Length of Stay	5.1	4.9	5.0	5.0	5.0
Personnel					
Total Full Time	259,932	271,754	256,346	244,904	235,081
Total Part Time	73,231	80,147	71,329	68,430	65,522
Revenue and Expenses - Totals					
(Includes Inpatient and Outpatient)					
Total Net Revenue	$36,298,364,734	$37,341,333,037	$34,060,819,744	$31,310,742,372	$29,559,557,540
Total Expenses	34,698,028,587	35,232,988,561	31,986,666,215	29,673,466,971	27,745,269,836
COMMUNITY HEALTH INDICATORS PER 1000 POPULATION					
Total Population (in thousands)	18,085	17,933	17,752	17,585	17,434
Inpatient					
Beds	3.5	3.6	3.6	3.6	3.7
Admissions	143.1	150.3	144.5	146.0	147.7
Inpatient Days	799.6	824.6	805.6	822.4	831.4
Inpatient Surgeries	40.7	43.1	42.6	43.1	42.0
Births	13.6	14.1	13.4	13.5	13.3
Outpatient					
Emergency Outpatient Visits	528.5	532.4	498.0	514.8	507.3
Other Outpatient Visits	1,403.5	1,361.1	1,300.0	1,314.4	1,306.5
Total Outpatient Visits	1,932.0	1,893.5	1,798.0	1,829.2	1,813.7
Outpatient Surgeries	72.4	75.9	72.7	71.9	70.8
Expense per Capita (per person)	$1,931.7	$1,977.7	$1,815.5	$1,703.1	$1,606.1

TABLE 5

U.S. CENSUS DIVISION 6: WEST NORTH CENTRAL

U.S. Registered Community Hospitals
(Nonfederal, short-term general and other special hospitals)

Overview 2004–2008

	2008	2007	2006	2005	2004
Total Community Hospitals					
in Census Division 6, West North Central . . .	683	670	674	678	676
Bed Size Category					
6-24	103	94	93	97	91
25-49	214	212	213	206	204
50-99	166	163	167	170	175
100-199	105	106	106	110	108
200-299	38	40	41	41	43
300-399	26	23	23	24	23
400-499	15	15	15	14	15
500 + ...	16	17	16	16	17
Location					
Hospitals Urban.	220	207	209	211	179
Hospitals Rural	463	463	465	467	497
Control					
State and Local Government.	236	241	241	242	242
Not for Profit	395	391	396	398	399
Investor owned	52	38	37	38	35
Physician Models					
Independent Practice Association	82	86	97	105	104
Group Practice without Walls.	13	15	21	23	24
Open Physician-Hospital Organization	89	88	89	91	79
Closed Physician-Hospital Organization	26	30	32	36	36
Management Service Organization	25	28	31	30	29
Integrated Salary Model	315	305	306	284	272
Equity Model	6	6	6	5	6
Foundation.	21	20	20	21	17
Insurance Products					
Health Maintenance Organization	59	62	69	73	81
Preferred Provider Organization.	93	121	133	142	144
Indemnity Fee for Service	32	27	31	32	32
Managed Care Contracts					
Health Maintenance Organization	313	312	312	320	319
Preferred Provider Organization.	471	471	488	483	494
Affiliations					
Hospitals in a System.	339	326	326	328	323
Hospitals in a Network	280	279	296	284	281
Hospitals in a Group Purchasing Organization. .	570	571	587	568	570

TABLE 5

U.S. CENSUS DIVISION 6: WEST NORTH CENTRAL

U.S. Registered Community Hospitals
(Nonfederal, short-term general and other special hospitals)

Utilization, Personnel, Revenue and Expenses, Community Health Indicators 2004–2008

	2008	2007	2006	2005	2004
TOTAL FACILITY (Includes Hospital and Nursing Home Units)					
Utilization - Inpatient					
Beds	70,208	70,058	70,501	71,352	72,051
Admissions	2,589,852	2,565,443	2,560,628	2,568,163	2,551,432
Inpatient Days	15,912,612	15,932,234	16,030,245	16,388,106	16,307,901
Average Length of Stay	6.1	6.2	6.3	6.4	6.4
Inpatient Surgeries	722,817	721,238	714,989	744,891	745,555
Births	279,320	281,227	278,721	273,627	271,804
Utilization - Outpatient					
Emergency Outpatient Visits	8,056,684	7,704,372	7,485,813	7,453,038	7,141,393
Other Outpatient Visits	45,865,406	43,815,430	42,934,077	42,642,247	41,490,877
Total Outpatient Visits	53,922,090	51,519,802	50,419,890	50,095,285	48,632,270
Outpatient Surgeries	1,420,972	1,413,357	1,420,795	1,446,527	1,419,118
Personnel					
Full Time RNs	67,029	64,883	61,457	58,415	55,868
Full Time LPNs	7,692	7,799	8,037	8,153	8,234
Part Time RNs	55,475	51,436	51,894	51,624	47,731
Part Time LPNs	5,225	5,731	5,880	5,997	6,025
Total Full Time	285,576	278,512	271,798	267,846	260,541
Total Part Time	171,973	161,850	162,593	164,041	155,334
Revenue - Inpatient					
Gross Inpatient Revenue	$65,013,165,311	$59,939,612,338	$55,534,317,918	$51,732,783,137	$47,049,223,539
Revenue - Outpatient					
Gross Outpatient Revenue	$50,949,559,907	$45,736,849,741	$41,298,026,667	$37,165,785,892	$32,547,024,877
Revenue and Expenses - Totals					
(Includes Inpatient and Outpatient)					
Total Gross Revenue	$115,962,725,218	$105,676,462,079	$96,832,344,585	$88,898,569,029	$79,596,248,416
Deductions from Revenue	67,883,978,998	61,925,172,023	55,264,598,641	50,223,009,185	44,019,202,341
Net Patient Revenue	48,078,746,220	43,751,290,056	41,567,745,944	38,675,559,544	35,577,046,075
Other Operating Revenue	2,675,404,595	2,616,805,771	2,479,210,752	2,106,710,807	2,124,848,618
Other Nonoperating Revenue	(524,235,863)	1,412,620,373	1,109,745,510	696,073,822	708,088,869
Total Net Revenue	50,229,914,952	47,780,716,200	45,156,702,206	41,478,344,173	38,409,983,562
Total Expenses	48,227,547,446	44,256,405,517	41,972,965,544	39,136,861,595	36,013,631,175
HOSPITAL UNIT (Excludes Separate Nursing Home Units)					
Utilization - Inpatient					
Beds	58,879	58,121	58,156	58,980	59,383
Admissions	2,561,317	2,534,429	2,526,301	2,532,903	2,514,990
Inpatient Days	12,328,044	12,109,078	12,011,373	12,377,417	12,288,035
Average Length of Stay	4.8	4.8	4.8	4.9	4.9
Personnel					
Total Full Time	279,159	271,540	264,519	260,310	251,059
Total Part Time	166,260	155,511	156,092	157,231	147,559
Revenue and Expenses - Totals					
(Includes Inpatient and Outpatient)					
Total Net Revenue	$49,501,040,808	$47,065,541,644	$44,374,251,964	$40,819,418,642	$37,728,656,760
Total Expenses	47,573,291,977	43,615,288,526	41,265,906,225	38,534,012,886	35,392,518,478
COMMUNITY HEALTH INDICATORS PER 1000 POPULATION					
Total Population (in thousands)	20,166	20,025	19,883	19,750	19,646
Inpatient					
Beds	3.5	3.5	3.5	3.6	3.7
Admissions	128.4	128.1	128.8	130.0	129.9
Inpatient Days	789.1	795.6	806.2	829.8	830.1
Inpatient Surgeries	35.8	36.0	36.0	37.7	38.0
Births	13.9	14.0	14.0	13.9	13.8
Outpatient					
Emergency Outpatient Visits	399.5	384.7	376.5	377.4	363.5
Other Outpatient Visits	2,274.4	2,188.1	2,159.3	2,159.1	2,112.0
Total Outpatient Visits	2,673.9	2,572.8	2,535.8	2,536.5	2,475.5
Outpatient Surgeries	70.5	70.6	71.5	73.2	72.2
Expense per Capita (per person)	$2,391.6	$2,210.1	$2,111.0	$1,981.7	$1,833.2

TABLE 5

U.S. CENSUS DIVISION 7: WEST SOUTH CENTRAL

U.S. Registered Community Hospitals
(Nonfederal, short-term general and other special hospitals)

Overview 2004–2008

	2008	2007	2006	2005	2004
Total Community Hospitals					
in Census Division 7, West South Central...	757	735	745	738	745
Bed Size Category					
6-24	112	105	105	96	95
25-49	219	213	217	214	212
50-99	151	147	149	147	149
100-199	124	118	122	134	140
200-299	61	65	64	65	62
300-399	37	39	39	37	42
400-499	21	20	21	19	18
500 + ...	32	28	28	26	27
Location					
Hospitals Urban...........................	442	422	430	424	413
Hospitals Rural	315	313	315	314	332
Control					
State and Local Government................	225	226	230	231	239
Not for Profit	273	268	266	270	279
Investor owned	259	241	249	237	227
Physician Models					
Independent Practice Association	103	122	129	128	130
Group Practice without Walls...............	28	32	27	34	32
Open Physician-Hospital Organization	143	146	150	139	141
Closed Physician-Hospital Organization	32	28	30	32	30
Management Service Organization	92	93	85	80	80
Integrated Salary Model....................	155	142	150	130	134
Equity Model	19	14	11	15	10
Foundation...............................	50	49	47	51	40
Insurance Products					
Health Maintenance Organization	78	84	83	100	104
Preferred Provider Organization.............	93	116	124	141	138
Indemnity Fee for Service	32	30	35	41	35
Managed Care Contracts					
Health Maintenance Organization	453	445	429	432	433
Preferred Provider Organization.............	551	551	536	539	532
Affiliations					
Hospitals in a System......................	454	432	432	418	420
Hospitals in a Network	177	181	182	176	179
Hospitals in a Group Purchasing Organization..	622	600	602	588	576

TABLE 5

U.S. CENSUS DIVISION 7: WEST SOUTH CENTRAL

U.S. Registered Community Hospitals
(Nonfederal, short-term general and other special hospitals)

Utilization, Personnel, Revenue and Expenses, Community Health Indicators 2004–2008

	2008	2007	2006	2005	2004
TOTAL FACILITY (Includes Hospital and Nursing Home Units)					
Utilization - Inpatient					
Beds	97,720	94,072	94,910	93,890	95,699
Admissions	4,061,559	3,919,411	3,979,239	3,965,504	4,050,583
Inpatient Days	21,234,945	20,533,725	20,852,125	20,850,457	21,478,464
Average Length of Stay	5.2	5.2	5.2	5.3	5.3
Inpatient Surgeries	1,169,284	1,187,576	1,173,512	1,153,649	1,172,389
Births	546,219	536,959	540,951	513,917	506,460
Utilization - Outpatient					
Emergency Outpatient Visits	14,148,116	13,551,624	13,210,287	13,045,463	13,013,965
Other Outpatient Visits	42,236,693	39,885,211	39,010,692	39,473,305	39,980,656
Total Outpatient Visits	56,384,809	53,436,835	52,220,979	52,518,768	52,994,621
Outpatient Surgeries	1,642,752	1,624,911	1,625,425	1,601,209	1,654,307
Personnel					
Full Time RNs	110,558	107,131	102,597	100,220	97,021
Full Time LPNs	17,702	17,350	18,288	19,416	20,830
Part Time RNs	33,899	32,312	31,471	29,783	30,363
Part Time LPNs	4,592	4,559	5,154	5,378	5,676
Total Full Time	419,150	413,130	403,194	401,825	402,207
Total Part Time	102,483	96,722	99,179	96,029	99,129
Revenue - Inpatient					
Gross Inpatient Revenue	$122,760,036,602	$109,628,591,480	$101,979,867,848	$93,601,076,744	$87,369,160,822
Revenue - Outpatient					
Gross Outpatient Revenue	$73,261,517,369	$63,422,381,320	$57,034,788,275	$52,052,044,098	$46,336,452,782
Revenue and Expenses - Totals					
(Includes Inpatient and Outpatient)					
Total Gross Revenue	$196,021,553,971	$173,050,972,800	$159,014,656,123	$145,653,120,842	$133,705,613,604
Deductions from Revenue	136,945,981,599	118,940,845,500	106,872,525,570	96,016,085,892	86,617,124,034
Net Patient Revenue	59,075,572,372	54,110,127,300	52,142,130,553	49,637,034,950	47,088,489,570
Other Operating Revenue	4,942,957,894	4,713,837,579	4,747,889,502	4,040,443,738	3,981,823,882
Other Nonoperating Revenue	412,762,180	1,530,873,066	895,311,146	633,323,118	629,583,829
Total Net Revenue	64,431,292,446	60,354,837,945	57,797,925,303	54,310,801,806	51,699,897,281
Total Expenses	60,693,798,710	55,938,005,973	53,806,425,890	50,793,309,760	48,477,859,590
HOSPITAL UNIT (Excludes Separate Nursing Home Units)					
Utilization - Inpatient					
Beds	95,219	91,393	91,780	90,900	92,867
Admissions	4,044,358	3,902,159	3,957,541	3,940,077	4,024,745
Inpatient Days	20,585,465	19,711,788	19,937,670	19,956,488	20,620,040
Average Length of Stay	5.1	5.1	5.0	5.1	5.1
Personnel					
Total Full Time	416,608	410,704	400,215	399,460	390,268
Total Part Time	101,661	96,037	98,302	95,377	96,313
Revenue and Expenses - Totals					
(Includes Inpatient and Outpatient)					
Total Net Revenue	$64,269,536,853	$60,143,040,802	$57,559,802,328	$54,058,291,289	$51,509,676,207
Total Expenses	60,516,951,798	55,631,442,741	53,542,353,988	50,527,566,604	48,325,807,692
COMMUNITY HEALTH INDICATORS PER 1000 POPULATION					
Total Population (in thousands)	35,236	34,655	33,983	33,606	33,165
Inpatient					
Beds	2.8	2.7	2.8	2.8	2.9
Admissions	115.3	113.1	117.1	118.0	122.1
Inpatient Days	602.7	592.5	613.6	620.4	647.6
Inpatient Surgeries	33.2	34.3	34.5	34.3	35.4
Births	15.5	15.5	15.9	15.3	15.3
Outpatient					
Emergency Outpatient Visits	401.5	391.0	388.7	388.2	392.4
Other Outpatient Visits	1,198.7	1,150.9	1,147.9	1,174.6	1,205.5
Total Outpatient Visits	1,600.2	1,541.9	1,536.7	1,562.8	1,597.9
Outpatient Surgeries	46.6	46.9	47.8	47.6	49.9
Expense per Capita (per person)	$1,722.5	$1,614.1	$1,583.3	$1,511.4	$1,461.7

TABLE 5

U.S. CENSUS DIVISION 8: MOUNTAIN

U.S. Registered Community Hospitals
(Nonfederal, short-term general and other special hospitals)

Overview 2004–2008

	2008	2007	2006	2005	2004
Total Community Hospitals					
in Census Division 8, Mountain............	374	365	365	367	359
Bed Size Category					
6-24	48	46	57	52	49
25-49	94	90	88	86	79
50-99	92	92	82	89	91
100-199	66	66	66	65	65
200-299	34	34	35	39	39
300-399	17	15	17	20	21
400-499	9	9	10	7	7
500 + ...	14	13	10	9	8
Location					
Hospitals Urban...........................	183	169	169	170	148
Hospitals Rural	191	196	196	197	211
Control					
State and Local Government................	96	95	100	102	104
Not for Profit............................	189	192	184	182	181
Investor owned	89	78	81	83	74
Physician Models					
Independent Practice Association	46	48	45	44	46
Group Practice without Walls...............	8	10	9	7	13
Open Physician-Hospital Organization	33	33	40	41	42
Closed Physician-Hospital Organization	16	17	15	17	14
Management Service Organization	22	24	18	22	19
Integrated Salary Model...................	122	120	112	113	99
Equity Model.............................	6	6	6	7	5
Foundation...............................	14	14	13	13	5
Insurance Products					
Health Maintenance Organization	53	55	57	56	51
Preferred Provider Organization..............	49	61	63	76	60
Indemnity Fee for Service	25	36	32	34	30
Managed Care Contracts					
Health Maintenance Organization	156	155	152	159	149
Preferred Provider Organization..............	199	196	197	203	195
Affiliations					
Hospitals in a System.....................	225	211	213	213	203
Hospitals in a Network....................	110	107	104	103	101
Hospitals in a Group Purchasing Organization..	255	258	254	260	238

TABLE 5

U.S. CENSUS DIVISION 8: MOUNTAIN

U.S. Registered Community Hospitals
(Nonfederal, short-term general and other special hospitals)

Utilization, Personnel, Revenue and Expenses, Community Health Indicators 2004–2008

	2008	2007	2006	2005	2004
TOTAL FACILITY (Includes Hospital and Nursing Home Units)					
Utilization - Inpatient					
Beds	46,293	44,564	43,792	43,796	43,182
Admissions	2,098,239	2,033,246	2,013,762	2,004,384	1,959,133
Inpatient Days	10,533,261	10,290,695	10,300,681	10,165,433	10,015,692
Average Length of Stay	5.0	5.1	5.1	5.1	5.1
Inpatient Surgeries	638,455	633,790	640,838	604,787	590,717
Births	314,340	313,570	312,461	303,119	294,508
Utilization - Outpatient					
Emergency Outpatient Visits	7,302,452	7,077,571	6,901,098	6,851,313	6,243,490
Other Outpatient Visits	28,396,866	26,578,776	25,201,852	26,019,382	24,571,238
Total Outpatient Visits	35,699,318	33,656,347	32,102,950	32,870,695	30,814,728
Outpatient Surgeries	936,167	856,886	842,579	886,545	881,616
Personnel					
Full Time RNs	62,485	57,336	52,261	49,918	48,001
Full Time LPNs	4,011	4,199	4,308	4,502	4,521
Part Time RNs	24,804	22,170	23,766	23,173	21,260
Part Time LPNs	1,594	1,768	1,982	1,975	2,009
Total Full Time	224,101	218,760	204,327	201,681	190,186
Total Part Time	75,630	68,111	73,473	71,634	64,583
Revenue - Inpatient					
Gross Inpatient Revenue	$65,876,774,754	$58,788,545,403	$53,107,976,721	$48,458,007,228	$42,470,879,422
Revenue - Outpatient					
Gross Outpatient Revenue	$41,380,379,213	$35,716,383,231	$30,552,510,790	$27,312,023,316	$23,013,525,198
Revenue and Expenses - Totals					
(Includes Inpatient and Outpatient)					
Total Gross Revenue	$107,257,153,967	$94,504,928,634	$83,660,487,511	$75,770,030,544	$65,484,404,620
Deductions from Revenue	70,987,810,766	61,088,641,713	53,002,070,673	47,144,479,539	39,364,474,737
Net Patient Revenue	36,269,343,201	33,416,286,921	30,658,416,838	28,625,551,005	26,119,929,883
Other Operating Revenue	1,612,417,661	1,585,270,393	1,599,894,899	1,363,620,777	1,222,669,757
Other Nonoperating Revenue	(20,098,533)	870,215,218	481,150,834	357,911,606	358,187,063
Total Net Revenue	37,861,662,329	35,871,772,532	32,739,462,571	30,347,083,388	27,700,786,703
Total Expenses	35,816,821,042	32,708,537,125	29,827,199,413	27,941,395,174	25,258,325,366
HOSPITAL UNIT (Excludes Separate Nursing Home Units)					
Utilization - Inpatient					
Beds	42,780	40,648	39,887	39,623	39,064
Admissions	2,087,447	2,022,366	2,001,347	1,993,334	1,948,586
Inpatient Days	9,502,108	9,123,808	9,089,752	8,898,953	8,802,367
Average Length of Stay	4.6	4.5	4.5	4.5	4.5
Personnel					
Total Full Time	220,221	214,707	201,619	198,836	184,390
Total Part Time	74,179	66,557	72,021	69,885	62,492
Revenue and Expenses - Totals					
(Includes Inpatient and Outpatient)					
Total Net Revenue	$37,657,242,332	$35,656,821,227	$32,520,772,718	$30,134,818,660	$27,502,747,526
Total Expenses	35,628,245,086	32,520,257,859	29,635,161,921	27,747,618,911	25,083,681,922
COMMUNITY HEALTH INDICATORS PER 1000 POPULATION					
Total Population (in thousands)	21,785	21,360	20,856	20,305	19,823
Inpatient					
Beds	2.1	2.1	2.1	2.2	2.2
Admissions	96.3	95.2	96.6	98.7	98.8
Inpatient Days	483.5	481.8	493.9	500.6	505.3
Inpatient Surgeries	29.3	29.7	30.7	29.8	29.8
Births	14.4	14.7	15.0	14.9	14.9
Outpatient					
Emergency Outpatient Visits	335.2	331.3	330.9	337.4	315.0
Other Outpatient Visits	1,303.5	1,244.3	1,208.4	1,281.4	1,239.6
Total Outpatient Visits	1,638.7	1,575.7	1,539.3	1,618.9	1,554.5
Outpatient Surgeries	43.0	40.1	40.4	43.7	44.5
Expense per Capita (per person)	$1,644.1	$1,531.3	$1,430.1	$1,376.1	$1,274.2

TABLE 5

U.S. CENSUS DIVISION 9: PACIFIC

U.S. Registered Community Hospitals
(Nonfederal, short-term general and other special hospitals)

Overview 2004–2008

	2008	2007	2006	2005	2004
Total Community Hospitals					
in Census Division 9, Pacific	**543**	**545**	**549**	**548**	**547**
Bed Size Category					
6-24	36	35	38	39	38
25-49	97	95	99	97	93
50-99	82	85	85	89	88
100-199	139	145	144	142	142
200-299	92	89	91	87	94
300-399	53	54	52	58	52
400-499	27	24	22	19	21
500 + ...	17	18	18	17	19
Location					
Hospitals Urban..........................	420	423	424	422	409
Hospitals Rural	123	122	125	126	138
Control					
State and Local Government................	141	139	144	136	137
Not for Profit	315	316	316	319	311
Investor owned	87	90	89	93	99
Physician Models					
Independent Practice Association	88	108	117	123	130
Group Practice without Walls................	22	20	21	18	19
Open Physician-Hospital Organization	22	26	31	29	29
Closed Physician-Hospital Organization	10	10	9	16	16
Management Service Organization	44	51	51	46	53
Integrated Salary Model....................	107	111	113	117	90
Equity Model	2	4	3	3	1
Foundation...............................	52	44	48	48	38
Insurance Products					
Health Maintenance Organization	64	69	70	75	76
Preferred Provider Organization..............	48	63	55	62	56
Indemnity Fee for Service	15	21	21	23	25
Managed Care Contracts					
Health Maintenance Organization	226	257	258	267	256
Preferred Provider Organization..............	263	287	285	289	281
Affiliations					
Hospitals in a System.....................	328	329	342	329	329
Hospitals in a Network	107	100	106	103	97
Hospitals in a Group Purchasing Organization..	333	346	350	352	325

TABLE 5

U.S. CENSUS DIVISION 9: PACIFIC

U.S. Registered Community Hospitals
(Nonfederal, short-term general and other special hospitals)

Utilization, Personnel, Revenue and Expenses, Community Health Indicators 2004–2008

	2008	2007	2006	2005	2004
TOTAL FACILITY (Includes Hospital and Nursing Home Units)					
Utilization - Inpatient					
Beds	92,389	91,955	92,077	91,864	93,975
Admissions	4,557,658	4,365,002	4,491,195	4,478,621	4,497,690
Inpatient Days	23,454,079	22,401,234	23,419,759	23,367,424	23,439,112
Average Length of Stay	5.1	5.1	5.2	5.2	5.2
Inpatient Surgeries	1,260,249	1,299,136	1,251,269	1,258,460	1,276,765
Births	676,180	662,060	670,591	644,267	645,833
Utilization - Outpatient					
Emergency Outpatient Visits	14,473,721	14,319,461	14,623,874	13,513,811	13,832,185
Other Outpatient Visits	58,052,120	54,654,796	61,615,935	57,116,950	54,773,146
Total Outpatient Visits	72,525,841	68,974,257	76,239,809	70,630,761	68,605,331
Outpatient Surgeries	1,886,717	1,811,593	1,783,808	1,817,189	1,825,002
Personnel					
Full Time RNs	126,718	114,266	109,551	102,846	100,389
Full Time LPNs	9,011	8,993	9,538	9,880	10,293
Part Time RNs	72,526	75,566	73,766	68,963	67,130
Part Time LPNs	4,274	4,950	5,058	4,669	5,036
Total Full Time	477,563	454,501	444,221	425,327	419,721
Total Part Time	201,710	211,443	202,571	191,425	185,090
Revenue - Inpatient					
Gross Inpatient Revenue	$181,416,247,444	$168,961,978,477	$162,753,461,850	$153,582,565,621	$142,652,359,980
Revenue - Outpatient					
Gross Outpatient Revenue	$98,528,236,224	$84,834,034,482	$78,665,367,009	$70,108,626,775	$61,627,750,175
Revenue and Expenses - Totals					
(Includes Inpatient and Outpatient)					
Total Gross Revenue	$279,944,483,668	$253,796,012,959	$241,418,828,859	$223,691,192,396	$204,280,110,155
Deductions from Revenue	194,777,375,687	175,398,585,106	167,168,229,819	154,243,546,060	139,866,102,129
Net Patient Revenue	85,167,107,981	78,397,427,853	74,250,599,040	69,447,646,336	64,414,008,026
Other Operating Revenue	5,041,401,269	4,653,195,596	4,361,003,114	3,540,496,528	3,375,512,005
Other Nonoperating Revenue	23,014,193	2,776,806,260	2,124,134,857	1,782,114,508	1,652,444,385
Total Net Revenue	90,231,523,443	85,827,429,709	80,706,061,954	74,770,257,372	69,441,964,416
Total Expenses	88,037,635,750	79,632,236,072	76,421,525,696	71,652,944,767	66,689,227,653
HOSPITAL UNIT (Excludes Separate Nursing Home Units)					
Utilization - Inpatient					
Beds	87,253	86,642	86,878	86,221	87,995
Admissions	4,527,176	4,330,186	4,456,404	4,441,580	4,455,935
Inpatient Days	21,897,397	20,880,648	21,889,072	21,675,035	21,541,278
Average Length of Stay	4.8	4.8	4.9	4.9	4.8
Personnel					
Total Full Time	473,367	449,821	438,331	420,531	411,223
Total Part Time	199,475	208,757	199,539	189,337	182,133
Revenue and Expenses - Totals					
(Includes Inpatient and Outpatient)					
Total Net Revenue	$89,624,997,242	$85,096,193,516	$79,957,542,841	$74,213,917,886	$68,863,776,071
Total Expenses	87,584,896,173	79,167,104,551	75,989,209,712	71,197,475,636	66,179,943,341
COMMUNITY HEALTH INDICATORS PER 1000 POPULATION					
Total Population (in thousands)	49,070	48,521	48,114	47,695	47,298
Inpatient					
Beds	1.9	1.9	1.9	1.9	2.0
Admissions	92.9	90.0	93.3	93.9	95.1
Inpatient Days	478.0	461.7	486.8	489.9	495.6
Inpatient Surgeries	25.7	26.8	26.0	26.4	27.0
Births	13.8	13.6	13.9	13.5	13.7
Outpatient					
Emergency Outpatient Visits	295.0	295.1	303.9	283.3	292.4
Other Outpatient Visits	1,183.0	1,126.4	1,280.6	1,197.5	1,158.0
Total Outpatient Visits	1,478.0	1,421.5	1,584.6	1,480.9	1,450.5
Outpatient Surgeries	38.4	37.3	37.1	38.1	38.6
Expense per Capita (per person)	$1,794.1	$1,641.2	$1,588.3	$1,502.3	$1,410.0

U.S. Census Divisions

TABLE 6

ALABAMA

U.S. Registered Community Hospitals
(Nonfederal, short-term general and other special hospitals)

Overview 2004–2008

	2008	2007	2006	2005	2004
Total Community Hospitals in Alabama	109	109	109	109	108
Bed Size Category					
6-24	8	6	6	7	7
25-49	25	25	22	23	20
50-99	27	26	24	24	25
100-199	25	29	34	31	33
200-299	11	11	11	13	13
300-399	7	6	7	6	5
400-499	3	2	1	1	1
500 + ...	3	4	4	4	4
Location					
Hospitals Urban	60	60	60	60	57
Hospitals Rural	49	49	49	49	51
Control					
State and Local Government	42	42	41	39	37
Not for Profit	27	27	26	31	35
Investor owned	40	40	42	39	36
Physician Models					
Independent Practice Association	8	7	7	7	6
Group Practice without Walls	2	3	1	0	0
Open Physician-Hospital Organization	3	5	3	4	3
Closed Physician-Hospital Organization	2	2	1	3	1
Management Service Organization	10	12	7	9	7
Integrated Salary Model	14	14	12	11	12
Equity Model	0	1	0	0	0
Foundation	5	6	2	5	3
Insurance Products					
Health Maintenance Organization	13	12	9	7	5
Preferred Provider Organization	10	8	8	12	11
Indemnity Fee for Service	3	2	2	3	2
Managed Care Contracts					
Health Maintenance Organization	35	32	27	35	36
Preferred Provider Organization	49	42	39	50	46
Affiliations					
Hospitals in a System	68	67	65	68	63
Hospitals in a Network	12	12	10	12	13
Hospitals in a Group Purchasing Organization . .	68	64	55	60	52

TABLE 6

ALABAMA

U.S. Registered Community Hospitals
(Nonfederal, short-term general and other special hospitals)

Utilization, Personnel, Revenue and Expenses, Community Health Indicators 2004–2008

	2008	2007	2006	2005	2004
TOTAL FACILITY (Includes Hospital and Nursing Home Units)					
Utilization - Inpatient					
Beds	15,250	15,682	15,639	15,486	15,328
Admissions	687,446	696,131	683,726	706,442	715,709
Inpatient Days	3,524,687	3,551,293	3,556,939	3,628,012	3,664,493
Average Length of Stay	5.1	5.1	5.2	5.1	5.1
Inpatient Surgeries	202,900	221,162	223,876	210,076	204,461
Births	62,436	62,617	59,456	59,570	57,793
Utilization - Outpatient					
Emergency Outpatient Visits	2,271,755	2,253,215	2,192,221	2,085,573	2,026,709
Other Outpatient Visits	6,746,766	5,934,478	5,831,133	5,461,629	6,235,601
Total Outpatient Visits	9,018,521	8,187,693	8,023,354	7,547,202	8,262,310
Outpatient Surgeries	364,648	365,487	373,688	356,034	340,943
Personnel					
Full Time RNs	17,930	17,077	17,308	16,617	15,209
Full Time LPNs	1,795	2,005	2,225	2,356	2,488
Part Time RNs	6,708	7,708	6,677	6,097	5,804
Part Time LPNs	755	885	890	716	780
Total Full Time	64,821	63,949	65,120	65,221	62,248
Total Part Time	18,103	20,423	18,703	16,142	15,825
Revenue - Inpatient					
Gross Inpatient Revenue	$18,436,910,861	$17,301,065,902	$16,275,203,299	$15,022,125,418	$14,229,244,584
Revenue - Outpatient					
Gross Outpatient Revenue	$11,949,849,370	$10,302,085,003	$9,484,229,706	$8,417,319,841	$7,369,023,127
Revenue and Expenses - Totals (Includes Inpatient and Outpatient)					
Total Gross Revenue	$30,386,760,231	$27,603,150,905	$25,759,433,005	$23,439,445,259	$21,598,267,711
Deductions from Revenue	22,550,588,921	19,968,905,297	18,197,677,398	16,193,032,176	15,026,334,977
Net Patient Revenue	7,836,171,310	7,634,245,608	7,561,755,607	7,246,413,083	6,571,932,734
Other Operating Revenue	499,586,864	522,333,646	441,333,070	371,786,311	407,758,534
Other Nonoperating Revenue	(56,405,573)	268,802,396	203,736,118	149,232,438	139,283,436
Total Net Revenue	8,279,352,601	8,425,381,650	8,206,824,795	7,767,431,832	7,118,974,704
Total Expenses	8,288,702,647	7,960,186,498	7,550,751,275	7,180,554,012	6,733,585,986
HOSPITAL UNIT (Excludes Separate Nursing Home Units)					
Utilization - Inpatient					
Beds	14,824	15,042	14,917	14,692	14,615
Admissions	686,256	693,215	680,564	703,117	713,126
Inpatient Days	3,377,540	3,347,267	3,335,678	3,367,589	3,441,086
Average Length of Stay	4.9	4.8	4.9	4.8	4.8
Personnel					
Total Full Time	64,502	63,572	64,631	64,700	61,790
Total Part Time	18,073	20,305	18,617	16,035	15,768
Revenue and Expenses - Totals (Includes Inpatient and Outpatient)					
Total Net Revenue	$8,258,544,123	$8,397,411,188	$8,172,214,723	$7,734,917,420	$7,067,657,683
Total Expenses	8,268,150,713	7,937,260,895	7,526,811,142	7,153,872,718	6,691,220,104
COMMUNITY HEALTH INDICATORS PER 1000 POPULATION					
Total Population (in thousands)	4,662	4,627	4,588	4,537	4,507
Inpatient					
Beds	3.3	3.4	3.4	3.4	3.4
Admissions	147.5	150.5	149.0	155.7	158.8
Inpatient Days	756.1	767.6	775.3	799.6	813.1
Inpatient Surgeries	43.5	47.8	48.8	46.3	45.4
Births	13.4	13.5	13.0	13.1	12.8
Outpatient					
Emergency Outpatient Visits	487.3	487.0	477.9	459.7	449.7
Other Outpatient Visits	1,447.2	1,282.7	1,271.1	1,203.7	1,383.7
Total Outpatient Visits	1,934.5	1,769.7	1,748.9	1,663.4	1,833.4
Outpatient Surgeries	78.2	79.0	81.5	78.5	75.7
Expense per Capita (per person)	$1,778.0	$1,720.5	$1,645.9	$1,582.6	$1,494.2

TABLE 6   **ALASKA**

U.S. Registered Community Hospitals
(Nonfederal, short-term general and other special hospitals)

Overview 2004–2008

	2008	2007	2006	2005	2004
Total Community Hospitals in Alaska.........	22	22	22	22	19
Bed Size Category					
6-24....................................	6	6	7	7	5
25-49....................................	7	7	7	8	8
50-99....................................	4	4	4	3	2
100-199................................	3	3	2	3	2
200-299................................	1	1	1	0	1
300-399................................	1	1	1	1	1
400-499................................	0	0	0	0	0
500 +....................................	0	0	0	0	0
Location					
Hospitals Urban...........................	5	5	5	5	3
Hospitals Rural...........................	17	17	17	17	16
Control					
State and Local Government................	7	7	7	7	7
Not for Profit............................	13	13	13	13	10
Investor owned..........................	2	2	2	2	2
Physician Models					
Independent Practice Association	0	2	2	1	2
Group Practice without Walls................	0	0	1	1	3
Open Physician-Hospital Organization	2	3	2	1	1
Closed Physician-Hospital Organization	0	0	0	1	0
Management Service Organization	0	0	0	0	0
Integrated Salary Model....................	4	4	6	6	2
Equity Model............................	0	0	0	0	0
Foundation...............................	0	0	1	1	0
Insurance Products					
Health Maintenance Organization	0	0	0	0	0
Preferred Provider Organization..............	2	3	2	3	1
Indemnity Fee for Service	1	0	0	0	0
Managed Care Contracts					
Health Maintenance Organization	0	0	0	0	0
Preferred Provider Organization..............	8	9	8	6	4
Affiliations					
Hospitals in a System......................	8	8	8	8	12
Hospitals in a Network.....................	3	4	4	4	4
Hospitals in a Group Purchasing Organization..	11	11	13	11	6

States

TABLE 6

ALASKA

U.S. Registered Community Hospitals
(Nonfederal, short-term general and other special hospitals)

Utilization, Personnel, Revenue and Expenses, Community Health Indicators 2004–2008

	2008	2007	2006	2005	2004
TOTAL FACILITY (Includes Hospital and Nursing Home Units)					
Utilization - Inpatient					
Beds	1,553	1,554	1,551	1,393	1,427
Admissions	58,204	56,584	52,357	51,022	45,359
Inpatient Days	346,837	337,028	304,978	306,027	285,999
Average Length of Stay	6.0	6.0	5.8	6.0	6.3
Inpatient Surgeries	20,522	18,924	26,787	18,091	27,473
Births	8,882	9,047	9,128	8,554	7,366
Utilization - Outpatient					
Emergency Outpatient Visits	328,164	328,947	610,324	326,528	253,405
Other Outpatient Visits	1,365,178	1,455,616	1,165,596	1,340,089	1,077,327
Total Outpatient Visits	1,693,342	1,784,563	1,775,920	1,666,617	1,330,732
Outpatient Surgeries	43,567	44,193	34,522	41,155	44,071
Personnel					
Full Time RNs	2,090	2,091	2,071	2,135	1,583
Full Time LPNs	163	197	191	222	184
Part Time RNs	848	512	826	702	509
Part Time LPNs	48	45	56	55	58
Total Full Time	8,809	8,712	8,668	8,299	6,191
Total Part Time	2,435	1,661	2,304	2,031	1,532
Revenue - Inpatient					
Gross Inpatient Revenue	$2,045,394,009	$1,688,213,313	$1,619,128,443	$1,503,737,136	$1,338,181,466
Revenue - Outpatient					
Gross Outpatient Revenue	$1,623,182,947	$1,379,909,276	$1,283,765,424	$1,156,015,492	$971,620,399
Revenue and Expenses - Totals					
(Includes Inpatient and Outpatient)					
Total Gross Revenue	$3,668,576,956	$3,068,122,589	$2,902,893,867	$2,659,752,628	$2,309,801,865
Deductions from Revenue	2,054,343,109	1,623,832,318	1,529,429,013	1,433,497,046	1,302,835,817
Net Patient Revenue	1,614,233,847	1,444,290,271	1,373,464,854	1,226,255,582	1,006,966,048
Other Operating Revenue	66,832,290	78,687,582	73,602,633	53,752,321	43,170,801
Other Nonoperating Revenue	16,635,452	41,367,990	27,681,282	18,810,420	13,685,375
Total Net Revenue	1,697,701,589	1,564,345,843	1,474,748,769	1,298,818,323	1,063,822,224
Total Expenses	1,570,873,845	1,458,281,758	1,424,479,572	1,281,505,051	1,053,847,164
HOSPITAL UNIT (Excludes Separate Nursing Home Units)					
Utilization - Inpatient					
Beds	1,381	1,280	1,359	1,268	1,344
Admissions	58,081	56,310	51,957	50,773	45,140
Inpatient Days	293,939	252,315	242,591	270,302	261,976
Average Length of Stay	5.1	4.5	4.7	5.3	5.8
Personnel					
Total Full Time	8,712	8,469	8,483	8,182	6,115
Total Part Time	2,350	1,546	2,203	1,969	1,486
Revenue and Expenses - Totals					
(Includes Inpatient and Outpatient)					
Total Net Revenue	$1,678,203,874	$1,502,363,012	$1,446,879,893	$1,283,490,046	$1,055,506,617
Total Expenses	1,560,050,288	1,432,798,379	1,402,317,116	1,272,419,936	1,048,048,983
COMMUNITY HEALTH INDICATORS PER 1000 POPULATION					
Total Population (in thousands)	686	681	676	669	661
Inpatient					
Beds	2.3	2.3	2.3	2.1	2.2
Admissions	84.8	83.1	77.4	76.3	68.6
Inpatient Days	505.4	494.8	451.0	457.7	432.7
Inpatient Surgeries	29.9	27.8	39.6	27.1	41.6
Births	12.9	13.3	13.5	12.8	11.1
Outpatient					
Emergency Outpatient Visits	478.2	483.0	902.4	488.4	383.4
Other Outpatient Visits	1,989.2	2,137.1	1,723.5	2,004.2	1,629.9
Total Outpatient Visits	2,467.4	2,620.1	2,625.9	2,492.6	2,013.3
Outpatient Surgeries	63.5	64.9	51.0	61.6	66.7
Expense per Capita (per person)	$2,288.9	$2,141.0	$2,106.3	$1,916.6	$1,594.4

TABLE **6**

ARIZONA

U.S. Registered Community Hospitals
(Nonfederal, short-term general and other special hospitals)

Overview 2004–2008

	2008	2007	2006	2005	2004
Total Community Hospitals in Arizona	71	66	66	67	62
Bed Size Category					
6-24	4	4	5	6	6
25-49	10	10	9	8	7
50-99	18	14	14	13	10
100-199	12	13	13	15	15
200-299	11	11	12	13	12
300-399	7	6	6	7	6
400-499	4	3	2	0	1
500 + ...	5	5	5	5	5
Location					
Hospitals Urban.	57	48	50	51	47
Hospitals Rural	14	18	16	16	15
Control					
State and Local Government	4	4	5	5	5
Not for Profit	44	43	41	40	38
Investor owned	23	19	20	22	19
Physician Models					
Independent Practice Association	10	9	6	7	5
Group Practice without Walls.	2	3	2	3	4
Open Physician-Hospital Organization	5	7	9	10	7
Closed Physician-Hospital Organization	4	4	5	5	2
Management Service Organization	3	4	2	3	2
Integrated Salary Model	12	12	11	10	12
Equity Model	0	0	1	1	1
Foundation.	3	3	4	4	2
Insurance Products					
Health Maintenance Organization	10	11	10	10	9
Preferred Provider Organization.	3	10	9	9	7
Indemnity Fee for Service	3	9	7	7	6
Managed Care Contracts					
Health Maintenance Organization	33	33	28	31	28
Preferred Provider Organization.	31	33	32	36	32
Affiliations					
Hospitals in a System.	48	44	45	47	44
Hospitals in a Network	14	11	12	14	12
Hospitals in a Group Purchasing Organization. .	43	39	37	42	35

States

TABLE 6

ARIZONA

U.S. Registered Community Hospitals
(Nonfederal, short-term general and other special hospitals)

Utilization, Personnel, Revenue and Expenses, Community Health Indicators 2004–2008

	2008	2007	2006	2005	2004
TOTAL FACILITY (Includes Hospital and Nursing Home Units)					
Utilization - Inpatient					
Beds	13,138	12,157	11,947	11,767	11,166
Admissions	716,136	675,216	664,773	664,595	624,583
Inpatient Days	3,235,063	3,041,795	3,023,329	2,936,640	2,781,888
Average Length of Stay	4.5	4.5	4.5	4.4	4.5
Inpatient Surgeries	225,735	209,707	218,604	186,097	179,548
Births	96,193	97,159	96,797	92,519	87,924
Utilization - Outpatient					
Emergency Outpatient Visits	2,172,149	2,122,695	2,073,320	2,050,938	1,747,614
Other Outpatient Visits	5,542,202	5,190,865	4,482,315	4,725,513	3,661,990
Total Outpatient Visits	7,714,351	7,313,560	6,555,635	6,776,451	5,409,604
Outpatient Surgeries	254,546	221,754	224,424	217,836	217,574
Personnel					
Full Time RNs	20,898	18,124	16,858	15,017	13,772
Full Time LPNs	957	920	1,041	1,042	964
Part Time RNs	6,462	6,140	5,535	5,982	5,195
Part Time LPNs	251	274	298	364	335
Total Full Time	65,568	64,315	61,165	58,488	52,349
Total Part Time	18,272	17,536	16,607	18,331	14,547
Revenue - Inpatient					
Gross Inpatient Revenue	$23,681,284,471	$21,143,464,204	$19,051,058,791	$17,448,393,885	$14,738,387,044
Revenue - Outpatient					
Gross Outpatient Revenue	$12,097,995,360	$10,534,254,958	$9,001,251,090	$8,162,904,498	$6,246,095,056
Revenue and Expenses - Totals (Includes Inpatient and Outpatient)					
Total Gross Revenue	$35,779,279,831	$31,677,719,162	$28,052,309,881	$25,611,298,383	$20,984,482,100
Deductions from Revenue	25,364,507,854	21,946,070,382	19,016,673,089	17,078,729,257	13,840,885,226
Net Patient Revenue	10,414,771,977	9,731,648,780	9,035,636,792	8,532,569,126	7,143,596,874
Other Operating Revenue	363,332,345	367,303,347	512,917,408	330,874,226	254,898,935
Other Nonoperating Revenue	(141,211,261)	203,652,122	103,114,887	83,188,540	61,100,042
Total Net Revenue	10,636,893,061	10,302,604,249	9,651,669,087	8,946,631,892	7,459,595,851
Total Expenses	10,461,227,615	9,586,339,104	8,959,776,857	8,025,631,963	6,861,149,144
HOSPITAL UNIT (Excludes Separate Nursing Home Units)					
Utilization - Inpatient					
Beds	12,954	11,949	11,739	11,630	11,093
Admissions	713,487	672,878	662,251	664,082	624,492
Inpatient Days	3,189,855	2,981,340	2,953,137	2,893,566	2,756,345
Average Length of Stay	4.5	4.4	4.5	4.4	4.4
Personnel					
Total Full Time	63,940	62,623	61,087	58,341	49,656
Total Part Time	17,993	17,258	16,567	18,288	14,076
Revenue and Expenses - Totals (Includes Inpatient and Outpatient)					
Total Net Revenue	$10,627,564,240	$10,291,634,189	$9,632,434,792	$8,939,787,932	$7,456,265,078
Total Expenses	10,447,130,955	9,573,110,290	8,946,668,918	8,012,166,227	6,856,080,845
COMMUNITY HEALTH INDICATORS PER 1000 POPULATION					
Total Population (in thousands)	6,500	6,353	6,178	5,961	5,750
Inpatient					
Beds	2.0	1.9	1.9	2.0	1.9
Admissions	110.2	106.3	107.6	111.5	108.6
Inpatient Days	497.7	478.8	489.4	492.6	483.8
Inpatient Surgeries	34.7	33.0	35.4	31.2	31.2
Births	14.8	15.3	15.7	15.5	15.3
Outpatient					
Emergency Outpatient Visits	334.2	334.1	335.6	344.0	303.9
Other Outpatient Visits	852.6	817.0	725.5	792.7	636.8
Total Outpatient Visits	1,186.8	1,151.1	1,061.1	1,136.8	940.7
Outpatient Surgeries	39.2	34.9	36.3	36.5	37.8
Expense per Capita (per person)	$1,609.4	$1,508.8	$1,450.2	$1,346.3	$1,193.1

TABLE 6

ARKANSAS

U.S. Registered Community Hospitals
(Nonfederal, short-term general and other special hospitals)

Overview 2004–2008

	2008	2007	2006	2005	2004
Total Community Hospitals in Arkansas.......	86	84	84	85	87
Bed Size Category					
6-24	7	5	5	6	5
25-49	30	30	29	29	28
50-99	18	17	20	19	21
100-199	18	19	16	18	20
200-299	6	6	7	6	7
300-399	5	5	5	5	4
400-499	0	0	0	0	0
500 + ...	2	2	2	2	2
Location					
Hospitals Urban.........................	37	35	35	35	32
Hospitals Rural	49	49	49	50	55
Control					
State and Local Government................	13	14	15	15	15
Not for Profit	46	45	45	47	50
Investor owned	27	25	24	23	22
Physician Models					
Independent Practice Association	17	17	20	20	21
Group Practice without Walls...............	6	6	5	8	5
Open Physician-Hospital Organization	28	28	32	32	30
Closed Physician-Hospital Organization	4	3	4	4	6
Management Service Organization	10	12	13	12	13
Integrated Salary Model....................	18	16	18	16	15
Equity Model	2	2	2	2	2
Foundation...............................	11	8	8	7	8
Insurance Products					
Health Maintenance Organization	15	14	14	15	22
Preferred Provider Organization..............	13	14	11	17	23
Indemnity Fee for Service	4	4	4	5	7
Managed Care Contracts					
Health Maintenance Organization	47	49	45	45	47
Preferred Provider Organization..............	65	68	62	66	70
Affiliations					
Hospitals in a System.....................	46	45	47	47	47
Hospitals in a Network....................	29	27	28	29	29
Hospitals in a Group Purchasing Organization..	80	82	78	80	79

TABLE 6

ARKANSAS

U.S. Registered Community Hospitals
(Nonfederal, short-term general and other special hospitals)

Utilization, Personnel, Revenue and Expenses, Community Health Indicators 2004–2008

	2008	2007	2006	2005	2004
TOTAL FACILITY (Includes Hospital and Nursing Home Units)					
Utilization - Inpatient					
Beds	9,686	9,502	9,309	9,389	9,580
Admissions	376,158	366,452	373,067	380,067	382,836
Inpatient Days	1,989,969	1,908,909	1,943,363	2,002,721	2,050,766
Average Length of Stay............	5.3	5.2	5.2	5.3	5.4
Inpatient Surgeries...............	102,681	116,019	108,651	126,374	115,512
Births..........................	39,013	39,602	39,232	37,939	36,734
Utilization - Outpatient					
Emergency Outpatient Visits........	1,301,330	1,294,119	1,267,198	1,263,822	1,220,658
Other Outpatient Visits............	3,671,422	3,942,397	3,818,276	3,707,485	3,621,645
Total Outpatient Visits	4,972,752	5,236,516	5,085,474	4,971,307	4,842,303
Outpatient Surgeries	136,565	147,222	144,619	141,104	146,074
Personnel					
Full Time RNs	9,700	9,678	9,699	9,578	8,903
Full Time LPNs	2,455	2,313	2,572	2,670	2,674
Part Time RNs..................	3,596	3,478	3,309	3,299	3,557
Part Time LPNs.................	824	824	859	884	1,015
Total Full Time.................	38,483	37,486	37,651	37,444	36,721
Total Part Time	11,549	10,872	10,845	10,766	11,816
Revenue - Inpatient					
Gross Inpatient Revenue...........	$8,250,771,568	$7,750,748,662	$7,346,539,305	$6,962,421,549	$6,513,778,911
Revenue - Outpatient					
Gross Outpatient Revenue	$5,568,220,057	$5,054,791,861	$4,655,737,561	$4,238,194,924	$3,861,410,128
Revenue and Expenses - Totals					
(Includes Inpatient and Outpatient)					
Total Gross Revenue..............	$13,818,991,625	$12,805,540,523	$12,002,276,866	$11,200,616,473	$10,375,189,039
Deductions from Revenue..........	9,011,385,599	8,220,632,392	7,572,665,742	6,945,017,078	6,360,783,014
Net Patient Revenue	4,807,606,026	4,584,908,131	4,429,611,124	4,255,599,395	4,014,406,025
Other Operating Revenue	169,341,834	162,135,731	154,744,439	153,253,789	134,780,857
Other Nonoperating Revenue	31,674,701	56,666,788	74,174,385	51,496,442	57,186,707
Total Net Revenue...............	5,008,622,561	4,803,710,650	4,658,529,948	4,460,349,626	4,206,373,589
Total Expenses..................	4,921,858,438	4,585,732,810	4,437,596,804	4,225,289,800	4,015,475,758
HOSPITAL UNIT (Excludes Separate Nursing Home Units)					
Utilization - Inpatient					
Beds	9,250	9,067	8,855	8,914	9,107
Admissions	374,159	364,431	371,143	377,594	380,311
Inpatient Days	1,854,685	1,767,173	1,799,422	1,852,272	1,903,513
Average Length of Stay............	5.0	4.8	4.8	4.9	5.0
Personnel					
Total Full Time..................	38,028	37,156	37,231	37,086	36,344
Total Part Time	11,398	10,768	10,671	10,632	11,689
Revenue and Expenses - Totals					
(Includes Inpatient and Outpatient)					
Total Net Revenue...............	$4,986,288,187	$4,782,794,055	$4,637,882,611	$4,435,802,386	$4,184,016,644
Total Expenses..................	4,902,909,300	4,567,507,045	4,419,957,774	4,206,167,940	4,001,964,554
COMMUNITY HEALTH INDICATORS PER 1000 POPULATION					
Total Population (in thousands)	2,855	2,831	2,804	2,769	2,740
Inpatient					
Beds	3.4	3.4	3.3	3.4	3.5
Admissions	131.7	129.5	133.0	137.3	139.7
Inpatient Days	696.9	674.4	693.0	723.3	748.4
Inpatient Surgeries...............	36.0	41.0	38.7	45.6	42.2
Births..........................	13.7	14.0	14.0	13.7	13.4
Outpatient					
Emergency Outpatient Visits........	455.7	457.2	451.9	456.4	445.5
Other Outpatient Visits............	1,285.8	1,392.8	1,361.6	1,339.0	1,321.7
Total Outpatient Visits	1,741.5	1,850.0	1,813.5	1,795.4	1,767.1
Outpatient Surgeries	47.8	52.0	51.6	51.0	53.3
Expense per Capita (per person).....	$1,723.7	$1,620.1	$1,582.5	$1,526.0	$1,465.4

TABLE 6

CALIFORNIA

U.S. Registered Community Hospitals
(Nonfederal, short-term general and other special hospitals)

Overview 2004–2008

	2008	2007	2006	2005	2004
Total Community Hospitals in California	352	355	357	357	361
Bed Size Category					
6-24	14	14	11	11	14
25-49	36	34	39	39	37
50-99	50	53	53	54	59
100-199	107	111	109	107	102
200-299	66	66	71	70	74
300-399	44	45	43	49	44
400-499	22	18	16	12	14
500 + ...	13	14	15	15	17
Location					
Hospitals Urban..........................	321	323	324	323	321
Hospitals Rural	31	32	33	34	40
Control					
State and Local Government................	71	71	76	69	72
Not for Profit	202	203	202	204	200
Investor owned	79	81	79	84	89
Physician Models					
Independent Practice Association	72	89	93	94	108
Group Practice without Walls...............	12	12	13	10	10
Open Physician-Hospital Organization	6	10	12	11	16
Closed Physician-Hospital Organization	7	4	3	6	9
Management Service Organization	27	33	38	32	41
Integrated Salary Model....................	30	32	36	35	30
Equity Model	1	4	2	2	1
Foundation...............................	39	39	41	40	35
Insurance Products					
Health Maintenance Organization	46	48	52	54	58
Preferred Provider Organization..............	19	27	25	27	30
Indemnity Fee for Service	10	15	15	15	18
Managed Care Contracts					
Health Maintenance Organization	154	179	182	183	182
Preferred Provider Organization..............	158	183	184	186	189
Affiliations					
Hospitals in a System.....................	231	235	240	237	234
Hospitals in a Network....................	59	55	61	58	56
Hospitals in a Group Purchasing Organization..	206	206	212	211	217

TABLE 6

CALIFORNIA

U.S. Registered Community Hospitals
(Nonfederal, short-term general and other special hospitals)

Utilization, Personnel, Revenue and Expenses, Community Health Indicators 2004–2008

	2008	2007	2006	2005	2004
TOTAL FACILITY (Includes Hospital and Nursing Home Units)					
Utilization - Inpatient					
Beds	69,587	69,325	70,021	70,192	71,910
Admissions	3,460,688	3,276,372	3,428,885	3,434,221	3,468,538
Inpatient Days	18,044,888	17,154,514	18,278,223	18,235,884	18,351,443
Average Length of Stay	5.2	5.2	5.3	5.3	5.3
Inpatient Surgeries	904,722	951,529	913,228	918,661	933,289
Births	526,946	514,164	524,279	502,721	507,236
Utilization - Outpatient					
Emergency Outpatient Visits	10,068,613	10,006,018	10,276,370	9,483,972	10,035,153
Other Outpatient Visits	38,808,536	35,930,559	43,662,065	39,548,508	37,430,411
Total Outpatient Visits	48,877,149	45,936,577	53,938,435	49,032,480	47,465,564
Outpatient Surgeries	1,309,864	1,250,377	1,238,695	1,272,041	1,280,528
Personnel					
Full Time RNs	98,152	86,556	82,703	78,208	76,315
Full Time LPNs	7,531	7,494	7,835	8,258	8,464
Part Time RNs	49,205	54,152	52,774	47,279	45,608
Part Time LPNs	3,281	3,948	4,023	3,593	3,885
Total Full Time	356,834	338,268	328,016	316,517	314,622
Total Part Time	134,602	150,145	141,985	130,350	122,989
Revenue - Inpatient					
Gross Inpatient Revenue	$150,337,219,745	$141,494,365,112	$137,778,920,000	$130,814,700,988	$122,088,752,099
Revenue - Outpatient					
Gross Outpatient Revenue	$74,357,000,289	$63,410,673,627	$59,664,515,444	$53,085,704,335	$46,806,272,994
Revenue and Expenses - Totals					
(Includes Inpatient and Outpatient)					
Total Gross Revenue	$224,694,220,034	$204,905,038,739	$197,443,435,444	$183,900,405,323	$168,895,025,093
Deductions from Revenue	162,955,378,616	147,778,238,783	142,916,546,652	132,790,253,113	121,210,414,502
Net Patient Revenue	61,738,841,418	57,126,799,956	54,526,888,792	51,110,152,210	47,684,610,591
Other Operating Revenue	3,808,102,197	3,501,284,745	3,340,457,320	2,603,323,550	2,434,927,648
Other Nonoperating Revenue	139,168,261	2,141,531,027	1,675,375,040	1,513,766,473	1,389,431,023
Total Net Revenue	65,686,111,876	62,769,615,728	59,513,046,095	55,227,242,233	51,508,969,262
Total Expenses	64,441,142,995	58,050,140,085	56,137,019,009	52,941,027,828	49,655,611,093
HOSPITAL UNIT (Excludes Separate Nursing Home Units)					
Utilization - Inpatient					
Beds	65,773	65,169	65,789	65,715	67,188
Admissions	3,435,099	3,246,140	3,398,774	3,402,199	3,432,533
Inpatient Days	16,911,379	15,982,046	17,052,324	16,904,055	16,838,780
Average Length of Stay	4.9	4.9	5.0	5.0	4.9
Personnel					
Total Full Time	353,564	334,625	323,030	312,625	307,259
Total Part Time	132,907	147,999	139,310	128,632	120,423
Revenue and Expenses - Totals					
(Includes Inpatient and Outpatient)					
Total Net Revenue	$65,179,794,371	$62,185,142,736	$58,848,516,663	$54,774,015,404	$51,021,631,137
Total Expenses	64,094,102,118	57,679,563,342	55,775,213,595	52,565,839,598	49,229,372,270
COMMUNITY HEALTH INDICATORS PER 1000 POPULATION					
Total Population (in thousands)	36,757	36,378	36,121	35,885	35,630
Inpatient					
Beds	1.9	1.9	1.9	2.0	2.0
Admissions	94.2	90.1	94.9	95.7	97.3
Inpatient Days	490.9	471.6	506.0	508.2	515.1
Inpatient Surgeries	24.6	26.2	25.3	25.6	26.2
Births	14.3	14.1	14.5	14.0	14.2
Outpatient					
Emergency Outpatient Visits	273.9	275.1	284.5	264.3	281.7
Other Outpatient Visits	1,055.8	987.7	1,208.8	1,102.1	1,050.5
Total Outpatient Visits	1,329.7	1,262.8	1,493.3	1,366.4	1,332.2
Outpatient Surgeries	35.6	34.4	34.3	35.4	35.9
Expense per Capita (per person)	$1,753.2	$1,595.8	$1,554.1	$1,475.3	$1,393.7

States

TABLE 6

COLORADO

U.S. Registered Community Hospitals
(Nonfederal, short-term general and other special hospitals)

Overview 2004–2008

	2008	2007	2006	2005	2004
Total Community Hospitals in Colorado.......	78	75	73	71	70
Bed Size Category					
6-24	10	10	13	10	9
25-49	21	18	18	15	14
50-99	16	17	13	16	18
100-199	13	12	11	11	10
200-299	9	9	8	8	8
300-399	4	4	5	7	8
400-499	3	4	4	3	3
500 + ...	2	1	1	1	0
Location					
Hospitals Urban..........................	41	38	36	35	34
Hospitals Rural	37	37	37	36	36
Control					
State and Local Government................	28	28	27	27	27
Not for Profit	37	37	35	33	32
Investor owned	13	10	11	11	11
Physician Models					
Independent Practice Association	9	7	6	5	9
Group Practice without Walls...............	1	2	3	1	3
Open Physician-Hospital Organization	12	8	7	5	9
Closed Physician-Hospital Organization	2	3	2	4	5
Management Service Organization	3	3	2	4	4
Integrated Salary Model....................	32	29	26	24	21
Equity Model	2	3	2	1	0
Foundation...............................	2	2	1	1	2
Insurance Products					
Health Maintenance Organization	9	8	6	6	8
Preferred Provider Organization..............	9	10	8	9	10
Indemnity Fee for Service	3	4	2	3	3
Managed Care Contracts					
Health Maintenance Organization	48	40	41	45	41
Preferred Provider Organization..............	54	46	47	48	46
Affiliations					
Hospitals in a System......................	44	41	38	35	34
Hospitals in a Network.....................	25	23	25	24	24
Hospitals in a Group Purchasing Organization..	57	53	51	52	47

States

TABLE 6

COLORADO

U.S. Registered Community Hospitals
(Nonfederal, short-term general and other special hospitals)

Utilization, Personnel, Revenue and Expenses, Community Health Indicators 2004–2008

	2008	2007	2006	2005	2004
TOTAL FACILITY (Includes Hospital and Nursing Home Units)					
Utilization - Inpatient					
Beds	10,053	9,708	9,518	9,620	9,250
Admissions	442,161	425,959	420,547	417,338	435,001
Inpatient Days	2,210,340	2,169,902	2,164,588	2,103,711	2,147,534
Average Length of Stay.	5.0	5.1	5.1	5.0	4.9
Inpatient Surgeries	141,724	139,125	134,773	132,150	134,772
Births.	68,659	66,512	66,612	66,379	65,270
Utilization - Outpatient					
Emergency Outpatient Visits	1,621,056	1,548,319	1,496,363	1,502,264	1,345,618
Other Outpatient Visits.	6,786,916	6,206,101	5,768,007	5,875,842	5,608,487
Total Outpatient Visits	8,407,972	7,754,420	7,264,370	7,378,106	6,954,105
Outpatient Surgeries	204,045	185,515	174,314	192,456	195,372
Personnel					
Full Time RNs	15,300	14,201	11,937	11,602	11,234
Full Time LPNs	775	823	866	818	723
Part Time RNs.	5,123	3,543	4,957	4,967	4,793
Part Time LPNs	240	181	300	242	254
Total Full Time.	53,002	53,751	47,656	46,274	44,821
Total Part Time	16,290	10,814	14,718	13,994	13,651
Revenue - Inpatient					
Gross Inpatient Revenue.	$16,296,367,033	$14,291,552,936	$13,112,287,510	$11,633,947,618	$10,574,795,347
Revenue - Outpatient					
Gross Outpatient Revenue	$11,343,750,441	$9,499,093,812	$8,259,901,579	$7,357,897,067	$6,385,848,467
Revenue and Expenses - Totals					
(Includes Inpatient and Outpatient)					
Total Gross Revenue.	$27,640,117,474	$23,790,646,748	$21,372,189,089	$18,991,844,685	$16,960,643,814
Deductions from Revenue	18,781,874,571	15,715,614,730	13,916,531,235	12,247,238,186	10,376,000,752
Net Patient Revenue	8,858,242,903	8,075,032,018	7,455,657,854	6,744,606,499	6,584,643,062
Other Operating Revenue	518,570,378	603,828,098	499,204,326	454,470,676	417,924,144
Other Nonoperating Revenue	(27,071,112)	258,400,086	185,613,712	130,487,562	139,970,924
Total Net Revenue.	9,349,742,169	8,937,260,202	8,140,475,892	7,329,564,737	7,142,538,130
Total Expenses.	8,889,584,362	8,011,595,534	7,269,883,043	6,679,054,011	6,307,604,445
HOSPITAL UNIT (Excludes Separate Nursing Home Units)					
Utilization - Inpatient					
Beds	9,518	9,016	8,968	8,903	8,535
Admissions	441,061	424,899	419,404	416,085	433,821
Inpatient Days	2,076,120	1,986,909	1,990,815	1,877,955	1,919,383
Average Length of Stay.	4.7	4.7	4.7	4.5	4.4
Personnel					
Total Full Time.	52,602	53,421	47,280	45,860	44,414
Total Part Time	16,131	10,670	14,548	13,744	13,435
Revenue and Expenses - Totals					
(Includes Inpatient and Outpatient)					
Total Net Revenue.	$9,321,879,151	$8,905,534,902	$8,111,396,372	$7,298,142,254	$7,101,090,580
Total Expenses.	8,862,237,046	7,977,887,275	7,245,463,125	6,650,327,035	6,271,131,736
COMMUNITY HEALTH INDICATORS PER 1000 POPULATION					
Total Population (in thousands)	4,939	4,843	4,751	4,663	4,600
Inpatient					
Beds	2.0	2.0	2.0	2.1	2.0
Admissions	89.5	88.0	88.5	89.5	94.6
Inpatient Days	447.5	448.1	455.6	451.2	466.9
Inpatient Surgeries	28.7	28.7	28.4	28.3	29.3
Births.	13.9	13.7	14.0	14.2	14.2
Outpatient					
Emergency Outpatient Visits	328.2	319.7	314.9	322.2	292.5
Other Outpatient Visits.	1,374.0	1,281.5	1,213.9	1,260.2	1,219.2
Total Outpatient Visits	1,702.2	1,601.2	1,528.9	1,582.4	1,511.7
Outpatient Surgeries	41.3	38.3	36.7	41.3	42.5
Expense per Capita (per person).	$1,799.7	$1,654.3	$1,530.0	$1,432.4	$1,371.2

States

TABLE 6

CONNECTICUT

U.S. Registered Community Hospitals
(Nonfederal, short-term general and other special hospitals)

Overview 2004–2008

	2008	2007	2006	2005	2004
Total Community Hospitals in Connecticut	35	34	35	36	35
Bed Size Category					
6-24	0	0	0	0	0
25-49	1	1	1	2	1
50-99	8	8	8	9	9
100-199	12	11	11	11	11
200-299	4	5	5	5	5
300-399	5	5	5	4	4
400-499	2	1	1	1	1
500 + ...	3	3	4	4	4
Location					
Hospitals Urban..........................	30	29	30	31	29
Hospitals Rural	5	5	5	5	6
Control					
State and Local Government................	1	1	1	1	1
Not for Profit	32	32	33	34	33
Investor owned	2	1	1	1	1
Physician Models					
Independent Practice Association	8	8	6	9	9
Group Practice without Walls................	1	1	0	1	1
Open Physician-Hospital Organization	3	5	9	9	9
Closed Physician-Hospital Organization	2	2	2	0	0
Management Service Organization	3	4	2	3	3
Integrated Salary Model....................	18	13	14	11	7
Equity Model	1	0	0	0	0
Foundation...............................	0	1	0	0	0
Insurance Products					
Health Maintenance Organization	3	2	1	2	3
Preferred Provider Organization..............	0	3	4	6	7
Indemnity Fee for Service	1	0	0	2	2
Managed Care Contracts					
Health Maintenance Organization	22	22	22	26	27
Preferred Provider Organization..............	22	23	22	26	26
Affiliations					
Hospitals in a System......................	9	9	10	9	8
Hospitals in a Network.....................	13	14	12	13	10
Hospitals in a Group Purchasing Organization..	28	29	29	31	30

TABLE 6

CONNECTICUT

U.S. Registered Community Hospitals
(Nonfederal, short-term general and other special hospitals)

Utilization, Personnel, Revenue and Expenses, Community Health Indicators 2004–2008

	2008	2007	2006	2005	2004
TOTAL FACILITY (Includes Hospital and Nursing Home Units)					
Utilization - Inpatient					
Beds	7,000	7,400	7,988	7,862	7,828
Admissions	400,632	396,895	406,498	404,989	389,728
Inpatient Days	2,296,558	2,128,239	2,303,485	2,312,197	2,249,861
Average Length of Stay.	5.7	5.4	5.7	5.7	5.8
Inpatient Surgeries.	107,611	111,119	114,762	112,582	111,966
Births.	40,963	41,620	41,476	42,535	42,064
Utilization - Outpatient					
Emergency Outpatient Visits	1,524,545	1,461,985	1,463,125	1,452,412	1,419,179
Other Outpatient Visits.	6,550,089	6,088,953	6,315,889	5,693,448	5,586,684
Total Outpatient Visits	8,074,634	7,550,938	7,779,014	7,145,860	7,005,863
Outpatient Surgeries	192,544	198,022	194,238	200,903	199,724
Personnel					
Full Time RNs	10,057	9,736	9,636	8,807	8,500
Full Time LPNs	348	363	367	327	339
Part Time RNs	6,883	7,422	7,200	6,724	7,386
Part Time LPNs	361	353	277	272	352
Total Full Time.	42,558	41,918	41,961	39,801	38,142
Total Part Time	23,152	22,594	21,899	21,822	23,471
Revenue - Inpatient					
Gross Inpatient Revenue.	$11,484,375,092	$10,507,210,277	$9,889,922,333	$8,773,033,682	$8,121,680,854
Revenue - Outpatient					
Gross Outpatient Revenue	$8,402,315,796	$7,345,514,961	$6,623,255,839	$5,827,212,980	$5,173,445,929
Revenue and Expenses - Totals					
(Includes Inpatient and Outpatient)					
Total Gross Revenue.	$19,886,690,888	$17,852,725,238	$16,513,178,172	$14,600,246,662	$13,295,126,783
Deductions from Revenue.	12,234,710,097	10,801,568,841	9,681,601,278	8,182,392,169	7,327,059,905
Net Patient Revenue	7,651,980,791	7,051,156,397	6,831,576,894	6,417,854,493	5,968,066,878
Other Operating Revenue	368,547,369	303,008,601	288,671,225	271,833,254	247,319,933
Other Nonoperating Revenue	(125,823,897)	157,150,928	141,753,252	124,430,009	96,210,339
Total Net Revenue.	7,894,704,263	7,511,315,926	7,262,001,371	6,814,117,756	6,311,597,150
Total Expenses.	7,906,958,696	7,221,249,850	7,066,962,056	6,589,084,173	6,111,901,479
HOSPITAL UNIT (Excludes Separate Nursing Home Units)					
Utilization - Inpatient					
Beds	7,237	7,196	7,699	7,575	7,537
Admissions	399,384	396,101	405,883	404,170	388,802
Inpatient Days	2,060,023	2,028,334	2,198,706	2,199,618	2,132,517
Average Length of Stay.	5.2	5.1	5.4	5.4	5.5
Personnel					
Total Full Time.	41,790	41,538	41,600	39,499	37,698
Total Part Time	22,313	22,178	21,794	21,539	23,140
Revenue and Expenses - Totals					
(Includes Inpatient and Outpatient)					
Total Net Revenue.	$7,822,208,146	$7,478,024,431	$7,230,095,664	$6,790,731,034	$6,284,285,277
Total Expenses.	7,846,566,914	7,189,144,542	7,031,531,481	6,560,898,866	6,080,770,231
COMMUNITY HEALTH INDICATORS PER 1000 POPULATION					
Total Population (in thousands)	3,501	3,490	3,488	3,479	3,475
Inpatient					
Beds	2.3	2.1	2.3	2.3	2.3
Admissions	114.4	113.7	116.5	116.4	112.1
Inpatient Days	655.9	609.8	660.4	664.7	647.4
Inpatient Surgeries.	30.7	31.8	32.9	32.4	32.2
Births.	11.7	11.9	11.9	12.2	12.1
Outpatient					
Emergency Outpatient Visits	435.4	418.9	419.5	417.5	408.4
Other Outpatient Visits.	1,870.8	1,744.8	1,810.8	1,636.7	1,607.5
Total Outpatient Visits	2,306.2	2,163.7	2,230.3	2,054.2	2,015.9
Outpatient Surgeries	55.0	56.7	55.7	57.8	57.5
Expense per Capita (per person).	$2,258.3	$2,069.2	$2,026.1	$1,894.1	$1,758.6

States

TABLE 6

DELAWARE

U.S. Registered Community Hospitals
(Nonfederal, short-term general and other special hospitals)

Overview 2004–2008

	2008	2007	2006	2005	2004
Total Community Hospitals in Delaware.......	7	6	6	6	6
Bed Size Category					
6-24.....................................	0	0	0	0	0
25-49....................................	1	0	0	0	0
50-99....................................	0	0	0	0	0
100-199..................................	3	1	1	2	2
200-299..................................	1	3	2	2	2
300-399..................................	1	1	2	1	1
400-499..................................	0	0	0	0	0
500 +....................................	1	1	1	1	1
Location					
Hospitals Urban..........................	5	4	4	4	4
Hospitals Rural	2	2	2	2	2
Control					
State and Local Government................	0	0	0	0	0
Not for Profit	6	6	6	6	6
Investor owned	1	0	0	0	0
Physician Models					
Independent Practice Association	0	0	1	0	0
Group Practice without Walls...............	0	0	0	0	0
Open Physician-Hospital Organization	0	1	1	1	1
Closed Physician-Hospital Organization	0	0	0	0	0
Management Service Organization	0	1	1	1	0
Integrated Salary Model....................	2	3	4	3	4
Equity Model	0	0	0	0	0
Foundation...............................	1	1	0	0	0
Insurance Products					
Health Maintenance Organization	0	0	0	0	1
Preferred Provider Organization..............	0	0	0	0	1
Indemnity Fee for Service	0	0	1	0	1
Managed Care Contracts					
Health Maintenance Organization	5	5	4	4	4
Preferred Provider Organization..............	5	5	4	4	4
Affiliations					
Hospitals in a System.....................	3	2	2	2	2
Hospitals in a Network....................	0	0	0	0	0
Hospitals in a Group Purchasing Organization..	6	5	5	4	4

TABLE 6

DELAWARE

U.S. Registered Community Hospitals
(Nonfederal, short-term general and other special hospitals)

Utilization, Personnel, Revenue and Expenses, Community Health Indicators 2004–2008

	2008	2007	2006	2005	2004
TOTAL FACILITY (Includes Hospital and Nursing Home Units)					
Utilization - Inpatient					
Beds	2,071	2,288	2,138	1,900	1,955
Admissions	103,726	107,037	105,164	103,863	103,169
Inpatient Days	613,049	671,628	669,392	639,855	642,401
Average Length of Stay	5.9	6.3	6.4	6.2	6.2
Inpatient Surgeries	30,845	32,039	31,881	32,532	31,553
Births	12,536	12,312	12,361	12,014	11,974
Utilization - Outpatient					
Emergency Outpatient Visits	363,979	343,713	382,935	330,570	325,692
Other Outpatient Visits	1,317,097	1,495,036	1,456,973	1,537,157	1,540,257
Total Outpatient Visits	1,681,076	1,838,749	1,839,908	1,867,727	1,865,949
Outpatient Surgeries	60,343	63,526	62,593	60,754	62,461
Personnel					
Full Time RNs	3,334	3,010	2,995	2,918	2,605
Full Time LPNs	164	179	212	179	185
Part Time RNs	2,326	2,021	2,107	2,162	2,063
Part Time LPNs	156	148	126	109	108
Total Full Time	13,954	12,707	12,774	13,019	12,452
Total Part Time	6,340	5,485	5,541	5,809	5,704
Revenue - Inpatient					
Gross Inpatient Revenue	$2,385,974,140	$2,244,196,638	$2,060,178,931	$1,995,823,039	$1,753,513,945
Revenue - Outpatient					
Gross Outpatient Revenue	$1,569,559,056	$1,352,820,078	$1,315,656,776	$1,157,724,434	$990,566,571
Revenue and Expenses - Totals					
(Includes Inpatient and Outpatient)					
Total Gross Revenue	$3,955,533,196	$3,597,016,716	$3,375,835,707	$3,153,547,473	$2,744,080,516
Deductions from Revenue	1,865,226,783	1,679,045,929	1,626,506,667	1,461,877,504	1,219,630,928
Net Patient Revenue	2,090,306,413	1,917,970,787	1,749,329,040	1,691,669,969	1,524,449,588
Other Operating Revenue	121,047,453	167,718,247	144,361,451	133,359,882	119,498,615
Other Nonoperating Revenue	81,948,435	62,950,703	52,564,940	28,598,147	27,000,467
Total Net Revenue	2,293,302,301	2,148,639,737	1,946,255,431	1,853,627,998	1,670,948,670
Total Expenses	2,119,860,075	1,949,799,885	1,802,837,132	1,738,206,074	1,584,087,451
HOSPITAL UNIT (Excludes Separate Nursing Home Units)					
Utilization - Inpatient					
Beds	1,967	1,892	1,742	1,727	1,765
Admissions	103,438	105,462	104,253	103,078	102,359
Inpatient Days	577,278	538,981	532,566	578,748	580,519
Average Length of Stay	5.6	5.1	5.1	5.6	5.7
Personnel					
Total Full Time	13,883	12,391	12,551	12,851	12,292
Total Part Time	6,316	5,297	5,450	5,724	5,647
Revenue and Expenses - Totals					
(Includes Inpatient and Outpatient)					
Total Net Revenue	$2,283,604,301	$2,109,958,350	$1,913,476,298	$1,835,773,035	$1,654,004,709
Total Expenses	2,110,993,075	1,902,038,450	1,760,866,423	1,708,544,323	1,561,247,907
COMMUNITY HEALTH INDICATORS PER 1000 POPULATION					
Total Population (in thousands)	873	862	850	839	826
Inpatient					
Beds	2.4	2.7	2.5	2.3	2.4
Admissions	118.8	124.2	123.7	123.9	125.0
Inpatient Days	702.2	779.2	787.2	763.1	778.0
Inpatient Surgeries	35.3	37.2	37.5	38.8	38.2
Births	14.4	14.3	14.5	14.3	14.5
Outpatient					
Emergency Outpatient Visits	416.9	398.8	450.3	394.2	394.5
Other Outpatient Visits	1,508.5	1,734.5	1,713.3	1,833.2	1,865.4
Total Outpatient Visits	1,925.4	2,133.2	2,163.7	2,227.4	2,259.9
Outpatient Surgeries	69.1	73.7	73.6	72.5	75.6
Expense per Capita (per person)	$2,428.0	$2,262.1	$2,120.1	$2,072.9	$1,918.5

States

TABLE 6

DISTRICT OF COLUMBIA

U.S. Registered Community Hospitals
(Nonfederal, short-term general and other special hospitals)

Overview 2004–2008

	2008	2007	2006	2005	2004
Total Community Hospitals in					
District of Columbia	10	10	11	11	11
Bed Size Category					
6-24	0	0	0	0	0
25-49	0	0	0	0	0
50-99	1	1	1	0	0
100-199	1	1	2	4	4
200-299	3	2	2	2	3
300-399	3	4	4	3	2
400-499	0	0	0	0	0
500 + ...	2	2	2	2	2
Location					
Hospitals Urban	10	10	11	11	11
Hospitals Rural	0	0	0	0	0
Control					
State and Local Government	0	0	0	0	0
Not for Profit	7	7	7	7	7
Investor owned	3	3	4	4	4
Physician Models					
Independent Practice Association	1	0	0	1	1
Group Practice without Walls	1	1	1	0	0
Open Physician-Hospital Organization	0	1	1	1	1
Closed Physician-Hospital Organization	1	1	1	1	1
Management Service Organization	1	1	1	1	1
Integrated Salary Model	4	5	6	3	5
Equity Model	0	0	0	0	0
Foundation	1	1	1	1	0
Insurance Products					
Health Maintenance Organization	3	4	4	4	4
Preferred Provider Organization	0	1	1	1	1
Indemnity Fee for Service	0	1	1	1	1
Managed Care Contracts					
Health Maintenance Organization	7	7	8	7	6
Preferred Provider Organization	7	5	8	6	6
Affiliations					
Hospitals in a System	7	7	8	6	5
Hospitals in a Network	2	2	0	0	1
Hospitals in a Group Purchasing Organization . .	8	7	8	7	7

States

TABLE 6

DISTRICT OF COLUMBIA

U.S. Registered Community Hospitals
(Nonfederal, short-term general and other special hospitals)

Utilization, Personnel, Revenue and Expenses, Community Health Indicators 2004–2008

	2008	2007	2006	2005	2004
TOTAL FACILITY (Includes Hospital and Nursing Home Units)					
Utilization - Inpatient					
Beds	3,358	3,418	3,601	3,534	3,453
Admissions	137,260	136,488	139,515	140,500	140,765
Inpatient Days	954,416	908,940	979,850	995,971	981,412
Average Length of Stay.	7.0	6.7	7.0	7.1	7.0
Inpatient Surgeries.	43,173	42,870	42,206	46,856	44,031
Births.	14,901	14,871	14,120	14,446	13,675
Utilization - Outpatient					
Emergency Outpatient Visits	436,918	461,465	396,343	358,164	374,237
Other Outpatient Visits.	1,919,145	1,905,247	1,212,621	1,291,120	1,251,186
Total Outpatient Visits	2,356,063	2,366,712	1,608,964	1,649,284	1,625,423
Outpatient Surgeries	65,742	59,336	57,955	60,208	62,370
Personnel					
Full Time RNs	4,447	4,357	4,374	4,336	3,849
Full Time LPNs	215	296	362	309	384
Part Time RNs.	1,796	1,796	1,648	1,962	1,179
Part Time LPNs	38	46	84	59	111
Total Full Time.	21,247	20,507	20,779	20,229	18,019
Total Part Time	4,463	4,946	4,811	5,031	3,803
Revenue - Inpatient					
Gross Inpatient Revenue.	$5,686,127,872	$5,672,805,649	$5,144,465,380	$4,655,163,186	$4,225,075,708
Revenue - Outpatient					
Gross Outpatient Revenue	$2,835,491,356	$2,666,461,627	$2,288,315,622	$2,185,930,249	$1,860,118,198
Revenue and Expenses - Totals					
(Includes Inpatient and Outpatient)					
Total Gross Revenue.	$8,521,619,228	$8,339,267,276	$7,432,781,002	$6,841,093,435	$6,085,193,906
Deductions from Revenue.	5,300,645,413	5,229,606,649	4,529,081,776	4,155,896,247	3,574,955,972
Net Patient Revenue	3,220,973,815	3,109,660,627	2,903,699,226	2,685,197,188	2,510,237,934
Other Operating Revenue	192,446,948	187,903,112	174,433,561	136,161,036	160,603,714
Other Nonoperating Revenue	(139,712,361)	67,564,569	69,896,434	27,474,658	12,544,341
Total Net Revenue.	3,273,708,402	3,365,128,308	3,148,029,221	2,848,832,882	2,683,385,989
Total Expenses.	3,392,800,661	3,224,779,035	2,998,369,380	2,777,290,830	2,591,189,818
HOSPITAL UNIT (Excludes Separate Nursing Home Units)					
Utilization - Inpatient					
Beds	3,061	3,123	3,161	3,372	3,058
Admissions	135,521	134,769	137,343	138,963	139,720
Inpatient Days	850,769	805,786	827,871	940,331	844,876
Average Length of Stay.	6.3	6.0	6.0	6.8	6.0
Personnel					
Total Full Time.	21,151	20,210	20,365	20,081	17,581
Total Part Time	4,437	4,882	4,666	5,003	3,640
Revenue and Expenses - Totals					
(Includes Inpatient and Outpatient)					
Total Net Revenue.	$3,244,092,304	$3,331,993,244	$3,094,272,498	$2,830,249,399	$2,641,209,758
Total Expenses.	3,363,055,134	3,196,280,439	2,959,472,207	2,761,556,434	2,554,808,556
COMMUNITY HEALTH INDICATORS PER 1000 POPULATION					
Total Population (in thousands)	592	588	585	582	580
Inpatient					
Beds	5.7	5.8	6.2	6.1	6.0
Admissions	231.9	232.2	238.3	241.4	242.9
Inpatient Days	1,612.6	1,546.2	1,673.8	1,711.1	1,693.5
Inpatient Surgeries.	72.9	72.9	72.1	80.5	76.0
Births.	25.2	25.3	24.1	24.8	23.6
Outpatient					
Emergency Outpatient Visits	738.2	785.0	677.0	615.4	645.8
Other Outpatient Visits.	3,242.7	3,240.9	2,071.4	2,218.2	2,159.0
Total Outpatient Visits	3,981.0	4,025.9	2,748.4	2,833.6	2,804.8
Outpatient Surgeries	111.1	100.9	99.0	103.4	107.6
Expense per Capita (per person).	$5,732.7	$5,485.5	$5,121.7	$4,771.6	$4,471.3

States

TABLE 6

FLORIDA

U.S. Registered Community Hospitals
(Nonfederal, short-term general and other special hospitals)

Overview 2004–2008

	2008	2007	2006	2005	2004
Total Community Hospitals in Florida.........	211	200	203	205	203
Bed Size Category					
6-24	3	2	2	4	5
25-49	23	18	16	15	17
50-99	35	33	32	32	35
100-199	55	53	57	54	52
200-299	37	35	35	39	34
300-399	25	27	28	28	26
400-499	11	10	10	12	11
500 + ...	22	22	23	21	23
Location					
Hospitals Urban..........................	181	169	173	175	169
Hospitals Rural	30	31	30	30	34
Control					
State and Local Government................	25	26	24	19	20
Not for Profit	86	82	84	91	89
Investor owned	100	92	95	95	94
Physician Models					
Independent Practice Association	6	6	8	10	9
Group Practice without Walls................	3	3	2	2	2
Open Physician-Hospital Organization	12	9	14	18	16
Closed Physician-Hospital Organization	10	7	7	6	6
Management Service Organization	5	6	8	7	11
Integrated Salary Model....................	52	59	44	30	31
Equity Model	0	1	0	0	2
Foundation...............................	2	5	4	1	1
Insurance Products					
Health Maintenance Organization	8	9	19	19	16
Preferred Provider Organization..............	10	8	19	22	19
Indemnity Fee for Service	5	5	10	8	7
Managed Care Contracts					
Health Maintenance Organization	81	98	102	98	95
Preferred Provider Organization..............	82	97	103	102	98
Affiliations					
Hospitals in a System......................	159	149	155	154	153
Hospitals in a Network	38	38	40	35	36
Hospitals in a Group Purchasing Organization..	118	123	123	113	109

TABLE 6

FLORIDA

U.S. Registered Community Hospitals
(Nonfederal, short-term general and other special hospitals)

Utilization, Personnel, Revenue and Expenses, Community Health Indicators 2004–2008

	2008	2007	2006	2005	2004
TOTAL FACILITY (Includes Hospital and Nursing Home Units)					
Utilization - Inpatient					
Beds	60,000	51,010	51,420	51,174	49,902
Admissions	2,396,691	2,387,525	2,373,712	2,371,397	2,322,370
Inpatient Days	12,192,327	12,351,368	12,432,951	12,367,864	12,099,072
Average Length of Stay	5.1	5.2	5.2	5.2	5.2
Inpatient Surgeries	659,237	660,217	672,998	666,247	642,711
Births	218,035	223,202	225,049	214,930	205,910
Utilization - Outpatient					
Emergency Outpatient Visits	7,161,108	7,085,930	7,165,036	6,895,641	6,782,103
Other Outpatient Visits	17,268,832	16,410,090	15,593,993	15,402,669	15,584,678
Total Outpatient Visits	24,429,940	23,496,020	22,759,029	22,298,310	22,366,781
Outpatient Surgeries	846,551	796,945	783,330	821,180	816,023
Personnel					
Full Time RNs	62,639	62,349	59,518	55,398	53,156
Full Time LPNs	4,563	5,159	5,212	5,337	5,423
Part Time RNs	20,188	18,904	18,411	18,364	15,950
Part Time LPNs	1,154	1,318	1,310	1,621	1,494
Total Full Time	220,165	220,065	213,259	212,095	201,102
Total Part Time	54,335	54,010	53,611	53,818	46,121
Revenue - Inpatient					
Gross Inpatient Revenue	$80,168,815,722	$76,599,198,509	$70,860,708,525	$64,094,470,693	$55,347,346,986
Revenue - Outpatient					
Gross Outpatient Revenue	$44,224,777,407	$39,745,819,297	$34,594,178,527	$31,857,827,748	$26,785,318,334
Revenue and Expenses - Totals					
(Includes Inpatient and Outpatient)					
Total Gross Revenue	$124,393,593,129	$116,345,017,806	$105,454,887,052	$95,952,298,441	$82,132,665,320
Deductions from Revenue	91,084,229,921	84,506,636,341	75,260,615,364	67,717,148,688	55,715,118,691
Net Patient Revenue	33,309,363,208	31,838,381,465	30,194,271,688	28,235,149,753	26,417,546,629
Other Operating Revenue	2,104,002,109	1,913,000,678	1,737,406,049	1,639,114,853	1,496,693,528
Other Nonoperating Revenue	64,179,556	592,244,508	431,835,226	417,868,629	305,555,865
Total Net Revenue	35,477,544,873	34,343,626,651	32,363,512,963	30,292,133,235	28,219,796,022
Total Expenses	33,117,894,364	31,504,674,840	30,009,185,777	28,094,396,517	27,326,085,175
HOSPITAL UNIT (Excludes Separate Nursing Home Units)					
Utilization - Inpatient					
Beds	51,863	50,444	50,173	50,039	48,429
Admissions	2,392,911	2,382,000	2,368,632	2,365,467	2,316,363
Inpatient Days	11,874,879	11,954,597	12,062,565	12,002,797	11,584,815
Average Length of Stay	5.0	5.0	5.1	5.1	5.0
Personnel					
Total Full Time	219,027	218,802	209,939	210,698	198,423
Total Part Time	54,203	53,792	52,895	53,585	45,576
Revenue and Expenses - Totals					
(Includes Inpatient and Outpatient)					
Total Net Revenue	$35,402,114,525	$34,260,176,558	$32,235,490,697	$30,168,171,118	$27,945,858,623
Total Expenses	33,027,271,463	31,421,178,984	29,908,580,552	27,961,204,642	27,061,192,395
COMMUNITY HEALTH INDICATORS PER 1000 POPULATION					
Total Population (in thousands)	18,328	18,200	18,019	17,702	17,314
Inpatient					
Beds	2.9	2.8	2.9	2.9	2.9
Admissions	130.8	131.2	131.7	134.0	134.1
Inpatient Days	665.2	678.7	690.0	698.7	698.8
Inpatient Surgeries	36.0	36.3	37.3	37.6	37.1
Births	11.9	12.3	12.5	12.1	11.9
Outpatient					
Emergency Outpatient Visits	390.7	389.3	397.6	389.5	391.7
Other Outpatient Visits	942.2	901.7	865.4	870.1	900.1
Total Outpatient Visits	1,332.9	1,291.0	1,263.1	1,259.6	1,291.8
Outpatient Surgeries	46.2	43.8	43.5	46.4	47.1
Expense per Capita (per person)	$1,806.9	$1,731.1	$1,665.4	$1,587.0	$1,578.3

States

TABLE 6

GEORGIA

U.S. Registered Community Hospitals
(Nonfederal, short-term general and other special hospitals)

Overview 2004–2008

	2008	2007	2006	2005	2004
Total Community Hospitals in Georgia	153	147	147	149	146
Bed Size Category					
6-24	4	3	4	3	3
25-49	41	35	35	34	35
50-99	22	22	24	26	24
100-199	44	42	40	42	41
200-299	15	18	17	17	15
300-399	9	8	8	10	11
400-499	9	11	13	11	13
500 + ...	9	8	6	6	4
Location					
Hospitals Urban	87	82	83	84	63
Hospitals Rural	66	65	64	65	83
Control					
State and Local Government	56	57	56	58	54
Not for Profit	63	59	59	59	62
Investor owned	34	31	32	32	30
Physician Models					
Independent Practice Association	10	8	12	15	17
Group Practice without Walls	2	1	2	4	2
Open Physician-Hospital Organization	19	22	19	27	23
Closed Physician-Hospital Organization	15	17	16	17	15
Management Service Organization	8	8	8	8	8
Integrated Salary Model	35	34	33	27	30
Equity Model	6	4	4	2	1
Foundation	5	5	5	4	4
Insurance Products					
Health Maintenance Organization	10	6	9	11	12
Preferred Provider Organization	20	24	35	34	37
Indemnity Fee for Service	7	6	10	13	10
Managed Care Contracts					
Health Maintenance Organization	79	67	67	70	60
Preferred Provider Organization	89	83	91	96	92
Affiliations					
Hospitals in a System	81	74	72	71	67
Hospitals in a Network	42	42	50	59	55
Hospitals in a Group Purchasing Organization . .	100	92	100	106	95

TABLE 6

GEORGIA

U.S. Registered Community Hospitals
(Nonfederal, short-term general and other special hospitals)

Utilization, Personnel, Revenue and Expenses, Community Health Indicators 2004–2008

	2008	2007	2006	2005	2004
TOTAL FACILITY (Includes Hospital and Nursing Home Units)					
Utilization - Inpatient					
Beds	25,583	25,483	24,772	25,015	24,700
Admissions	959,375	963,583	956,395	961,195	943,837
Inpatient Days	6,172,510	6,278,894	6,221,330	6,191,628	6,093,697
Average Length of Stay	6.4	6.5	6.5	6.4	6.5
Inpatient Surgeries	269,766	277,885	273,420	300,754	286,215
Births	142,382	146,746	140,741	139,577	136,501
Utilization - Outpatient					
Emergency Outpatient Visits	3,843,244	3,747,532	3,629,453	3,683,883	3,492,747
Other Outpatient Visits	10,340,848	10,010,319	10,153,274	10,119,196	9,905,204
Total Outpatient Visits	14,184,092	13,757,851	13,782,727	13,803,079	13,397,951
Outpatient Surgeries	487,070	491,459	504,293	556,126	513,356
Personnel					
Full Time RNs	27,823	27,684	25,671	25,269	23,256
Full Time LPNs	3,651	3,738	3,965	4,217	4,043
Part Time RNs	11,963	13,312	12,286	12,174	11,800
Part Time LPNs	1,035	1,253	1,230	1,285	1,361
Total Full Time	108,871	107,711	104,111	104,406	99,205
Total Part Time	32,169	35,093	32,617	32,953	33,537
Revenue - Inpatient					
Gross Inpatient Revenue	$25,139,478,750	$24,285,401,220	$22,163,780,319	$20,093,353,401	$18,156,528,430
Revenue - Outpatient					
Gross Outpatient Revenue	$18,392,697,423	$16,838,734,295	$14,777,650,188	$13,622,377,234	$11,618,489,833
Revenue and Expenses - Totals					
(Includes Inpatient and Outpatient)					
Total Gross Revenue	$43,532,176,173	$41,124,135,515	$36,941,430,507	$33,715,730,635	$29,775,018,263
Deductions from Revenue	28,602,816,610	26,341,808,978	23,269,007,568	20,520,952,593	17,743,170,185
Net Patient Revenue	14,929,359,563	14,782,326,537	13,672,422,939	13,194,778,042	12,031,848,078
Other Operating Revenue	788,733,742	594,706,811	830,795,303	613,617,105	609,415,034
Other Nonoperating Revenue	(102,237,534)	373,626,935	257,847,975	179,448,150	163,439,074
Total Net Revenue	15,615,855,771	15,750,660,283	14,761,066,217	13,987,843,297	12,804,702,186
Total Expenses	15,098,639,746	14,769,627,733	13,846,913,245	13,345,809,666	12,162,763,316
HOSPITAL UNIT (Excludes Separate Nursing Home Units)					
Utilization - Inpatient					
Beds	22,332	22,171	21,036	21,121	21,291
Admissions	953,328	957,240	950,054	954,725	936,806
Inpatient Days	5,113,980	5,168,328	4,942,793	4,864,313	4,945,631
Average Length of Stay	5.4	5.4	5.2	5.1	5.3
Personnel					
Total Full Time	106,600	105,488	101,590	101,435	95,311
Total Part Time	31,471	34,314	31,890	32,052	32,682
Revenue and Expenses - Totals					
(Includes Inpatient and Outpatient)					
Total Net Revenue	$15,449,511,224	$15,588,075,384	$14,592,684,941	$13,807,327,170	$12,641,676,379
Total Expenses	14,947,753,769	14,621,668,884	13,687,516,954	13,178,754,987	12,012,826,005
COMMUNITY HEALTH INDICATORS PER 1000 POPULATION					
Total Population (in thousands)	9,686	9,523	9,319	9,094	8,911
Inpatient					
Beds	2.6	2.7	2.7	2.8	2.8
Admissions	99.1	101.2	102.6	105.7	105.9
Inpatient Days	637.3	659.3	667.6	680.9	683.9
Inpatient Surgeries	27.9	29.2	29.3	33.1	32.1
Births	14.7	15.4	15.1	15.3	15.3
Outpatient					
Emergency Outpatient Visits	396.8	393.5	389.5	405.1	392.0
Other Outpatient Visits	1,067.6	1,051.1	1,089.6	1,112.7	1,111.6
Total Outpatient Visits	1,464.4	1,444.7	1,479.0	1,517.8	1,503.6
Outpatient Surgeries	50.3	51.6	54.1	61.2	57.6
Expense per Capita (per person)	$1,558.9	$1,550.9	$1,485.9	$1,467.5	$1,365.0

TABLE 6

HAWAII

U.S. Registered Community Hospitals
(Nonfederal, short-term general and other special hospitals)

Overview 2004–2008

	2008	2007	2006	2005	2004
Total Community Hospitals in Hawaii	25	23	24	25	24
Bed Size Category					
6-24	4	3	4	4	2
25-49	4	4	4	4	5
50-99	5	3	3	5	3
100-199	6	7	7	7	9
200-299	5	5	5	4	4
300-399	0	0	0	0	0
400-499	1	1	1	1	1
500 + ...	0	0	0	0	0
Location					
Hospitals Urban.	14	13	13	13	13
Hospitals Rural	11	10	11	12	11
Control					
State and Local Government.	8	7	7	8	7
Not for Profit	17	16	17	17	17
Investor owned	0	0	0	0	0
Physician Models					
Independent Practice Association	1	0	1	2	1
Group Practice without Walls.	0	0	0	0	0
Open Physician-Hospital Organization	3	2	2	3	4
Closed Physician-Hospital Organization	1	1	1	1	0
Management Service Organization	0	0	0	0	0
Integrated Salary Model.	4	4	5	5	3
Equity Model	0	0	0	0	0
Foundation.	1	1	1	1	1
Insurance Products					
Health Maintenance Organization	0	1	1	1	2
Preferred Provider Organization.	1	1	1	1	2
Indemnity Fee for Service	0	0	0	0	2
Managed Care Contracts					
Health Maintenance Organization	9	11	11	11	9
Preferred Provider Organization.	9	10	9	11	10
Affiliations					
Hospitals in a System.	21	18	20	21	20
Hospitals in a Network	1	1	4	4	4
Hospitals in a Group Purchasing Organization. .	13	12	14	15	15

TABLE 6

HAWAII

U.S. Registered Community Hospitals
(Nonfederal, short-term general and other special hospitals)

Utilization, Personnel, Revenue and Expenses, Community Health Indicators 2004–2008

	2008	2007	2006	2005	2004
TOTAL FACILITY (Includes Hospital and Nursing Home Units)					
Utilization - Inpatient					
Beds	3,087	2,920	2,969	3,001	3,110
Admissions	111,310	110,788	111,713	113,876	114,341
Inpatient Days	846,756	796,898	841,667	853,247	875,714
Average Length of Stay	7.6	7.2	7.5	7.5	7.7
Inpatient Surgeries	30,723	32,305	32,495	34,801	29,168
Births	10,522	9,921	11,543	11,286	10,645
Utilization - Outpatient					
Emergency Outpatient Visits	361,068	339,004	339,863	336,483	325,843
Other Outpatient Visits	1,658,064	1,538,987	1,543,551	1,572,459	1,530,113
Total Outpatient Visits	2,019,132	1,877,991	1,883,414	1,908,942	1,855,956
Outpatient Surgeries	59,191	57,484	54,946	50,453	46,276
Personnel					
Full Time RNs	3,776	3,724	3,656	3,459	3,476
Full Time LPNs	298	302	339	345	372
Part Time RNs	1,254	1,052	1,029	1,121	1,237
Part Time LPNs	78	57	75	86	124
Total Full Time	14,550	14,045	13,537	13,744	13,295
Total Part Time	3,712	3,186	3,436	3,666	3,841
Revenue - Inpatient					
Gross Inpatient Revenue	$3,209,458,842	$2,947,813,604	$2,786,116,929	$2,694,034,423	$2,347,974,631
Revenue - Outpatient					
Gross Outpatient Revenue	$2,484,934,032	$2,190,455,686	$1,971,471,114	$1,759,937,510	$1,487,369,001
Revenue and Expenses - Totals					
(Includes Inpatient and Outpatient)					
Total Gross Revenue	$5,694,392,874	$5,138,269,290	$4,757,588,043	$4,453,971,933	$3,835,343,632
Deductions from Revenue	3,484,200,407	3,151,824,643	2,884,449,692	2,678,439,273	2,232,324,478
Net Patient Revenue	2,210,192,467	1,986,444,647	1,873,138,351	1,775,532,660	1,603,019,154
Other Operating Revenue	150,555,239	137,045,681	131,661,720	125,797,552	103,982,850
Other Nonoperating Revenue	21,263,753	67,676,101	89,618,454	37,170,475	20,697,246
Total Net Revenue	2,382,011,459	2,191,166,429	2,094,418,525	1,938,500,687	1,727,699,250
Total Expenses	2,321,587,503	2,144,699,750	2,017,583,352	1,886,966,333	1,756,444,575
HOSPITAL UNIT (Excludes Separate Nursing Home Units)					
Utilization - Inpatient					
Beds	2,589	2,706	2,706	2,554	2,700
Admissions	108,918	108,877	109,755	111,560	112,004
Inpatient Days	667,147	716,562	754,872	714,106	721,088
Average Length of Stay	6.1	6.6	6.9	6.4	6.4
Personnel					
Total Full Time	14,172	13,832	13,278	13,393	12,785
Total Part Time	3,610	3,146	3,405	3,612	3,753
Revenue and Expenses - Totals					
(Includes Inpatient and Outpatient)					
Total Net Revenue	$2,353,764,329	$2,164,235,821	$2,079,708,741	$1,908,563,083	$1,696,652,491
Total Expenses	2,275,182,714	2,126,689,282	2,005,122,969	1,857,830,469	1,726,905,064
COMMUNITY HEALTH INDICATORS PER 1000 POPULATION					
Total Population (in thousands)	1,288	1,277	1,275	1,264	1,252
Inpatient					
Beds	2.4	2.3	2.3	2.4	2.5
Admissions	86.4	86.7	87.6	90.1	91.4
Inpatient Days	657.3	623.9	660.0	674.8	699.7
Inpatient Surgeries	23.8	25.3	25.5	27.5	23.3
Births	8.2	7.8	9.1	8.9	8.5
Outpatient					
Emergency Outpatient Visits	280.3	265.4	266.5	266.1	260.4
Other Outpatient Visits	1,287.1	1,204.8	1,210.4	1,243.6	1,222.6
Total Outpatient Visits	1,567.4	1,470.2	1,476.9	1,509.7	1,482.9
Outpatient Surgeries	45.9	45.0	43.1	39.9	37.0
Expense per Capita (per person)	$1,802.2	$1,679.0	$1,582.1	$1,492.3	$1,403.4

States

TABLE 6

IDAHO

U.S. Registered Community Hospitals
(Nonfederal, short-term general and other special hospitals)

Overview 2004–2008

	2008	2007	2006	2005	2004
Total Community Hospitals in Idaho..........	39	39	38	39	39
Bed Size Category					
6-24	11	10	11	13	11
25-49	10	10	9	8	9
50-99	9	9	8	8	9
100-199	5	6	5	4	4
200-299	2	2	3	4	4
300-399	1	1	1	1	1
400-499	0	0	1	1	1
500 + ...	1	1	0	0	0
Location					
Hospitals Urban..........................	14	14	14	14	6
Hospitals Rural	25	25	24	25	33
Control					
State and Local Government................	22	21	21	23	24
Not for Profit	14	15	14	13	13
Investor owned	3	3	3	3	2
Physician Models					
Independent Practice Association	7	9	7	7	7
Group Practice without Walls................	2	2	1	1	2
Open Physician-Hospital Organization	3	3	5	5	5
Closed Physician-Hospital Organization	4	5	4	4	4
Management Service Organization	4	5	3	4	3
Integrated Salary Model....................	11	10	7	7	7
Equity Model	1	1	2	1	1
Foundation...............................	1	2	2	1	0
Insurance Products					
Health Maintenance Organization	2	2	2	4	3
Preferred Provider Organization..............	4	3	3	8	3
Indemnity Fee for Service	1	1	1	2	1
Managed Care Contracts					
Health Maintenance Organization	16	15	11	12	13
Preferred Provider Organization..............	21	22	18	21	21
Affiliations					
Hospitals in a System......................	22	19	20	18	15
Hospitals in a Network.....................	15	19	16	14	12
Hospitals in a Group Purchasing Organization..	26	30	27	28	26

TABLE 6

IDAHO

U.S. Registered Community Hospitals
(Nonfederal, short-term general and other special hospitals)

Utilization, Personnel, Revenue and Expenses, Community Health Indicators 2004–2008

	2008	2007	2006	2005	2004
TOTAL FACILITY (Includes Hospital and Nursing Home Units)					
Utilization - Inpatient					
Beds	3,311	3,296	3,303	3,320	3,191
Admissions	135,697	133,895	141,839	129,666	127,381
Inpatient Days	643,039	654,818	678,059	645,598	667,687
Average Length of Stay.	4.7	4.9	4.8	5.0	5.2
Inpatient Surgeries.	41,234	42,964	43,284	43,272	43,633
Births.	23,014	23,236	21,341	20,411	20,283
Utilization - Outpatient					
Emergency Outpatient Visits	520,941	521,382	511,381	509,964	479,734
Other Outpatient Visits.	2,419,470	2,346,680	2,192,224	2,209,546	1,950,153
Total Outpatient Visits	2,940,411	2,868,062	2,703,605	2,719,510	2,429,887
Outpatient Surgeries	70,154	65,946	63,077	61,995	57,542
Personnel					
Full Time RNs	3,730	3,634	3,375	3,071	2,984
Full Time LPNs	421	429	402	398	443
Part Time RNs	2,641	2,228	2,265	2,331	2,303
Part Time LPNs	215	226	204	232	259
Total Full Time	16,336	15,868	14,449	13,672	13,316
Total Part Time	7,728	7,213	7,177	7,163	7,023
Revenue - Inpatient					
Gross Inpatient Revenue.	$2,561,301,943	$2,248,997,324	$2,059,962,522	$1,843,887,676	$1,717,713,040
Revenue - Outpatient					
Gross Outpatient Revenue	$2,451,235,258	$2,086,866,647	$1,843,045,507	$1,532,057,016	$1,281,184,735
Revenue and Expenses - Totals					
(Includes Inpatient and Outpatient)					
Total Gross Revenue.	$5,012,537,201	$4,335,863,971	$3,903,008,029	$3,375,944,692	$2,998,897,775
Deductions from Revenue.	2,484,822,454	1,983,781,556	1,717,092,865	1,444,375,282	1,245,981,416
Net Patient Revenue	2,527,714,747	2,352,082,415	2,185,915,164	1,931,569,410	1,752,916,359
Other Operating Revenue	90,838,094	82,800,813	75,440,778	69,587,347	71,615,996
Other Nonoperating Revenue	15,092,420	77,705,507	39,175,538	25,675,802	14,730,380
Total Net Revenue.	2,633,645,261	2,512,588,735	2,300,531,480	2,026,832,559	1,839,262,735
Total Expenses.	2,406,259,158	2,224,117,950	2,083,181,465	1,886,169,323	1,716,607,087
HOSPITAL UNIT (Excludes Separate Nursing Home Units)					
Utilization - Inpatient					
Beds	3,004	2,895	2,857	2,879	2,929
Admissions	134,364	132,563	140,455	126,999	124,565
Inpatient Days	553,925	541,539	554,457	521,885	525,298
Average Length of Stay.	4.1	4.1	3.9	4.1	4.2
Personnel					
Total Full Time	16,134	15,619	14,134	13,366	12,942
Total Part Time	7,599	7,060	6,963	6,964	6,742
Revenue and Expenses - Totals					
(Includes Inpatient and Outpatient)					
Total Net Revenue.	$2,607,116,770	$2,485,446,404	$2,270,617,640	$1,987,654,602	$1,806,044,478
Total Expenses.	2,389,059,009	2,205,976,897	2,056,627,846	1,849,929,427	1,686,865,340
COMMUNITY HEALTH INDICATORS PER 1000 POPULATION					
Total Population (in thousands)	1,524	1,496	1,461	1,424	1,390
Inpatient					
Beds	2.2	2.2	2.3	2.3	2.5
Admissions	89.1	89.5	97.1	91.0	91.6
Inpatient Days	422.0	437.7	464.0	453.3	480.2
Inpatient Surgeries.	27.1	28.7	29.6	30.4	31.4
Births.	15.1	15.5	14.6	14.3	14.6
Outpatient					
Emergency Outpatient Visits	341.9	348.5	350.0	358.1	345.1
Other Outpatient Visits.	1,587.8	1,568.5	1,500.3	1,551.5	1,402.7
Total Outpatient Visits	1,929.6	1,917.0	1,850.3	1,909.6	1,747.7
Outpatient Surgeries	46.0	44.1	43.2	43.5	41.4
Expense per Capita (per person)	$1,579.1	$1,486.6	$1,425.7	$1,324.4	$1,234.7

TABLE 6

ILLINOIS

U.S. Registered Community Hospitals
(Nonfederal, short-term general and other special hospitals)

Overview 2004–2008

	2008	2007	2006	2005	2004
Total Community Hospitals in Illinois.........	191	190	190	191	191
Bed Size Category					
6-24....................................	6	3	3	3	3
25-49...................................	33	34	34	32	28
50-99...................................	34	32	34	31	37
100-199.................................	50	53	53	59	57
200-299.................................	30	34	31	30	28
300-399.................................	21	16	17	17	20
400-499.................................	9	10	9	11	9
500 +..................................	8	8	9	8	9
Location					
Hospitals Urban..........................	127	126	126	127	119
Hospitals Rural	64	64	64	64	72
Control					
State and Local Government................	26	27	27	29	29
Not for Profit	149	150	150	154	152
Investor owned	16	13	13	8	10
Physician Models					
Independent Practice Association	29	32	33	30	33
Group Practice without Walls...............	8	7	6	7	4
Open Physician-Hospital Organization	41	41	41	52	48
Closed Physician-Hospital Organization	8	10	13	10	15
Management Service Organization	24	26	27	30	27
Integrated Salary Model....................	61	57	52	52	48
Equity Model	3	3	1	1	0
Foundation...............................	7	7	8	10	10
Insurance Products					
Health Maintenance Organization	20	22	21	23	20
Preferred Provider Organization..............	18	22	24	25	27
Indemnity Fee for Service	10	7	6	5	4
Managed Care Contracts					
Health Maintenance Organization	120	120	127	127	125
Preferred Provider Organization..............	133	131	140	143	141
Affiliations					
Hospitals in a System.....................	105	103	100	98	97
Hospitals in a Network....................	45	44	43	42	45
Hospitals in a Group Purchasing Organization..	149	144	151	154	152

TABLE 6

ILLINOIS

U.S. Registered Community Hospitals
(Nonfederal, short-term general and other special hospitals)

Utilization, Personnel, Revenue and Expenses, Community Health Indicators 2004–2008

	2008	2007	2006	2005	2004
TOTAL FACILITY (Includes Hospital and Nursing Home Units)					
Utilization - Inpatient					
Beds	34,506	34,560	34,178	34,498	34,844
Admissions	1,610,844	1,606,241	1,583,620	1,583,328	1,586,401
Inpatient Days	8,069,859	8,107,743	8,072,145	8,258,893	8,405,800
Average Length of Stay.	5.0	5.0	5.1	5.2	5.3
Inpatient Surgeries.	406,437	412,696	407,498	398,425	418,369
Births.	176,458	172,896	170,858	169,531	173,700
Utilization - Outpatient					
Emergency Outpatient Visits	5,123,091	5,068,338	5,079,148	5,021,453	4,947,646
Other Outpatient Visits.	25,863,666	25,579,122	24,485,471	23,707,111	23,387,196
Total Outpatient Visits	30,986,757	30,647,460	29,564,619	28,728,564	28,334,842
Outpatient Surgeries	728,072	723,558	729,602	715,216	715,470
Personnel					
Full Time RNs	39,613	39,478	36,521	35,229	33,613
Full Time LPNs	2,142	2,308	2,271	2,297	2,542
Part Time RNs	23,785	22,555	24,837	24,748	25,332
Part Time LPNs	1,051	1,086	1,220	1,222	1,365
Total Full Time	164,936	165,962	158,757	156,434	153,720
Total Part Time	73,769	72,865	79,025	77,647	77,912
Revenue - Inpatient					
Gross Inpatient Revenue.	$45,587,537,606	$42,978,477,154	$38,493,305,193	$36,286,660,043	$33,428,553,596
Revenue - Outpatient					
Gross Outpatient Revenue	$34,572,195,642	$30,813,226,194	$26,754,990,338	$23,617,488,823	$20,355,331,327
Revenue and Expenses - Totals					
(Includes Inpatient and Outpatient)					
Total Gross Revenue.	$80,159,733,248	$73,791,703,348	$65,248,295,531	$59,904,148,866	$53,783,884,923
Deductions from Revenue.	53,322,130,324	47,626,354,101	42,114,856,257	37,220,464,082	32,823,525,854
Net Patient Revenue	26,837,602,924	26,165,349,247	23,133,439,274	22,683,684,784	20,960,359,069
Other Operating Revenue	1,822,911,841	1,776,488,686	1,399,916,299	1,368,531,305	1,314,989,573
Other Nonoperating Revenue	38,822,875	1,235,227,543	713,723,481	606,480,110	369,884,276
Total Net Revenue.	28,699,337,640	29,177,065,476	25,247,079,054	24,658,696,199	22,645,232,918
Total Expenses.	27,982,801,609	26,624,446,808	24,077,972,512	23,329,645,752	21,729,619,998
HOSPITAL UNIT (Excludes Separate Nursing Home Units)					
Utilization - Inpatient					
Beds	32,847	32,590	31,932	32,006	32,180
Admissions	1,597,722	1,593,560	1,565,855	1,562,755	1,563,815
Inpatient Days	7,595,924	7,592,769	7,450,541	7,577,711	7,637,905
Average Length of Stay.	4.8	4.8	4.8	4.8	4.9
Personnel					
Total Full Time.	163,669	159,417	157,039	154,165	150,603
Total Part Time	73,011	72,017	77,948	76,823	76,889
Revenue and Expenses - Totals					
(Includes Inpatient and Outpatient)					
Total Net Revenue.	$28,605,435,197	$29,063,650,445	$25,089,859,015	$24,503,316,065	$22,478,149,114
Total Expenses.	27,899,476,892	26,479,602,469	23,875,608,006	23,137,091,202	21,520,879,222
COMMUNITY HEALTH INDICATORS PER 1000 POPULATION					
Total Population (in thousands)	12,902	12,826	12,760	12,704	12,666
Inpatient					
Beds	2.7	2.7	2.7	2.7	2.8
Admissions	124.9	125.2	124.1	124.6	125.3
Inpatient Days	625.5	632.1	632.6	650.1	663.7
Inpatient Surgeries.	31.5	32.2	31.9	31.4	33.0
Births.	13.7	13.5	13.4	13.3	13.7
Outpatient					
Emergency Outpatient Visits	397.1	395.2	398.1	395.3	390.6
Other Outpatient Visits.	2,004.7	1,994.3	1,919.0	1,866.1	1,846.5
Total Outpatient Visits	2,401.8	2,389.5	2,317.0	2,261.4	2,237.1
Outpatient Surgeries	56.4	56.4	57.2	56.3	56.5
Expense per Capita (per person).	$2,168.9	$2,075.8	$1,887.0	$1,836.4	$1,715.6

States

TABLE 6

INDIANA

U.S. Registered Community Hospitals
(Nonfederal, short-term general and other special hospitals)

Overview 2004–2008

	2008	2007	2006	2005	2004
Total Community Hospitals in Indiana	123	114	114	113	113
Bed Size Category					
6-24	6	5	5	5	5
25-49	40	37	35	32	27
50-99	28	23	20	26	31
100-199	20	18	22	20	18
200-299	16	18	17	14	15
300-399	4	3	3	6	6
400-499	2	3	5	3	3
500 + ...	7	7	7	7	8
Location					
Hospitals Urban.........................	83	74	74	72	68
Hospitals Rural	40	40	40	41	45
Control					
State and Local Government................	39	39	39	36	37
Not for Profit	59	56	56	58	60
Investor owned	25	19	19	19	16
Physician Models					
Independent Practice Association	8	6	8	7	11
Group Practice without Walls...............	4	4	4	5	2
Open Physician-Hospital Organization	25	28	26	29	26
Closed Physician-Hospital Organization	9	11	9	8	10
Management Service Organization	9	13	12	12	16
Integrated Salary Model....................	49	48	41	40	38
Equity Model	2	1	1	0	0
Foundation..............................	6	4	6	3	2
Insurance Products					
Health Maintenance Organization	26	30	29	31	26
Preferred Provider Organization..............	25	43	42	45	40
Indemnity Fee for Service	5	7	9	11	9
Managed Care Contracts					
Health Maintenance Organization	64	68	60	58	64
Preferred Provider Organization..............	80	82	75	80	79
Affiliations					
Hospitals in a System.....................	79	70	68	66	65
Hospitals in a Network....................	42	41	41	39	37
Hospitals in a Group Purchasing Organization..	103	101	94	91	87

TABLE 6

INDIANA

U.S. Registered Community Hospitals
(Nonfederal, short-term general and other special hospitals)

Utilization, Personnel, Revenue and Expenses, Community Health Indicators 2004–2008

	2008	2007	2006	2005	2004
TOTAL FACILITY (Includes Hospital and Nursing Home Units)					
Utilization - Inpatient					
Beds	17,612	17,066	18,076	17,750	10,790
Admissions	732,627	690,866	726,020	717,490	730,610
Inpatient Days	3,829,835	3,513,575	3,801,325	3,763,741	4,059,031
Average Length of Stay	5.2	5.1	5.2	5.2	5.6
Inpatient Surgeries	217,917	196,104	201,896	212,497	210,455
Births	82,040	82,852	85,960	83,336	85,670
Utilization - Outpatient					
Emergency Outpatient Visits	3,041,160	3,080,110	2,704,727	2,594,196	2,624,977
Other Outpatient Visits	13,981,154	13,641,278	13,815,730	13,857,787	12,887,708
Total Outpatient Visits	17,022,314	16,721,388	16,520,457	16,451,983	15,512,685
Outpatient Surgeries	433,467	420,587	443,997	415,756	430,099
Personnel					
Full Time RNs	20,417	17,979	18,592	17,532	17,385
Full Time LPNs	2,092	2,075	2,197	2,259	2,217
Part Time RNs	14,045	14,638	14,729	14,843	14,650
Part Time LPNs	1,275	1,348	1,381	1,523	1,507
Total Full Time	83,800	79,310	81,503	78,337	78,178
Total Part Time	43,202	42,633	43,210	42,031	41,619
Revenue - Inpatient					
Gross Inpatient Revenue	$18,735,608,044	$16,424,288,617	$15,861,935,722	$14,091,962,851	$13,296,387,383
Revenue - Outpatient					
Gross Outpatient Revenue	$16,228,904,838	$14,405,730,848	$13,095,278,016	$11,464,712,812	$10,362,964,783
Revenue and Expenses - Totals					
(Includes Inpatient and Outpatient)					
Total Gross Revenue	$34,964,512,882	$30,830,019,465	$28,957,213,738	$25,556,675,663	$23,659,352,166
Deductions from Revenue	20,658,195,492	17,923,123,410	16,266,448,623	13,874,036,226	12,303,799,992
Net Patient Revenue	14,306,317,390	12,906,896,055	12,690,765,115	11,682,639,437	11,355,552,174
Other Operating Revenue	837,647,729	847,569,677	729,382,635	660,605,999	495,987,318
Other Nonoperating Revenue	(665,292,556)	543,156,760	394,167,657	224,037,175	252,320,225
Total Net Revenue	14,478,672,563	14,297,622,492	13,814,315,407	12,567,282,611	12,103,859,717
Total Expenses	14,654,457,324	13,178,097,122	12,642,920,543	11,413,287,976	10,916,451,392
HOSPITAL UNIT (Excludes Separate Nursing Home Units)					
Utilization - Inpatient					
Beds	16,911	16,295	17,194	16,841	17,907
Admissions	724,499	682,827	716,630	707,682	720,545
Inpatient Days	3,612,957	3,287,612	3,532,765	3,484,986	3,812,707
Average Length of Stay	5.0	4.8	4.9	4.9	5.3
Personnel					
Total Full Time	82,933	78,394	80,597	77,768	77,283
Total Part Time	42,676	42,129	42,664	41,496	40,858
Revenue and Expenses - Totals					
(Includes Inpatient and Outpatient)					
Total Net Revenue	$14,424,793,981	$14,228,510,655	$13,752,934,410	$12,495,533,140	$12,051,572,873
Total Expenses	14,603,238,942	13,123,516,451	12,580,110,810	11,352,451,392	10,871,754,546
COMMUNITY HEALTH INDICATORS PER 1000 POPULATION					
Total Population (in thousands)	6,377	6,336	6,294	6,249	6,211
Inpatient					
Beds	2.8	2.7	2.9	2.8	3.0
Admissions	114.9	109.0	115.3	114.8	117.6
Inpatient Days	600.6	554.6	603.9	602.3	653.5
Inpatient Surgeries	34.2	31.0	32.1	34.0	33.9
Births	12.9	13.1	13.7	13.3	13.8
Outpatient					
Emergency Outpatient Visits	476.9	486.1	429.7	415.2	422.6
Other Outpatient Visits	2,192.5	2,153.0	2,195.0	2,217.8	2,075.0
Total Outpatient Visits	2,669.4	2,639.2	2,624.7	2,632.9	2,497.7
Outpatient Surgeries	68.0	66.4	70.5	66.5	69.3
Expense per Capita (per person)	$2,298.1	$2,079.9	$2,008.7	$1,826.5	$1,757.7

States

Overview 2004–2008

	2008	2007	2006	2005	2004
Total Community Hospitals in Iowa...........	118	117	117	116	115
Bed Size Category					
6-24	13	13	13	13	10
25-49	53	50	51	50	49
50-99	26	28	26	25	28
100-199	11	11	12	13	13
200-299	6	6	7	6	6
300-399	5	5	4	5	4
400-499	2	2	2	2	3
500 + ...	2	2	2	2	2
Location					
Hospitals Urban...........................	34	33	33	32	20
Hospitals Rural	84	84	84	84	95
Control					
State and Local Government................	59	59	59	59	59
Not for Profit	58	58	58	57	56
Investor owned	1	0	0	0	0
Physician Models					
Independent Practice Association	15	15	17	20	19
Group Practice without Walls................	3	3	3	3	4
Open Physician-Hospital Organization	27	26	26	24	21
Closed Physician-Hospital Organization	10	11	11	11	12
Management Service Organization	12	12	12	13	13
Integrated Salary Model....................	65	64	62	59	56
Equity Model	0	1	1	1	2
Foundation...............................	6	5	6	6	5
Insurance Products					
Health Maintenance Organization	9	13	13	13	17
Preferred Provider Organization..............	20	26	29	31	37
Indemnity Fee for Service	4	6	7	7	8
Managed Care Contracts					
Health Maintenance Organization	70	69	66	65	65
Preferred Provider Organization..............	97	97	99	93	94
Affiliations					
Hospitals in a System.....................	64	63	64	62	61
Hospitals in a Network....................	70	70	73	70	65
Hospitals in a Group Purchasing Organization..	112	111	110	108	105

States

TABLE 6   **IOWA**

U.S. Registered Community Hospitals
(Nonfederal, short-term general and other special hospitals)

Utilization, Personnel, Revenue and Expenses, Community Health Indicators 2004–2008

	2008	2007	2006	2005	2004
TOTAL FACILITY (Includes Hospital and Nursing Home Units)					
Utilization - Inpatient					
Beds	10,531	10,515	10,500	10,760	10,010
Admissions	373,330	368,272	363,077	362,541	359,611
Inpatient Days	2,248,874	2,266,094	2,267,449	2,323,346	2,358,165
Average Length of Stay	6.0	6.2	6.2	6.4	6.6
Inpatient Surgeries	101,343	100,151	99,335	102,520	108,042
Births	39,060	40,274	39,560	38,899	38,419
Utilization - Outpatient					
Emergency Outpatient Visits	1,226,568	1,165,305	1,122,636	1,118,233	1,065,819
Other Outpatient Visits	9,154,060	9,390,580	9,172,457	8,979,828	8,619,047
Total Outpatient Visits	10,380,628	10,555,885	10,295,093	10,098,061	9,684,866
Outpatient Surgeries	337,632	337,757	335,367	348,557	334,652
Personnel					
Full Time RNs	10,589	10,263	10,218	9,842	9,268
Full Time LPNs	902	915	904	978	901
Part Time RNs	7,573	7,388	7,211	6,683	7,207
Part Time LPNs	734	824	759	737	836
Total Full Time	45,177	44,058	43,563	43,891	41,397
Total Part Time	26,052	25,304	25,228	23,884	25,233
Revenue - Inpatient					
Gross Inpatient Revenue	$7,173,320,596	$6,622,133,635	$6,041,189,863	$5,691,952,810	$5,138,048,080
Revenue - Outpatient					
Gross Outpatient Revenue	$7,008,785,229	$6,341,069,890	$5,765,745,834	$5,140,873,851	$4,509,250,053
Revenue and Expenses - Totals					
(Includes Inpatient and Outpatient)					
Total Gross Revenue	$14,182,105,825	$12,963,203,525	$11,806,935,697	$10,832,826,661	$9,647,298,133
Deductions from Revenue	7,919,893,373	7,059,676,768	6,158,463,230	5,563,253,766	4,779,712,534
Net Patient Revenue	6,262,212,452	5,903,526,757	5,648,472,467	5,269,572,895	4,867,585,599
Other Operating Revenue	479,246,797	468,286,796	423,197,979	422,215,028	397,098,611
Other Nonoperating Revenue	(17,782,222)	235,126,914	141,353,867	122,389,633	74,842,671
Total Net Revenue	6,723,677,027	6,606,940,467	6,213,024,313	5,814,177,556	5,339,526,881
Total Expenses	6,518,050,247	6,082,343,644	5,830,164,533	5,446,874,403	5,081,276,194
HOSPITAL UNIT (Excludes Separate Nursing Home Units)					
Utilization - Inpatient					
Beds	8,524	8,486	8,491	8,664	8,829
Admissions	365,727	360,207	354,676	353,704	351,217
Inpatient Days	1,616,630	1,626,922	1,605,060	1,653,640	1,685,270
Average Length of Stay	4.4	4.5	4.5	4.7	4.8
Personnel					
Total Full Time	44,290	43,130	42,578	42,873	39,785
Total Part Time	25,160	24,397	24,254	22,882	23,980
Revenue and Expenses - Totals					
(Includes Inpatient and Outpatient)					
Total Net Revenue	$6,614,103,911	$6,497,382,484	$6,108,192,223	$5,707,539,421	$5,244,048,673
Total Expenses	6,429,352,282	5,997,176,987	5,746,268,857	5,359,185,888	5,006,432,721
COMMUNITY HEALTH INDICATORS PER 1000 POPULATION					
Total Population (in thousands)	3,003	2,983	2,967	2,952	2,943
Inpatient					
Beds	3.5	3.5	3.5	3.6	3.7
Admissions	124.3	123.4	122.4	122.8	122.2
Inpatient Days	749.0	759.6	764.2	787.1	801.4
Inpatient Surgeries	33.8	33.6	33.5	34.7	36.7
Births	13.0	13.5	13.3	13.2	13.1
Outpatient					
Emergency Outpatient Visits	408.5	390.6	378.3	378.8	362.2
Other Outpatient Visits	3,048.8	3,147.7	3,091.2	3,042.2	2,928.9
Total Outpatient Visits	3,457.3	3,538.3	3,469.6	3,421.0	3,291.1
Outpatient Surgeries	112.4	113.2	113.0	118.1	113.7
Expense per Capita (per person)	$2,170.8	$2,038.8	$1,964.8	$1,845.3	$1,726.7

TABLE 6

KANSAS

U.S. Registered Community Hospitals
(Nonfederal, short-term general and other special hospitals)

Overview 2004–2008

	2008	2007	2006	2005	2004
Total Community Hospitals in Kansas	**132**	**128**	**129**	**131**	**134**
Bed Size Category					
6-24	15	14	15	16	15
25-49	51	51	52	50	50
50-99	39	38	38	42	47
100-199	17	14	13	13	12
200-299	5	6	6	6	5
300-399	2	2	2	1	2
400-499	0	0	1	1	1
500 + ...	3	3	2	2	2
Location					
Hospitals Urban............................	33	29	29	30	27
Hospitals Rural	99	99	100	101	107
Control					
State and Local Government................	62	62	61	61	61
Not for Profit	53	55	57	58	60
Investor owned	17	11	11	12	13
Physician Models					
Independent Practice Association	14	13	17	19	20
Group Practice without Walls...............	3	2	5	4	5
Open Physician-Hospital Organization	15	15	14	16	14
Closed Physician-Hospital Organization	2	2	2	1	1
Management Service Organization	4	4	6	3	3
Integrated Salary Model....................	65	62	66	58	51
Equity Model	1	1	1	0	0
Foundation...............................	3	4	5	4	3
Insurance Products					
Health Maintenance Organization	5	6	5	6	8
Preferred Provider Organization..............	11	28	31	35	36
Indemnity Fee for Service	3	5	4	4	6
Managed Care Contracts					
Health Maintenance Organization	51	46	44	45	43
Preferred Provider Organization..............	112	107	113	111	111
Affiliations					
Hospitals in a System......................	52	47	48	50	51
Hospitals in a Network	82	79	81	83	83
Hospitals in a Group Purchasing Organization..	126	124	124	125	127

States

TABLE 6

KANSAS

U.S. Registered Community Hospitals
(Nonfederal, short-term general and other special hospitals)

Utilization, Personnel, Revenue and Expenses, Community Health Indicators 2004–2008

	2008	2007	2006	2005	2004
TOTAL FACILITY (Includes Hospital and Nursing Home Units)					
Utilization - Inpatient					
Beds	10,269	10,079	10,019	10,075	10,362
Admissions	328,279	325,355	332,524	330,429	330,712
Inpatient Days	2,079,667	2,025,564	2,024,257	2,070,956	2,115,015
Average Length of Stay	6.3	6.2	6.1	6.3	6.4
Inpatient Surgeries	82,907	84,061	82,929	95,685	96,928
Births	41,592	41,753	40,729	40,039	39,489
Utilization - Outpatient					
Emergency Outpatient Visits	1,028,706	1,003,181	972,761	959,699	933,816
Other Outpatient Visits	5,497,497	5,394,624	5,173,496	4,985,081	4,926,831
Total Outpatient Visits	6,526,203	6,397,805	6,146,257	5,944,780	5,860,647
Outpatient Surgeries	162,784	158,129	160,808	169,295	168,004
Personnel					
Full Time RNs	9,924	9,353	8,599	8,396	8,081
Full Time LPNs	1,104	1,085	1,055	1,066	1,085
Part Time RNs	4,448	4,483	4,671	4,756	4,046
Part Time LPNs	502	533	484	485	530
Total Full Time	38,038	36,715	35,113	34,326	33,963
Total Part Time	14,394	14,215	14,162	14,570	13,957
Revenue - Inpatient					
Gross Inpatient Revenue	$8,347,025,856	$7,570,341,842	$7,121,171,892	$6,492,436,141	$6,041,564,302
Revenue - Outpatient					
Gross Outpatient Revenue	$6,341,227,760	$5,585,998,443	$5,152,612,930	$4,575,808,221	$4,008,314,363
Revenue and Expenses - Totals					
(Includes Inpatient and Outpatient)					
Total Gross Revenue	$14,688,253,616	$13,156,340,285	$12,273,784,822	$11,068,244,362	$10,049,878,665
Deductions from Revenue	9,366,195,974	8,521,152,481	7,575,131,231	6,722,580,237	5,989,750,259
Net Patient Revenue	5,322,057,642	4,635,187,804	4,698,653,591	4,345,664,125	4,060,128,406
Other Operating Revenue	194,026,086	190,949,651	183,451,488	160,393,655	167,277,373
Other Nonoperating Revenue	33,604,548	143,977,328	92,775,123	65,308,485	68,121,241
Total Net Revenue	5,549,688,276	4,970,114,783	4,974,880,202	4,571,366,265	4,295,527,020
Total Expenses	5,330,135,811	4,536,195,594	4,612,906,605	4,292,972,936	4,062,879,679
HOSPITAL UNIT (Excludes Separate Nursing Home Units)					
Utilization - Inpatient					
Beds	8,435	8,287	8,313	8,376	8,699
Admissions	325,383	322,629	329,818	327,686	327,208
Inpatient Days	1,551,696	1,496,858	1,498,214	1,547,593	1,588,632
Average Length of Stay	4.8	4.6	4.5	4.7	4.9
Personnel					
Total Full Time	36,923	35,595	34,042	33,277	32,568
Total Part Time	13,775	13,608	13,650	14,042	13,263
Revenue and Expenses - Totals					
(Includes Inpatient and Outpatient)					
Total Net Revenue	$5,472,326,781	$4,898,350,636	$4,908,181,882	$4,509,750,464	$4,236,126,636
Total Expenses	5,262,852,507	4,478,090,750	4,558,169,540	4,243,480,226	4,010,808,623
COMMUNITY HEALTH INDICATORS PER 1000 POPULATION					
Total Population (in thousands)	2,802	2,777	2,756	2,742	2,731
Inpatient					
Beds	3.7	3.6	3.6	3.7	3.8
Admissions	117.2	117.1	120.6	120.5	121.1
Inpatient Days	742.2	729.3	734.4	755.2	774.4
Inpatient Surgeries	29.6	30.3	30.1	34.9	35.5
Births	14.8	15.0	14.8	14.6	14.5
Outpatient					
Emergency Outpatient Visits	367.1	361.2	352.9	350.0	341.9
Other Outpatient Visits	1,961.9	1,942.3	1,877.0	1,817.9	1,804.0
Total Outpatient Visits	2,329.0	2,303.5	2,229.9	2,167.9	2,145.9
Outpatient Surgeries	58.1	56.9	58.3	61.7	61.5
Expense per Capita (per person)	$1,902.2	$1,633.3	$1,673.6	$1,565.5	$1,487.7

States

TABLE 6

KENTUCKY

U.S. Registered Community Hospitals
(Nonfederal, short-term general and other special hospitals)

Overview 2004–2008

	2008	2007	2006	2005	2004
Total Community Hospitals in Kentucky.......	105	104	104	105	105
Bed Size Category					
6-24	1	1	2	2	1
25-49	34	32	31	29	28
50-99	23	24	24	27	27
100-199	22	19	19	20	20
200-299	10	14	13	12	15
300-399	9	8	8	7	6
400-499	3	3	5	6	6
500 + ...	3	3	2	2	2
Location					
Hospitals Urban...........................	41	40	40	41	35
Hospitals Rural	64	64	64	64	70
Control					
State and Local Government................	14	12	13	13	13
Not for Profit	71	73	71	72	72
Investor owned	20	19	20	20	20
Physician Models					
Independent Practice Association	7	7	7	8	3
Group Practice without Walls...............	2	3	2	2	1
Open Physician-Hospital Organization	11	11	11	11	12
Closed Physician-Hospital Organization	5	5	4	3	2
Management Service Organization	2	3	3	2	2
Integrated Salary Model....................	39	38	34	30	27
Equity Model	1	0	0	0	0
Foundation...............................	3	2	3	2	3
Insurance Products					
Health Maintenance Organization	4	9	17	20	21
Preferred Provider Organization..............	9	17	23	31	23
Indemnity Fee for Service	3	2	3	4	3
Managed Care Contracts					
Health Maintenance Organization	41	43	45	46	51
Preferred Provider Organization..............	60	63	67	66	64
Affiliations					
Hospitals in a System......................	72	68	74	69	69
Hospitals in a Network.....................	24	27	26	25	23
Hospitals in a Group Purchasing Organization..	82	83	83	80	77

TABLE 6

KENTUCKY

U.S. Registered Community Hospitals
(Nonfederal, short-term general and other special hospitals)

Utilization, Personnel, Revenue and Expenses, Community Health Indicators 2004–2008

	2008	2007	2006	2005	2004
TOTAL FACILITY (Includes Hospital and Nursing Home Units)					
Utilization - Inpatient					
Beds	14,180	14,423	14,574	14,891	15,276
Admissions	610,449	611,689	612,842	617,969	605,707
Inpatient Days	3,216,149	3,188,902	3,239,168	3,385,604	3,384,932
Average Length of Stay	5.3	5.2	5.3	5.5	5.6
Inpatient Surgeries	176,178	178,549	178,264	178,250	169,692
Births	54,872	56,096	54,614	53,835	53,067
Utilization - Outpatient					
Emergency Outpatient Visits	2,339,390	2,305,046	2,191,969	2,238,194	2,257,276
Other Outpatient Visits	7,319,408	7,219,771	6,623,337	6,620,883	6,622,870
Total Outpatient Visits	9,658,798	9,524,817	8,815,306	8,859,077	8,880,146
Outpatient Surgeries	385,428	376,310	373,174	375,953	365,854
Personnel					
Full Time RNs	16,222	15,410	15,106	14,515	14,319
Full Time LPNs	1,807	2,045	2,146	2,178	2,163
Part Time RNs	6,151	6,335	6,400	6,668	6,436
Part Time LPNs	445	539	547	665	614
Total Full Time	61,610	60,572	59,725	57,617	56,989
Total Part Time	18,576	18,836	18,967	21,061	19,236
Revenue - Inpatient					
Gross Inpatient Revenue	$13,943,782,950	$13,031,881,310	$12,527,888,281	$11,140,011,986	$10,211,530,486
Revenue - Outpatient					
Gross Outpatient Revenue	$11,459,995,978	$10,354,782,898	$9,475,429,030	$8,208,360,194	$7,156,929,150
Revenue and Expenses - Totals					
(Includes Inpatient and Outpatient)					
Total Gross Revenue	$25,403,778,928	$23,386,664,208	$22,003,317,311	$19,348,372,180	$17,368,459,636
Deductions from Revenue	16,462,600,038	14,766,322,595	13,658,377,781	11,792,754,141	10,353,176,805
Net Patient Revenue	8,941,178,890	8,620,341,613	8,344,939,530	7,555,618,039	7,015,282,831
Other Operating Revenue	309,734,161	282,137,777	257,873,549	292,730,942	314,482,516
Other Nonoperating Revenue	(81,140,239)	206,333,489	190,808,469	84,227,172	80,671,058
Total Net Revenue	9,169,772,812	9,108,812,879	8,793,621,548	7,932,576,153	7,410,436,405
Total Expenses	8,831,617,722	8,398,874,713	7,943,139,511	7,397,991,998	6,893,069,255
HOSPITAL UNIT (Excludes Separate Nursing Home Units)					
Utilization - Inpatient					
Beds	13,383	13,437	13,581	13,794	13,980
Admissions	603,967	604,725	606,435	609,253	597,247
Inpatient Days	2,975,158	2,886,705	2,928,444	3,010,129	2,992,615
Average Length of Stay	4.9	4.8	4.8	4.9	5.0
Personnel					
Total Full Time	60,776	59,665	58,711	56,719	54,461
Total Part Time	18,322	18,550	18,596	20,725	18,269
Revenue and Expenses - Totals					
(Includes Inpatient and Outpatient)					
Total Net Revenue	$9,092,827,775	$9,023,023,649	$8,703,572,762	$7,815,800,206	$7,312,879,356
Total Expenses	8,766,577,356	8,337,062,529	7,869,950,752	7,301,705,467	6,825,631,885
COMMUNITY HEALTH INDICATORS PER 1000 POPULATION					
Total Population (in thousands)	4,269	4,236	4,199	4,166	4,136
Inpatient					
Beds	3.3	3.4	3.5	3.6	3.7
Admissions	143.0	144.4	145.9	148.3	146.5
Inpatient Days	753.3	752.8	771.3	812.7	818.5
Inpatient Surgeries	41.3	42.1	42.4	42.8	41.0
Births	12.9	13.2	13.0	12.9	12.8
Outpatient					
Emergency Outpatient Visits	548.0	544.1	522.0	537.3	545.8
Other Outpatient Visits	1,714.5	1,704.3	1,577.2	1,589.3	1,601.4
Total Outpatient Visits	2,262.4	2,248.4	2,099.2	2,126.5	2,147.3
Outpatient Surgeries	90.3	88.8	88.9	90.2	88.5
Expense per Capita (per person)	$2,068.7	$1,982.6	$1,891.5	$1,775.8	$1,666.8

TABLE 6

LOUISIANA

U.S. Registered Community Hospitals
(Nonfederal, short-term general and other special hospitals)

Overview 2004–2008

	2008	2007	2006	2005	2004
Total Community Hospitals in Louisiana	130	129	132	128	131
Bed Size Category					
6-24	19	16	16	16	15
25-49	37	39	40	35	33
50-99	22	24	27	27	30
100-199	28	28	27	26	27
200-299	9	9	10	13	10
300-399	7	6	4	4	6
400-499	5	5	4	4	6
500 + ...	3	2	4	3	4
Location					
Hospitals Urban.	80	79	81	78	82
Hospitals Rural	50	50	51	50	49
Control					
State and Local Government.	50	50	51	51	53
Not for Profit	38	38	38	32	34
Investor owned	42	41	43	45	44
Physician Models					
Independent Practice Association	8	9	14	8	12
Group Practice without Walls.	4	5	4	4	5
Open Physician-Hospital Organization	14	14	14	11	13
Closed Physician-Hospital Organization	8	5	6	3	4
Management Service Organization	8	3	7	6	7
Integrated Salary Model.	24	22	18	13	19
Equity Model	4	2	1	1	1
Foundation.	4	3	4	2	1
Insurance Products					
Health Maintenance Organization	9	5	7	8	12
Preferred Provider Organization.	6	7	12	10	12
Indemnity Fee for Service	2	2	6	2	2
Managed Care Contracts					
Health Maintenance Organization	51	50	41	45	50
Preferred Provider Organization.	61	58	54	52	60
Affiliations					
Hospitals in a System.	70	70	72	65	67
Hospitals in a Network	24	20	19	17	22
Hospitals in a Group Purchasing Organization. .	72	63	64	60	60

TABLE 6

LOUISIANA

U.S. Registered Community Hospitals
(Nonfederal, short-term general and other special hospitals)

Utilization, Personnel, Revenue and Expenses, Community Health Indicators 2004–2008

	2008	2007	2006	2005	2004
TOTAL FACILITY (Includes Hospital and Nursing Home Units)					
Utilization - Inpatient					
Beds	16,007	15,516	15,861	15,504	17,199
Admissions	636,767	630,873	623,144	619,500	696,154
Inpatient Days	3,378,368	3,448,099	3,556,169	3,404,395	3,856,768
Average Length of Stay	5.3	5.5	5.7	5.5	5.5
Inpatient Surgeries	184,754	187,991	176,644	150,594	170,141
Births	67,081	69,359	69,455	56,499	56,218
Utilization - Outpatient					
Emergency Outpatient Visits	2,381,889	2,194,465	2,096,962	2,147,600	2,468,882
Other Outpatient Visits	8,779,479	8,233,730	7,764,689	7,659,204	7,911,215
Total Outpatient Visits	11,161,368	10,428,195	9,861,651	9,806,804	10,380,097
Outpatient Surgeries	278,141	288,118	281,956	239,027	269,918
Personnel					
Full Time RNs	17,187	16,261	15,502	15,017	16,231
Full Time LPNs	3,034	2,675	2,761	2,898	3,394
Part Time RNs	5,039	4,942	5,545	5,358	5,552
Part Time LPNs	773	616	778	786	936
Total Full Time	70,862	69,031	65,516	62,785	69,516
Total Part Time	15,367	14,004	17,124	16,770	18,508
Revenue - Inpatient					
Gross Inpatient Revenue	$15,609,477,577	$14,226,935,015	$12,833,233,745	$12,486,431,054	$12,631,245,465
Revenue - Outpatient					
Gross Outpatient Revenue	$10,443,222,809	$8,622,281,370	$7,529,943,140	$7,056,479,417	$7,060,262,549
Revenue and Expenses - Totals					
(Includes Inpatient and Outpatient)					
Total Gross Revenue	$26,052,700,386	$22,849,216,385	$20,363,176,885	$19,542,910,471	$19,691,508,014
Deductions from Revenue	17,411,142,732	15,075,589,108	13,060,049,470	12,631,005,388	12,335,668,769
Net Patient Revenue	8,641,557,654	7,773,627,277	7,303,127,415	6,911,905,083	7,355,839,245
Other Operating Revenue	521,425,542	530,981,708	495,512,730	394,178,196	383,145,135
Other Nonoperating Revenue	33,327,586	276,902,027	168,610,943	99,333,406	115,137,849
Total Net Revenue	9,196,310,782	8,581,511,012	7,979,845,190	7,405,416,685	7,854,122,229
Total Expenses	9,014,212,755	8,192,722,277	7,552,791,081	7,158,276,605	7,419,160,281
HOSPITAL UNIT (Excludes Separate Nursing Home Units)					
Utilization - Inpatient					
Beds	15,323	14,832	14,964	14,881	16,826
Admissions	634,313	629,620	621,068	617,435	693,562
Inpatient Days	3,273,703	3,236,493	3,276,461	3,212,644	3,737,214
Average Length of Stay	5.2	5.1	5.3	5.2	5.4
Personnel					
Total Full Time	70,017	68,659	64,629	62,136	68,744
Total Part Time	15,147	13,879	16,905	16,612	18,142
Revenue and Expenses - Totals					
(Includes Inpatient and Outpatient)					
Total Net Revenue	$9,161,979,219	$8,548,109,513	$7,947,920,310	$7,375,447,859	$7,829,455,901
Total Expenses	8,973,038,466	8,161,833,462	7,514,898,181	7,124,471,067	7,393,898,853
COMMUNITY HEALTH INDICATORS PER 1000 POPULATION					
Total Population (in thousands)	4,411	4,373	4,244	4,496	4,488
Inpatient					
Beds	3.6	3.5	3.7	3.5	3.8
Admissions	144.4	144.3	146.8	137.8	155.1
Inpatient Days	765.9	788.4	838.0	757.3	859.4
Inpatient Surgeries	41.9	43.0	41.6	33.5	37.9
Births	15.2	15.9	16.4	12.6	12.5
Outpatient					
Emergency Outpatient Visits	540.0	501.8	494.1	477.7	550.1
Other Outpatient Visits	1,990.5	1,882.7	1,829.7	1,703.7	1,762.8
Total Outpatient Visits	2,530.5	2,384.5	2,323.9	2,181.4	2,312.9
Outpatient Surgeries	63.1	65.9	66.4	53.2	60.1
Expense per Capita (per person)	$2,043.7	$1,873.3	$1,779.8	$1,592.3	$1,653.2

States

TABLE 6

MAINE

U.S. Registered Community Hospitals
(Nonfederal, short-term general and other special hospitals)

Overview 2004–2008

	2008	2007	2006	2005	2004
Total Community Hospitals in Maine..........	37	37	37	37	37
Bed Size Category					
6-24	2	2	2	2	1
25-49	16	16	15	14	15
50-99	9	9	10	11	11
100-199	7	7	7	7	7
200-299	1	1	1	1	1
300-399	1	1	1	1	1
400-499	0	0	0	0	0
500 + ...	1	1	1	1	1
Location					
Hospitals Urban..........................	15	15	15	15	8
Hospitals Rural	22	22	22	22	29
Control					
State and Local Government................	2	2	2	2	2
Not for Profit	34	34	34	34	34
Investor owned	1	1	1	1	1
Physician Models					
Independent Practice Association	3	4	4	4	4
Group Practice without Walls...............	2	2	2	1	1
Open Physician-Hospital Organization	12	12	14	15	14
Closed Physician-Hospital Organization	0	0	0	1	1
Management Service Organization	5	4	3	4	4
Integrated Salary Model....................	20	21	21	21	18
Equity Model	1	1	1	1	1
Foundation...............................	0	0	0	0	1
Insurance Products					
Health Maintenance Organization	5	4	3	2	2
Preferred Provider Organization..............	4	5	5	6	5
Indemnity Fee for Service	2	3	3	2	2
Managed Care Contracts					
Health Maintenance Organization	21	22	21	22	22
Preferred Provider Organization..............	20	17	20	22	20
Affiliations					
Hospitals in a System......................	14	15	15	14	13
Hospitals in a Network.....................	17	18	20	20	18
Hospitals in a Group Purchasing Organization..	31	34	33	32	30

States

TABLE 6

MAINE

U.S. Registered Community Hospitals
(Nonfederal, short-term general and other special hospitals)

Utilization, Personnel, Revenue and Expenses, Community Health Indicators 2004–2008

	2008	2007	2006	2005	2004
TOTAL FACILITY (Includes Hospital and Nursing Home Units)					
Utilization - Inpatient					
Beds	3,504	3,509	3,489	3,526	3,549
Admissions	148,635	151,877	150,990	151,303	151,135
Inpatient Days	845,428	839,900	851,520	848,195	820,114
Average Length of Stay.	5.7	5.5	5.6	5.6	5.4
Inpatient Surgeries	44,812	43,205	44,380	42,857	43,761
Births.	13,489	13,707	13,736	13,667	13,504
Utilization - Outpatient					
Emergency Outpatient Visits	780,874	718,242	757,685	728,701	711,570
Other Outpatient Visits.	4,312,504	3,982,761	3,447,664	3,570,798	3,406,226
Total Outpatient Visits	5,093,378	4,701,003	4,205,349	4,299,499	4,117,796
Outpatient Surgeries	130,708	128,931	125,183	118,469	118,131
Personnel					
Full Time RNs	4,707	4,702	4,337	4,369	4,132
Full Time LPNs	234	222	270	256	291
Part Time RNs.	3,384	3,571	3,596	3,349	3,437
Part Time LPNs	159	143	150	169	171
Total Full Time.	23,172	22,259	21,285	20,969	19,205
Total Part Time	11,058	11,809	11,494	10,914	10,723
Revenue - Inpatient					
Gross Inpatient Revenue.	$3,043,869,279	$2,773,541,415	$2,679,113,113	$2,540,202,810	$2,467,189,637
Revenue - Outpatient					
Gross Outpatient Revenue	$3,446,970,975	$3,066,834,815	$2,828,799,712	$2,491,229,223	$2,211,215,695
Revenue and Expenses - Totals					
(Includes Inpatient and Outpatient)					
Total Gross Revenue.	$6,490,840,254	$5,840,376,230	$5,507,912,825	$5,031,432,033	$4,678,405,332
Deductions from Revenue.	2,989,235,436	2,569,231,346	2,428,063,405	2,169,148,932	2,111,297,150
Net Patient Revenue	3,501,604,818	3,271,144,884	3,079,849,420	2,862,283,101	2,567,108,182
Other Operating Revenue	93,262,738	95,971,646	90,802,554	86,008,208	80,994,871
Other Nonoperating Revenue	13,684,134	74,855,385	61,676,959	54,877,774	52,626,519
Total Net Revenue.	3,608,551,690	3,441,971,915	3,232,328,933	3,003,169,083	2,700,729,572
Total Expenses.	3,516,496,379	3,265,842,064	3,060,867,876	2,762,713,712	2,549,574,659
HOSPITAL UNIT (Excludes Separate Nursing Home Units)					
Utilization - Inpatient					
Beds	3,108	3,090	3,099	3,112	3,310
Admissions	147,524	150,702	149,665	150,031	150,073
Inpatient Days	712,754	709,283	721,622	714,678	745,357
Average Length of Stay.	4.8	4.7	4.8	4.8	5.0
Personnel					
Total Full Time.	22,480	21,683	20,709	20,647	18,517
Total Part Time	10,596	11,516	11,123	10,639	10,225
Revenue and Expenses - Totals					
(Includes Inpatient and Outpatient)					
Total Net Revenue.	$3,580,910,825	$3,413,422,605	$3,203,268,060	$2,976,406,866	$2,684,324,134
Total Expenses.	3,486,675,727	3,236,639,252	3,034,440,927	2,736,792,556	2,533,017,594
COMMUNITY HEALTH INDICATORS PER 1000 POPULATION					
Total Population (in thousands)	1,316	1,315	1,313	1,311	1,308
Inpatient					
Beds	2.7	2.7	2.7	2.7	2.7
Admissions	112.9	115.5	115.0	115.4	115.6
Inpatient Days	642.2	638.5	648.4	647.0	627.0
Inpatient Surgeries	34.0	32.8	33.8	32.7	33.5
Births.	10.2	10.4	10.5	10.4	10.3
Outpatient					
Emergency Outpatient Visits	593.2	546.0	576.9	555.8	544.1
Other Outpatient Visits.	3,275.8	3,027.8	2,625.1	2,723.6	2,604.3
Total Outpatient Visits	3,869.0	3,573.8	3,202.0	3,279.4	3,148.4
Outpatient Surgeries	99.3	98.0	95.3	90.4	90.3
Expense per Capita (per person).	$2,671.2	$2,482.8	$2,330.6	$2,107.3	$1,949.4

TABLE 6

MARYLAND

U.S. Registered Community Hospitals
(Nonfederal, short-term general and other special hospitals)

Overview 2004–2008

	2008	2007	2006	2005	2004
Total Community Hospitals in Maryland.......	50	49	50	50	50
Bed Size Category					
6-24	0	0	0	0	0
25-49	2	3	3	3	2
50-99	6	5	7	5	6
100-199	13	13	13	16	17
200-299	15	14	16	15	11
300-399	8	8	6	6	8
400-499	3	3	2	2	3
500 + ...	3	3	3	3	3
Location					
Hospitals Urban.........................	44	43	44	44	41
Hospitals Rural	6	6	6	6	9
Control					
State and Local Government................	0	0	0	0	0
Not for Profit............................	48	47	48	48	48
Investor owned	2	2	2	2	2
Physician Models					
Independent Practice Association	3	3	4	3	6
Group Practice without Walls...............	3	4	2	1	2
Open Physician-Hospital Organization	4	5	7	8	10
Closed Physician-Hospital Organization	2	3	4	4	1
Management Service Organization	6	6	6	5	4
Integrated Salary Model....................	27	25	26	23	26
Equity Model	4	3	2	2	4
Foundation..............................	5	2	2	1	1
Insurance Products					
Health Maintenance Organization	12	10	8	8	9
Preferred Provider Organization..............	5	6	4	4	5
Indemnity Fee for Service	2	3	2	1	3
Managed Care Contracts					
Health Maintenance Organization	36	36	36	33	36
Preferred Provider Organization..............	33	34	32	33	35
Affiliations					
Hospitals in a System.....................	32	30	32	30	30
Hospitals in a Network....................	15	13	10	9	13
Hospitals in a Group Purchasing Organization..	44	45	46	45	46

States

TABLE 6

MARYLAND

U.S. Registered Community Hospitals
(Nonfederal, short-term general and other special hospitals)

Utilization, Personnel, Revenue and Expenses, Community Health Indicators 2004–2008

	2008	2007	2006	2005	2004
TOTAL FACILITY (Includes Hospital and Nursing Home Units)					
Utilization - Inpatient					
Beds	12,018	11,713	11,470	11,404	11,409
Admissions	711,267	698,057	690,371	679,838	661,449
Inpatient Days	3,298,930	3,243,033	3,167,502	3,187,739	3,189,302
Average Length of Stay	4.6	4.6	4.6	4.7	4.8
Inpatient Surgeries	196,641	195,341	192,341	188,592	189,945
Births	73,595	72,022	69,138	67,813	68,201
Utilization - Outpatient					
Emergency Outpatient Visits	2,282,417	2,285,417	2,299,181	2,160,010	2,162,198
Other Outpatient Visits	5,800,698	5,016,402	4,708,636	4,590,267	4,769,543
Total Outpatient Visits	8,083,115	7,301,819	7,007,817	6,750,277	6,931,741
Outpatient Surgeries	355,489	350,768	349,370	357,194	361,757
Personnel					
Full Time RNs	16,216	15,333	14,709	13,933	13,664
Full Time LPNs	554	592	578	579	589
Part Time RNs	8,857	8,651	8,972	8,096	8,348
Part Time LPNs	271	257	264	252	326
Total Full Time	66,471	63,954	62,875	61,492	58,981
Total Part Time	27,048	25,034	25,458	23,583	25,011
Revenue - Inpatient					
Gross Inpatient Revenue	$8,955,048,928	$8,470,935,614	$7,817,701,056	$7,328,324,384	$6,825,359,796
Revenue - Outpatient					
Gross Outpatient Revenue	$4,920,676,123	$4,305,767,399	$4,043,062,566	$3,806,641,962	$3,472,795,225
Revenue and Expenses - Totals					
(Includes Inpatient and Outpatient)					
Total Gross Revenue	$13,875,725,051	$12,776,703,013	$11,860,763,622	$11,134,966,346	$10,298,155,021
Deductions from Revenue	2,596,608,560	2,295,774,013	2,108,964,137	2,153,177,051	1,940,994,076
Net Patient Revenue	11,279,116,491	10,480,929,000	9,751,799,485	8,981,789,295	8,357,160,945
Other Operating Revenue	462,807,673	432,880,309	395,195,238	326,183,274	322,420,713
Other Nonoperating Revenue	(106,798,785)	189,549,902	132,820,364	121,915,311	53,498,715
Total Net Revenue	11,635,125,379	11,103,359,211	10,279,815,087	9,429,887,880	8,733,080,373
Total Expenses	11,389,973,159	10,520,002,176	9,794,446,454	8,998,802,051	8,424,555,436
HOSPITAL UNIT (Excludes Separate Nursing Home Units)					
Utilization - Inpatient					
Beds	11,272	10,986	10,733	10,706	10,675
Admissions	704,669	690,355	682,097	671,054	652,166
Inpatient Days	3,104,039	3,007,468	2,948,727	2,965,422	2,928,619
Average Length of Stay	4.4	4.4	4.3	4.4	4.5
Personnel					
Total Full Time	65,813	63,276	62,242	60,750	58,217
Total Part Time	26,682	24,731	25,092	23,194	24,621
Revenue and Expenses - Totals					
(Includes Inpatient and Outpatient)					
Total Net Revenue	$11,517,892,326	$10,987,997,184	$10,172,144,312	$9,330,092,287	$8,631,033,566
Total Expenses	11,280,192,702	10,409,152,064	9,685,250,847	8,900,701,029	8,316,968,289
COMMUNITY HEALTH INDICATORS PER 1000 POPULATION					
Total Population (in thousands)	5,634	5,619	5,602	5,576	5,539
Inpatient					
Beds	2.1	2.1	2.0	2.0	2.1
Admissions	126.3	124.2	123.2	121.9	119.4
Inpatient Days	585.6	577.2	565.4	571.7	575.8
Inpatient Surgeries	34.9	34.8	34.3	33.8	34.3
Births	13.1	12.8	12.3	12.2	12.3
Outpatient					
Emergency Outpatient Visits	405.1	406.7	410.4	387.4	390.4
Other Outpatient Visits	1,029.7	892.8	840.5	823.3	861.1
Total Outpatient Visits	1,434.8	1,299.5	1,250.9	1,210.7	1,251.4
Outpatient Surgeries	63.1	62.4	62.4	64.1	65.3
Expense per Capita (per person)	$2,021.8	$1,872.3	$1,748.3	$1,614.0	$1,521.0

TABLE 6

MASSACHUSETTS

U.S. Registered Community Hospitals
(Nonfederal, short-term general and other special hospitals)

Overview 2004–2008

	2008	2007	2006	2005	2004
Total Community Hospitals in Massachusetts..	75	78	80	80	78
Bed Size Category					
6-24	6	5	6	5	2
25-49	7	7	7	11	13
50-99	11	14	12	10	8
100-199	22	23	25	23	25
200-299	11	11	14	17	13
300-399	9	8	8	6	9
400-499	2	3	1	1	1
500 + ...	7	7	7	7	7
Location					
Hospitals Urban............................	73	76	78	78	67
Hospitals Rural	2	2	2	2	11
Control					
State and Local Government................	2	3	3	3	3
Not for Profit	65	67	67	67	66
Investor owned	8	8	10	10	9
Physician Models					
Independent Practice Association	21	25	30	33	30
Group Practice without Walls................	2	2	6	8	7
Open Physician-Hospital Organization	15	15	15	15	18
Closed Physician-Hospital Organization	6	10	11	9	6
Management Service Organization	10	10	10	11	12
Integrated Salary Model.....................	30	30	37	36	37
Equity Model	4	4	4	3	2
Foundation...............................	4	7	7	7	4
Insurance Products					
Health Maintenance Organization	6	11	11	11	10
Preferred Provider Organization..............	3	9	8	8	7
Indemnity Fee for Service	1	6	4	4	3
Managed Care Contracts					
Health Maintenance Organization	48	53	64	65	61
Preferred Provider Organization..............	45	52	59	61	58
Affiliations					
Hospitals in a System......................	39	39	42	38	37
Hospitals in a Network.....................	22	24	25	27	25
Hospitals in a Group Purchasing Organization..	58	60	62	56	52

TABLE 6

MASSACHUSETTS

U.S. Registered Community Hospitals
(Nonfederal, short-term general and other special hospitals)

Utilization, Personnel, Revenue and Expenses, Community Health Indicators 2004–2008

	2008	2007	2006	2005	2004
TOTAL FACILITY (Includes Hospital and Nursing Home Units)					
Utilization - Inpatient					
Beds	15,710	16,496	16,311	16,213	16,215
Admissions	808,489	842,417	834,895	799,653	801,137
Inpatient Days	4,190,441	4,391,528	4,432,313	4,386,690	4,428,800
Average Length of Stay	5.2	5.2	5.3	5.5	5.5
Inpatient Surgeries	216,569	229,481	201,727	222,012	209,418
Births	77,002	77,250	94,228	99,215	79,299
Utilization - Outpatient					
Emergency Outpatient Visits	3,119,580	3,187,172	3,139,255	2,866,187	2,874,936
Other Outpatient Visits	17,340,178	16,393,033	16,404,673	15,998,978	16,161,749
Total Outpatient Visits	20,459,758	19,580,205	19,543,928	18,865,165	19,036,685
Outpatient Surgeries	451,925	462,064	515,027	507,335	543,250
Personnel					
Full Time RNs	20,635	20,433	17,773	17,644	17,751
Full Time LPNs	857	935	873	907	1,101
Part Time RNs	21,666	21,460	20,521	19,190	18,435
Part Time LPNs	814	905	827	1,280	971
Total Full Time	108,893	106,269	95,358	91,708	94,873
Total Part Time	64,047	64,652	61,747	56,704	54,831
Revenue - Inpatient					
Gross Inpatient Revenue	$21,768,649,075	$21,032,291,099	$18,131,480,820	$16,062,562,936	$16,030,894,805
Revenue - Outpatient					
Gross Outpatient Revenue	$22,264,309,254	$20,101,218,739	$18,765,595,188	$16,256,621,729	$14,502,126,803
Revenue and Expenses - Totals					
(Includes Inpatient and Outpatient)					
Total Gross Revenue	$44,032,958,329	$41,133,509,838	$36,897,076,008	$32,319,184,665	$30,533,021,608
Deductions from Revenue	25,449,205,856	23,579,085,229	20,747,996,172	17,830,536,310	17,030,539,095
Net Patient Revenue	18,583,752,473	17,554,424,609	16,149,079,836	14,488,648,355	13,502,482,513
Other Operating Revenue	2,794,111,079	2,603,492,463	2,378,723,094	1,919,801,409	1,999,130,082
Other Nonoperating Revenue	(71,544,749)	710,404,019	410,670,072	246,123,264	257,876,135
Total Net Revenue	21,306,318,803	20,868,321,091	18,938,473,002	16,654,573,028	15,759,488,730
Total Expenses	20,772,347,640	19,480,349,556	18,075,916,295	16,079,248,699	15,124,176,850
HOSPITAL UNIT (Excludes Separate Nursing Home Units)					
Utilization - Inpatient					
Beds	15,586	16,311	15,959	15,552	15,565
Admissions	805,960	837,201	824,881	788,780	790,876
Inpatient Days	4,156,756	4,324,089	4,316,301	4,176,350	4,220,730
Average Length of Stay	5.2	5.2	5.2	5.3	5.3
Personnel					
Total Full Time	108,805	106,159	95,080	91,414	93,735
Total Part Time	63,855	64,470	61,339	56,275	53,268
Revenue and Expenses - Totals					
(Includes Inpatient and Outpatient)					
Total Net Revenue	$21,279,253,160	$20,834,366,846	$18,830,494,898	$16,584,625,538	$15,695,985,452
Total Expenses	20,753,005,237	19,457,179,959	18,007,708,627	16,036,372,144	15,066,414,424
COMMUNITY HEALTH INDICATORS PER 1000 POPULATION					
Total Population (in thousands)	6,498	6,468	6,443	6,434	6,437
Inpatient					
Beds	2.4	2.6	2.5	2.5	2.5
Admissions	124.4	130.2	129.6	124.3	124.5
Inpatient Days	644.9	679.0	687.9	681.8	688.0
Inpatient Surgeries	33.3	35.5	31.3	34.5	32.5
Births	11.9	11.9	14.6	15.4	12.3
Outpatient					
Emergency Outpatient Visits	480.1	492.8	487.2	445.5	446.6
Other Outpatient Visits	2,668.6	2,534.5	2,546.0	2,486.5	2,510.6
Total Outpatient Visits	3,148.6	3,027.3	3,033.2	2,931.9	2,957.2
Outpatient Surgeries	69.5	71.4	79.9	78.8	84.4
Expense per Capita (per person)	$3,196.7	$3,011.8	$2,805.3	$2,499.0	$2,349.4

States

TABLE 6

U.S. Registered Community Hospitals
(Nonfederal, short-term general and other special hospitals)

Overview 2004–2008

	2008	2007	2006	2005	2004
Total Community Hospitals in Michigan.......	153	143	142	146	144
Bed Size Category					
6-24	9	8	10	11	11
25-49	40	30	25	25	21
50-99	39	42	41	45	47
100-199	20	18	21	20	20
200-299	15	15	16	14	14
300-399	14	13	12	16	16
400-499	6	7	6	5	4
500 + ...	10	10	11	10	11
Location					
Hospitals Urban..........................	94	84	84	87	85
Hospitals Rural	59	59	58	59	59
Control					
State and Local Government................	15	16	17	18	18
Not for Profit	123	123	120	124	122
Investor owned	15	4	5	4	4
Physician Models					
Independent Practice Association	13	13	12	16	15
Group Practice without Walls...............	5	4	6	5	8
Open Physician-Hospital Organization	41	40	36	39	46
Closed Physician-Hospital Organization	14	17	19	17	15
Management Service Organization	12	15	16	23	19
Integrated Salary Model....................	85	81	70	69	66
Equity Model	0	2	2	2	2
Foundation...............................	7	7	8	8	9
Insurance Products					
Health Maintenance Organization	40	42	49	51	49
Preferred Provider Organization..............	42	49	61	61	60
Indemnity Fee for Service	16	15	17	21	17
Managed Care Contracts					
Health Maintenance Organization	117	110	111	106	110
Preferred Provider Organization..............	123	116	113	113	116
Affiliations					
Hospitals in a System.....................	89	79	74	77	76
Hospitals in a Network	71	66	64	66	63
Hospitals in a Group Purchasing Organization..	132	128	128	128	122

States

TABLE 6

MICHIGAN

U.S. Registered Community Hospitals
(Nonfederal, short-term general and other special hospitals)

Utilization, Personnel, Revenue and Expenses, Community Health Indicators 2004–2008

	2008	2007	2006	2005	2004
TOTAL FACILITY (Includes Hospital and Nursing Home Units)					
Utilization - Inpatient					
Beds	25,272	25,306	25,016	25,214	25,950
Admissions	1,221,970	1,204,263	1,205,481	1,198,076	1,190,293
Inpatient Days	6,350,025	6,275,096	6,245,033	6,412,561	6,279,987
Average Length of Stay	5.2	5.2	5.2	5.4	5.3
Inpatient Surgeries	370,118	347,370	349,826	349,441	354,425
Births	118,965	122,072	123,600	124,808	127,666
Utilization - Outpatient					
Emergency Outpatient Visits	4,428,070	4,468,623	4,326,912	4,177,255	4,155,147
Other Outpatient Visits	23,570,226	23,417,840	23,798,191	21,972,261	23,580,862
Total Outpatient Visits	27,998,296	27,886,463	28,125,103	26,149,516	27,736,009
Outpatient Surgeries	707,236	726,158	755,353	769,424	780,943
Personnel					
Full Time RNs	33,536	32,510	30,490	29,501	27,994
Full Time LPNs	1,770	1,772	1,770	2,006	1,990
Part Time RNs	18,989	19,064	19,793	18,959	18,418
Part Time LPNs	1,156	1,151	1,241	1,420	1,518
Total Full Time	139,918	139,154	135,402	132,063	127,386
Total Part Time	65,331	63,156	65,321	63,532	62,069
Revenue - Inpatient					
Gross Inpatient Revenue	$29,869,338,749	$27,912,729,445	$26,450,363,373	$24,395,111,754	$22,587,070,811
Revenue - Outpatient					
Gross Outpatient Revenue	$26,487,242,565	$24,527,347,942	$22,637,487,899	$19,689,965,942	$17,786,301,382
Revenue and Expenses - Totals (Includes Inpatient and Outpatient)					
Total Gross Revenue	$56,356,581,314	$52,440,077,387	$49,087,851,272	$44,085,077,696	$40,373,372,193
Deductions from Revenue	33,607,413,797	31,030,821,925	28,905,181,590	25,570,765,697	23,170,867,760
Net Patient Revenue	22,749,167,517	21,409,255,462	20,182,669,682	18,514,311,999	17,202,504,433
Other Operating Revenue	1,094,570,561	1,094,719,240	1,018,637,486	888,745,004	811,237,389
Other Nonoperating Revenue	(268,360,656)	919,654,570	566,746,298	441,671,050	400,368,184
Total Net Revenue	23,575,377,422	23,423,629,272	21,768,053,466	19,844,728,053	18,414,110,006
Total Expenses	23,392,920,738	21,728,603,773	20,701,788,855	18,818,318,860	17,506,296,112
HOSPITAL UNIT (Excludes Separate Nursing Home Units)					
Utilization - Inpatient					
Beds	23,838	23,682	24,542	24,282	24,243
Admissions	1,217,600	1,199,366	1,201,976	1,192,956	1,186,198
Inpatient Days	5,868,107	5,699,371	5,766,423	5,811,312	5,779,770
Average Length of Stay	4.8	4.8	4.8	4.9	4.9
Personnel					
Total Full Time	138,950	138,010	134,441	130,712	125,902
Total Part Time	64,550	62,250	64,532	62,686	61,210
Revenue and Expenses - Totals (Includes Inpatient and Outpatient)					
Total Net Revenue	$23,455,611,994	$23,302,680,432	$21,641,889,153	$19,696,234,106	$18,292,566,711
Total Expenses	23,316,518,420	21,640,135,083	20,619,312,307	18,683,610,130	17,436,971,373
COMMUNITY HEALTH INDICATORS PER 1000 POPULATION					
Total Population (in thousands)	10,003	10,050	10,084	10,093	10,090
Inpatient					
Beds	2.5	2.5	2.6	2.6	2.6
Admissions	122.2	119.8	119.5	118.7	118.0
Inpatient Days	634.8	624.4	619.3	635.3	622.4
Inpatient Surgeries	37.0	34.6	34.7	34.6	35.1
Births	11.9	12.1	12.3	12.4	12.7
Outpatient					
Emergency Outpatient Visits	442.7	444.6	429.1	413.9	411.8
Other Outpatient Visits	2,356.2	2,330.2	2,360.0	2,176.9	2,337.0
Total Outpatient Visits	2,798.9	2,774.8	2,789.1	2,590.8	2,748.8
Outpatient Surgeries	70.7	72.3	74.9	76.2	77.4
Expense per Capita (per person)	$2,338.5	$2,162.1	$2,053.0	$1,864.4	$1,735.0

States

TABLE 6

MINNESOTA

U.S. Registered Community Hospitals
(Nonfederal, short-term general and other special hospitals)

Overview 2004–2008

	2008	2007	2006	2005	2004
Total Community Hospitals in Minnesota......	130	131	131	133	132
Bed Size Category					
6-24	17	18	17	18	17
25-49	25	25	23	23	23
50-99	37	36	40	38	36
100-199	35	36	35	38	40
200-299	4	4	4	4	4
300-399	4	3	4	5	5
400-499	5	6	5	4	4
500 + ...	3	3	3	3	3
Location					
Hospitals Urban...........................	49	49	49	50	46
Hospitals Rural	81	82	82	83	86
Control					
State and Local Government................	37	40	40	41	41
Not for Profit	93	91	91	91	91
Investor owned	0	0	0	1	0
Physician Models					
Independent Practice Association	20	25	28	27	30
Group Practice without Walls...............	2	4	5	4	5
Open Physician-Hospital Organization	11	9	9	10	9
Closed Physician-Hospital Organization	3	5	5	8	7
Management Service Organization	2	1	3	4	4
Integrated Salary Model....................	47	44	42	38	41
Equity Model	1	1	1	1	2
Foundation...............................	2	1	1	2	3
Insurance Products					
Health Maintenance Organization	9	8	11	13	13
Preferred Provider Organization..............	14	12	16	17	15
Indemnity Fee for Service	4	1	3	4	4
Managed Care Contracts					
Health Maintenance Organization	51	53	53	55	63
Preferred Provider Organization..............	55	58	59	61	70
Affiliations					
Hospitals in a System......................	69	70	70	71	68
Hospitals in a Network.....................	24	25	28	24	25
Hospitals in a Group Purchasing Organization..	91	92	95	85	92

TABLE 6

MINNESOTA

U.S. Registered Community Hospitals
(Nonfederal, short-term general and other special hospitals)

Utilization, Personnel, Revenue and Expenses, Community Health Indicators 2004–2008

	2008	2007	2006	2005	2004
TOTAL FACILITY (Includes Hospital and Nursing Home Units)					
Utilization - Inpatient					
Beds	15,001	15,000	15,040	15,993	16,101
Admissions	640,976	635,133	633,225	635,162	626,693
Inpatient Days	3,873,690	3,929,879	3,955,503	4,020,255	4,004,183
Average Length of Stay............	6.0	6.2	6.2	6.3	6.4
Inpatient Surgeries................	186,775	186,218	182,856	204,762	190,791
Births........................	69,360	70,789	71,999	70,784	69,799
Utilization - Outpatient					
Emergency Outpatient Visits........	1,772,982	1,727,682	1,711,528	1,717,155	1,558,720
Other Outpatient Visits.............	8,233,087	8,125,800	8,397,658	7,725,310	7,971,965
Total Outpatient Visits	10,006,069	9,853,482	10,109,186	9,442,465	9,530,685
Outpatient Surgeries	294,628	299,076	300,661	300,667	298,323
Personnel					
Full Time RNs	9,744	9,704	8,980	8,609	8,440
Full Time LPNs	1,365	1,429	1,481	1,477	1,436
Part Time RNs..................	22,355	20,379	20,193	21,070	17,218
Part Time LPNs	2,031	2,206	2,300	2,354	2,293
Total Full Time..................	51,432	50,937	48,647	47,471	46,782
Total Part Time	64,764	58,808	59,057	61,469	51,444
Revenue - Inpatient					
Gross Inpatient Revenue...........	$17,008,252,322	$15,698,619,417	$14,591,084,241	$13,866,748,412	$12,319,629,780
Revenue - Outpatient					
Gross Outpatient Revenue	$12,005,677,625	$11,064,301,671	$10,131,993,797	$9,152,203,023	$7,932,681,220
Revenue and Expenses - Totals					
(Includes Inpatient and Outpatient)					
Total Gross Revenue..............	$29,013,929,947	$26,762,921,088	$24,723,078,038	$23,018,951,435	$20,252,311,000
Deductions from Revenue..........	16,742,727,027	15,261,878,579	13,936,215,046	12,923,611,920	11,069,414,757
Net Patient Revenue	12,271,202,920	11,501,042,509	10,786,862,992	10,095,339,515	9,182,896,243
Other Operating Revenue	615,406,723	596,121,525	579,265,096	513,674,553	483,299,164
Other Nonoperating Revenue	(172,569,600)	316,210,452	241,843,240	131,543,838	125,102,720
Total Net Revenue...............	12,714,040,043	12,413,374,486	11,607,971,328	10,740,557,906	9,791,298,127
Total Expenses..................	12,401,406,555	11,693,354,628	10,886,427,005	10,169,803,966	9,202,353,673
HOSPITAL UNIT (Excludes Separate Nursing Home Units)					
Utilization - Inpatient					
Beds	12,837	12,895	12,729	12,969	12,881
Admissions	637,183	631,175	629,069	630,577	621,925
Inpatient Days	2,943,441	2,927,784	2,901,267	2,987,706	2,888,972
Average Length of Stay............	4.6	4.6	4.6	4.7	4.6
Personnel					
Total Full Time..................	50,078	49,542	47,079	45,979	44,919
Total Part Time	62,661	56,612	56,638	59,124	48,693
Revenue and Expenses - Totals					
(Includes Inpatient and Outpatient)					
Total Net Revenue...............	$12,531,828,490	$12,245,206,091	$11,431,135,431	$10,568,197,592	$9,614,263,388
Total Expenses..................	12,221,469,706	11,521,791,897	10,704,577,635	9,999,347,164	9,023,305,159
COMMUNITY HEALTH INDICATORS PER 1000 POPULATION					
Total Population (in thousands)	5,220	5,182	5,143	5,105	5,078
Inpatient					
Beds	3.0	3.1	3.1	3.1	3.2
Admissions	122.8	122.6	123.1	124.4	123.4
Inpatient Days	742.0	758.3	769.1	787.5	788.5
Inpatient Surgeries...............	35.8	35.9	35.6	40.1	37.6
Births........................	13.3	13.7	14.0	13.9	13.7
Outpatient					
Emergency Outpatient Visits........	339.6	333.4	332.8	336.4	307.0
Other Outpatient Visits.............	1,577.1	1,568.0	1,632.8	1,513.3	1,569.9
Total Outpatient Visits	1,916.7	1,901.4	1,965.6	1,849.7	1,876.9
Outpatient Surgeries	56.4	57.7	58.5	58.9	58.7
Expense per Capita (per person).....	$2,375.6	$2,256.4	$2,116.7	$1,992.2	$1,812.2

States

TABLE 6

MISSISSIPPI

U.S. Registered Community Hospitals
(Nonfederal, short-term general and other special hospitals)

Overview 2004–2008

	2008	2007	2006	2005	2004
Total Community Hospitals in Mississippi	98	95	94	94	93
Bed Size Category					
6-24	2	2	1	1	1
25-49	31	30	28	26	25
50-99	25	25	26	25	23
100-199	23	22	24	27	29
200-299	6	4	4	3	4
300-399	3	4	3	7	4
400-499	3	3	3	1	2
500 + ...	5	5	5	4	5
Location					
Hospitals Urban	29	26	27	27	19
Hospitals Rural	69	69	67	67	74
Control					
State and Local Government	41	42	41	41	42
Not for Profit	30	29	29	29	25
Investor owned	27	24	24	24	26
Physician Models					
Independent Practice Association	6	6	7	6	9
Group Practice without Walls	2	2	4	4	3
Open Physician-Hospital Organization	16	18	18	21	8
Closed Physician-Hospital Organization	5	2	2	1	0
Management Service Organization	7	7	9	10	1
Integrated Salary Model	22	16	19	19	7
Equity Model	1	0	1	2	0
Foundation	6	7	7	8	2
Insurance Products					
Health Maintenance Organization	8	7	7	8	1
Preferred Provider Organization	38	40	43	39	7
Indemnity Fee for Service	12	9	10	11	2
Managed Care Contracts					
Health Maintenance Organization	14	8	6	1	6
Preferred Provider Organization	37	26	28	20	20
Affiliations					
Hospitals in a System	42	39	39	41	38
Hospitals in a Network	30	31	32	31	35
Hospitals in a Group Purchasing Organization . .	1	10	24	31	31

TABLE 6

MISSISSIPPI

U.S. Registered Community Hospitals
(Nonfederal, short-term general and other special hospitals)

Utilization, Personnel, Revenue and Expenses, Community Health Indicators 2004–2008

	2008	2007	2006	2005	2004
TOTAL FACILITY (Includes Hospital and Nursing Home Units)					
Utilization - Inpatient					
Beds	13,094	12,712	12,973	l2,753	13,143
Admissions	430,680	417,929	415,577	414,373	427,401
Inpatient Days	2,807,964	2,675,307	2,697,952	2,679,961	2,771,304
Average Length of Stay	6.5	6.4	6.5	6.5	6.5
Inpatient Surgeries	113,847	115,564	122,509	116,048	122,339
Births	43,775	44,650	42,729	43,202	40,431
Utilization - Outpatient					
Emergency Outpatient Visits	1,694,645	1,736,141	1,650,523	1,665,894	1,602,016
Other Outpatient Visits	3,320,962	2,688,325	2,567,848	2,427,582	2,613,026
Total Outpatient Visits	5,015,607	4,424,466	4,218,371	4,093,476	4,215,042
Outpatient Surgeries	173,799	176,076	162,127	146,338	150,301
Personnel					
Full Time RNs	11,143	10,987	10,092	10,552	9,881
Full Time LPNs	1,726	1,799	1,803	1,742	1,929
Part Time RNs	3,757	3,670	3,583	3,493	3,757
Part Time LPNs	487	502	475	525	629
Total Full Time	46,424	45,895	43,338	42,140	42,182
Total Part Time	12,158	11,902	11,648	11,124	12,109
Revenue - Inpatient					
Gross Inpatient Revenue	$11,036,455,713	$9,436,579,499	$8,470,744,247	$7,660,349,400	$7,255,099,763
Revenue - Outpatient					
Gross Outpatient Revenue	$7,520,162,560	$6,352,192,000	$5,402,234,688	$4,830,456,007	$4,286,884,357
Revenue and Expenses - Totals					
(Includes Inpatient and Outpatient)					
Total Gross Revenue	$18,556,618,273	$15,788,771,499	$13,872,978,935	$12,490,805,407	$11,541,984,120
Deductions from Revenue	12,632,981,913	10,466,830,159	8,822,388,239	7,955,298,330	6,899,022,514
Net Patient Revenue	5,923,636,360	5,321,941,340	5,050,590,696	4,535,507,077	4,642,961,606
Other Operating Revenue	319,430,782	335,839,429	231,893,393	193,477,120	163,436,087
Other Nonoperating Revenue	36,224,687	126,182,224	62,006,706	71,401,765	63,508,641
Total Net Revenue	6,279,291,829	5,783,962,993	5,344,490,795	4,800,385,962	4,869,906,334
Total Expenses	5,817,368,267	5,702,007,832	5,237,172,195	4,738,973,161	4,470,158,941
HOSPITAL UNIT (Excludes Separate Nursing Home Units)					
Utilization - Inpatient					
Beds	11,401	11,013	11,247	11,190	11,695
Admissions	429,960	417,221	414,554	413,368	426,552
Inpatient Days	2,233,999	2,088,193	2,123,492	2,153,451	2,297,184
Average Length of Stay	5.2	5.0	5.1	5.2	5.4
Personnel					
Total Full Time	45,125	44,537	41,925	40,919	36,915
Total Part Time	11,832	11,547	11,290	10,802	11,523
Revenue and Expenses - Totals					
(Includes Inpatient and Outpatient)					
Total Net Revenue	$6,211,348,322	$5,699,630,012	$5,251,964,574	$4,752,934,290	$4,815,226,678
Total Expenses	5,767,228,058	5,640,280,980	5,189,913,198	4,700,533,201	4,429,693,154
COMMUNITY HEALTH INDICATORS PER 1000 POPULATION					
Total Population (in thousands)	2,939	2,921	2,897	2,898	2,885
Inpatient					
Beds	4.5	4.4	4.5	4.4	4.6
Admissions	146.6	143.1	143.5	143.0	148.2
Inpatient Days	955.5	915.9	931.4	924.7	960.7
Inpatient Surgeries	38.7	39.6	42.3	40.0	42.4
Births	14.9	15.3	14.8	14.9	14.0
Outpatient					
Emergency Outpatient Visits	576.7	594.4	569.8	574.8	555.4
Other Outpatient Visits	1,130.1	920.3	886.5	837.6	905.9
Total Outpatient Visits	1,706.8	1,514.7	1,456.3	1,412.4	1,461.2
Outpatient Surgeries	59.1	60.3	56.0	50.5	52.1
Expense per Capita (per person)	$1,979.6	$1,952.1	$1,808.0	$1,635.1	$1,549.7

TABLE 6

MISSOURI

U.S. Registered Community Hospitals
(Nonfederal, short-term general and other special hospitals)

Overview 2004–2008

	2008	2007	2006	2005	2004
Total Community Hospitals in Missouri	123	117	119	119	119
Bed Size Category					
6-24	8	5	5	7	6
25-49	38	36	36	32	33
50-99	19	17	18	19	21
100-199	26	27	28	28	23
200-299	12	15	13	14	17
300-399	9	7	9	9	8
400-499	5	4	4	4	5
500 + ...	6	6	6	6	6
Location					
Hospitals Urban.............................	70	64	66	66	61
Hospitals Rural	53	53	53	53	58
Control					
State and Local Government................	35	35	36	36	36
Not for Profit	62	61	62	63	64
Investor owned	26	21	21	20	19
Physician Models					
Independent Practice Association	10	13	13	17	15
Group Practice without Walls................	0	0	1	2	3
Open Physician-Hospital Organization	14	14	19	21	18
Closed Physician-Hospital Organization	8	7	9	10	13
Management Service Organization	2	4	5	5	4
Integrated Salary Model.....................	66	65	59	59	60
Equity Model	1	0	0	0	0
Foundation.................................	3	3	2	2	3
Insurance Products					
Health Maintenance Organization	16	16	19	20	21
Preferred Provider Organization..............	14	14	14	15	15
Indemnity Fee for Service	5	5	7	7	6
Managed Care Contracts					
Health Maintenance Organization	97	99	99	104	102
Preferred Provider Organization..............	106	107	107	111	111
Affiliations					
Hospitals in a System......................	72	66	68	69	67
Hospitals in a Network.....................	38	40	40	34	35
Hospitals in a Group Purchasing Organization..	115	114	114	114	113

TABLE 6

MISSOURI

U.S. Registered Community Hospitals
(Nonfederal, short-term general and other special hospitals)

Utilization, Personnel, Revenue and Expenses, Community Health Indicators 2004–2008

	2008	2007	2006	2005	2004
TOTAL FACILITY (Includes Hospital and Nursing Home Units)					
Utilization - Inpatient					
Beds	18,968	18,454	18,888	19,146	19,131
Admissions	841,118	833,114	830,882	836,179	831,892
Inpatient Days	4,396,779	4,310,130	4,331,742	4,421,138	4,407,818
Average Length of Stay	5.2	5.2	5.2	5.3	5.3
Inpatient Surgeries	222,378	220,098	219,027	210,112	216,568
Births	80,282	79,940	79,240	77,542	77,638
Utilization - Outpatient					
Emergency Outpatient Visits	2,860,410	2,677,716	2,641,586	2,617,778	2,561,625
Other Outpatient Visits	15,968,175	14,297,938	13,696,600	14,595,386	13,624,807
Total Outpatient Visits	18,828,585	16,975,654	16,338,186	17,213,164	16,186,432
Outpatient Surgeries	377,592	378,013	384,189	398,992	397,142
Personnel					
Full Time RNs	24,084	23,139	21,839	20,275	19,212
Full Time LPNs	2,711	2,719	2,811	2,849	2,950
Part Time RNs	12,367	11,264	11,942	11,598	11,774
Part Time LPNs	837	922	1,001	1,069	1,133
Total Full Time	96,722	93,628	92,126	90,985	88,747
Total Part Time	36,336	34,771	35,565	36,195	36,403
Revenue - Inpatient					
Gross Inpatient Revenue	$22,713,673,771	$20,986,021,738	$19,488,280,323	$18,091,147,295	$16,624,521,378
Revenue - Outpatient					
Gross Outpatient Revenue	$17,415,385,697	$15,502,302,919	$13,820,205,178	$12,666,683,321	$11,220,642,518
Revenue and Expenses - Totals					
(Includes Inpatient and Outpatient)					
Total Gross Revenue	$40,129,059,468	$36,488,324,657	$33,308,485,501	$30,757,830,616	$27,845,163,896
Deductions from Revenue	24,102,018,264	22,479,673,810	20,127,195,935	18,464,345,424	16,534,751,958
Net Patient Revenue	16,027,041,204	14,008,650,847	13,181,289,566	12,293,485,192	11,310,411,938
Other Operating Revenue	985,155,809	969,705,284	882,120,238	646,016,294	745,387,376
Other Nonoperating Revenue	(360,477,386)	443,559,855	414,857,246	245,980,140	314,383,075
Total Net Revenue	16,651,719,627	15,421,915,986	14,478,267,050	13,185,481,626	12,370,182,389
Total Expenses	15,824,162,545	14,391,329,687	13,503,914,459	12,612,917,341	11,559,349,647
HOSPITAL UNIT (Excludes Separate Nursing Home Units)					
Utilization - Inpatient					
Beds	17,970	17,293	17,664	17,767	17,735
Admissions	834,653	824,907	820,375	825,255	819,702
Inpatient Days	4,109,631	3,971,643	3,966,608	4,022,789	4,040,112
Average Length of Stay	4.9	4.8	4.8	4.9	4.9
Personnel					
Total Full Time	96,023	92,704	91,235	89,670	87,147
Total Part Time	35,963	34,258	35,082	35,617	35,705
Revenue and Expenses - Totals					
(Includes Inpatient and Outpatient)					
Total Net Revenue	$16,539,007,342	$15,292,838,772	$14,267,051,695	$13,071,840,233	$12,222,272,066
Total Expenses	15,727,570,466	14,270,140,082	13,315,304,412	12,505,733,147	11,428,018,346
COMMUNITY HEALTH INDICATORS PER 1000 POPULATION					
Total Population (in thousands)	5,912	5,878	5,833	5,785	5,743
Inpatient					
Beds	3.2	3.1	3.2	3.3	3.3
Admissions	142.3	141.7	142.4	144.5	144.9
Inpatient Days	743.8	733.2	742.6	764.2	767.6
Inpatient Surgeries	37.6	37.4	37.5	36.3	37.7
Births	13.6	13.6	13.6	13.4	13.5
Outpatient					
Emergency Outpatient Visits	483.9	455.5	452.9	452.5	446.1
Other Outpatient Visits	2,701.2	2,432.3	2,348.1	2,522.9	2,372.6
Total Outpatient Visits	3,185.0	2,887.8	2,801.0	2,975.4	2,818.6
Outpatient Surgeries	63.9	64.3	65.9	69.0	69.2
Expense per Capita (per person)	$2,676.8	$2,448.2	$2,315.1	$2,180.2	$2,012.9

States

TABLE 6

MONTANA

U.S. Registered Community Hospitals
(Nonfederal, short-term general and other special hospitals)

Overview 2004–2008

	2008	2007	2006	2005	2004
Total Community Hospitals in Montana	48	52	52	54	54
Bed Size Category					
6-24	9	9	10	9	10
25-49	14	15	15	16	15
50-99	15	17	14	16	17
100-199	7	8	10	10	8
200-299	1	1	1	1	2
300-399	1	1	1	1	1
400-499	1	1	1	1	1
500 + ...	0	0	0	0	0
Location					
Hospitals Urban..........................	5	6	6	6	3
Hospitals Rural	43	46	46	48	51
Control					
State and Local Government................	8	9	9	10	10
Not for Profit	39	42	42	44	44
Investor owned	1	1	1	0	0
Physician Models					
Independent Practice Association	9	10	9	10	9
Group Practice without Walls...............	3	3	2	2	3
Open Physician-Hospital Organization	6	7	8	8	8
Closed Physician-Hospital Organization	2	2	1	1	0
Management Service Organization	6	6	8	8	6
Integrated Salary Model....................	29	30	28	31	27
Equity Model	2	1	0	1	2
Foundation..............................	5	5	3	5	0
Insurance Products					
Health Maintenance Organization	4	5	7	6	5
Preferred Provider Organization..............	9	9	9	17	13
Indemnity Fee for Service	4	6	7	9	8
Managed Care Contracts					
Health Maintenance Organization	13	14	15	15	16
Preferred Provider Organization..............	27	31	29	32	31
Affiliations					
Hospitals in a System.....................	11	11	12	15	14
Hospitals in a Network	24	24	24	25	27
Hospitals in a Group Purchasing Organization..	47	48	48	50	48

TABLE 6

MONTANA

U.S. Registered Community Hospitals
(Nonfederal, short-term general and other special hospitals)

Utilization, Personnel, Revenue and Expenses, Community Health Indicators 2004–2008

	2008	2007	2006	2005	2004
TOTAL FACILITY (Includes Hospital and Nursing Home Units)					
Utilization - Inpatient					
Beds	3,765	4,002	4,080	4,200	4,007
Admissions	103,840	106,860	106,826	106,457	106,619
Inpatient Days	903,981	957,251	975,390	1,023,301	1,042,530
Average Length of Stay	8.7	9.0	9.1	9.6	9.8
Inpatient Surgeries	30,697	32,021	32,099	32,081	32,550
Births	10,708	10,714	10,681	10,426	10,418
Utilization - Outpatient					
Emergency Outpatient Visits	346,670	354,943	333,504	311,144	294,359
Other Outpatient Visits	2,807,604	2,680,087	2,568,374	2,548,342	2,600,951
Total Outpatient Visits	3,154,274	3,035,030	2,901,878	2,859,486	2,895,310
Outpatient Surgeries	45,012	43,987	44,129	37,910	38,428
Personnel					
Full Time RNs	2,496	2,654	2,508	2,333	2,304
Full Time LPNs	497	530	490	502	501
Part Time RNs	1,936	1,847	1,882	1,979	1,736
Part Time LPNs	328	330	315	351	335
Total Full Time	13,974	14,098	13,081	12,773	12,372
Total Part Time	7,358	7,091	7,059	7,325	6,612
Revenue - Inpatient					
Gross Inpatient Revenue	$1,868,192,302	$1,749,392,120	$1,669,626,014	$1,566,799,646	$1,442,716,805
Revenue - Outpatient					
Gross Outpatient Revenue	$1,879,526,779	$1,692,878,144	$1,490,075,406	$1,315,545,776	$1,159,001,092
Revenue and Expenses - Totals					
(Includes Inpatient and Outpatient)					
Total Gross Revenue	$3,747,719,081	$3,442,270,264	$3,159,701,420	$2,882,345,422	$2,601,717,897
Deductions from Revenue	1,670,030,190	1,497,426,748	1,333,944,188	1,215,530,442	1,068,216,515
Net Patient Revenue	2,077,688,891	1,944,843,516	1,825,757,232	1,666,814,980	1,533,501,382
Other Operating Revenue	80,597,184	82,175,840	69,888,745	67,644,799	69,423,086
Other Nonoperating Revenue	16,554,468	73,552,521	54,093,518	43,783,036	40,895,332
Total Net Revenue	2,174,840,543	2,100,571,877	1,949,739,495	1,778,242,815	1,643,819,800
Total Expenses	2,077,753,777	1,933,325,734	1,800,736,855	1,648,588,537	1,528,310,065
HOSPITAL UNIT (Excludes Separate Nursing Home Units)					
Utilization - Inpatient					
Beds	2,292	2,426	2,484	2,421	2,453
Admissions	101,233	103,637	103,686	103,371	103,105
Inpatient Days	440,713	465,512	471,793	460,351	482,021
Average Length of Stay	4.4	4.5	4.6	4.5	4.7
Personnel					
Total Full Time	12,999	13,047	11,960	11,620	11,127
Total Part Time	6,770	6,498	6,352	6,403	5,771
Revenue and Expenses - Totals					
(Includes Inpatient and Outpatient)					
Total Net Revenue	$2,092,696,080	$2,015,682,825	$1,870,972,965	$1,700,302,201	$1,565,817,386
Total Expenses	2,002,337,963	1,859,283,771	1,727,928,485	1,578,014,372	1,458,411,635
COMMUNITY HEALTH INDICATORS PER 1000 POPULATION					
Total Population (in thousands)	967	957	945	935	926
Inpatient					
Beds	3.9	4.2	4.3	4.6	4.7
Admissions	107.3	111.7	113.0	113.9	115.1
Inpatient Days	934.4	1,000.7	1,031.7	1,094.6	1,125.9
Inpatient Surgeries	31.7	33.5	34.0	34.3	35.2
Births	11.1	11.2	11.3	11.2	11.3
Outpatient					
Emergency Outpatient Visits	358.3	371.0	352.8	332.8	317.9
Other Outpatient Visits	2,902.1	2,801.6	2,716.6	2,725.8	2,808.9
Total Outpatient Visits	3,260.4	3,172.6	3,069.4	3,058.6	3,126.8
Outpatient Surgeries	46.5	46.0	46.7	40.6	41.5
Expense per Capita (per person)	$2,147.7	$2,021.0	$1,904.7	$1,763.4	$1,650.5

States

TABLE 6

NEBRASKA

U.S. Registered Community Hospitals
(Nonfederal, short-term general and other special hospitals)

Overview 2004–2008

	2008	2007	2006	2005	2004
Total Community Hospitals in Nebraska.......	86	85	85	87	85
Bed Size Category					
6-24	21	18	19	22	22
25-49	23	26	24	23	22
50-99	23	22	23	22	20
100-199	7	8	8	8	10
200-299	7	4	6	7	6
300-399	4	5	3	3	3
400-499	0	1	1	1	1
500 + ...	1	1	1	1	1
Location					
Hospitals Urban..........................	16	16	16	17	13
Hospitals Rural	70	69	69	70	72
Control					
State and Local Government................	38	40	40	40	39
Not for Profit	46	43	43	45	44
Investor owned	2	2	2	2	2
Physician Models					
Independent Practice Association	8	6	7	7	8
Group Practice without Walls................	2	3	3	3	3
Open Physician-Hospital Organization	13	13	13	13	11
Closed Physician-Hospital Organization	0	0	0	0	0
Management Service Organization	3	3	3	2	1
Integrated Salary Model....................	32	31	37	33	31
Equity Model	0	0	0	0	0
Foundation...............................	2	2	0	2	1
Insurance Products					
Health Maintenance Organization	3	4	5	4	5
Preferred Provider Organization..............	14	19	20	19	19
Indemnity Fee for Service	4	4	3	3	3
Managed Care Contracts					
Health Maintenance Organization	19	21	23	23	21
Preferred Provider Organization..............	53	53	58	52	54
Affiliations					
Hospitals in a System......................	29	28	26	27	26
Hospitals in a Network.....................	36	38	44	42	43
Hospitals in a Group Purchasing Organization..	56	57	66	60	62

TABLE 6

NEBRASKA

U.S. Registered Community Hospitals
(Nonfederal, short-term general and other special hospitals)

Utilization, Personnel, Revenue and Expenses, Community Health Indicators 2004–2008

	2008	2007	2006	2005	2004
TOTAL FACILITY (Includes Hospital and Nursing Home Units)					
Utilization - Inpatient					
Beds	7,264	7,468	7,375	7,566	7,336
Admissions	214,808	214,628	215,219	214,240	211,025
Inpatient Days	1,562,960	1,619,546	1,666,078	1,757,311	1,612,857
Average Length of Stay.	7.3	7.5	7.7	8.2	7.6
Inpatient Surgeries.	71,248	68,537	67,255	69,536	71,164
Births.	26,802	26,659	26,226	25,725	25,986
Utilization - Outpatient					
Emergency Outpatient Visits	639,756	630,134	551,914	554,269	551,836
Other Outpatient Visits.	3,987,333	3,569,670	3,497,191	3,336,135	3,397,641
Total Outpatient Visits	4,627,089	4,199,804	4,049,105	3,890,404	3,949,477
Outpatient Surgeries	130,440	133,820	131,698	133,477	125,001
Personnel					
Full Time RNs	7,104	6,962	6,799	6,249	5,851
Full Time LPNs	913	906	1,039	1,050	1,049
Part Time RNs.	4,477	4,018	3,646	3,457	3,817
Part Time LPNs	530	550	590	624	657
Total Full Time.	27,407	27,636	27,907	26,636	25,601
Total Part Time	15,212	13,899	13,082	12,871	14,200
Revenue - Inpatient					
Gross Inpatient Revenue.	$5,994,545,329	$5,595,875,292	$5,152,084,912	$4,582,880,874	$4,120,664,079
Revenue - Outpatient					
Gross Outpatient Revenue	$4,349,628,655	$3,960,071,473	$3,474,072,754	$3,035,020,244	$2,616,253,431
Revenue and Expenses - Totals					
(Includes Inpatient and Outpatient)					
Total Gross Revenue.	$10,344,173,984	$9,555,946,765	$8,626,157,666	$7,617,901,118	$6,736,917,510
Deductions from Revenue.	5,885,164,745	5,361,837,259	4,630,561,170	3,976,606,980	3,385,802,054
Net Patient Revenue	4,459,009,239	4,194,109,506	3,995,596,496	3,641,294,138	3,351,114,556
Other Operating Revenue	210,752,208	186,903,385	192,326,079	184,632,186	157,573,205
Other Nonoperating Revenue	(24,908,037)	165,706,153	132,919,108	66,496,703	61,483,416
Total Net Revenue.	4,644,853,410	4,546,719,044	4,320,841,683	3,892,423,027	3,570,171,177
Total Expenses.	4,380,337,731	4,013,619,694	3,862,460,549	3,568,319,403	3,254,039,649
HOSPITAL UNIT (Excludes Separate Nursing Home Units)					
Utilization - Inpatient					
Beds	5,793	5,929	5,734	6,043	5,795
Admissions	211,021	211,109	211,591	210,663	207,634
Inpatient Days	1,117,877	1,157,386	1,151,365	1,261,063	1,152,562
Average Length of Stay.	5.3	5.5	5.4	6.0	5.6
Personnel					
Total Full Time.	26,467	26,664	26,795	25,596	24,552
Total Part Time	14,524	13,150	12,430	12,086	13,421
Revenue and Expenses - Totals					
(Includes Inpatient and Outpatient)					
Total Net Revenue.	$4,527,469,170	$4,444,144,173	$4,235,396,340	$3,814,957,460	$3,491,161,406
Total Expenses.	4,274,392,152	3,932,011,095	3,778,967,078	3,489,172,670	3,172,415,483
COMMUNITY HEALTH INDICATORS PER 1000 POPULATION					
Total Population (in thousands)	1,783	1,769	1,760	1,751	1,741
Inpatient					
Beds	4.1	4.2	4.2	4.3	4.2
Admissions	120.4	121.3	122.3	122.3	121.2
Inpatient Days	876.4	915.3	946.8	1,003.6	926.2
Inpatient Surgeries.	39.9	38.7	38.2	39.7	40.9
Births.	15.0	15.1	14.9	14.7	14.9
Outpatient					
Emergency Outpatient Visits	358.7	356.1	313.6	316.5	316.9
Other Outpatient Visits.	2,235.8	2,017.4	1,987.3	1,905.2	1,951.0
Total Outpatient Visits	2,594.5	2,373.5	2,300.9	2,221.7	2,267.9
Outpatient Surgeries	73.1	75.6	74.8	76.2	71.8
Expense per Capita (per person).	$2,456.1	$2,268.3	$2,194.9	$2,037.8	$1,868.6

States

TABLE 6

NEVADA

U.S. Registered Community Hospitals
(Nonfederal, short-term general and other special hospitals)

Overview 2004–2008

	2008	2007	2006	2005	2004
Total Community Hospitals in Nevada	35	33	33	32	30
Bed Size Category					
6-24	4	3	6	4	1
25-49	6	6	5	6	6
50-99	11	10	9	9	9
100-199	6	6	5	5	7
200-299	3	3	3	3	2
300-399	2	2	2	2	2
400-499	0	0	0	0	0
500 + ...	3	3	3	3	3
Location					
Hospitals Urban...........................	24	23	22	22	21
Hospitals Rural	11	10	11	10	9
Control					
State and Local Government...............	6	6	7	6	6
Not for Profit	13	13	11	11	10
Investor owned	16	14	15	15	14
Physician Models					
Independent Practice Association	3	3	4	3	2
Group Practice without Walls...............	0	0	0	0	1
Open Physician-Hospital Organization	0	1	3	3	2
Closed Physician-Hospital Organization	1	1	1	1	1
Management Service Organization	3	2	1	1	1
Integrated Salary Model....................	4	3	3	3	3
Equity Model............................	0	0	0	0	0
Foundation..............................	0	0	1	0	0
Insurance Products					
Health Maintenance Organization	4	4	3	4	4
Preferred Provider Organization..............	5	4	4	5	4
Indemnity Fee for Service	3	3	2	2	2
Managed Care Contracts					
Health Maintenance Organization	11	13	12	10	10
Preferred Provider Organization..............	14	13	16	10	13
Affiliations					
Hospitals in a System......................	24	22	21	20	19
Hospitals in a Network.....................	5	6	4	3	4
Hospitals in a Group Purchasing Organization..	18	17	17	14	11

States

TABLE 6

NEVADA

U.S. Registered Community Hospitals
(Nonfederal, short-term general and other special hospitals)

Utilization, Personnel, Revenue and Expenses, Community Health Indicators 2004–2008

	2008	2007	2006	2005	2004
TOTAL FACILITY (Includes Hospital and Nursing Home Units)					
Utilization - Inpatient					
Beds	5,144	5,051	4,826	4,685	4,752
Admissions	247,232	244,187	245,649	240,596	232,603
Inpatient Days	1,300,514	1,275,671	1,307,303	1,268,272	1,246,727
Average Length of Stay	5.3	5.2	5.3	5.3	5.4
Inpatient Surgeries	68,365	71,526	71,718	71,701	71,927
Births	29,248	30,441	32,737	31,210	29,196
Utilization - Outpatient					
Emergency Outpatient Visits	780,500	751,845	697,906	712,484	606,094
Other Outpatient Visits	2,135,809	1,903,945	1,689,902	1,901,170	1,839,386
Total Outpatient Visits	2,916,309	2,655,790	2,387,808	2,613,654	2,445,480
Outpatient Surgeries	100,526	90,820	83,381	96,495	106,988
Personnel					
Full Time RNs	6,457	6,112	5,317	5,290	5,163
Full Time LPNs	452	445	452	504	540
Part Time RNs	1,521	1,617	1,633	1,390	1,429
Part Time LPNs	83	88	111	77	100
Total Full Time	21,672	20,043	17,567	18,716	17,751
Total Part Time	3,766	4,061	4,255	3,716	3,799
Revenue - Inpatient					
Gross Inpatient Revenue	$10,133,945,714	$9,157,234,146	$8,318,719,056	$7,471,884,853	$6,156,363,442
Revenue - Outpatient					
Gross Outpatient Revenue	$4,647,890,751	$3,939,962,372	$3,245,923,076	$2,899,874,111	$2,529,847,264
Revenue and Expenses - Totals					
(Includes Inpatient and Outpatient)					
Total Gross Revenue	$14,781,836,465	$13,097,196,518	$11,564,642,132	$10,371,758,964	$8,686,210,706
Deductions from Revenue	10,926,597,214	9,514,175,359	8,554,764,914	7,387,212,650	5,805,707,829
Net Patient Revenue	3,855,239,251	3,583,021,159	3,009,877,218	2,984,546,314	2,880,502,877
Other Operating Revenue	94,718,637	93,358,804	79,167,789	79,622,920	103,442,479
Other Nonoperating Revenue	49,631,516	86,652,018	31,991,694	12,140,050	17,918,332
Total Net Revenue	3,999,589,404	3,763,031,981	3,121,036,701	3,076,309,284	3,001,863,688
Total Expenses	3,912,575,991	3,536,781,905	2,930,773,692	3,105,816,107	2,787,592,070
HOSPITAL UNIT (Excludes Separate Nursing Home Units)					
Utilization - Inpatient					
Beds	5,119	5,026	4,670	4,655	4,673
Admissions	247,208	244,175	245,070	240,224	232,527
Inpatient Days	1,293,475	1,267,602	1,257,697	1,257,630	1,220,754
Average Length of Stay	5.2	5.2	5.1	5.2	5.2
Personnel					
Total Full Time	21,651	20,025	17,471	18,696	17,707
Total Part Time	3,763	4,056	4,236	3,712	3,788
Revenue and Expenses - Totals					
(Includes Inpatient and Outpatient)					
Total Net Revenue	$3,997,480,744	$3,760,531,168	$3,112,151,041	$3,073,496,634	$2,998,131,909
Total Expenses	3,911,278,159	3,535,439,430	2,922,980,821	3,104,642,195	2,786,047,490
COMMUNITY HEALTH INDICATORS PER 1000 POPULATION					
Total Population (in thousands)	2,600	2,554	2,484	2,402	2,324
Inpatient					
Beds	2.0	2.0	1.9	2.0	2.0
Admissions	95.1	95.6	98.9	100.2	100.1
Inpatient Days	500.2	499.4	526.2	528.1	536.5
Inpatient Surgeries	26.3	28.0	28.9	29.9	31.0
Births	11.2	11.9	13.2	13.0	12.6
Outpatient					
Emergency Outpatient Visits	300.2	294.3	280.9	296.7	260.8
Other Outpatient Visits	821.4	745.4	680.3	791.6	791.5
Total Outpatient Visits	1,121.6	1,039.7	961.2	1,088.3	1,052.3
Outpatient Surgeries	38.7	35.6	33.6	40.2	46.0
Expense per Capita (per person)	$1,504.7	$1,384.6	$1,179.8	$1,293.2	$1,199.5

States

TABLE **6**

NEW HAMPSHIRE

U.S. Registered Community Hospitals
(Nonfederal, short-term general and other special hospitals)

Overview 2004–2008

	2008	2007	2006	2005	2004
Total Community Hospitals in					
New Hampshire..........................	28	28	28	28	28
Bed Size Category					
6-24	1	1	1	1	1
25-49	8	8	8	8	7
50-99	9	9	9	9	10
100-199	6	6	6	6	6
200-299	3	3	3	3	3
300-399	1	1	1	1	1
400-499	0	0	0	0	0
500 + ...	0	0	0	0	0
Location					
Hospitals Urban..........................	11	11	11	11	10
Hospitals Rural	17	17	17	17	18
Control					
State and Local Government................	0	0	0	0	0
Not for Profit	24	24	24	24	24
Investor owned	4	4	4	4	4
Physician Models					
Independent Practice Association	2	3	3	4	4
Group Practice without Walls................	2	2	0	0	0
Open Physician-Hospital Organization	10	10	10	10	10
Closed Physician-Hospital Organization	1	2	2	2	3
Management Service Organization	0	2	3	3	3
Integrated Salary Model	16	16	15	14	14
Equity Model	0	0	0	1	0
Foundation...............................	1	1	1	2	1
Insurance Products					
Health Maintenance Organization	0	0	0	1	2
Preferred Provider Organization..............	1	0	0	1	1
Indemnity Fee for Service	0	0	0	1	1
Managed Care Contracts					
Health Maintenance Organization	25	25	24	23	24
Preferred Provider Organization..............	24	24	23	23	24
Affiliations					
Hospitals in a System.....................	6	6	6	7	7
Hospitals in a Network.....................	11	12	12	11	11
Hospitals in a Group Purchasing Organization..	26	27	26	25	26

TABLE 6

NEW HAMPSHIRE

U.S. Registered Community Hospitals
(Nonfederal, short-term general and other special hospitals)

Utilization, Personnel, Revenue and Expenses, Community Health Indicators 2004–2008

	2008	2007	2006	2005	2004
TOTAL FACILITY (Includes Hospital and Nursing Home Units)					
Utilization - Inpatient					
Beds	2,858	2,841	2,825	2,843	2,807
Admissions	124,184	121,747	118,956	117,468	117,130
Inpatient Days	664,659	659,511	644,096	647,457	648,454
Average Length of Stay	5.4	5.4	5.4	5.5	5.5
Inpatient Surgeries	35,022	34,217	33,612	35,584	37,755
Births	13,636	13,995	13,615	13,696	14,043
Utilization - Outpatient					
Emergency Outpatient Visits	623,814	619,714	604,317	621,217	563,318
Other Outpatient Visits	3,844,709	3,479,378	3,266,700	3,160,825	2,403,954
Total Outpatient Visits	4,468,523	4,099,092	3,871,017	3,782,042	2,967,272
Outpatient Surgeries	91,320	85,548	86,761	90,385	94,192
Personnel					
Full Time RNs	4,181	4,070	3,852	3,775	3,423
Full Time LPNs	223	199	208	215	147
Part Time RNs	3,102	2,604	2,453	2,462	2,513
Part Time LPNs	156	151	123	136	135
Total Full Time	20,853	19,705	18,632	18,390	15,560
Total Part Time	10,452	9,465	8,674	8,459	8,314
Revenue - Inpatient					
Gross Inpatient Revenue	$3,458,246,012	$3,409,556,142	$2,702,075,606	$2,428,565,909	$2,020,888,964
Revenue - Outpatient					
Gross Outpatient Revenue	$4,446,890,786	$3,772,204,893	$3,488,005,564	$2,985,681,639	$2,373,162,075
Revenue and Expenses - Totals					
(Includes Inpatient and Outpatient)					
Total Gross Revenue	$7,905,136,798	$7,181,761,035	$6,190,081,170	$5,414,247,548	$4,394,051,039
Deductions from Revenue	4,413,714,285	3,943,723,858	3,195,298,030	2,798,961,017	2,142,869,543
Net Patient Revenue	3,491,422,513	3,238,037,177	2,994,783,140	2,615,286,531	2,251,181,496
Other Operating Revenue	87,274,249	83,643,504	79,223,066	80,767,166	63,792,812
Other Nonoperating Revenue	(67,525,945)	99,299,362	57,646,499	57,076,374	36,058,708
Total Net Revenue	3,511,170,817	3,420,980,043	3,131,652,705	2,753,130,071	2,351,033,016
Total Expenses	3,330,628,143	3,070,122,158	2,848,299,424	2,548,210,216	2,188,643,072
HOSPITAL UNIT (Excludes Separate Nursing Home Units)					
Utilization - Inpatient					
Beds	2,678	2,661	2,645	2,655	2,627
Admissions	123,622	121,196	118,323	116,803	116,654
Inpatient Days	605,089	600,484	584,931	586,625	588,035
Average Length of Stay	4.9	5.0	4.9	5.0	5.0
Personnel					
Total Full Time	20,767	19,612	18,545	18,278	15,453
Total Part Time	10,380	9,388	8,594	8,372	8,246
Revenue and Expenses - Totals					
(Includes Inpatient and Outpatient)					
Total Net Revenue	$3,496,911,705	$3,407,280,709	$3,118,367,395	$2,741,511,410	$2,339,709,215
Total Expenses	3,319,098,045	3,059,851,657	2,837,832,481	2,537,711,796	2,178,924,493
COMMUNITY HEALTH INDICATORS PER 1000 POPULATION					
Total Population (in thousands)	1,316	1,312	1,309	1,301	1,292
Inpatient					
Beds	2.2	2.2	2.2	2.2	2.2
Admissions	94.4	92.8	90.9	90.3	90.7
Inpatient Days	505.1	502.6	492.1	497.8	501.9
Inpatient Surgeries	26.6	26.1	25.7	27.4	29.2
Births	10.4	10.7	10.4	10.5	10.9
Outpatient					
Emergency Outpatient Visits	474.1	472.3	461.7	477.7	436.0
Other Outpatient Visits	2,921.9	2,651.4	2,495.9	2,430.4	1,860.6
Total Outpatient Visits	3,396.0	3,123.7	2,957.6	2,908.1	2,296.5
Outpatient Surgeries	69.4	65.2	66.3	69.5	72.9
Expense per Capita (per person)	$2,531.2	$2,339.6	$2,176.2	$1,959.4	$1,693.9

States

TABLE 6

NEW JERSEY

U.S. Registered Community Hospitals
(Nonfederal, short-term general and other special hospitals)

Overview 2004–2008

	2008	2007	2006	2005	2004
Total Community Hospitals in New Jersey.....	73	73	79	80	80
Bed Size Category					
6-24	0	0	0	0	0
25-49	3	0	0	0	0
50-99	4	6	7	7	6
100-199	19	18	23	22	25
200-299	16	17	17	18	20
300-399	13	14	15	16	11
400-499	11	12	11	11	11
500 + ...	7	6	6	6	7
Location					
Hospitals Urban..........................	73	73	79	80	80
Hospitals Rural	0	0	0	0	0
Control					
State and Local Government................	4	3	1	2	1
Not for Profit	61	65	74	74	75
Investor owned	8	5	4	4	4
Physician Models					
Independent Practice Association	16	17	24	24	30
Group Practice without Walls................	2	2	2	2	3
Open Physician-Hospital Organization	10	6	5	9	10
Closed Physician-Hospital Organization	2	2	2	3	5
Management Service Organization	12	10	11	12	16
Integrated Salary Model	17	19	17	15	15
Equity Model	0	1	0	0	1
Foundation...............................	3	1	1	1	1
Insurance Products					
Health Maintenance Organization	4	7	10	7	8
Preferred Provider Organization..............	6	12	12	10	9
Indemnity Fee for Service	3	5	4	2	4
Managed Care Contracts					
Health Maintenance Organization	52	48	52	55	56
Preferred Provider Organization..............	53	49	49	55	53
Affiliations					
Hospitals in a System......................	42	41	45	44	46
Hospitals in a Network.....................	33	29	31	30	32
Hospitals in a Group Purchasing Organization..	61	52	52	55	53

TABLE 6

NEW JERSEY

U.S. Registered Community Hospitals
(Nonfederal, short-term general and other special hospitals)

Utilization, Personnel, Revenue and Expenses, Community Health Indicators 2004–2008

	2008	2007	2006	2005	2004
TOTAL FACILITY (Includes Hospital and Nursing Home Units)					
Utilization - Inpatient					
Beds	20,007	21,544	22,094	22,090	21,952
Admissions	1,086,445	1,084,226	1,111,101	1,109,705	1,103,743
Inpatient Days	5,595,966	5,613,126	5,835,422	5,925,414	5,911,631
Average Length of Stay	5.2	5.2	5.3	5.3	5.4
Inpatient Surgeries	255,641	266,546	284,822	282,259	284,886
Births	107,580	107,824	108,995	109,227	108,029
Utilization - Outpatient					
Emergency Outpatient Visits	3,350,786	3,175,910	3,256,298	3,078,419	3,027,063
Other Outpatient Visits	14,789,129	14,013,705	13,734,887	13,748,497	14,695,340
Total Outpatient Visits	18,139,915	17,189,615	16,991,185	16,826,916	17,722,403
Outpatient Surgeries	378,011	379,519	407,085	417,084	423,269
Personnel					
Full Time RNs	26,330	27,020	26,071	25,241	23,858
Full Time LPNs	988	1,239	1,400	1,652	1,676
Part Time RNs	11,559	12,682	11,367	13,117	11,838
Part Time LPNs	341	446	478	624	577
Total Full Time	100,758	106,135	104,148	103,106	97,242
Total Part Time	37,240	39,675	37,053	39,603	37,057
Revenue - Inpatient					
Gross Inpatient Revenue	$55,005,071,849	$49,634,356,051	$45,310,317,960	$43,952,410,001	$40,437,203,818
Revenue - Outpatient					
Gross Outpatient Revenue	$21,188,946,872	$18,690,116,226	$17,267,735,947	$15,777,247,986	$14,458,714,520
Revenue and Expenses - Totals					
(Includes Inpatient and Outpatient)					
Total Gross Revenue	$76,194,018,721	$68,324,472,277	$62,578,053,907	$59,729,657,987	$54,895,918,338
Deductions from Revenue	60,144,230,629	53,091,395,932	47,643,352,686	45,310,599,793	41,382,302,648
Net Patient Revenue	16,049,788,092	15,233,076,345	14,934,701,221	14,419,058,194	13,513,615,690
Other Operating Revenue	843,164,744	994,975,114	1,010,071,748	922,878,762	738,399,866
Other Nonoperating Revenue	(674,159,972)	387,392,141	283,078,006	219,417,576	198,750,109
Total Net Revenue	16,218,792,864	16,615,443,600	16,227,850,975	15,561,354,532	14,450,765,665
Total Expenses	17,087,597,199	16,016,305,676	15,863,979,000	14,923,445,789	13,989,784,649
HOSPITAL UNIT (Excludes Separate Nursing Home Units)					
Utilization - Inpatient					
Beds	20,358	21,151	21,663	21,607	21,482
Admissions	1,082,467	1,080,885	1,107,354	1,104,354	1,099,223
Inpatient Days	5,429,164	5,482,670	5,706,480	5,766,665	5,755,885
Average Length of Stay	5.0	5.1	5.2	5.2	5.2
Personnel					
Total Full Time	99,958	105,444	103,669	102,583	96,664
Total Part Time	36,951	39,453	36,787	39,383	36,822
Revenue and Expenses - Totals					
(Includes Inpatient and Outpatient)					
Total Net Revenue	$16,159,968,959	$16,577,766,424	$16,177,529,982	$15,514,141,581	$14,399,602,815
Total Expenses	17,039,861,968	15,991,283,969	15,839,497,100	14,885,121,726	13,940,628,001
COMMUNITY HEALTH INDICATORS PER 1000 POPULATION					
Total Population (in thousands)	8,683	8,653	8,640	8,635	8,621
Inpatient					
Beds	2.4	2.5	2.6	2.6	2.5
Admissions	125.1	125.3	128.6	128.5	128.0
Inpatient Days	644.5	648.7	675.4	686.2	685.7
Inpatient Surgeries	29.4	30.8	33.0	32.7	33.0
Births	12.4	12.5	12.6	12.6	12.5
Outpatient					
Emergency Outpatient Visits	385.9	367.0	376.9	356.5	351.1
Other Outpatient Visits	1,703.3	1,619.5	1,589.6	1,592.2	1,704.6
Total Outpatient Visits	2,089.2	1,986.5	1,966.5	1,948.8	2,055.8
Outpatient Surgeries	43.5	43.9	47.1	48.3	49.1
Expense per Capita (per person)	$1,968.0	$1,850.9	$1,836.1	$1,728.3	$1,622.8

TABLE 6

NEW MEXICO

U.S. Registered Community Hospitals
(Nonfederal, short-term general and other special hospitals)

Overview 2004–2008

	2008	2007	2006	2005	2004
Total Community Hospitals in New Mexico	36	35	36	37	37
Bed Size Category					
6-24	4	4	6	4	4
25-49	9	9	8	10	9
50-99	10	10	9	10	10
100-199	10	9	10	9	9
200-299	1	1	1	3	4
300-399	0	0	1	1	1
400-499	0	0	0	0	0
500 + ...	2	2	1	0	0
Location					
Hospitals Urban...........................	14	13	14	15	15
Hospitals Rural	22	22	22	22	22
Control					
State and Local Government...............	7	7	8	8	9
Not for Profit	14	15	15	15	18
Investor owned	15	13	13	14	10
Physician Models					
Independent Practice Association	3	5	8	6	8
Group Practice without Walls...............	0	0	0	0	0
Open Physician-Hospital Organization	4	4	4	6	6
Closed Physician-Hospital Organization	1	0	0	0	0
Management Service Organization	1	2	0	0	0
Integrated Salary Model	10	11	9	11	8
Equity Model	1	1	1	2	1
Foundation...............................	2	2	2	2	1
Insurance Products					
Health Maintenance Organization	7	8	8	7	6
Preferred Provider Organization..............	6	5	6	6	5
Indemnity Fee for Service	4	4	4	4	2
Managed Care Contracts					
Health Maintenance Organization	17	21	21	22	18
Preferred Provider Organization..............	19	22	23	23	19
Affiliations					
Hospitals in a System......................	28	26	29	30	30
Hospitals in a Network.....................	7	6	6	6	5
Hospitals in a Group Purchasing Organization..	22	25	24	26	23

TABLE 6

NEW MEXICO

U.S. Registered Community Hospitals
(Nonfederal, short-term general and other special hospitals)

Utilization, Personnel, Revenue and Expenses, Community Health Indicators 2004–2008

	2008	2007	2006	2005	2004
TOTAL FACILITY (Includes Hospital and Nursing Home Units)					
Utilization - Inpatient					
Beds	3,035	0,005	3,525	3,505	3,678
Admissions	174,169	170,081	160,792	171,547	163,416
Inpatient Days	809,916	764,458	762,267	807,324	781,150
Average Length of Stay	4.7	4.5	4.7	4.7	4.8
Inpatient Surgeries	48,698	52,350	57,642	52,087	48,648
Births	24,127	24,530	24,275	24,477	24,571
Utilization - Outpatient					
Emergency Outpatient Visits	770,475	650,026	777,671	742,439	725,603
Other Outpatient Visits	3,481,084	3,458,967	3,566,448	3,971,938	4,315,563
Total Outpatient Visits	4,251,559	4,108,993	4,344,119	4,714,377	5,041,166
Outpatient Surgeries	84,596	85,918	78,948	81,852	81,127
Personnel					
Full Time RNs	5,151	4,690	4,555	4,890	4,955
Full Time LPNs	401	415	484	545	588
Part Time RNs	1,997	2,025	2,726	2,415	2,183
Part Time LPNs	143	220	338	312	299
Total Full Time	19,610	18,112	18,746	20,955	20,275
Total Part Time	5,789	5,808	8,132	7,273	6,348
Revenue - Inpatient					
Gross Inpatient Revenue	$4,955,498,423	$4,068,780,483	$3,696,095,782	$3,740,792,937	$3,213,735,333
Revenue - Outpatient					
Gross Outpatient Revenue	$4,098,164,016	$3,553,788,776	$3,022,732,688	$2,754,519,275	$2,383,978,355
Revenue and Expenses - Totals					
(Includes Inpatient and Outpatient)					
Total Gross Revenue	$9,053,662,439	$7,622,569,259	$6,718,828,470	$6,495,312,212	$5,597,713,688
Deductions from Revenue	5,863,897,074	4,772,970,882	4,102,007,203	3,950,367,545	3,293,098,514
Net Patient Revenue	3,189,765,365	2,849,598,377	2,616,821,267	2,544,944,667	2,304,615,174
Other Operating Revenue	201,317,481	147,824,626	141,948,486	147,448,779	125,469,086
Other Nonoperating Revenue	25,179,087	67,325,548	29,409,340	21,735,358	34,435,552
Total Net Revenue	3,416,261,933	3,064,748,551	2,788,179,093	2,714,128,804	2,464,519,812
Total Expenses	3,078,569,624	2,857,121,542	2,532,320,664	2,634,907,395	2,303,636,339
HOSPITAL UNIT (Excludes Separate Nursing Home Units)					
Utilization - Inpatient					
Beds	3,838	3,582	3,478	3,470	3,631
Admissions	173,883	169,533	160,746	171,494	163,374
Inpatient Days	788,033	736,788	751,554	798,081	772,542
Average Length of Stay	4.5	4.3	4.7	4.7	4.7
Personnel					
Total Full Time	19,566	18,009	18,692	20,900	20,175
Total Part Time	5,778	5,765	8,122	7,260	6,348
Revenue and Expenses - Totals					
(Includes Inpatient and Outpatient)					
Total Net Revenue	$3,409,480,468	$3,054,320,532	$2,785,047,800	$2,711,389,967	$2,462,884,622
Total Expenses	3,074,660,998	2,852,899,697	2,530,199,604	2,632,999,432	2,301,783,109
COMMUNITY HEALTH INDICATORS PER 1000 POPULATION					
Total Population (in thousands)	1,984	1,964	1,938	1,913	1,889
Inpatient					
Beds	2.0	1.9	1.8	1.8	1.9
Admissions	87.8	86.6	83.0	89.7	86.5
Inpatient Days	408.2	389.2	393.3	422.0	413.5
Inpatient Surgeries	24.5	26.6	29.7	27.2	25.7
Births	12.2	12.5	12.5	12.8	13.0
Outpatient					
Emergency Outpatient Visits	388.3	330.9	401.3	388.1	384.1
Other Outpatient Visits	1,754.3	1,760.8	1,840.4	2,076.4	2,284.3
Total Outpatient Visits	2,142.5	2,091.7	2,241.6	2,464.5	2,668.3
Outpatient Surgeries	42.6	43.7	40.7	42.8	42.9
Expense per Capita (per person)	$1,551.4	$1,454.4	$1,306.7	$1,377.5	$1,219.3

States

TABLE 6

NEW YORK

U.S. Registered Community Hospitals
(Nonfederal, short-term general and other special hospitals)

Overview 2004–2008

	2008	2007	2006	2005	2004
Total Community Hospitals in New York	194	202	203	203	206
Bed Size Category					
6-24	5	6	5	5	5
25-49	9	8	8	7	7
50-99	19	21	23	24	23
100-199	47	48	50	51	49
200-299	38	41	42	40	45
300-399	29	31	28	29	25
400-499	14	14	9	14	18
500 + ...	33	33	38	33	34
Location					
Hospitals Urban............................	154	162	163	163	170
Hospitals Rural	40	40	40	40	36
Control					
State and Local Government................	26	26	23	22	23
Not for Profit	167	174	177	179	180
Investor owned	1	2	3	2	3
Physician Models					
Independent Practice Association	38	43	31	33	33
Group Practice without Walls................	5	5	5	4	5
Open Physician-Hospital Organization	13	18	20	15	16
Closed Physician-Hospital Organization	9	11	7	8	5
Management Service Organization	13	16	14	9	11
Integrated Salary Model	56	56	54	50	49
Equity Model	4	3	3	4	2
Foundation...............................	2	6	2	2	0
Insurance Products					
Health Maintenance Organization	50	42	35	35	41
Preferred Provider Organization..............	30	23	19	23	33
Indemnity Fee for Service	15	14	10	12	17
Managed Care Contracts					
Health Maintenance Organization	115	119	113	107	108
Preferred Provider Organization..............	105	105	106	101	102
Affiliations					
Hospitals in a System......................	73	76	79	74	72
Hospitals in a Network	73	74	68	65	66
Hospitals in a Group Purchasing Organization..	116	125	130	124	118

States

TABLE 6

NEW YORK

U.S. Registered Community Hospitals
(Nonfederal, short-term general and other special hospitals)

Utilization, Personnel, Revenue and Expenses, Community Health Indicators 2004–2008

	2008	2007	2006	2005	2004
TOTAL FACILITY (Includes Hospital and Nursing Home Units)					
Utilization - Inpatient					
Beds	61,237	62,367	63,591	63,068	64,205
Admissions	2,528,191	2,540,711	2,571,572	2,537,762	2,525,777
Inpatient Days	17,973,047	18,344,398	18,510,969	18,277,363	18,482,900
Average Length of Stay	7.1	7.2	7.2	7.2	7.3
Inpatient Surgeries	660,660	679,506	698,078	668,566	668,644
Births	242,326	247,523	249,648	250,417	250,456
Utilization - Outpatient					
Emergency Outpatient Visits	8,114,078	8,193,513	7,924,843	7,639,381	7,612,589
Other Outpatient Visits	44,455,562	44,944,035	46,104,567	43,898,912	42,117,477
Total Outpatient Visits	52,569,640	53,137,548	54,029,410	51,538,293	49,730,066
Outpatient Surgeries	1,340,449	1,362,222	1,354,724	1,259,196	1,288,074
Personnel					
Full Time RNs	76,900	76,438	72,165	67,837	67,182
Full Time LPNs	5,964	6,184	6,174	6,423	6,792
Part Time RNs	22,118	22,590	22,604	23,521	23,412
Part Time LPNs	1,561	1,696	1,850	2,036	2,135
Total Full Time	340,045	335,364	319,765	311,322	313,844
Total Part Time	74,972	75,084	74,473	74,617	75,365
Revenue - Inpatient					
Gross Inpatient Revenue	$76,153,885,959	$73,373,569,851	$71,010,568,325	$66,080,727,158	$59,845,203,393
Revenue - Outpatient					
Gross Outpatient Revenue	$43,198,790,671	$38,929,448,202	$37,230,180,894	$33,027,420,524	$30,028,806,702
Revenue and Expenses - Totals					
(Includes Inpatient and Outpatient)					
Total Gross Revenue	$119,352,676,630	$112,303,018,053	$108,240,749,219	$99,108,147,682	$89,874,010,095
Deductions from Revenue	71,744,138,399	66,207,959,482	64,798,876,462	58,467,022,570	51,448,977,266
Net Patient Revenue	47,608,538,231	46,095,058,571	43,441,872,757	40,641,125,112	38,425,032,829
Other Operating Revenue	3,624,584,884	3,905,891,729	4,156,988,495	3,738,648,013	3,735,758,067
Other Nonoperating Revenue	(31,698,081)	1,052,459,422	959,995,822	636,663,624	736,713,307
Total Net Revenue	51,201,425,034	51,053,409,722	48,558,857,074	45,016,436,749	42,897,504,203
Total Expenses	52,930,511,542	50,122,518,825	47,808,815,271	44,701,048,591	42,332,666,603
HOSPITAL UNIT (Excludes Separate Nursing Home Units)					
Utilization - Inpatient					
Beds	55,922	56,413	58,005	58,596	58,524
Admissions	2,514,606	2,525,283	2,557,311	2,527,409	2,513,339
Inpatient Days	16,133,356	16,221,721	16,556,677	16,772,641	16,471,866
Average Length of Stay	6.4	6.4	6.5	6.6	6.6
Personnel					
Total Full Time	334,474	330,451	315,355	307,991	303,125
Total Part Time	72,541	72,893	72,457	71,379	72,486
Revenue and Expenses - Totals					
(Includes Inpatient and Outpatient)					
Total Net Revenue	$50,719,366,889	$50,534,703,285	$48,111,502,694	$44,687,516,050	$42,533,180,009
Total Expenses	52,469,154,258	49,634,461,793	47,414,611,530	44,410,483,707	42,017,458,035
COMMUNITY HEALTH INDICATORS PER 1000 POPULATION					
Total Population (in thousands)	19,490	19,429	19,367	19,336	19,301
Inpatient					
Beds	3.1	3.2	3.3	3.3	3.3
Admissions	129.7	130.8	132.8	131.2	130.9
Inpatient Days	922.2	944.2	955.8	945.2	957.6
Inpatient Surgeries	33.9	35.0	36.0	34.6	34.6
Births	12.4	12.7	12.9	13.0	13.0
Outpatient					
Emergency Outpatient Visits	416.3	421.7	409.2	395.1	394.4
Other Outpatient Visits	2,280.9	2,313.2	2,380.6	2,270.3	2,182.1
Total Outpatient Visits	2,697.2	2,734.9	2,789.8	2,665.4	2,576.5
Outpatient Surgeries	68.8	70.1	70.0	65.1	66.7
Expense per Capita (per person)	$2,715.7	$2,579.7	$2,468.6	$2,311.8	$2,193.3

States

TABLE 6

NORTH CAROLINA

U.S. Registered Community Hospitals
(Nonfederal, short-term general and other special hospitals)

Overview 2004–2008

	2008	2007	2006	2005	2004
Total Community Hospitals in North Carolina ..	116	113	114	115	115
Bed Size Category					
6-24	4	4	3	4	4
25-49	16	14	15	16	12
50-99	22	19	22	22	25
100-199	40	40	38	37	38
200-299	12	14	13	15	15
300-399	7	7	9	7	7
400-499	2	2	1	2	1
500 + ...	13	13	13	12	13
Location					
Hospitals Urban	58	55	56	56	53
Hospitals Rural	58	58	58	59	62
Control					
State and Local Government	32	32	32	32	32
Not for Profit	74	75	75	75	74
Investor owned	10	6	7	8	9
Physician Models					
Independent Practice Association	11	13	13	14	15
Group Practice without Walls	2	2	3	3	4
Open Physician-Hospital Organization	10	11	14	17	20
Closed Physician-Hospital Organization	6	7	8	8	6
Management Service Organization	16	13	14	10	11
Integrated Salary Model	57	48	45	38	37
Equity Model	3	2	3	2	2
Foundation	5	4	4	4	4
Insurance Products					
Health Maintenance Organization	7	9	12	9	11
Preferred Provider Organization	10	20	21	19	19
Indemnity Fee for Service	2	3	4	4	6
Managed Care Contracts					
Health Maintenance Organization	80	78	74	70	71
Preferred Provider Organization	89	88	86	80	85
Affiliations					
Hospitals in a System	69	60	59	65	65
Hospitals in a Network	41	40	43	37	43
Hospitals in a Group Purchasing Organization ..	102	102	102	90	89

States

TABLE 6

NORTH CAROLINA

U.S. Registered Community Hospitals
(Nonfederal, short-term general and other special hospitals)

Utilization, Personnel, Revenue and Expenses, Community Health Indicators 2004–2008

	2008	2007	2006	2005	2004
TOTAL FACILITY (Includes Hospital and Nursing Home Units)					
Utilization - Inpatient					
Beds	23,140	23,158	23,441	23,344	23,498
Admissions	1,041,918	1,027,909	1,015,594	1,013,094	1,005,965
Inpatient Days	6,019,401	6,069,660	6,131,924	6,089,400	6,115,774
Average Length of Stay	5.8	5.9	6.0	6.0	6.1
Inpatient Surgeries	292,208	292,262	294,298	301,188	304,921
Births	126,934	125,276	120,778	117,137	114,108
Utilization - Outpatient					
Emergency Outpatient Visits	4,166,718	4,068,389	3,849,736	3,784,070	3,483,332
Other Outpatient Visits	13,566,350	13,699,957	13,363,083	13,017,649	11,831,202
Total Outpatient Visits	17,733,068	17,768,346	17,212,819	16,801,719	15,314,534
Outpatient Surgeries	561,677	548,944	561,285	588,276	608,488
Personnel					
Full Time RNs	33,527	32,542	31,642	29,786	28,825
Full Time LPNs	1,847	1,867	2,000	2,215	2,157
Part Time RNs	15,014	13,391	13,498	13,730	12,470
Part Time LPNs	717	765	761	834	828
Total Full Time	127,114	124,066	121,023	118,275	116,111
Total Part Time	39,645	36,185	36,764	37,399	34,438
Revenue - Inpatient					
Gross Inpatient Revenue	$23,694,080,318	$22,069,980,664	$20,338,755,428	$18,580,679,238	$17,237,298,617
Revenue - Outpatient					
Gross Outpatient Revenue	$19,809,416,116	$17,851,201,525	$15,852,323,132	$13,815,373,836	$11,892,189,064
Revenue and Expenses - Totals					
(Includes Inpatient and Outpatient)					
Total Gross Revenue	$43,503,496,434	$39,921,182,189	$36,191,078,560	$32,396,053,074	$29,129,487,681
Deductions from Revenue	26,008,781,838	23,217,172,845	20,163,280,087	17,752,655,424	15,475,967,403
Net Patient Revenue	17,494,714,596	16,704,009,344	16,027,797,573	14,643,397,650	13,653,520,278
Other Operating Revenue	988,309,628	844,581,143	774,858,487	723,646,759	725,740,871
Other Nonoperating Revenue	(560,668,606)	571,143,345	556,662,511	340,797,263	357,649,552
Total Net Revenue	17,922,355,618	18,119,733,832	17,359,318,571	15,707,841,672	14,736,910,701
Total Expenses	17,662,604,664	16,635,094,264	15,721,863,715	14,661,849,081	13,310,632,196
HOSPITAL UNIT (Excludes Separate Nursing Home Units)					
Utilization - Inpatient					
Beds	20,496	20,302	20,428	20,767	20,739
Admissions	1,031,609	1,016,854	1,004,707	1,003,543	995,794
Inpatient Days	5,128,782	5,093,680	5,164,167	5,253,458	5,203,268
Average Length of Stay	5.0	5.0	5.1	5.2	5.2
Personnel					
Total Full Time	125,088	121,526	118,627	116,358	113,268
Total Part Time	38,721	35,164	35,802	36,432	33,255
Revenue and Expenses - Totals					
(Includes Inpatient and Outpatient)					
Total Net Revenue	$17,753,404,722	$17,925,776,886	$17,183,454,204	$15,559,562,668	$14,590,640,384
Total Expenses	17,488,022,607	16,444,335,265	15,526,247,079	14,505,827,063	13,163,805,794
COMMUNITY HEALTH INDICATORS PER 1000 POPULATION					
Total Population (in thousands)	9,222	9,042	8,845	8,661	8,523
Inpatient					
Beds	2.5	2.6	2.7	2.7	2.8
Admissions	113.0	113.7	114.8	117.0	118.0
Inpatient Days	652.7	671.3	693.2	703.1	717.5
Inpatient Surgeries	31.7	32.3	33.3	34.8	35.8
Births	13.8	13.9	13.7	13.5	13.4
Outpatient					
Emergency Outpatient Visits	451.8	450.0	435.2	436.9	408.7
Other Outpatient Visits	1,471.0	1,515.2	1,510.7	1,503.0	1,388.1
Total Outpatient Visits	1,922.8	1,965.2	1,946.0	1,939.9	1,796.8
Outpatient Surgeries	60.9	60.7	63.5	67.9	71.4
Expense per Capita (per person)	$1,915.2	$1,839.8	$1,777.4	$1,692.8	$1,561.7

States

TABLE 6

NORTH DAKOTA

U.S. Registered Community Hospitals
(Nonfederal, short-term general and other special hospitals)

Overview 2004–2008

	2008	2007	2006	2005	2004
Total Community Hospitals in North Dakota ...	41	41	41	40	40
Bed Size Category					
6-24	11	11	9	8	8
25-49	12	11	13	13	14
50-99	11	12	12	12	11
100-199	2	2	2	3	3
200-299	3	3	3	2	2
300-399	0	0	0	0	0
400-499	1	1	1	1	0
500 + ...	1	1	1	1	2
Location					
Hospitals Urban..........................	7	6	6	6	6
Hospitals Rural	34	35	35	34	34
Control					
State and Local Government................	0	0	0	0	0
Not for Profit	39	40	41	40	40
Investor owned	2	1	0	0	0
Physician Models					
Independent Practice Association	4	4	4	4	4
Group Practice without Walls...............	0	0	1	3	2
Open Physician-Hospital Organization	3	3	2	1	1
Closed Physician-Hospital Organization	0	1	2	2	1
Management Service Organization	0	1	0	0	1
Integrated Salary Model....................	15	14	16	16	10
Equity Model	1	1	1	1	1
Foundation..............................	4	3	5	4	1
Insurance Products					
Health Maintenance Organization	0	0	1	0	0
Preferred Provider Organization..............	7	4	5	5	3
Indemnity Fee for Service	4	1	1	0	0
Managed Care Contracts					
Health Maintenance Organization	1	2	4	6	4
Preferred Provider Organization..............	16	17	19	19	18
Affiliations					
Hospitals in a System......................	15	16	14	13	12
Hospitals in a Network.....................	8	7	10	10	10
Hospitals in a Group Purchasing Organization..	25	29	32	28	24

TABLE 6

NORTH DAKOTA

U.S. Registered Community Hospitals
(Nonfederal, short-term general and other special hospitals)

Utilization, Personnel, Revenue and Expenses, Community Health Indicators 2004–2008

	2008	2007	2006	2005	2004
TOTAL FACILITY (Includes Hospital and Nursing Home Units)					
Utilization - Inpatient					
Beds	3,442	3,488	3,550	3,494	3,567
Admissions	89,225	89,010	88,737	87,485	88,004
Inpatient Days	744,876	772,643	762,500	767,324	769,880
Average Length of Stay	8.3	8.7	8.6	8.8	8.7
Inpatient Surgeries	26,451	28,861	28,577	27,730	28,678
Births	9,966	9,687	9,587	9,281	9,238
Utilization - Outpatient					
Emergency Outpatient Visits	289,070	274,223	263,144	263,489	254,409
Other Outpatient Visits	1,406,490	1,474,224	1,446,140	1,599,948	1,594,764
Total Outpatient Visits	1,695,560	1,748,447	1,709,284	1,863,437	1,849,173
Outpatient Surgeries	46,734	45,328	44,257	42,892	47,079
Personnel					
Full Time RNs	2,424	2,356	2,110	2,089	2,296
Full Time LPNs	512	556	544	521	584
Part Time RNs	2,002	2,030	2,244	2,153	1,756
Part Time LPNs	460	566	602	571	424
Total Full Time	12,312	12,036	11,623	11,714	11,744
Total Part Time	7,148	7,666	8,050	7,866	6,776
Revenue - Inpatient					
Gross Inpatient Revenue	$1,483,180,662	$1,414,871,895	$1,334,432,797	$1,265,396,292	$1,188,078,532
Revenue - Outpatient					
Gross Outpatient Revenue	$1,953,610,192	$1,687,925,226	$1,527,971,411	$1,411,506,368	$1,261,112,345
Revenue and Expenses - Totals					
(Includes Inpatient and Outpatient)					
Total Gross Revenue	$3,436,790,854	$3,102,797,121	$2,862,404,208	$2,676,902,660	$2,449,190,877
Deductions from Revenue	1,680,883,923	1,444,698,089	1,303,212,416	1,204,587,282	1,070,387,845
Net Patient Revenue	1,755,906,931	1,658,099,032	1,559,191,792	1,472,315,378	1,378,803,032
Other Operating Revenue	87,201,376	83,258,147	78,157,365	79,881,629	70,301,224
Other Nonoperating Revenue	(13,097,663)	43,988,926	38,911,418	23,059,817	25,078,701
Total Net Revenue	1,830,010,644	1,785,346,105	1,676,260,575	1,575,256,824	1,474,182,957
Total Expenses	1,853,693,024	1,748,248,300	1,630,169,448	1,508,285,775	1,414,152,181
HOSPITAL UNIT (Excludes Separate Nursing Home Units)					
Utilization - Inpatient					
Beds	2,649	2,610	2,589	2,497	2,559
Admissions	86,795	86,408	85,589	84,778	85,546
Inpatient Days	479,593	472,732	446,177	446,887	439,666
Average Length of Stay	5.5	5.5	5.2	5.3	5.1
Personnel					
Total Full Time	11,728	11,350	10,927	11,072	10,773
Total Part Time	6,808	7,147	7,481	7,274	6,153
Revenue and Expenses - Totals					
(Includes Inpatient and Outpatient)					
Total Net Revenue	$1,780,423,431	$1,729,923,488	$1,621,940,757	$1,525,993,700	$1,423,651,440
Total Expenses	1,809,203,400	1,702,249,310	1,587,820,886	1,470,178,178	1,373,930,577
COMMUNITY HEALTH INDICATORS PER 1000 POPULATION					
Total Population (in thousands)	641	638	636	635	636
Inpatient					
Beds	5.4	5.5	5.6	5.5	5.6
Admissions	139.1	139.5	139.4	137.7	138.3
Inpatient Days	1,161.2	1,211.2	1,198.0	1,208.0	1,210.1
Inpatient Surgeries	41.2	45.2	44.9	43.7	45.1
Births	15.5	15.2	15.1	14.6	14.5
Outpatient					
Emergency Outpatient Visits	450.6	429.9	413.5	414.8	399.9
Other Outpatient Visits	2,192.6	2,311.0	2,272.2	2,518.7	2,506.7
Total Outpatient Visits	2,643.2	2,740.9	2,685.6	2,933.5	2,906.6
Outpatient Surgeries	72.9	71.1	69.5	67.5	74.0
Expense per Capita (per person)	$2,889.7	$2,740.6	$2,561.3	$2,374.4	$2,222.8

States

TABLE 6

OHIO

U.S. Registered Community Hospitals
(Nonfederal, short-term general and other special hospitals)

Overview 2004–2008

	2008	2007	2006	2005	2004
Total Community Hospitals in Ohio..........	181	171	171	170	166
Bed Size Category					
6-24.....................................	4	3	4	5	3
25-49...................................	44	37	36	32	31
50-99...................................	29	26	26	27	23
100-199.................................	45	47	45	43	47
200-299.................................	25	24	26	25	24
300-399.................................	11	12	14	19	17
400-499.................................	10	11	8	8	10
500 +...................................	13	11	12	11	11
Location					
Hospitals Urban..........................	126	117	117	116	117
Hospitals Rural..........................	55	54	54	54	49
Control					
State and Local Government................	21	23	23	23	23
Not for Profit............................	139	137	136	137	138
Investor owned..........................	21	11	12	10	5
Physician Models					
Independent Practice Association............	25	27	26	19	20
Group Practice without Walls...............	9	11	11	11	7
Open Physician-Hospital Organization........	41	41	45	47	45
Closed Physician-Hospital Organization.......	13	25	24	24	25
Management Service Organization...........	49	39	38	39	37
Integrated Salary Model...................	68	65	64	58	56
Equity Model............................	8	6	7	7	5
Foundation..............................	27	24	25	22	23
Insurance Products					
Health Maintenance Organization............	31	35	35	23	27
Preferred Provider Organization..............	34	45	45	32	33
Indemnity Fee for Service..................	11	26	17	14	19
Managed Care Contracts					
Health Maintenance Organization............	112	110	109	110	107
Preferred Provider Organization..............	120	120	122	127	117
Affiliations					
Hospitals in a System.....................	107	99	93	92	88
Hospitals in a Network....................	74	70	74	66	67
Hospitals in a Group Purchasing Organization..	141	139	144	144	133

TABLE 6

OHIO

U.S. Registered Community Hospitals
(Nonfederal, short-term general and other special hospitals)

Utilization, Personnel, Revenue and Expenses, Community Health Indicators 2004–2008

	2008	2007	2006	2005	2004
TOTAL FACILITY (Includes Hospital and Nursing Home Units)					
Utilization - Inpatient					
Beds	33,860	32,866	32,822	33,250	33,398
Admissions	1,547,720	1,542,176	1,542,333	1,511,171	1,474,876
Inpatient Days	7,814,849	7,753,839	7,742,312	7,801,663	7,718,229
Average Length of Stay	5.0	5.0	5.0	5.2	5.2
Inpatient Surgeries	413,959	416,220	414,838	414,613	415,641
Births	143,941	146,861	147,992	146,625	147,087
Utilization - Outpatient					
Emergency Outpatient Visits	6,023,705	5,918,218	5,840,398	5,593,421	5,401,226
Other Outpatient Visits	26,868,157	27,167,211	26,846,119	25,756,970	25,145,977
Total Outpatient Visits	32,891,862	33,085,429	32,686,517	31,350,391	30,547,203
Outpatient Surgeries	787,850	763,623	782,568	806,211	791,207
Personnel					
Full Time RNs	45,914	44,637	43,114	42,180	39,184
Full Time LPNs	3,769	4,022	4,279	4,510	4,325
Part Time RNs	24,600	23,100	23,277	22,608	22,851
Part Time LPNs	2,080	2,113	2,122	2,278	2,311
Total Full Time	194,709	185,526	181,475	183,355	171,655
Total Part Time	76,454	69,946	70,557	67,961	67,388
Revenue - Inpatient					
Gross Inpatient Revenue	$41,893,875,454	$38,144,462,997	$35,776,947,886	$32,838,049,256	$29,068,190,645
Revenue - Outpatient					
Gross Outpatient Revenue	$35,108,967,663	$30,960,953,256	$28,562,090,312	$25,659,811,203	$22,371,774,845
Revenue and Expenses - Totals					
(Includes Inpatient and Outpatient)					
Total Gross Revenue	$77,002,843,117	$69,105,416,253	$64,339,038,198	$58,497,860,459	$51,439,965,490
Deductions from Revenue	48,579,748,500	42,732,933,128	39,005,578,638	34,669,271,066	29,452,662,017
Net Patient Revenue	28,423,094,617	26,372,483,125	25,333,459,560	23,828,589,393	21,987,303,473
Other Operating Revenue	1,902,066,455	1,781,044,376	1,572,944,936	1,418,198,645	1,271,069,402
Other Nonoperating Revenue	(1,531,882,065)	696,280,084	665,928,838	405,904,678	360,710,829
Total Net Revenue	28,793,279,007	28,849,807,585	27,572,333,334	25,652,692,716	23,619,083,704
Total Expenses	29,074,986,966	26,781,375,793	25,712,641,988	24,084,934,719	22,138,349,794
HOSPITAL UNIT (Excludes Separate Nursing Home Units)					
Utilization - Inpatient					
Beds	32,422	31,350	30,827	31,422	31,516
Admissions	1,532,848	1,526,090	1,521,553	1,493,794	1,459,452
Inpatient Days	7,365,607	7,283,480	7,158,331	7,246,049	7,127,973
Average Length of Stay	4.8	4.8	4.7	4.9	4.9
Personnel					
Total Full Time	193,511	184,300	179,982	182,022	162,601
Total Part Time	75,671	69,255	69,778	67,196	62,931
Revenue and Expenses - Totals					
(Includes Inpatient and Outpatient)					
Total Net Revenue	$28,664,373,342	$28,691,701,961	$27,333,636,562	$25,417,810,898	$23,467,323,085
Total Expenses	28,951,022,330	26,629,876,388	25,525,939,444	23,846,822,087	22,008,158,681
COMMUNITY HEALTH INDICATORS PER 1000 POPULATION					
Total Population (in thousands)	11,486	11,478	11,458	11,451	11,445
Inpatient					
Beds	2.9	2.9	2.9	2.9	2.9
Admissions	134.7	134.4	134.6	132.0	128.9
Inpatient Days	680.4	675.6	675.7	681.3	674.4
Inpatient Surgeries	36.0	36.3	36.2	36.2	36.3
Births	12.5	12.8	12.9	12.8	12.9
Outpatient					
Emergency Outpatient Visits	524.4	515.6	509.7	488.5	471.9
Other Outpatient Visits	2,339.2	2,367.0	2,342.9	2,249.3	2,197.1
Total Outpatient Visits	2,863.7	2,882.6	2,852.6	2,737.8	2,669.0
Outpatient Surgeries	68.6	66.5	68.3	70.4	69.1
Expense per Capita (per person)	$2,531.4	$2,333.4	$2,244.0	$2,103.3	$1,934.3

States

TABLE 6

OKLAHOMA

U.S. Registered Community Hospitals
(Nonfederal, short-term general and other special hospitals)

Overview 2004–2008

	2008	2007	2006	2005	2004
Total Community Hospitals in Oklahoma	**115**	**113**	**112**	**110**	**109**
Bed Size Category					
6-24	23	24	23	18	18
25-49	41	38	37	38	40
50-99	24	25	25	25	21
100-199	14	12	13	15	16
200-299	2	4	3	5	5
300-399	5	4	5	3	3
400-499	2	2	2	1	2
500 + ...	4	4	4	5	4
Location					
Hospitals Urban...........................	50	48	46	45	41
Hospitals Rural	65	65	66	65	68
Control					
State and Local Government................	45	45	44	41	45
Not for Profit	37	35	35	39	42
Investor owned	33	33	33	30	22
Physician Models					
Independent Practice Association	11	16	15	17	11
Group Practice without Walls...............	4	7	3	4	3
Open Physician-Hospital Organization	11	16	17	14	14
Closed Physician-Hospital Organization	3	3	5	9	7
Management Service Organization	11	13	10	13	15
Integrated Salary Model	22	17	25	22	26
Equity Model	1	1	1	4	1
Foundation..............................	1	0	1	4	2
Insurance Products					
Health Maintenance Organization	5	9	7	8	10
Preferred Provider Organization..............	8	12	13	11	14
Indemnity Fee for Service	3	3	3	3	4
Managed Care Contracts					
Health Maintenance Organization	41	41	35	32	28
Preferred Provider Organization..............	64	68	60	63	50
Affiliations					
Hospitals in a System......................	57	58	56	58	53
Hospitals in a Network	20	25	24	22	22
Hospitals in a Group Purchasing Organization..	85	86	85	81	76

TABLE 6

OKLAHOMA

U.S. Registered Community Hospitals
(Nonfederal, short-term general and other special hospitals)

Utilization, Personnel, Revenue and Expenses, Community Health Indicators 2004–2008

	2008	2007	2006	2005	2004
TOTAL FACILITY (Includes Hospital and Nursing Home Units)					
Utilization - Inpatient					
Beds	10,988	10,862	10,773	10,814	10,804
Admissions	462,954	453,977	454,085	456,759	454,875
Inpatient Days	2,436,253	2,359,878	2,307,539	2,341,597	2,370,273
Average Length of Stay.	5.3	5.2	5.1	5.1	5.2
Inpatient Surgeries.	117,982	115,503	112,716	114,376	127,837
Births.	49,851	49,623	47,489	45,225	43,167
Utilization - Outpatient					
Emergency Outpatient Visits.	1,645,625	1,618,741	1,554,914	1,428,028	1,358,288
Other Outpatient Visits.	3,785,996	3,654,371	3,779,892	3,983,463	3,972,073
Total Outpatient Visits	5,431,621	5,273,112	5,334,806	5,411,491	5,330,361
Outpatient Surgeries	198,007	197,718	188,902	189,427	189,338
Personnel					
Full Time RNs	10,585	10,229	9,638	9,382	8,571
Full Time LPNs	1,986	2,275	2,209	2,246	2,553
Part Time RNs.	3,684	3,523	3,508	2,746	3,223
Part Time LPNs	508	650	690	642	678
Total Full Time.	43,201	43,508	42,811	42,957	39,573
Total Part Time	12,279	12,348	12,270	9,893	12,209
Revenue - Inpatient					
Gross Inpatient Revenue.	$11,758,611,895	$10,320,519,778	$9,412,503,176	$8,557,722,404	$7,876,618,375
Revenue - Outpatient					
Gross Outpatient Revenue	$7,423,183,911	$6,214,687,591	$5,508,080,380	$4,920,113,693	$4,120,562,889
Revenue and Expenses - Totals					
(Includes Inpatient and Outpatient)					
Total Gross Revenue.	$19,181,795,806	$16,535,207,369	$14,920,583,556	$13,477,836,097	$11,997,181,264
Deductions from Revenue.	12,656,733,800	10,641,812,711	9,331,819,127	8,181,135,336	7,260,891,202
Net Patient Revenue	6,525,062,006	5,893,394,658	5,588,764,429	5,296,700,761	4,736,290,062
Other Operating Revenue	211,578,156	234,090,824	247,484,700	246,057,846	286,260,545
Other Nonoperating Revenue	37,213,785	137,588,524	86,916,871	60,680,859	51,828,639
Total Net Revenue.	6,773,853,947	6,265,074,006	5,923,166,000	5,603,439,466	5,074,379,246
Total Expenses.	6,361,690,040	5,731,142,311	5,384,898,786	5,189,657,883	4,731,185,235
HOSPITAL UNIT (Excludes Separate Nursing Home Units)					
Utilization - Inpatient					
Beds	10,699	10,542	10,392	10,533	10,465
Admissions	461,577	452,687	451,626	453,877	451,720
Inpatient Days	2,339,600	2,256,043	2,204,009	2,260,754	2,268,446
Average Length of Stay.	5.1	5.0	4.9	5.0	5.0
Personnel					
Total Full Time.	42,916	43,203	42,351	42,764	39,420
Total Part Time	12,202	12,267	12,075	9,815	12,159
Revenue and Expenses - Totals					
(Includes Inpatient and Outpatient)					
Total Net Revenue.	$6,759,273,857	$6,249,707,579	$5,904,273,214	$5,578,528,213	$5,045,401,661
Total Expenses.	6,348,305,959	5,658,213,009	5,367,863,128	5,158,908,800	4,712,397,152
COMMUNITY HEALTH INDICATORS PER 1000 POPULATION					
Total Population (in thousands)	3,642	3,608	3,568	3,530	3,512
Inpatient					
Beds	3.0	3.0	3.0	3.1	3.1
Admissions	127.1	125.8	127.3	129.4	129.5
Inpatient Days	668.9	654.0	646.7	663.3	674.9
Inpatient Surgeries.	32.4	32.0	31.6	32.4	36.4
Births.	13.7	13.8	13.3	12.8	12.3
Outpatient					
Emergency Outpatient Visits.	451.8	448.6	435.8	404.5	386.8
Other Outpatient Visits.	1,039.4	1,012.8	1,059.3	1,128.4	1,131.0
Total Outpatient Visits	1,491.2	1,461.5	1,495.1	1,533.0	1,517.8
Outpatient Surgeries	54.4	54.8	52.9	53.7	53.9
Expense per Capita (per person).	$1,746.6	$1,588.4	$1,509.2	$1,470.1	$1,347.2

TABLE 6

OREGON

U.S. Registered Community Hospitals
(Nonfederal, short-term general and other special hospitals)

Overview 2004–2008

	2008	2007	2006	2005	2004
Total Community Hospitals in Oregon	**58**	**58**	**58**	**58**	**58**
Bed Size Category					
6-24	8	7	8	8	8
25-49	19	20	19	19	19
50-99	11	11	12	12	12
100-199	9	9	9	9	10
200-299	5	4	4	4	3
300-399	0	1	0	0	0
400-499	4	4	5	6	6
500 + ...	2	2	1	0	0
Location					
Hospitals Urban..........................	29	29	29	29	26
Hospitals Rural	29	29	29	29	32
Control					
State and Local Government................	13	13	13	12	12
Not for Profit	43	43	42	43	43
Investor owned	2	2	3	3	3
Physician Models					
Independent Practice Association	13	13	14	17	13
Group Practice without Walls...............	8	7	6	6	4
Open Physician-Hospital Organization	6	6	10	10	4
Closed Physician-Hospital Organization	2	3	3	3	3
Management Service Organization	14	14	9	9	7
Integrated Salary Model....................	35	36	31	29	21
Equity Model	1	0	1	1	0
Foundation..............................	5	3	4	3	1
Insurance Products					
Health Maintenance Organization	14	16	13	14	10
Preferred Provider Organization..............	14	21	19	20	15
Indemnity Fee for Service	3	5	6	6	3
Managed Care Contracts					
Health Maintenance Organization	30	34	34	36	31
Preferred Provider Organization..............	51	47	46	45	35
Affiliations					
Hospitals in a System.....................	37	37	34	34	34
Hospitals in a Network....................	25	24	22	22	19
Hospitals in a Group Purchasing Organization..	56	57	57	57	45

TABLE 6

OREGON

U.S. Registered Community Hospitals
(Nonfederal, short-term general and other special hospitals)

Utilization, Personnel, Revenue and Expenses, Community Health Indicators 2004–2008

	2008	2007	2006	2005	2004
TOTAL FACILITY (Includes Hospital and Nursing Home Units)					
Utilization - Inpatient					
Beds	6,614	6,641	6,609	6,515	6,505
Admissions	348,600	347,089	341,540	336,173	341,307
Inpatient Days	1,551,894	1,534,999	1,508,314	1,490,898	1,461,923
Average Length of Stay	4.5	4.4	4.4	4.4	4.3
Inpatient Surgeries	120,048	119,933	117,402	114,513	114,611
Births	47,273	48,230	47,369	45,475	45,957
Utilization - Outpatient					
Emergency Outpatient Visits	1,330,142	1,301,629	1,250,008	1,216,163	1,147,196
Other Outpatient Visits	7,228,022	6,877,816	7,007,868	6,757,046	6,712,041
Total Outpatient Visits	8,558,164	8,179,445	8,257,876	7,973,209	7,859,237
Outpatient Surgeries	210,333	213,159	206,125	197,263	188,638
Personnel					
Full Time RNs	9,498	9,248	8,633	8,404	8,144
Full Time LPNs	214	179	219	251	431
Part Time RNs	7,753	7,217	7,901	7,976	7,510
Part Time LPNs	171	212	240	259	260
Total Full Time	37,581	36,209	35,767	34,474	33,571
Total Part Time	20,437	19,627	20,862	21,368	20,868
Revenue - Inpatient					
Gross Inpatient Revenue	$7,942,127,860	$7,305,555,599	$6,636,156,491	$6,178,760,391	$5,702,413,613
Revenue - Outpatient					
Gross Outpatient Revenue	$6,403,379,909	$5,753,564,088	$5,193,062,718	$4,697,819,458	$4,128,678,383
Revenue and Expenses - Totals (Includes Inpatient and Outpatient)					
Total Gross Revenue	$14,345,507,769	$13,059,119,687	$11,829,219,209	$10,876,579,849	$9,831,091,996
Deductions from Revenue	7,249,042,014	6,506,212,357	5,737,941,726	5,249,271,986	4,651,055,624
Net Patient Revenue	7,096,465,755	6,552,907,330	6,091,277,483	5,627,307,863	5,180,036,372
Other Operating Revenue	351,902,221	303,815,392	299,687,588	255,942,976	260,818,230
Other Nonoperating Revenue	(55,685,102)	238,442,802	138,893,278	92,691,720	67,106,324
Total Net Revenue	7,392,682,874	7,095,165,524	6,529,858,349	5,975,942,559	5,507,960,926
Total Expenses	7,376,298,400	6,704,406,099	6,192,331,481	5,665,479,466	5,206,775,669
HOSPITAL UNIT (Excludes Separate Nursing Home Units)					
Utilization - Inpatient					
Beds	6,551	6,577	6,345	6,251	6,265
Admissions	348,313	346,747	341,242	335,831	340,958
Inpatient Days	1,485,018	1,464,066	1,437,308	1,418,888	1,398,492
Average Length of Stay	4.3	4.2	4.2	4.2	4.1
Personnel					
Total Full Time	37,436	36,068	35,615	34,331	33,429
Total Part Time	20,381	19,561	20,784	21,280	20,784
Revenue and Expenses - Totals (Includes Inpatient and Outpatient)					
Total Net Revenue	$7,380,524,478	$7,083,566,291	$6,520,330,928	$5,964,862,021	$5,498,352,090
Total Expenses	7,366,061,834	6,693,285,719	6,183,003,680	5,653,222,094	5,196,487,284
COMMUNITY HEALTH INDICATORS PER 1000 POPULATION					
Total Population (in thousands)	3,790	3,736	3,681	3,622	3,576
Inpatient					
Beds	1.8	1.8	1.8	1.8	1.8
Admissions	92.0	92.9	92.8	92.8	95.4
Inpatient Days	409.5	410.9	409.8	411.6	408.8
Inpatient Surgeries	31.7	32.1	31.9	31.6	32.0
Births	12.5	12.9	12.9	12.6	12.9
Outpatient					
Emergency Outpatient Visits	351.0	348.4	339.6	335.8	320.8
Other Outpatient Visits	1,907.1	1,841.2	1,903.8	1,865.6	1,876.8
Total Outpatient Visits	2,258.1	2,189.6	2,243.4	2,201.4	2,197.6
Outpatient Surgeries	55.5	57.1	56.0	54.5	52.7
Expense per Capita (per person)	$1,946.2	$1,794.8	$1,682.3	$1,564.2	$1,455.9

States

TABLE 6

PENNSYLVANIA

U.S. Registered Community Hospitals
(Nonfederal, short-term general and other special hospitals)

Overview 2004–2008

	2008	2007	2006	2005	2004
Total Community Hospitals in Pennsylvania ...	201	187	188	191	197
Bed Size Category					
6-24	2	2	3	3	4
25-49	29	21	22	19	16
50-99	42	33	29	33	36
100-199	49	53	57	58	63
200-299	41	40	37	40	42
300-399	14	12	15	16	13
400-499	9	12	12	10	12
500 + ...	15	14	13	12	11
Location					
Hospitals Urban..........................	152	139	140	143	153
Hospitals Rural	49	48	48	48	44
Control					
State and Local Government................	3	2	2	2	1
Not for Profit	160	158	161	165	172
Investor owned	38	27	25	24	24
Physician Models					
Independent Practice Association	9	9	9	9	12
Group Practice without Walls................	13	12	12	13	15
Open Physician-Hospital Organization	32	31	30	31	37
Closed Physician-Hospital Organization	4	5	6	7	5
Management Service Organization	27	25	30	26	27
Integrated Salary Model....................	69	75	72	69	66
Equity Model	2	2	4	4	5
Foundation...............................	6	5	5	6	9
Insurance Products					
Health Maintenance Organization	29	29	29	28	30
Preferred Provider Organization..............	44	41	39	41	42
Indemnity Fee for Service	15	12	13	11	11
Managed Care Contracts					
Health Maintenance Organization	116	122	125	115	138
Preferred Provider Organization..............	112	117	121	109	131
Affiliations					
Hospitals in a System......................	116	101	107	106	104
Hospitals in a Network.....................	48	49	52	39	48
Hospitals in a Group Purchasing Organization..	131	138	142	124	143

States

TABLE 6

PENNSYLVANIA

U.S. Registered Community Hospitals
(Nonfederal, short-term general and other special hospitals)

Utilization, Personnel, Revenue and Expenses, Community Health Indicators 2004–2008

	2008	2007	2006	2005	2004
TOTAL FACILITY (Includes Hospital and Nursing Home Units)					
Utilization - Inpatient					
Beds	40,407	39,728	39,567	39,602	40,079
Admissions	1,901,417	1,880,382	1,866,261	1,863,299	1,846,702
Inpatient Days	10,353,793	10,257,605	10,110,336	10,170,812	10,259,088
Average Length of Stay	5.4	5.5	5.4	5.5	5.6
Inpatient Surgeries	558,918	549,182	553,061	550,986	546,837
Births	143,674	143,281	141,971	140,089	134,864
Utilization - Outpatient					
Emergency Outpatient Visits	6,006,841	5,771,876	5,583,228	5,379,119	5,277,055
Other Outpatient Visits	32,449,554	31,012,536	30,127,411	29,531,995	28,135,789
Total Outpatient Visits	38,456,395	36,784,412	35,710,639	34,911,114	33,412,844
Outpatient Surgeries	948,852	931,789	998,156	1,000,746	993,636
Personnel					
Full Time RNs	51,379	49,838	47,217	46,105	43,382
Full Time LPNs	4,183	4,225	4,342	4,703	4,727
Part Time RNs	25,909	26,044	25,541	24,832	25,620
Part Time LPNs	2,013	2,050	2,105	2,256	2,431
Total Full Time	211,389	204,480	200,061	196,471	190,861
Total Part Time	75,418	75,971	75,335	73,870	74,959
Revenue - Inpatient					
Gross Inpatient Revenue	$72,947,964,529	$68,794,426,900	$61,367,161,956	$57,094,838,770	$50,833,106,752
Revenue - Outpatient					
Gross Outpatient Revenue	$43,951,207,740	$39,611,381,052	$35,511,165,044	$31,755,327,351	$27,569,043,380
Revenue and Expenses - Totals					
(Includes Inpatient and Outpatient)					
Total Gross Revenue	$116,899,172,269	$108,405,807,952	$96,878,327,000	$88,850,166,121	$78,402,150,132
Deductions from Revenue	85,447,182,883	78,990,384,684	69,114,526,615	63,021,240,504	54,797,070,047
Net Patient Revenue	31,451,989,386	29,415,423,268	27,763,800,385	25,828,925,617	23,605,080,085
Other Operating Revenue	1,437,920,156	1,437,490,621	1,410,478,499	1,277,949,356	1,141,606,635
Other Nonoperating Revenue	183,327,965	696,634,527	521,348,733	349,212,193	345,413,069
Total Net Revenue	33,073,237,507	31,549,548,416	29,695,627,707	27,456,087,166	25,092,099,789
Total Expenses	31,323,216,832	28,750,837,150	27,714,356,897	25,733,953,779	23,881,154,851
HOSPITAL UNIT (Excludes Separate Nursing Home Units)					
Utilization - Inpatient					
Beds	38,441	37,762	37,449	37,640	37,931
Admissions	1,880,413	1,859,317	1,843,785	1,840,409	1,820,785
Inpatient Days	9,836,158	9,655,775	9,458,378	9,565,533	9,585,201
Average Length of Stay	5.2	5.2	5.1	5.2	5.3
Personnel					
Total Full Time	209,962	202,951	198,398	195,064	174,983
Total Part Time	74,556	75,053	74,360	72,851	72,378
Revenue and Expenses - Totals					
(Includes Inpatient and Outpatient)					
Total Net Revenue	$32,864,948,434	$31,356,583,352	$29,511,480,040	$27,289,851,511	$24,903,242,365
Total Expenses	31,124,814,383	28,586,982,718	27,484,488,144	25,604,477,946	23,719,764,958
COMMUNITY HEALTH INDICATORS PER 1000 POPULATION					
Total Population (in thousands)	12,448	12,420	12,388	12,352	12,336
Inpatient					
Beds	3.2	3.2	3.2	3.2	3.2
Admissions	152.7	151.4	150.7	150.9	149.7
Inpatient Days	831.7	825.9	816.1	823.4	831.7
Inpatient Surgeries	44.9	44.2	44.6	44.6	44.3
Births	11.5	11.5	11.5	11.3	10.9
Outpatient					
Emergency Outpatient Visits	482.5	464.7	450.7	435.5	427.8
Other Outpatient Visits	2,606.8	2,497.0	2,432.0	2,390.9	2,280.9
Total Outpatient Visits	3,089.3	2,961.7	2,882.7	2,826.4	2,708.6
Outpatient Surgeries	76.2	75.0	80.6	81.0	80.5
Expense per Capita (per person)	$2,516.3	$2,314.9	$2,237.2	$2,083.4	$1,935.9

States

TABLE 6

RHODE ISLAND

U.S. Registered Community Hospitals
(Nonfederal, short-term general and other special hospitals)

Overview 2004–2008

	2008	2007	2006	2005	2004
Total Community Hospitals in Rhode Island ...	11	11	11	11	11
Bed Size Category					
6-24	0	0	0	0	0
25-49	0	0	0	0	0
50-99	1	1	1	1	1
100-199	6	6	6	6	6
200-299	2	2	2	2	2
300-399	1	1	1	1	1
400-499	0	0	0	0	0
500 + ...	1	1	1	1	1
Location					
Hospitals Urban...........................	11	11	11	11	10
Hospitals Rural	0	0	0	0	1
Control					
State and Local Government................	0	0	0	0	0
Not for Profit	11	11	11	11	11
Investor owned	0	0	0	0	0
Physician Models					
Independent Practice Association	6	6	6	6	6
Group Practice without Walls................	0	0	0	0	0
Open Physician-Hospital Organization	7	7	7	7	6
Closed Physician-Hospital Organization	1	1	1	1	1
Management Service Organization	2	2	2	1	2
Integrated Salary Model....................	5	5	5	5	5
Equity Model	0	0	0	0	0
Foundation...............................	3	3	3	3	3
Insurance Products					
Health Maintenance Organization	2	2	2	2	3
Preferred Provider Organization..............	1	2	2	2	3
Indemnity Fee for Service	0	1	1	1	2
Managed Care Contracts					
Health Maintenance Organization	9	10	10	10	9
Preferred Provider Organization..............	10	9	10	10	9
Affiliations					
Hospitals in a System......................	5	5	5	5	5
Hospitals in a Network	1	1	3	3	1
Hospitals in a Group Purchasing Organization..	9	10	10	10	9

TABLE 6

RHODE ISLAND

U.S. Registered Community Hospitals
(Nonfederal, short-term general and other special hospitals)

Utilization, Personnel, Revenue and Expenses, Community Health Indicators 2004–2008

	2008	2007	2006	2005	2004
TOTAL FACILITY (Includes Hospital and Nursing Home Units)					
Utilization - Inpatient					
Beds	2,463	2,440	2,004	2,405	2,397
Admissions	127,413	128,519	127,179	126,619	125,308
Inpatient Days	666,745	672,831	680,881	684,067	663,734
Average Length of Stay	5.2	5.2	5.4	5.4	5.3
Inpatient Surgeries	38,970	37,084	36,517	36,321	38,190
Births	12,785	13,305	13,171	13,408	13,662
Utilization - Outpatient					
Emergency Outpatient Visits	494,817	485,624	466,720	454,840	431,433
Other Outpatient Visits	2,139,409	2,082,179	1,973,903	2,027,908	1,712,231
Total Outpatient Visits	2,634,226	2,567,803	2,440,623	2,482,748	2,143,664
Outpatient Surgeries	82,597	91,082	92,416	93,706	89,784
Personnel					
Full Time RNs	2,301	2,269	2,074	1,849	1,804
Full Time LPNs	92	119	128	143	146
Part Time RNs	3,147	2,840	2,862	2,823	2,757
Part Time LPNs	118	149	148	173	195
Total Full Time	12,908	12,810	12,612	13,006	12,218
Total Part Time	8,873	8,459	8,239	7,966	8,180
Revenue - Inpatient					
Gross Inpatient Revenue	$3,383,235,261	$3,157,359,726	$2,969,325,063	$2,782,209,685	$2,503,098,985
Revenue - Outpatient					
Gross Outpatient Revenue	$3,067,731,603	$2,874,889,949	$2,667,727,132	$2,431,758,707	$2,159,431,575
Revenue and Expenses - Totals (Includes Inpatient and Outpatient)					
Total Gross Revenue	$6,450,966,864	$6,032,249,675	$5,637,052,195	$5,213,968,392	$4,662,530,560
Deductions from Revenue	4,018,043,505	3,748,195,534	3,451,826,897	3,165,053,391	2,761,763,453
Net Patient Revenue	2,432,923,359	2,284,054,141	2,185,225,298	2,048,915,001	1,900,767,107
Other Operating Revenue	247,620,663	241,675,507	233,392,317	217,801,657	194,307,111
Other Nonoperating Revenue	6,024,220	26,894,546	15,205,663	14,066,548	13,381,409
Total Net Revenue	2,686,568,242	2,552,624,194	2,433,823,278	2,280,783,206	2,108,455,627
Total Expenses	2,649,565,524	2,504,792,635	2,395,122,194	2,242,386,790	2,084,652,695
HOSPITAL UNIT (Excludes Separate Nursing Home Units)					
Utilization - Inpatient					
Beds	2,439	2,425	2,370	2,346	2,354
Admissions	127,095	127,928	126,326	125,280	124,322
Inpatient Days	662,377	665,265	669,632	667,664	651,049
Average Length of Stay	5.2	5.2	5.3	5.3	5.2
Personnel					
Total Full Time	12,846	12,799	12,601	12,967	10,959
Total Part Time	8,790	8,451	8,231	7,931	8,001
Revenue and Expenses - Totals (Includes Inpatient and Outpatient)					
Total Net Revenue	$2,679,872,351	$2,549,240,364	$2,429,083,387	$2,265,259,405	$2,100,669,005
Total Expenses	2,643,600,577	2,501,997,062	2,391,044,858	2,231,955,395	2,081,390,651
COMMUNITY HEALTH INDICATORS PER 1000 POPULATION					
Total Population (in thousands)	1,051	1,053	1,059	1,064	1,071
Inpatient					
Beds	2.3	2.3	2.3	2.3	2.2
Admissions	121.3	122.0	120.1	119.0	117.0
Inpatient Days	634.5	638.9	643.0	642.7	619.7
Inpatient Surgeries	37.1	35.2	34.5	34.1	35.7
Births	12.2	12.6	12.4	12.6	12.8
Outpatient					
Emergency Outpatient Visits	470.9	461.1	440.7	427.3	402.8
Other Outpatient Visits	2,036.0	1,977.1	1,863.9	1,905.1	1,598.6
Total Outpatient Visits	2,506.9	2,438.2	2,304.7	2,332.4	2,001.4
Outpatient Surgeries	78.6	86.5	87.3	88.0	83.8
Expense per Capita (per person)	$2,521.5	$2,378.4	$2,261.7	$2,106.6	$1,946.3

States

TABLE **6**

SOUTH CAROLINA

U.S. Registered Community Hospitals
(Nonfederal, short-term general and other special hospitals)

Overview 2004–2008

	2008	2007	2006	2005	2004
Total Community Hospitals in South Carolina..	69	67	66	63	62
Bed Size Category					
6-24	0	1	0	0	1
25-49	18	16	16	13	10
50-99	12	11	11	12	16
100-199	14	14	15	14	14
200-299	12	14	12	14	11
300-399	7	5	7	5	3
400-499	1	2	1	2	4
500 + ...	5	4	4	3	3
Location					
Hospitals Urban...........................	44	42	41	39	35
Hospitals Rural	25	25	25	24	27
Control					
State and Local Government................	20	19	19	19	19
Not for Profit	25	23	22	23	24
Investor owned	24	25	25	21	19
Physician Models					
Independent Practice Association	6	3	2	2	4
Group Practice without Walls...............	3	0	2	4	0
Open Physician-Hospital Organization	8	7	9	9	12
Closed Physician-Hospital Organization	1	1	1	6	1
Management Service Organization	0	1	4	4	6
Integrated Salary Model....................	14	13	12	10	7
Equity Model	0	0	0	0	0
Foundation...............................	0	0	0	0	0
Insurance Products					
Health Maintenance Organization	2	2	4	2	2
Preferred Provider Organization..............	5	7	9	6	7
Indemnity Fee for Service	1	1	2	1	0
Managed Care Contracts					
Health Maintenance Organization	37	33	40	40	40
Preferred Provider Organization..............	36	36	46	46	44
Affiliations					
Hospitals in a System.....................	45	43	42	40	40
Hospitals in a Network....................	15	16	14	13	18
Hospitals in a Group Purchasing Organization..	52	1	—	—	—

TABLE 6

SOUTH CAROLINA

U.S. Registered Community Hospitals
(Nonfederal, short-term general and other special hospitals)

Utilization, Personnel, Revenue and Expenses, Community Health Indicators 2004–2008

	2008	2007	2006	2005	2004
TOTAL FACILITY (Includes Hospital and Nursing Home Units)					
Utilization - Inpatient					
Beds	12,400	12,002	11,790	11,438	11,222
Admissions	528,872	518,994	521,773	528,122	512,908
Inpatient Days	2,962,830	3,006,247	3,083,647	3,079,884	2,921,052
Average Length of Stay.	5.6	5.8	5.9	5.8	5.7
Inpatient Surgeries.	196,304	190,349	189,509	193,467	178,005
Births.	56,068	56,616	52,676	51,142	50,634
Utilization - Outpatient					
Emergency Outpatient Visits	1,954,264	1,890,731	1,893,605	1,739,487	1,694,314
Other Outpatient Visits.	3,969,951	4,151,591	4,200,091	4,086,965	5,350,857
Total Outpatient Visits	5,924,215	6,042,322	6,093,696	5,826,452	7,045,171
Outpatient Surgeries	294,280	280,735	288,804	291,119	273,128
Personnel					
Full Time RNs	16,203	15,120	14,900	14,139	13,281
Full Time LPNs	1,292	1,363	1,462	1,417	1,420
Part Time RNs	5,834	5,826	5,429	5,406	5,474
Part Time LPNs	510	514	491	449	507
Total Full Time.	58,372	54,571	53,886	51,545	49,087
Total Part Time	16,302	16,040	15,478	15,267	15,768
Revenue - Inpatient					
Gross Inpatient Revenue.	$16,743,319,395	$14,774,254,035	$13,760,712,078	$12,608,535,831	$11,113,931,424
Revenue - Outpatient					
Gross Outpatient Revenue	$10,266,244,867	$8,994,634,785	$7,918,853,975	$7,126,463,984	$6,244,132,865
Revenue and Expenses - Totals					
(Includes Inpatient and Outpatient)					
Total Gross Revenue.	$27,009,564,262	$23,768,888,820	$21,679,566,053	$19,734,999,815	$17,358,064,289
Deductions from Revenue.	18,082,987,646	15,526,589,717	13,957,650,045	12,554,885,094	10,562,293,848
Net Patient Revenue	8,926,576,616	8,242,299,103	7,721,916,008	7,180,114,721	6,795,770,441
Other Operating Revenue	262,341,118	224,352,076	222,065,204	230,677,665	215,550,499
Other Nonoperating Revenue	85,822,937	161,793,047	12,894,836	89,246,136	76,686,995
Total Net Revenue.	9,274,740,671	8,628,444,226	7,956,876,048	7,500,038,522	7,088,007,935
Total Expenses.	8,890,465,525	7,888,982,140	7,522,995,957	7,322,103,356	6,779,371,913
HOSPITAL UNIT (Excludes Separate Nursing Home Units)					
Utilization - Inpatient					
Beds	11,728	11,080	10,695	11,089	10,594
Admissions	524,838	514,618	516,307	526,296	508,769
Inpatient Days	2,750,321	2,686,337	2,717,463	2,983,107	2,704,771
Average Length of Stay.	5.2	5.2	5.3	5.7	5.3
Personnel					
Total Full Time.	57,714	53,761	52,914	51,010	47,198
Total Part Time	16,043	15,737	15,161	15,177	15,470
Revenue and Expenses - Totals					
(Includes Inpatient and Outpatient)					
Total Net Revenue.	$9,217,872,804	$8,562,824,215	$5,684,998,987	$7,466,733,849	$6,977,895,609
Total Expenses.	8,842,007,632	7,826,701,269	7,443,633,754	7,304,244,135	6,701,411,300
COMMUNITY HEALTH INDICATORS PER 1000 POPULATION					
Total Population (in thousands)	4,480	4,405	4,325	4,249	4,197
Inpatient					
Beds	2.8	2.7	2.7	2.7	2.7
Admissions	118.1	117.8	120.6	124.3	122.2
Inpatient Days	661.4	682.5	713.0	724.8	696.0
Inpatient Surgeries.	43.8	43.2	43.8	45.5	42.4
Births.	12.5	12.9	12.2	12.0	12.1
Outpatient					
Emergency Outpatient Visits	436.2	429.2	437.8	409.4	403.7
Other Outpatient Visits.	886.2	942.5	971.2	961.8	1,275.0
Total Outpatient Visits	1,322.4	1,371.7	1,409.0	1,371.1	1,678.7
Outpatient Surgeries	65.7	63.7	66.8	68.5	65.1
Expense per Capita (per person).	$1,984.6	$1,791.0	$1,739.5	$1,723.1	$1,615.4

TABLE 6

SOUTH DAKOTA

U.S. Registered Community Hospitals
(Nonfederal, short-term general and other special hospitals)

Overview 2004–2008

	2008	2007	2006	2005	2004
Total Community Hospitals in South Dakota...	53	51	52	52	51
Bed Size Category					
6-24	18	15	15	13	13
25-49	12	13	14	15	13
50-99	11	10	10	12	12
100-199	7	8	8	7	7
200-299	1	2	2	2	3
300-399	2	1	1	1	1
400-499	2	1	1	1	1
500 + ...	0	1	1	1	1
Location					
Hospitals Urban...........................	11	10	10	10	6
Hospitals Rural	42	41	42	42	45
Control					
State and Local Government................	5	5	5	5	6
Not for Profit	44	43	44	44	44
Investor owned	4	3	3	3	1
Physician Models					
Independent Practice Association	11	10	11	11	8
Group Practice without Walls................	3	3	3	4	2
Open Physician-Hospital Organization	6	8	6	6	5
Closed Physician-Hospital Organization	3	4	3	4	2
Management Service Organization	2	3	2	3	3
Integrated Salary Model....................	25	25	24	21	23
Equity Model	2	2	2	2	1
Foundation...............................	1	2	1	1	1
Insurance Products					
Health Maintenance Organization	17	15	15	17	17
Preferred Provider Organization..............	13	18	18	20	19
Indemnity Fee for Service	8	5	6	7	5
Managed Care Contracts					
Health Maintenance Organization	24	22	23	22	21
Preferred Provider Organization..............	32	32	33	36	36
Affiliations					
Hospitals in a System......................	38	36	36	36	38
Hospitals in a Network.....................	22	20	20	21	20
Hospitals in a Group Purchasing Organization..	45	44	46	48	47

TABLE 6

SOUTH DAKOTA

U.S. Registered Community Hospitals
(Nonfederal, short-term general and other special hospitals)

Utilization, Personnel, Revenue and Expenses, Community Health Indicators 2004–2008

	2008	2007	2006	2005	2004
TOTAL FACILITY (Includes Hospital and Nursing Home Units)					
Utilization - Inpatient					
Beds	4,110	4,245	4,326	4,325	4,611
Admissions	102,116	99,931	96,964	102,127	103,495
Inpatient Days	1,005,766	1,008,378	1,022,716	1,027,776	1,039,983
Average Length of Stay	9.8	10.1	10.5	10.1	10.0
Inpatient Surgeries	31,715	33,312	35,010	34,546	33,384
Births	12,258	12,125	11,380	11,357	11,235
Utilization - Outpatient					
Emergency Outpatient Visits	239,192	226,131	222,244	222,415	215,168
Other Outpatient Visits	1,618,764	1,562,594	1,550,535	1,420,559	1,355,822
Total Outpatient Visits	1,857,956	1,788,725	1,772,779	1,642,974	1,570,990
Outpatient Surgeries	71,162	61,234	63,815	52,647	48,917
Personnel					
Full Time RNs	3,160	3,106	2,912	2,955	2,720
Full Time LPNs	185	189	203	212	229
Part Time RNs	2,253	1,874	1,987	1,907	1,913
Part Time LPNs	131	130	144	157	152
Total Full Time	14,488	13,502	12,819	12,823	12,307
Total Part Time	8,067	7,187	7,449	7,186	7,321
Revenue - Inpatient					
Gross Inpatient Revenue	$2,293,166,775	$2,051,748,519	$1,806,073,890	$1,742,221,313	$1,616,717,388
Revenue - Outpatient					
Gross Outpatient Revenue	$1,875,244,749	$1,595,180,119	$1,425,424,763	$1,183,690,864	$998,770,947
Revenue and Expenses - Totals					
(Includes Inpatient and Outpatient)					
Total Gross Revenue	$4,168,411,524	$3,646,928,638	$3,231,498,653	$2,925,912,177	$2,615,488,335
Deductions from Revenue	2,187,095,692	1,796,255,037	1,533,819,613	1,368,023,876	1,180,382,034
Net Patient Revenue	1,981,315,832	1,850,673,601	1,697,679,040	1,557,888,301	1,426,106,301
Other Operating Revenue	103,615,596	121,580,983	140,692,507	99,897,462	103,911,665
Other Nonoperating Revenue	30,994,497	64,050,745	47,085,508	41,295,206	39,077,045
Total Net Revenue	2,115,925,925	2,036,305,329	1,885,457,055	1,699,080,969	1,569,095,011
Total Expenses	1,919,761,533	1,791,313,970	1,646,922,945	1,537,687,771	1,439,580,152
HOSPITAL UNIT (Excludes Separate Nursing Home Units)					
Utilization - Inpatient					
Beds	2,671	2,621	2,636	2,664	2,885
Admissions	100,555	97,994	95,183	100,240	101,758
Inpatient Days	509,176	455,753	442,682	457,739	492,821
Average Length of Stay	5.1	4.7	4.7	4.6	4.8
Personnel					
Total Full Time	13,650	12,555	11,863	11,843	11,315
Total Part Time	7,369	6,339	6,557	6,206	6,344
Revenue and Expenses - Totals					
(Includes Inpatient and Outpatient)					
Total Net Revenue	$2,035,881,683	$1,957,696,000	$1,802,353,636	$1,621,139,772	$1,497,133,151
Total Expenses	1,848,451,464	1,713,828,405	1,574,797,817	1,466,915,613	1,377,607,569
COMMUNITY HEALTH INDICATORS PER 1000 POPULATION					
Total Population (in thousands)	804	796	787	779	774
Inpatient					
Beds	5.1	5.3	5.5	5.5	6.0
Admissions	127.0	125.6	123.1	131.0	133.8
Inpatient Days	1,250.7	1,267.3	1,298.9	1,318.8	1,344.4
Inpatient Surgeries	39.4	41.9	44.5	44.3	43.2
Births	15.2	15.2	14.5	14.6	14.5
Outpatient					
Emergency Outpatient Visits	297.4	284.2	282.3	285.4	278.2
Other Outpatient Visits	2,012.9	1,963.8	1,969.2	1,822.8	1,752.8
Total Outpatient Visits	2,310.3	2,248.0	2,251.5	2,108.2	2,030.9
Outpatient Surgeries	88.5	77.0	81.0	67.6	63.2
Expense per Capita (per person)	$2,387.2	$2,251.3	$2,091.6	$1,973.1	$1,861.0

States

TABLE 6

TENNESSEE

U.S. Registered Community Hospitals
(Nonfederal, short-term general and other special hospitals)

Overview 2004–2008

	2008	2007	2006	2005	2004
Total Community Hospitals in Tennessee	137	133	130	130	127
Bed Size Category					
6-24	7	7	6	4	4
25-49	36	28	28	30	28
50-99	32	34	33	35	36
100-199	29	33	35	31	28
200-299	12	12	8	11	12
300-399	7	5	8	6	6
400-499	5	6	5	5	5
500 + ...	9	8	7	8	8
Location					
Hospitals Urban.	81	77	74	74	62
Hospitals Rural	56	56	56	56	65
Control					
State and Local Government.	22	22	24	24	24
Not for Profit	60	61	60	62	64
Investor owned	55	50	46	44	39
Physician Models					
Independent Practice Association	14	16	13	14	19
Group Practice without Walls.	4	4	2	2	3
Open Physician-Hospital Organization	19	21	19	22	22
Closed Physician-Hospital Organization	5	5	3	2	2
Management Service Organization	15	17	18	17	22
Integrated Salary Model	19	16	11	14	13
Equity Model	0	0	0	0	0
Foundation.	8	6	4	7	4
Insurance Products					
Health Maintenance Organization	14	16	17	19	12
Preferred Provider Organization.	26	25	26	31	24
Indemnity Fee for Service	10	14	15	14	9
Managed Care Contracts					
Health Maintenance Organization	86	77	75	77	70
Preferred Provider Organization.	87	80	78	81	77
Affiliations					
Hospitals in a System.	104	101	98	98	94
Hospitals in a Network	45	38	41	40	40
Hospitals in a Group Purchasing Organization. .	89	85	82	83	81

TABLE 6

TENNESSEE

U.S. Registered Community Hospitals
(Nonfederal, short-term general and other special hospitals)

Utilization, Personnel, Revenue and Expenses, Community Health Indicators 2004–2008

	2008	2007	2006	2005	2004
TOTAL FACILITY (Includes Hospital and Nursing Home Units)					
Utilization - Inpatient					
Beds	21,102	21,688	20,020	20,570	20,000
Admissions	859,344	969,763	853,304	829,247	825,269
Inpatient Days	4,911,215	5,372,297	4,806,765	4,767,818	4,673,861
Average Length of Stay	5.7	5.5	5.6	5.7	5.7
Inpatient Surgeries	243,820	258,348	231,102	253,509	235,406
Births	83,978	90,042	81,067	81,454	81,088
Utilization - Outpatient					
Emergency Outpatient Visits	3,251,592	3,253,035	2,806,111	3,062,336	2,957,496
Other Outpatient Visits	7,995,403	8,565,760	8,055,773	8,603,983	7,304,854
Total Outpatient Visits	11,246,995	11,818,795	10,861,884	11,666,319	10,262,350
Outpatient Surgeries	385,344	443,649	380,827	386,061	376,841
Personnel					
Full Time RNs	24,727	27,626	23,420	21,295	20,374
Full Time LPNs	3,286	3,744	3,644	3,872	3,904
Part Time RNs	8,891	10,578	7,658	7,504	7,048
Part Time LPNs	881	1,028	989	996	1,033
Total Full Time	90,902	105,326	92,365	83,981	83,319
Total Part Time	25,311	30,136	23,142	21,350	20,385
Revenue - Inpatient					
Gross Inpatient Revenue	$24,012,198,547	$24,331,008,568	$19,934,787,410	$17,803,281,276	$16,239,786,328
Revenue - Outpatient					
Gross Outpatient Revenue	$15,732,131,119	$16,507,650,360	$13,015,442,619	$11,366,280,361	$10,132,787,849
Revenue and Expenses - Totals					
(Includes Inpatient and Outpatient)					
Total Gross Revenue	$39,744,329,666	$40,838,658,928	$32,950,230,029	$29,169,561,637	$26,372,574,177
Deductions from Revenue	27,469,500,901	27,397,484,207	21,525,822,289	18,614,613,384	16,471,811,012
Net Patient Revenue	12,274,828,765	13,441,174,721	11,424,407,740	10,554,948,253	9,900,763,165
Other Operating Revenue	496,258,779	523,978,490	415,142,709	360,314,741	392,768,909
Other Nonoperating Revenue	81,614,397	363,631,353	201,731,194	215,626,677	196,711,112
Total Net Revenue	12,852,701,941	14,328,784,564	12,041,281,643	11,130,889,671	10,490,243,186
Total Expenses	11,996,245,958	13,405,461,053	11,497,417,852	10,630,276,472	9,902,904,362
HOSPITAL UNIT (Excludes Separate Nursing Home Units)					
Utilization - Inpatient					
Beds	19,467	20,088	18,755	18,815	18,698
Admissions	849,060	958,480	841,956	815,516	811,465
Inpatient Days	4,396,275	4,889,474	4,300,755	4,191,641	4,123,042
Average Length of Stay	5.2	5.1	5.1	5.1	5.1
Personnel					
Total Full Time	89,529	103,980	91,079	82,566	81,915
Total Part Time	25,004	29,745	22,826	20,868	19,962
Revenue and Expenses - Totals					
(Includes Inpatient and Outpatient)					
Total Net Revenue	$12,735,644,514	$14,221,268,188	$11,933,067,685	$11,007,090,456	$10,363,793,823
Total Expenses	11,896,072,460	13,318,384,157	11,399,991,123	10,517,355,585	9,798,724,693
COMMUNITY HEALTH INDICATORS PER 1000 POPULATION					
Total Population (in thousands)	6,215	6,149	6,068	5,983	5,907
Inpatient					
Beds	3.4	3.5	3.3	3.4	3.4
Admissions	138.3	157.7	140.6	138.6	139.7
Inpatient Days	790.2	873.7	792.1	796.9	791.2
Inpatient Surgeries	39.2	42.0	38.1	42.4	39.9
Births	13.5	14.6	13.4	13.6	13.7
Outpatient					
Emergency Outpatient Visits	523.2	529.0	462.4	511.8	500.7
Other Outpatient Visits	1,286.5	1,393.0	1,327.5	1,438.0	1,236.7
Total Outpatient Visits	1,809.7	1,922.0	1,789.9	1,949.8	1,737.3
Outpatient Surgeries	62.0	72.1	62.8	64.5	63.8
Expense per Capita (per person)	$1,930.2	$2,180.1	$1,894.7	$1,776.7	$1,676.5

States

TABLE **6**

TEXAS

U.S. Registered Community Hospitals
(Nonfederal, short-term general and other special hospitals)

Overview 2004–2008

	2008	2007	2006	2005	2004
Total Community Hospitals in Texas..........	**426**	**409**	**417**	**415**	**418**
Bed Size Category					
6-24	63	60	61	56	57
25-49	111	106	111	112	111
50-99	87	81	77	76	77
100-199	64	59	66	75	77
200-299	44	46	44	41	40
300-399	20	24	25	25	29
400-499	14	13	15	14	10
500 + ...	23	20	18	16	17
Location					
Hospitals Urban..........................	275	260	268	266	258
Hospitals Rural	151	149	149	149	160
Control					
State and Local Government................	117	117	120	124	126
Not for Profit	152	150	148	152	153
Investor owned	157	142	149	139	139
Physician Models					
Independent Practice Association	67	80	80	83	86
Group Practice without Walls...............	14	14	15	18	19
Open Physician-Hospital Organization	90	88	87	82	84
Closed Physician-Hospital Organization	17	17	15	16	13
Management Service Organization	63	65	55	49	45
Integrated Salary Model....................	91	87	89	79	74
Equity Model	12	9	7	8	6
Foundation..............................	34	38	34	38	29
Insurance Products					
Health Maintenance Organization	49	56	55	69	60
Preferred Provider Organization..............	66	83	88	103	89
Indemnity Fee for Service	23	21	22	31	22
Managed Care Contracts					
Health Maintenance Organization	314	305	308	310	308
Preferred Provider Organization..............	361	357	360	358	352
Affiliations					
Hospitals in a System.....................	281	259	257	248	253
Hospitals in a Network	104	109	111	108	106
Hospitals in a Group Purchasing Organization..	385	369	375	367	361

TABLE 6

TEXAS

U.S. Registered Community Hospitals
(Nonfederal, short-term general and other special hospitals)

Utilization, Personnel, Revenue and Expenses, Community Health Indicators 2004–2008

	2008	2007	2006	2005	2004
TOTAL FACILITY (Includes Hospital and Nursing Home Units)					
Utilization - Inpatient					
Beds	61,039	58,192	58,964	58,153	58,116
Admissions	2,585,680	2,468,109	2,528,943	2,509,178	2,516,718
Inpatient Days	13,430,355	12,816,839	13,045,054	13,101,744	13,200,657
Average Length of Stay	5.2	5.2	5.2	5.2	5.2
Inpatient Surgeries	763,867	768,063	775,501	762,305	758,899
Births	390,274	378,375	384,775	374,254	370,341
Utilization - Outpatient					
Emergency Outpatient Visits	8,819,272	8,444,299	8,291,213	8,206,013	7,966,137
Other Outpatient Visits	25,999,796	24,054,713	23,647,835	24,123,153	24,475,723
Total Outpatient Visits	34,819,068	32,499,012	31,939,048	32,329,166	32,441,860
Outpatient Surgeries	1,030,039	991,853	1,009,948	1,031,651	1,048,977
Personnel					
Full Time RNs	73,086	70,963	67,758	66,243	63,316
Full Time LPNs	10,227	10,087	10,746	11,602	12,209
Part Time RNs	21,580	20,369	19,109	18,380	18,031
Part Time LPNs	2,487	2,469	2,827	3,066	3,047
Total Full Time	266,604	263,105	257,216	258,639	256,397
Total Part Time	63,288	59,498	58,940	58,600	56,596
Revenue - Inpatient					
Gross Inpatient Revenue	$87,141,175,562	$77,330,388,025	$72,387,591,622	$65,594,501,737	$60,347,518,071
Revenue - Outpatient					
Gross Outpatient Revenue	$49,826,890,592	$43,530,620,498	$39,341,027,194	$35,837,256,064	$31,294,217,216
Revenue and Expenses - Totals					
(Includes Inpatient and Outpatient)					
Total Gross Revenue	$136,968,066,154	$120,861,008,523	$111,728,618,816	$101,431,757,801	$91,641,735,287
Deductions from Revenue	97,866,719,468	85,002,811,289	76,907,991,231	68,258,928,090	60,659,781,049
Net Patient Revenue	39,101,346,686	35,858,197,234	34,820,627,585	33,172,829,711	30,981,954,238
Other Operating Revenue	4,040,612,362	3,786,629,316	3,850,147,633	3,246,953,907	3,177,637,345
Other Nonoperating Revenue	310,546,108	1,059,715,727	565,608,947	421,812,411	405,430,634
Total Net Revenue	43,452,505,156	40,704,542,277	39,236,384,165	36,841,596,029	34,565,022,217
Total Expenses	40,396,037,477	37,428,408,575	36,431,139,219	34,220,085,472	32,312,038,316
HOSPITAL UNIT (Excludes Separate Nursing Home Units)					
Utilization - Inpatient					
Beds	59,947	56,952	57,569	56,572	56,469
Admissions	2,574,309	2,455,421	2,513,704	2,491,171	2,499,152
Inpatient Days	13,117,477	12,452,079	12,657,778	12,630,818	12,710,867
Average Length of Stay	5.1	5.1	5.0	5.1	5.1
Personnel					
Total Full Time	265,647	261,686	256,004	257,474	245,760
Total Part Time	62,914	59,123	58,651	58,318	54,323
Revenue and Expenses - Totals					
(Includes Inpatient and Outpatient)					
Total Net Revenue	$43,361,995,590	$40,562,429,655	$39,069,726,193	$36,668,512,831	$34,450,802,001
Total Expenses	40,292,698,073	37,243,889,225	36,239,634,905	34,038,018,797	32,217,547,133
COMMUNITY HEALTH INDICATORS PER 1000 POPULATION					
Total Population (in thousands)	24,327	23,843	23,368	22,811	22,425
Inpatient					
Beds	2.5	2.4	2.5	2.5	2.6
Admissions	106.3	103.5	108.2	110.0	112.2
Inpatient Days	552.1	537.5	558.3	574.4	588.7
Inpatient Surgeries	31.4	32.2	33.2	33.4	33.8
Births	16.0	15.9	16.5	16.4	16.5
Outpatient					
Emergency Outpatient Visits	362.5	354.2	354.8	359.7	355.2
Other Outpatient Visits	1,068.8	1,008.9	1,012.0	1,057.5	1,091.5
Total Outpatient Visits	1,431.3	1,363.0	1,366.8	1,417.3	1,446.7
Outpatient Surgeries	42.3	41.6	43.2	45.2	46.8
Expense per Capita (per person)	$1,660.5	$1,569.8	$1,559.0	$1,500.1	$1,440.9

States

TABLE 6

UTAH

U.S. Registered Community Hospitals
(Nonfederal, short-term general and other special hospitals)

Overview 2004–2008

	2008	2007	2006	2005	2004
Total Community Hospitals in Utah...........	43	41	43	43	43
Bed Size Category					
6-24....................................	6	6	6	6	8
25-49...................................	14	12	14	13	10
50-99...................................	6	8	8	9	10
100-199.................................	9	8	8	8	8
200-299.................................	4	4	4	4	4
300-399.................................	2	1	1	1	2
400-499.................................	1	1	2	2	1
500 +...................................	1	1	0	0	0
Location					
Hospitals Urban..........................	26	25	25	25	20
Hospitals Rural..........................	17	16	18	18	23
Control					
State and Local Government................	5	4	6	6	6
Not for Profit............................	23	22	22	22	22
Investor owned..........................	15	15	15	15	15
Physician Models					
Independent Practice Association............	2	2	2	3	4
Group Practice without Walls...............	0	0	1	0	0
Open Physician-Hospital Organization........	2	2	3	3	3
Closed Physician-Hospital Organization.......	1	1	1	1	1
Management Service Organization...........	1	1	1	1	2
Integrated Salary Model....................	13	14	17	17	12
Equity Model............................	0	0	0	1	0
Foundation..............................	1	0	0	0	0
Insurance Products					
Health Maintenance Organization............	16	16	20	18	16
Preferred Provider Organization..............	12	15	19	17	14
Indemnity Fee for Service..................	7	9	9	7	7
Managed Care Contracts					
Health Maintenance Organization............	14	15	21	21	20
Preferred Provider Organization..............	19	17	21	20	19
Affiliations					
Hospitals in a System.....................	37	36	36	36	36
Hospitals in a Network....................	15	14	13	13	13
Hospitals in a Group Purchasing Organization..	19	23	27	25	25

TABLE **6**

UTAH

U.S. Registered Community Hospitals
(Nonfederal, short-term general and other special hospitals)

Utilization, Personnel, Revenue and Expenses, Community Health Indicators 2004–2008

	2008	2007	2006	2005	2004
TOTAL FACILITY (Includes Hospital and Nursing Home Units)					
Utilization - Inpatient					
Beds	4,874	4,584	4,528	4,555	4,517
Admissions	226,376	223,971	220,750	222,985	219,021
Inpatient Days	1,015,945	1,003,917	968,656	959,235	953,754
Average Length of Stay	4.5	4.5	4.4	4.3	4.4
Inpatient Surgeries	67,840	71,541	68,590	74,224	65,013
Births	55,088	53,731	53,194	51,094	50,626
Utilization - Outpatient					
Emergency Outpatient Visits	856,277	900,975	789,653	803,394	829,030
Other Outpatient Visits	4,449,171	4,062,804	4,192,042	3,995,682	3,890,088
Total Outpatient Visits	5,305,448	4,963,779	4,981,695	4,799,076	4,719,118
Outpatient Surgeries	152,105	138,824	149,004	170,810	156,181
Personnel					
Full Time RNs	6,780	6,318	6,125	6,227	6,106
Full Time LPNs	378	500	413	520	586
Part Time RNs	4,620	4,170	4,311	3,739	3,221
Part Time LPNs	277	380	359	341	368
Total Full Time	26,648	25,903	24,814	24,107	22,719
Total Part Time	14,535	13,269	13,536	12,056	10,887
Revenue - Inpatient					
Gross Inpatient Revenue	$5,428,255,474	$5,250,442,289	$4,396,532,960	$4,017,366,853	$3,952,050,264
Revenue - Outpatient					
Gross Outpatient Revenue	$4,060,507,024	$3,704,805,862	$3,068,647,875	$2,728,130,477	$2,511,704,075
Revenue and Expenses - Totals					
(Includes Inpatient and Outpatient)					
Total Gross Revenue	$9,488,762,498	$8,955,248,151	$7,465,180,835	$6,745,497,330	$6,463,754,339
Deductions from Revenue	5,093,986,033	4,961,871,950	3,754,113,535	3,286,143,364	3,247,500,404
Net Patient Revenue	4,394,776,465	3,993,376,201	3,711,067,300	3,459,353,966	3,216,253,935
Other Operating Revenue	207,762,710	158,758,359	175,237,458	173,824,984	145,434,265
Other Nonoperating Revenue	20,119,824	39,067,658	16,047,892	20,303,182	33,354,146
Total Net Revenue	4,622,658,999	4,191,202,218	3,902,352,650	3,653,482,132	3,395,042,346
Total Expenses	4,041,481,901	3,710,391,899	3,437,079,268	3,214,131,545	3,059,828,012
HOSPITAL UNIT (Excludes Separate Nursing Home Units)					
Utilization - Inpatient					
Beds	4,720	4,431	4,383	4,388	4,416
Admissions	225,065	223,089	218,711	221,525	217,621
Inpatient Days	976,402	960,104	929,668	911,303	928,859
Average Length of Stay	4.3	4.3	4.3	4.1	4.3
Personnel					
Total Full Time	26,562	25,822	24,704	23,933	22,612
Total Part Time	14,449	13,158	13,437	11,922	10,799
Revenue and Expenses - Totals					
(Includes Inpatient and Outpatient)					
Total Net Revenue	$4,612,854,633	$4,183,929,529	$3,892,595,169	$3,644,185,837	$3,388,971,273
Total Expenses	4,034,303,806	3,704,812,297	3,430,215,718	3,207,843,710	3,055,918,500
COMMUNITY HEALTH INDICATORS PER 1000 POPULATION					
Total Population (in thousands)	2,736	2,669	2,585	2,501	2,440
Inpatient					
Beds	1.8	1.7	1.8	1.8	1.9
Admissions	82.7	83.9	85.4	89.1	89.8
Inpatient Days	371.3	376.2	374.7	383.5	390.9
Inpatient Surgeries	24.8	26.8	26.5	29.7	26.6
Births	20.1	20.1	20.6	20.4	20.7
Outpatient					
Emergency Outpatient Visits	312.9	337.6	305.5	321.2	339.8
Other Outpatient Visits	1,625.9	1,522.3	1,621.6	1,597.5	1,594.4
Total Outpatient Visits	1,938.8	1,859.8	1,927.0	1,918.7	1,934.2
Outpatient Surgeries	55.6	52.0	57.6	68.3	64.0
Expense per Capita (per person)	$1,476.9	$1,390.2	$1,329.5	$1,285.0	$1,254.1

States

TABLE 6

VERMONT

U.S. Registered Community Hospitals
(Nonfederal, short-term general and other special hospitals)

Overview 2004–2008

	2008	2007	2006	2005	2004
Total Community Hospitals in Vermont	**14**	**14**	**14**	**14**	**14**
Bed Size Category					
6-24	1	0	0	0	0
25-49	6	7	7	7	7
50-99	4	4	4	4	4
100-199	1	1	1	1	1
200-299	1	1	1	1	1
300-399	0	0	0	0	0
400-499	1	1	1	1	0
500 + ...	0	0	0	0	1
Location					
Hospitals Urban..........................	2	2	2	2	2
Hospitals Rural	12	12	12	12	12
Control					
State and Local Government...............	0	0	0	0	0
Not for Profit	14	14	14	14	14
Investor owned	0	0	0	0	0
Physician Models					
Independent Practice Association	0	0	1	0	1
Group Practice without Walls...............	0	0	0	1	1
Open Physician-Hospital Organization	3	2	3	4	4
Closed Physician-Hospital Organization	1	1	1	1	1
Management Service Organization	0	1	1	1	1
Integrated Salary Model	9	7	9	9	9
Equity Model	0	0	0	0	0
Foundation...............................	0	0	0	0	0
Insurance Products					
Health Maintenance Organization	3	3	3	3	5
Preferred Provider Organization..............	0	2	2	2	4
Indemnity Fee for Service	0	2	1	1	1
Managed Care Contracts					
Health Maintenance Organization	7	7	8	9	9
Preferred Provider Organization..............	6	6	8	9	10
Affiliations					
Hospitals in a System......................	1	1	1	1	1
Hospitals in a Network	5	5	5	5	5
Hospitals in a Group Purchasing Organization..	12	11	14	14	13

TABLE 6

VERMONT

U.S. Registered Community Hospitals
(Nonfederal, short-term general and other special hospitals)

Utilization, Personnel, Revenue and Expenses, Community Health Indicators 2004–2008

	2008	2007	2006	2005	2004
TOTAL FACILITY (Includes Hospital and Nursing Home Units)					
Utilization - Inpatient					
Beds	1,302	1,362	1,313	1,058	1,470
Admissions	51,301	49,892	50,402	51,430	52,853
Inpatient Days	328,506	337,004	327,850	334,533	347,087
Average Length of Stay	6.4	6.8	6.5	6.5	6.6
Inpatient Surgeries	14,160	14,224	13,883	13,828	14,040
Births	5,982	5,981	5,944	6,107	6,043
Utilization - Outpatient					
Emergency Outpatient Visits	304,717	259,661	260,429	256,116	261,642
Other Outpatient Visits	3,001,378	2,514,148	2,240,292	2,220,552	2,012,991
Total Outpatient Visits	3,306,095	2,773,809	2,500,721	2,476,668	2,274,633
Outpatient Surgeries	47,401	44,800	43,286	57,091	59,210
Personnel					
Full Time RNs	1,690	1,551	1,454	1,280	1,242
Full Time LPNs	218	214	223	219	161
Part Time RNs	1,239	1,211	1,286	1,326	1,262
Part Time LPNs	160	162	181	169	216
Total Full Time	9,611	9,373	8,781	8,264	7,761
Total Part Time	3,763	3,624	3,960	4,303	4,250
Revenue - Inpatient					
Gross Inpatient Revenue	$903,264,654	$906,951,930	$798,941,048	$715,536,841	$681,045,908
Revenue - Outpatient					
Gross Outpatient Revenue	$2,017,330,510	$1,784,747,426	$1,551,689,704	$1,385,916,565	$1,218,097,479
Revenue and Expenses - Totals					
(Includes Inpatient and Outpatient)					
Total Gross Revenue	$2,920,595,164	$2,691,699,356	$2,350,630,752	$2,101,453,406	$1,899,143,387
Deductions from Revenue	1,383,550,785	1,256,738,757	1,011,115,676	879,046,314	787,254,423
Net Patient Revenue	1,537,044,379	1,434,960,599	1,339,515,076	1,222,407,092	1,111,888,964
Other Operating Revenue	46,804,137	45,513,360	43,167,369	24,996,233	21,000,354
Other Nonoperating Revenue	(27,559,443)	38,665,452	61,745,217	26,468,077	17,165,067
Total Net Revenue	1,556,289,073	1,519,139,411	1,444,427,662	1,273,871,402	1,150,054,385
Total Expenses	1,558,572,905	1,451,986,474	1,332,522,993	1,217,413,378	1,103,050,959
HOSPITAL UNIT (Excludes Separate Nursing Home Units)					
Utilization - Inpatient					
Beds	1,061	1,106	1,053	1,090	1,205
Admissions	51,001	49,396	50,100	51,104	52,516
Inpatient Days	245,411	249,628	237,419	241,632	253,201
Average Length of Stay	4.8	5.1	4.7	4.7	4.8
Personnel					
Total Full Time	9,218	8,963	8,494	8,093	7,530
Total Part Time	3,538	3,409	3,791	4,181	4,108
Revenue and Expenses - Totals					
(Includes Inpatient and Outpatient)					
Total Net Revenue	$1,536,579,410	$1,494,392,921	$1,426,818,942	$1,255,847,385	$1,132,671,726
Total Expenses	1,540,919,362	1,434,525,067	1,315,948,812	1,199,376,861	1,085,829,448
COMMUNITY HEALTH INDICATORS PER 1000 POPULATION					
Total Population (in thousands)	621	621	620	619	618
Inpatient					
Beds	2.1	2.2	2.1	2.2	2.4
Admissions	82.6	80.4	81.3	83.0	85.5
Inpatient Days	528.8	542.9	528.6	540.2	561.2
Inpatient Surgeries	22.8	22.9	22.4	22.3	22.7
Births	9.6	9.6	9.6	9.9	9.8
Outpatient					
Emergency Outpatient Visits	490.5	418.3	419.9	413.6	423.1
Other Outpatient Visits	4,831.0	4,050.2	3,612.2	3,585.7	3,255.0
Total Outpatient Visits	5,321.5	4,468.5	4,032.1	3,999.3	3,678.1
Outpatient Surgeries	76.3	72.2	69.8	92.2	95.7
Expense per Capita (per person)	$2,508.7	$2,339.1	$2,148.6	$1,965.8	$1,783.6

TABLE **6**

VIRGINIA

U.S. Registered Community Hospitals
(Nonfederal, short-term general and other special hospitals)

Overview 2004–2008

	2008	2007	2006	2005	2004
Total Community Hospitals in Virginia	90	87	88	87	88
Bed Size Category					
6-24	4	4	5	5	4
25-49	15	13	12	12	12
50-99	16	15	17	15	18
100-199	25	25	24	25	24
200-299	13	15	13	14	15
300-399	5	3	6	4	3
400-499	4	4	5	4	5
500 + ...	8	8	6	8	7
Location					
Hospitals Urban.........................	60	57	58	57	53
Hospitals Rural	30	30	30	30	35
Control					
State and Local Government................	4	4	4	4	4
Not for Profit	65	64	64	62	64
Investor owned	21	19	20	21	20
Physician Models					
Independent Practice Association	11	12	11	11	9
Group Practice without Walls...............	10	11	10	9	7
Open Physician-Hospital Organization	13	11	9	10	12
Closed Physician-Hospital Organization	1	2	2	2	3
Management Service Organization	10	9	7	8	4
Integrated Salary Model....................	39	37	30	30	27
Equity Model	7	7	7	7	7
Foundation...............................	2	2	2	2	3
Insurance Products					
Health Maintenance Organization	17	19	21	22	22
Preferred Provider Organization..............	18	22	26	29	28
Indemnity Fee for Service	5	14	13	13	13
Managed Care Contracts					
Health Maintenance Organization	50	56	50	54	53
Preferred Provider Organization..............	56	60	56	61	60
Affiliations					
Hospitals in a System......................	60	55	57	56	56
Hospitals in a Network.....................	38	45	38	37	32
Hospitals in a Group Purchasing Organization..	60	63	61	70	63

TABLE 6

VIRGINIA

U.S. Registered Community Hospitals
(Nonfederal, short-term general and other special hospitals)

Utilization, Personnel, Revenue and Expenses, Community Health Indicators 2004–2008

	2008	2007	2006	2005	2004
TOTAL FACILITY (Includes Hospital and Nursing Home Units)					
Utilization - Inpatient					
Bodo	17,040	10,095	17,274	17,483	17,339
Admissions	795,578	787,319	778,680	780,063	770,482
Inpatient Days	4,452,740	4,354,340	4,416,114	4,500,420	4,468,361
Average Length of Stay	5.6	5.5	5.7	5.8	5.8
Inpatient Surgeries	235,678	229,376	233,922	239,260	236,905
Births	98,991	98,733	98,948	96,713	94,851
Utilization - Outpatient					
Emergency Outpatient Visits	3,091,131	3,040,762	3,060,052	2,891,314	2,915,593
Other Outpatient Visits	10,223,288	9,892,129	10,592,692	10,407,953	9,033,065
Total Outpatient Visits	13,314,419	12,932,891	13,652,744	13,299,267	11,948,658
Outpatient Surgeries	463,342	463,212	473,915	498,917	484,775
Personnel					
Full Time RNs	23,382	22,863	21,187	20,788	19,372
Full Time LPNs	2,460	2,445	2,645	2,809	2,585
Part Time RNs	10,075	9,823	9,948	9,337	10,442
Part Time LPNs	861	777	793	783	929
Total Full Time	83,178	80,744	78,169	78,447	75,743
Total Part Time	28,749	27,126	26,965	25,534	27,658
Revenue - Inpatient					
Gross Inpatient Revenue	$22,555,481,294	$21,113,593,014	$19,234,761,450	$17,128,029,759	$15,465,159,071
Revenue - Outpatient					
Gross Outpatient Revenue	$17,042,951,627	$15,015,219,220	$13,231,876,352	$11,727,859,701	$9,538,948,095
Revenue and Expenses - Totals					
(Includes Inpatient and Outpatient)					
Total Gross Revenue	$39,598,432,921	$36,128,812,234	$32,466,637,802	$28,855,889,460	$25,004,107,166
Deductions from Revenue	25,464,931,182	23,062,020,224	20,174,935,834	17,355,317,448	14,542,142,131
Net Patient Revenue	14,133,501,739	13,066,792,010	12,291,701,968	11,500,572,012	10,461,965,035
Other Operating Revenue	404,136,415	356,732,830	379,912,278	312,151,277	288,809,114
Other Nonoperating Revenue	(269,241,513)	393,479,251	245,713,096	180,752,253	187,888,489
Total Net Revenue	14,268,396,641	13,817,004,091	12,917,327,342	11,993,475,542	10,938,662,638
Total Expenses	13,800,772,246	12,626,089,380	11,554,705,543	10,918,957,473	10,050,894,896
HOSPITAL UNIT (Excludes Separate Nursing Home Units)					
Utilization - Inpatient					
Beds	16,478	16,097	16,411	16,453	16,158
Admissions	790,203	782,324	775,367	776,841	767,241
Inpatient Days	4,052,958	3,977,976	4,129,270	4,160,425	4,022,345
Average Length of Stay	5.1	5.1	5.3	5.4	5.2
Personnel					
Total Full Time	82,241	79,956	77,634	77,653	74,916
Total Part Time	28,385	26,940	26,744	25,226	27,424
Revenue and Expenses - Totals					
(Includes Inpatient and Outpatient)					
Total Net Revenue	$14,180,093,186	$13,715,806,678	$12,814,301,298	$11,935,132,273	$10,869,203,315
Total Expenses	13,713,829,141	12,526,340,640	11,498,207,599	10,867,011,952	9,993,659,840
COMMUNITY HEALTH INDICATORS PER 1000 POPULATION					
Total Population (in thousands)	7,769	7,699	7,628	7,547	7,455
Inpatient					
Beds	2.3	2.2	2.3	2.3	2.3
Admissions	102.4	102.3	102.1	103.4	103.4
Inpatient Days	573.1	565.6	578.9	596.3	599.4
Inpatient Surgeries	30.3	29.8	30.7	31.7	31.8
Births	12.7	12.8	13.0	12.8	12.7
Outpatient					
Emergency Outpatient Visits	397.9	395.0	401.1	383.1	391.1
Other Outpatient Visits	1,315.9	1,284.9	1,388.6	1,379.1	1,211.7
Total Outpatient Visits	1,713.8	1,679.9	1,789.7	1,762.3	1,602.8
Outpatient Surgeries	59.6	60.2	62.1	66.1	65.0
Expense per Capita (per person)	$1,776.4	$1,640.0	$1,514.7	$1,446.8	$1,348.3

States

TABLE 6

WASHINGTON

U.S. Registered Community Hospitals
(Nonfederal, short-term general and other special hospitals)

Overview 2004–2008

	2008	2007	2006	2005	2004
Total Community Hospitals in Washington	86	87	88	86	85
Bed Size Category					
6-24	4	5	8	9	9
25-49	31	30	30	27	24
50-99	12	14	13	15	12
100-199	14	15	17	16	19
200-299	15	13	10	9	12
300-399	8	7	8	8	7
400-499	0	1	0	0	0
500 + ...	2	2	2	2	2
Location					
Hospitals Urban...........................	51	53	53	52	46
Hospitals Rural	35	34	35	34	39
Control					
State and Local Government................	42	41	41	40	39
Not for Profit	40	41	42	42	41
Investor owned	4	5	5	4	5
Physician Models					
Independent Practice Association	2	4	7	9	6
Group Practice without Walls................	2	1	1	1	2
Open Physician-Hospital Organization	5	5	5	4	4
Closed Physician-Hospital Organization	0	2	2	5	4
Management Service Organization	3	4	4	5	5
Integrated Salary Model....................	34	35	35	42	34
Equity Model	0	0	0	0	0
Foundation...............................	7	1	1	3	1
Insurance Products					
Health Maintenance Organization	4	4	4	6	6
Preferred Provider Organization..............	12	11	8	11	8
Indemnity Fee for Service	1	1	0	2	2
Managed Care Contracts					
Health Maintenance Organization	33	33	31	37	34
Preferred Provider Organization..............	37	38	38	41	43
Affiliations					
Hospitals in a System......................	31	31	40	29	29
Hospitals in a Network.....................	19	16	15	15	14
Hospitals in a Group Purchasing Organization..	47	60	54	58	42

States

TABLE 6

WASHINGTON

U.S. Registered Community Hospitals
(Nonfederal, short-term general and other special hospitals)

Utilization, Personnel, Revenue and Expenses, Community Health Indicators 2004–2008

	2008	2007	2006	2005	2004
TOTAL FACILITY (Includes Hospital and Nursing Home Units)					
Utilization - Inpatient					
Beds	11,040	11,315	10,927	10,703	10,984
Admissions	578,856	574,169	556,700	543,329	528,145
Inpatient Days	2,663,704	2,577,795	2,486,577	2,481,368	2,464,033
Average Length of Stay	4.6	4.5	4.5	4.6	4.7
Inpatient Surgeries	184,234	176,445	161,357	172,394	172,224
Births	82,557	80,698	78,272	76,231	74,629
Utilization - Outpatient					
Emergency Outpatient Visits	2,385,734	2,343,863	2,147,309	2,150,665	2,070,588
Other Outpatient Visits	8,992,320	8,851,818	8,236,855	7,898,848	8,023,254
Total Outpatient Visits	11,378,054	11,195,681	10,384,164	10,049,513	10,093,842
Outpatient Surgeries	263,762	246,380	249,520	256,277	265,489
Personnel					
Full Time RNs	13,202	12,647	12,488	10,640	10,871
Full Time LPNs	805	821	954	804	842
Part Time RNs	13,466	12,633	11,236	11,885	12,266
Part Time LPNs	696	688	664	676	709
Total Full Time	59,789	57,267	58,233	52,293	52,042
Total Part Time	40,524	36,824	33,984	34,010	35,860
Revenue - Inpatient					
Gross Inpatient Revenue	$17,882,046,988	$15,526,030,849	$13,933,139,987	$12,391,332,683	$11,175,038,171
Revenue - Outpatient					
Gross Outpatient Revenue	$13,659,739,047	$12,099,431,805	$10,552,552,309	$9,409,149,980	$8,233,809,398
Revenue and Expenses - Totals					
(Includes Inpatient and Outpatient)					
Total Gross Revenue	$31,541,786,035	$27,625,462,654	$24,485,692,296	$21,800,482,663	$19,408,847,569
Deductions from Revenue	19,034,411,541	16,338,477,005	14,099,862,736	12,092,084,642	10,469,471,708
Net Patient Revenue	12,507,374,494	11,286,985,649	10,385,829,560	9,708,398,021	8,939,375,861
Other Operating Revenue	664,009,322	632,362,196	515,593,853	501,680,129	532,612,476
Other Nonoperating Revenue	(98,368,171)	287,788,340	192,566,803	119,675,420	161,524,417
Total Net Revenue	13,073,015,645	12,207,136,185	11,093,990,216	10,329,753,570	9,633,512,754
Total Expenses	12,327,733,007	11,274,708,380	10,650,112,282	9,877,966,089	9,016,549,152
HOSPITAL UNIT (Excludes Separate Nursing Home Units)					
Utilization - Inpatient					
Beds	10,959	10,910	10,679	10,433	10,498
Admissions	576,765	572,112	554,676	541,217	525,300
Inpatient Days	2,539,914	2,465,659	2,401,977	2,367,684	2,320,942
Average Length of Stay	4.4	4.3	4.3	4.4	4.4
Personnel					
Total Full Time	59,483	56,827	57,925	52,000	51,635
Total Part Time	40,227	36,505	33,837	33,844	35,687
Revenue and Expenses - Totals					
(Includes Inpatient and Outpatient)					
Total Net Revenue	$13,032,710,190	$12,160,885,656	$11,062,106,616	$10,282,987,332	$9,591,633,736
Total Expenses	12,289,499,219	11,234,767,829	10,623,552,352	9,848,163,539	8,979,129,740
COMMUNITY HEALTH INDICATORS PER 1000 POPULATION					
Total Population (in thousands)	6,549	6,450	6,361	6,255	6,180
Inpatient					
Beds	1.7	1.8	1.7	1.7	1.8
Admissions	88.4	89.0	87.5	86.9	85.5
Inpatient Days	406.7	399.7	390.9	396.7	398.7
Inpatient Surgeries	28.1	27.4	25.4	27.6	27.9
Births	12.6	12.5	12.3	12.2	12.1
Outpatient					
Emergency Outpatient Visits	364.3	363.4	337.6	343.9	335.1
Other Outpatient Visits	1,373.0	1,372.5	1,295.0	1,262.9	1,298.3
Total Outpatient Visits	1,737.3	1,735.9	1,632.6	1,606.7	1,633.4
Outpatient Surgeries	40.3	38.2	39.2	41.0	43.0
Expense per Capita (per person)	$1,882.3	$1,748.1	$1,674.4	$1,579.3	$1,459.1

States

TABLE **6**

WEST VIRGINIA

U.S. Registered Community Hospitals
(Nonfederal, short-term general and other special hospitals)

Overview 2004–2008

	2008	2007	2006	2005	2004
Total Community Hospitals in West Virginia . . .	56	56	56	57	57
Bed Size Category					
6-24	3	3	3	4	4
25-49	13	13	14	13	11
50-99	14	14	14	15	17
100-199	14	14	13	13	13
200-299	8	7	8	8	7
300-399	2	3	2	2	3
400-499	0	1	1	1	1
500 + ...	2	1	1	1	1
Location					
Hospitals Urban	27	27	26	25	18
Hospitals Rural	29	29	30	32	39
Control					
State and Local Government	10	10	10	10	10
Not for Profit	32	31	31	31	31
Investor owned	14	15	15	16	16
Physician Models					
Independent Practice Association	4	6	6	6	4
Group Practice without Walls	0	2	2	2	1
Open Physician-Hospital Organization	14	14	15	16	15
Closed Physician-Hospital Organization	3	2	1	1	1
Management Service Organization	5	5	4	3	4
Integrated Salary Model	25	25	28	29	29
Equity Model	0	1	1	1	1
Foundation	0	0	0	1	0
Insurance Products					
Health Maintenance Organization	3	5	6	8	8
Preferred Provider Organization	7	9	9	11	12
Indemnity Fee for Service	2	4	3	5	4
Managed Care Contracts					
Health Maintenance Organization	27	27	25	28	31
Preferred Provider Organization	38	38	37	40	44
Affiliations					
Hospitals in a System	23	23	24	25	25
Hospitals in a Network	20	23	24	25	27
Hospitals in a Group Purchasing Organization . .	52	52	52	53	52

TABLE 6

WEST VIRGINIA

U.S. Registered Community Hospitals
(Nonfederal, short-term general and other special hospitals)

Utilization, Personnel, Revenue and Expenses, Community Health Indicators 2004–2008

	2008	2007	2006	2005	2004
TOTAL FACILITY (Includes Hospital and Nursing Home Units)					
Utilization - Inpatient					
Beds	7,470	7,438	7,197	7,243	7,412
Admissions	283,673	286,892	281,766	291,936	297,957
Inpatient Days	1,665,076	1,656,614	1,592,271	1,662,043	1,707,211
Average Length of Stay	5.9	5.8	5.7	5.7	5.7
Inpatient Surgeries	79,916	77,775	77,881	79,072	81,045
Births	20,856	21,296	21,137	20,817	21,164
Utilization - Outpatient					
Emergency Outpatient Visits	1,183,158	1,171,507	1,137,535	1,163,861	1,130,236
Other Outpatient Visits	5,431,951	5,283,575	5,074,611	4,951,884	4,915,115
Total Outpatient Visits	6,615,109	6,455,082	6,212,146	6,115,745	6,045,351
Outpatient Surgeries	212,489	207,785	213,317	207,093	209,671
Personnel					
Full Time RNs	8,084	7,949	7,271	7,298	7,111
Full Time LPNs	1,387	1,416	1,422	1,498	1,557
Part Time RNs	3,392	3,460	3,287	3,021	3,053
Part Time LPNs	435	392	481	465	490
Total Full Time	32,463	31,879	30,778	30,701	30,378
Total Part Time	10,244	10,145	10,013	9,906	9,794
Revenue - Inpatient					
Gross Inpatient Revenue	$4,927,056,831	$4,544,128,430	$4,197,327,290	$4,026,435,796	$4,044,864,251
Revenue - Outpatient					
Gross Outpatient Revenue	$4,531,051,911	$4,100,750,655	$3,747,433,060	$3,455,792,349	$3,060,476,434
Revenue and Expenses - Totals					
(Includes Inpatient and Outpatient)					
Total Gross Revenue	$9,458,108,742	$8,644,879,085	$7,944,760,350	$7,482,228,145	$7,105,340,685
Deductions from Revenue	5,198,077,289	4,577,611,437	4,125,056,133	3,830,700,396	3,631,517,398
Net Patient Revenue	4,260,031,453	4,067,267,648	3,819,704,217	3,651,527,749	3,473,823,287
Other Operating Revenue	71,741,101	125,951,483	126,071,335	116,366,406	105,961,591
Other Nonoperating Revenue	(125,408,354)	100,086,468	61,758,746	48,171,478	52,015,444
Total Net Revenue	4,206,364,200	4,293,305,599	4,007,534,298	3,816,065,633	3,631,800,322
Total Expenses	4,289,258,433	4,018,748,717	3,814,590,273	3,711,750,009	3,504,272,644
HOSPITAL UNIT (Excludes Separate Nursing Home Units)					
Utilization - Inpatient					
Beds	6,587	6,553	6,439	6,422	6,576
Admissions	277,157	280,751	275,550	285,425	291,135
Inpatient Days	1,381,747	1,375,020	1,350,098	1,396,933	1,433,988
Average Length of Stay	5.0	4.9	4.9	4.9	4.9
Personnel					
Total Full Time	31,838	31,203	30,217	30,096	29,662
Total Part Time	9,825	9,763	9,640	9,509	9,443
Revenue and Expenses - Totals					
(Includes Inpatient and Outpatient)					
Total Net Revenue	$4,123,228,602	$4,225,397,482	$3,947,204,453	$3,760,605,431	$3,573,095,326
Total Expenses	4,229,627,238	3,964,906,237	3,769,187,062	3,667,763,446	3,459,519,326
COMMUNITY HEALTH INDICATORS PER 1000 POPULATION					
Total Population (in thousands)	1,814	1,810	1,807	1,804	1,803
Inpatient					
Beds	4.1	4.1	4.0	4.0	4.1
Admissions	156.3	158.5	156.0	161.8	165.2
Inpatient Days	917.7	915.3	881.3	921.3	946.7
Inpatient Surgeries	44.0	43.0	43.1	43.8	44.9
Births	11.5	11.8	11.7	11.5	11.7
Outpatient					
Emergency Outpatient Visits	652.1	647.3	629.6	645.1	626.8
Other Outpatient Visits	2,993.7	2,919.4	2,808.7	2,744.9	2,725.6
Total Outpatient Visits	3,645.8	3,566.7	3,438.3	3,390.1	3,352.4
Outpatient Surgeries	117.1	114.8	118.1	114.8	116.3
Expense per Capita (per person)	$2,363.9	$2,220.5	$2,111.3	$2,057.5	$1,943.2

States

TABLE 6

WISCONSIN

U.S. Registered Community Hospitals
(Nonfederal, short-term general and other special hospitals)

Overview 2004–2008

	2008	2007	2006	2005	2004
Total Community Hospitals in Wisconsin......	**126**	**124**	**124**	**124**	**121**
Bed Size Category					
6-24	12	12	11	12	10
25-49	36	33	31	26	27
50-99	32	27	27	31	27
100-199	24	33	37	35	36
200-299	13	10	10	12	13
300-399	6	6	5	5	4
400-499	2	2	2	2	3
500 + ...	1	1	1	1	1
Location					
Hospitals Urban..........................	69	68	67	67	57
Hospitals Rural	57	56	57	57	64
Control					
State and Local Government................	2	2	2	2	2
Not for Profit	119	117	118	118	115
Investor owned	5	5	4	4	4
Physician Models					
Independent Practice Association	13	10	11	9	6
Group Practice without Walls...............	2	1	1	1	3
Open Physician-Hospital Organization	3	6	4	4	4
Closed Physician-Hospital Organization	3	4	4	3	2
Management Service Organization	2	1	1	1	3
Integrated Salary Model....................	32	30	30	30	34
Equity Model	17	3	5	3	2
Foundation...............................	2	2	2	3	3
Insurance Products					
Health Maintenance Organization	23	25	23	10	20
Preferred Provider Organization..............	36	38	25	9	20
Indemnity Fee for Service	15	16	9	3	5
Managed Care Contracts					
Health Maintenance Organization	116	83	111	108	105
Preferred Provider Organization..............	120	86	114	109	110
Affiliations					
Hospitals in a System......................	72	70	70	72	67
Hospitals in a Network.....................	39	31	42	40	42
Hospitals in a Group Purchasing Organization..	118	86	117	114	109

States

TABLE 6

WISCONSIN

U.S. Registered Community Hospitals
(Nonfederal, short-term general and other special hospitals)

Utilization, Personnel, Revenue and Expenses, Community Health Indicators 2004–2008

	2008	2007	2006	2005	2004
TOTAL FACILITY (Includes Hospital and Nursing Home Units)					
Utilization - Inpatient					
Beds	13,707	13,981	14,123	14,458	14,577
Admissions	617,295	613,356	609,108	611,669	598,542
Inpatient Days	3,172,566	3,168,542	3,210,210	3,302,565	3,335,415
Average Length of Stay	5.1	5.2	5.3	5.4	5.6
Inpatient Surgeries	233,044	239,199	195,968	189,662	183,304
Births	69,465	70,500	68,461	67,525	67,419
Utilization - Outpatient					
Emergency Outpatient Visits	2,066,654	2,106,402	2,091,172	1,965,535	1,861,206
Other Outpatient Visits	12,136,773	10,966,003	10,420,878	10,760,999	9,957,806
Total Outpatient Visits	14,203,427	13,072,405	12,512,050	12,726,534	11,819,012
Outpatient Surgeries	491,040	497,452	449,460	537,342	418,490
Personnel					
Full Time RNs	14,522	13,480	12,971	12,197	11,027
Full Time LPNs	707	711	689	824	725
Part Time RNs	15,398	15,499	15,682	14,867	14,663
Part Time LPNs	927	1,028	1,094	1,152	1,105
Total Full Time	63,883	61,173	58,923	58,349	56,306
Total Part Time	47,517	47,796	49,217	48,137	47,844
Revenue - Inpatient					
Gross Inpatient Revenue	$13,612,135,956	$12,925,578,410	$11,855,822,996	$11,202,143,456	$9,931,707,238
Revenue - Outpatient					
Gross Outpatient Revenue	$13,162,259,140	$11,746,652,525	$10,739,176,109	$9,561,512,469	$7,994,289,334
Revenue and Expenses - Totals					
(Includes Inpatient and Outpatient)					
Total Gross Revenue	$26,774,395,096	$24,672,230,935	$22,594,999,105	$20,763,655,925	$17,925,996,572
Deductions from Revenue	13,709,265,312	12,424,903,890	11,063,269,437	10,261,422,693	8,369,952,440
Net Patient Revenue	13,065,129,784	12,247,327,045	11,531,729,668	10,502,233,232	9,556,044,132
Other Operating Revenue	643,332,317	473,238,179	438,517,748	510,794,120	505,677,051
Other Nonoperating Revenue	(30,738,485)	294,160,363	227,736,515	161,419,465	197,222,441
Total Net Revenue	13,677,723,616	13,014,725,587	12,197,983,931	11,174,446,817	10,258,943,624
Total Expenses	12,923,890,000	11,916,247,096	11,210,657,463	10,255,161,431	9,417,648,940
HOSPITAL UNIT (Excludes Separate Nursing Home Units)					
Utilization - Inpatient					
Beds	12,067	12,337	12,196	12,387	12,516
Admissions	614,395	610,759	606,030	608,252	594,654
Inpatient Days	2,629,527	2,622,596	2,565,274	2,615,415	2,666,092
Average Length of Stay	4.3	4.3	4.2	4.3	4.5
Personnel					
Total Full Time	63,068	60,418	58,161	57,472	53,258
Total Part Time	46,533	46,827	48,062	47,114	44,410
Revenue and Expenses - Totals					
(Includes Inpatient and Outpatient)					
Total Net Revenue	$13,576,550,948	$12,892,939,703	$12,114,061,349	$11,078,760,380	$10,167,474,913
Total Expenses	12,830,682,268	11,827,708,589	11,125,842,547	10,169,684,929	9,333,710,663
COMMUNITY HEALTH INDICATORS PER 1000 POPULATION					
Total Population (in thousands)	5,628	5,599	5,569	5,539	5,509
Inpatient					
Beds	2.4	2.5	2.5	2.6	2.6
Admissions	109.7	109.5	109.4	110.4	108.7
Inpatient Days	563.7	565.9	576.5	596.3	605.5
Inpatient Surgeries	41.4	42.7	35.2	34.2	33.3
Births	12.3	12.6	12.3	12.2	12.2
Outpatient					
Emergency Outpatient Visits	367.2	376.2	375.5	354.9	337.9
Other Outpatient Visits	2,156.5	1,958.6	1,871.4	1,942.8	1,807.6
Total Outpatient Visits	2,523.7	2,334.8	2,246.9	2,297.7	2,145.5
Outpatient Surgeries	87.2	88.8	80.7	97.0	76.0
Expense per Capita (per person)	$2,296.4	$2,128.3	$2,013.2	$1,851.5	$1,709.6

TABLE 6

WYOMING

U.S. Registered Community Hospitals
(Nonfederal, short-term general and other special hospitals)

Overview 2004–2008

	2008	2007	2006	2005	2004
Total Community Hospitals in Wyoming.......	24	24	24	24	24
Bed Size Category					
6-24.....................................	0	0	0	0	0
25-49....................................	10	10	10	10	9
50-99....................................	7	7	7	8	8
100-199..................................	4	4	4	3	4
200-299..................................	3	3	3	3	3
300-399..................................	0	0	0	0	0
400-499..................................	0	0	0	0	0
500 +....................................	0	0	0	0	0
Location					
Hospitals Urban..........................	2	2	2	2	2
Hospitals Rural..........................	22	22	22	22	22
Control					
State and Local Government................	16	16	17	17	17
Not for Profit...........................	5	5	4	4	4
Investor owned...........................	3	3	3	3	3
Physician Models					
Independent Practice Association...........	3	3	3	3	2
Group Practice without Walls..............	0	0	0	0	0
Open Physician-Hospital Organization	1	1	1	1	2
Closed Physician-Hospital Organization	1	1	1	1	1
Management Service Organization	1	1	1	1	1
Integrated Salary Model...................	11	11	11	10	9
Equity Model.............................	0	0	0	0	0
Foundation...............................	0	0	0	0	0
Insurance Products					
Health Maintenance Organization	1	1	1	1	0
Preferred Provider Organization..............	1	5	5	5	4
Indemnity Fee for Service	0	0	0	0	1
Managed Care Contracts					
Health Maintenance Organization	4	4	3	3	3
Preferred Provider Organization..............	14	12	11	13	14
Affiliations					
Hospitals in a System.....................	11	12	12	12	11
Hospitals in a Network....................	5	4	4	4	4
Hospitals in a Group Purchasing Organization..	23	23	23	23	23

TABLE 6

WYOMING

U.S. Registered Community Hospitals
(Nonfederal, short-term general and other special hospitals)

Utilization, Personnel, Revenue and Expenses, Community Health Indicators 2004–2008

	2008	2007	2006	2005	2004
TOTAL FACILITY (Includes Hospital and Nursing Home Units)					
Utilization - Inpatient					
Beds	2,070	2,071	2,056	2,051	2,040
Admissions	52,628	53,077	52,586	51,200	50,509
Inpatient Days	414,463	422,883	421,089	421,352	394,422
Average Length of Stay	7.9	8.0	8.0	8.2	7.8
Inpatient Surgeries	14,162	14,556	14,128	13,175	14,626
Births	7,303	7,247	6,824	6,603	6,220
Utilization - Outpatient					
Emergency Outpatient Visits	234,384	227,386	221,300	218,686	215,438
Other Outpatient Visits	774,610	729,327	742,540	791,349	704,620
Total Outpatient Visits	1,008,994	956,713	963,840	1,010,035	920,058
Outpatient Surgeries	25,183	24,122	25,302	27,191	28,404
Personnel					
Full Time RNs	1,664	1,603	1,586	1,488	1,483
Full Time LPNs	130	137	160	173	176
Part Time RNs	504	600	457	370	400
Part Time LPNs	57	69	57	56	59
Total Full Time	7,291	6,670	6,849	6,696	6,583
Total Part Time	1,892	2,319	1,989	1,776	1,716
Revenue - Inpatient					
Gross Inpatient Revenue	$951,929,394	$878,681,901	$803,694,086	$734,933,760	$675,118,147
Revenue - Outpatient					
Gross Outpatient Revenue	$801,309,584	$704,732,660	$620,933,569	$561,095,096	$515,866,154
Revenue and Expenses - Totals					
(Includes Inpatient and Outpatient)					
Total Gross Revenue	$1,753,238,978	$1,583,414,561	$1,424,627,655	$1,296,028,856	$1,190,984,301
Deductions from Revenue	802,095,376	696,730,106	606,943,644	534,882,813	487,084,081
Net Patient Revenue	951,143,602	886,684,455	817,684,011	761,146,043	703,900,220
Other Operating Revenue	55,280,832	49,220,506	46,089,909	40,147,046	34,461,766
Other Nonoperating Revenue	21,606,525	63,859,758	21,704,253	20,598,076	15,782,355
Total Net Revenue	1,028,030,959	999,764,719	885,478,173	821,891,165	754,144,341
Total Expenses	949,368,614	848,863,457	813,447,569	747,096,293	693,598,204
HOSPITAL UNIT (Excludes Separate Nursing Home Units)					
Utilization - Inpatient					
Beds	1,335	1,323	1,308	1,277	1,334
Admissions	51,146	51,592	51,024	49,554	49,081
Inpatient Days	183,585	184,014	180,631	178,182	197,165
Average Length of Stay	3.6	3.6	3.5	3.6	4.0
Personnel					
Total Full Time	6,767	6,141	6,291	6,120	5,757
Total Part Time	1,696	2,092	1,796	1,592	1,533
Revenue and Expenses - Totals					
(Includes Inpatient and Outpatient)					
Total Net Revenue	$988,170,246	$959,741,678	$845,556,939	$779,859,233	$723,542,200
Total Expenses	907,237,150	810,848,202	775,077,404	711,696,513	667,443,267
COMMUNITY HEALTH INDICATORS PER 1000 POPULATION					
Total Population (in thousands)	533	523	513	506	503
Inpatient					
Beds	3.9	4.0	4.0	4.1	4.1
Admissions	98.8	101.4	102.6	101.2	100.5
Inpatient Days	778.1	808.2	821.5	832.7	784.4
Inpatient Surgeries	26.6	27.8	27.6	26.0	29.1
Births	13.7	13.8	13.3	13.0	12.4
Outpatient					
Emergency Outpatient Visits	440.0	434.6	431.7	432.2	428.5
Other Outpatient Visits	1,454.2	1,393.8	1,448.7	1,563.9	1,401.3
Total Outpatient Visits	1,894.2	1,828.4	1,880.4	1,996.1	1,829.8
Outpatient Surgeries	47.3	46.1	49.4	53.7	56.5
Expense per Capita (per person)	$1,782.3	$1,622.3	$1,587.0	$1,476.5	$1,379.4

States

Table 7

The facilities and services presented in Table 7 are listed below in alphabetical order by major heading (where applicable).

Facilities and Services

Table 7

2008 Facilities and Services in the U.S. Census Divisions and States

These data include only hospital-based facilities and services as reported by responding hospitals in Section C of the 2008 AHA Annual Survey, beginning on page 215. All hospitals are represented with Community Hospitals listed separately under United States. No estimates have been made for nonresponding hospitals. Definitions of facilities and services are listed in the Glossary, page 201.

CLASSIFICATION	HOSPITALS REPORTING	GEN MED SURG: ADULT No.	ADULT %	PEDIATRIC No.	PEDIATRIC %	OBSTETRICS INPATIENT No.	OBST %	NEONATAL INTERMEDIATE No.	%	NEONATAL No.	%	PEDIATRIC No.	%	INTENSIVE CARE: CARDIAC No.	%	MEDICAL SURGICAL No.	%	OTHER No.	%
UNITED STATES	4,862	4,158	85.5	2,136	43.9	2,751	56.6	733	15.1	963	19.8	466	9.6	1,449	29.8	3,064	63.0	530	10.9
COMMUNITY HOSPITALS	4,186	3,905	93.3	2,084	49.8	2,714	64.8	724	17.3	948	22.6	458	10.9	1,397	33.4	2,941	70.3	511	12.2
CENSUS DIVISION 1, NEW ENGLAND	210	175	83.3	115	54.8	136	64.8	28	13.3	38	18.1	18	8.6	65	31.0	160	76.2	15	7.1
Connecticut	33	27	81.8	20	60.6	26	78.8	4	12.1	13	39.4	2	6.1	15	45.5	26	78.8	0	0.0
Maine	38	33	86.8	18	47.4	27	71.1	4	10.5	4	10.5	4	10.5	6	15.8	30	78.9	6	15.8
Massachusetts	81	64	79.0	47	58.0	44	54.3	15	18.5	15	18.5	7	8.6	28	34.6	58	71.6	4	4.9
New Hampshire	30	26	86.7	18	60.0	23	76.7	2	6.7	4	13.3	3	10.0	7	23.3	25	83.3	3	10.0
Rhode Island	13	11	84.6	5	38.5	6	46.2	1	7.7	1	7.7	1	7.7	4	30.8	10	76.9	2	15.4
Vermont	15	14	93.3	7	46.7	10	66.7	2	13.3	1	6.7	1	6.7	5	33.3	11	73.3	0	0.0
CENSUS DIVISION 2, MIDDLE ATLANTIC	398	343	86.2	217	54.5	252	63.3	120	30.2	116	29.1	58	14.6	188	47.2	311	78.1	60	15.1
New Jersey	73	61	83.6	49	67.1	51	69.9	43	58.9	25	34.2	17	23.3	43	58.9	61	83.6	10	13.7
New York	157	143	91.1	97	61.8	106	67.5	52	33.1	50	31.8	34	21.7	82	52.2	128	81.5	26	16.6
Pennsylvania	168	139	82.7	71	42.3	95	56.5	25	14.9	41	24.4	7	4.2	63	37.5	122	72.6	24	14.3
CENSUS DIVISION 3, SOUTH ATLANTIC	678	582	85.8	310	45.7	391	57.7	142	20.9	154	22.7	73	10.8	230	33.9	499	73.6	109	16.1
Delaware	8	5	62.5	4	50.0	5	62.5	2	25.0	3	37.5	3	37.5	4	50.0	5	62.5	2	25.0
District of Columbia	13	8	61.5	4	30.8	7	53.8	3	23.1	6	46.2	3	23.1	7	53.8	8	61.5	1	7.7
Florida	142	128	90.1	58	40.8	82	57.7	23	16.2	44	31.0	25	17.6	58	40.8	119	83.8	16	11.3
Georgia	122	105	86.1	44	36.1	64	52.5	35	28.7	28	23.0	7	5.7	32	26.2	80	65.6	18	14.8
Maryland	59	49	83.1	36	61.0	34	57.6	15	25.4	15	25.4	6	10.2	25	42.4	47	79.7	7	11.9
North Carolina	121	110	90.9	59	48.8	81	66.9	34	28.1	27	22.3	15	12.4	37	30.6	91	75.2	20	16.5
South Carolina	80	62	77.5	47	58.8	43	53.8	26	32.5	8	10.0	6	7.5	28	35.0	53	66.3	33	41.3
Virginia	70	62	88.6	31	44.3	46	65.7	9	12.9	19	27.1	5	7.1	19	27.1	61	87.1	8	11.4
West Virginia	63	53	84.1	27	42.9	29	46.0	2	3.2	4	6.3	3	4.8	20	31.7	35	55.6	4	6.3
CENSUS DIVISION 4, EAST NORTH CENTRAL	753	662	87.9	408	54.2	482	64.0	93	12.4	134	17.8	85	11.3	261	34.7	526	69.9	126	16.7
Illinois	173	155	89.6	103	59.5	112	64.7	35	20.2	30	17.3	21	12.1	47	27.2	123	71.1	11	6.4
Indiana	121	106	87.6	60	49.6	86	71.1	14	11.6	21	17.4	9	7.4	32	26.4	89	73.6	9	7.4
Michigan	158	136	86.1	77	48.7	88	55.7	14	8.9	23	14.6	11	7.0	48	30.4	102	64.6	13	8.2
Ohio	159	144	90.6	68	42.8	104	65.4	30	18.9	35	22.0	14	8.8	61	38.4	129	81.1	22	13.8
Wisconsin	142	121	85.2	100	70.4	92	64.8	0	0.0	25	17.6	30	21.1	73	51.4	83	58.5	71	50.0
CENSUS DIVISION 5, EAST SOUTH CENTRAL	424	374	88.2	177	41.7	190	44.8	67	15.8	62	14.6	39	9.2	127	30.0	239	56.4	45	10.6
Alabama	104	92	88.5	32	30.8	50	48.1	7	6.7	16	15.4	8	7.7	30	28.8	67	64.4	15	14.4
Kentucky	100	85	85.0	39	39.0	46	46.0	18	18.0	13	13.0	5	5.0	28	28.0	60	60.0	11	11.0
Mississippi	109	102	93.6	72	66.1	44	40.4	28	25.7	14	12.8	16	14.7	42	38.5	46	42.2	4	3.7
Tennessee	111	95	85.6	34	30.6	50	45.0	14	12.6	19	17.1	10	9.0	27	24.3	66	59.5	15	13.5
CENSUS DIVISION 6, WEST NORTH CENTRAL	693	624	90.0	300	43.3	380	54.8	76	11.0	85	12.3	48	6.9	149	21.5	352	50.8	48	6.9
Iowa	125	120	96.0	62	49.6	80	64.0	13	10.4	19	15.2	12	9.6	24	19.2	76	60.8	9	7.2
Kansas	153	139	90.8	45	29.4	71	46.4	13	8.5	13	8.5	7	4.6	14	9.2	52	34.0	5	3.3
Minnesota	116	101	87.1	62	53.4	84	72.4	7	6.0	14	12.1	10	8.6	31	26.7	66	56.9	7	6.0
Missouri	149	119	79.9	78	52.3	74	49.7	29	19.5	20	13.4	8	5.4	41	27.5	89	59.7	15	10.1
Nebraska	65	62	95.4	23	35.4	37	56.9	5	7.7	8	12.3	2	3.1	18	27.7	27	41.5	5	7.7
North Dakota	31	30	96.8	14	45.2	13	41.9	5	16.1	6	19.4	4	12.9	10	32.3	18	58.1	3	9.7
South Dakota	54	53	98.1	16	29.6	21	38.9	4	7.4	5	9.3	5	9.3	11	20.4	24	44.4	4	7.4
CENSUS DIVISION 7, WEST SOUTH CENTRAL	852	642	75.4	269	31.6	370	43.4	99	11.6	147	17.3	62	7.3	162	19.0	406	47.7	51	6.0
Arkansas	98	74	75.5	29	29.6	45	45.9	10	10.2	10	10.2	3	3.1	29	29.6	46	46.9	4	4.1
Louisiana	96	78	81.3	42	43.8	44	45.8	11	11.5	30	31.3	14	14.6	24	25.0	60	62.5	5	5.2
Oklahoma	116	101	87.1	30	25.9	53	45.7	3	2.6	9	7.8	5	4.3	18	15.5	47	40.5	7	6.0
Texas	542	389	71.8	168	31.0	228	42.1	75	13.8	98	18.1	40	7.4	91	16.8	253	46.7	35	6.5
CENSUS DIVISION 8, MOUNTAIN	347	307	88.5	140	40.3	212	61.1	47	13.5	71	20.5	33	9.5	82	23.6	197	56.8	28	8.1
Arizona	59	49	83.1	24	40.7	36	61.0	12	20.3	12	20.3	7	11.9	26	44.1	41	69.5	3	5.1
Colorado	66	62	93.9	32	48.5	46	69.7	10	15.2	23	34.8	6	9.1	15	22.7	44	66.7	8	12.1
Idaho	34	31	91.2	13	38.2	20	58.8	2	5.9	5	14.7	3	8.8	7	20.6	15	44.1	3	8.8
Montana	59	57	96.6	21	35.6	28	47.5	4	6.8	7	11.9	4	6.8	12	20.3	22	37.3	3	5.1
Nevada	29	21	72.4	9	31.0	15	51.7	4	13.8	6	20.7	4	13.8	6	20.7	16	55.2	4	13.8
New Mexico	36	29	80.6	13	36.1	21	58.3	5	13.9	2	5.6	2	5.6	5	13.9	20	55.6	2	5.6
Utah	33	29	87.9	18	54.5	26	78.8	8	24.2	16	48.5	6	18.2	11	33.3	19	57.6	4	12.1
Wyoming	31	29	93.5	10	32.3	20	64.5	2	6.5	0	0.0	1	3.2	0	0.0	20	64.5	1	3.2
CENSUS DIVISION 9, PACIFIC	507	449	88.6	200	39.4	338	66.7	61	12.0	156	30.8	50	9.9	185	36.5	374	73.8	48	9.5
Alaska	14	12	85.7	5	35.7	9	64.3	2	14.3	3	21.4	2	14.3	2	14.3	10	71.4	0	0.0
California	334	291	87.1	132	39.5	214	64.1	38	11.4	131	39.2	40	12.0	139	41.6	252	75.4	35	10.5
Hawaii	20	16	80.0	2	10.0	10	50.0	1	5.0	0	0.0	0	0.0	5	25.0	13	65.0	0	0.0
Oregon	57	57	100.0	24	42.1	52	91.2	6	10.5	8	14.0	2	3.5	18	31.6	49	86.0	4	7.0
Washington	82	73	89.0	37	45.1	53	64.6	14	17.1	14	17.1	6	7.3	21	25.6	50	61.0	9	11.0

Table 7 (Continued)

These data include only hospital-based facilities and services as reported by responding hospitals in Section C of the 2008 AHA Annual Survey, beginning on page 215. All hospitals are represented with Community Hospitals listed separately under United States. No estimates have been made for nonresponding hospitals. Definitions of facilities and services are listed in the Glossary, page 201.

CLASSIFICATION	HOSPITALS REPORTING	BURN CARE Number	BURN CARE Percent	LONG-TERM CARE — ACUTE LONG-TERM CARE Number	Percent	SKILLED NURSING CARE Number	Percent	INTERMEDIATE CARE Number	Percent	OTHER LONG-TERM CARE Number	Percent	PSYCHIATRIC INPATIENT CARE Number	Percent	ALCOHOL/DRUG ABUSE OR DEPENDENCY INPATIENT CARE Number	Percent	OTHER SPECIAL CARE Number	Percent	PHYSICAL REHABILITATION INPATIENT CARE Number	Percent
UNITED STATES	4,862	213	4.4	383	7.9	1,305	26.8	441	9.1	303	6.2	1,682	34.6	498	10.2	758	15.6	1,469	30.2
COMMUNITY HOSPITALS	4,186	205	4.9	259	6.2	1,214	29.0	401	9.6	258	6.2	1,320	31.5	364	8.7	716	17.1	1,369	32.7
CENSUS DIVISION 1, NEW ENGLAND	210	13	6.2	16	7.6	43	20.5	23	11.0	12	5.7	111	52.9	28	13.3	24	11.4	53	25.2
Connecticut	33	1	3.0	2	6.1	2	5.1	1	3.0	1	3.0	27	81.8	8	24.2	7	21.2	12	36.4
Maine	38	3	7.9	3	7.9	11	28.9	9	23.7	5	3.2	13	34.2	7	18.4	8	7.9	11	28.9
Massachusetts	81	6	7.4	9	11.1	11	13.5	3	3.7	4	4.9	46	56.8	9	11.1	8	9.9	16	19.8
New Hampshire	30	1	3.3	1	3.3	9	30.0	8	26.7	1	3.3	12	40.0	1	3.3	5	16.7	7	23.3
Rhode Island	13	1	7.7	1	7.7	1	7.7	1	7.7	1	7.7	8	61.5	2	15.4	0	0.0	4	30.8
Vermont	15	1	6.7	0	0.0	5	33.3	1	6.7	0	0.0	5	33.3	1	6.7	1	6.7	3	20.0
CENSUS DIVISION 2, MIDDLE ATLANTIC	398	23	5.8	17	4.3	115	28.9	22	5.5	23	5.8	236	59.3	75	18.8	74	18.6	148	37.2
New Jersey	73	5	6.8	6	8.2	17	23.3	10	13.7	7	9.6	47	64.4	14	19.2	14	19.2	15	20.5
New York	157	11	7.0	7	4.5	47	29.9	8	5.1	11	7.0	99	63.1	48	30.6	30	19.1	67	42.7
Pennsylvania	168	7	4.2	4	2.4	51	30.4	4	2.4	5	3.0	90	53.6	13	7.7	30	17.9	66	39.3
CENSUS DIVISION 3, SOUTH ATLANTIC	678	28	4.1	73	10.8	199	29.4	62	9.1	57	8.4	256	37.8	80	11.8	135	19.9	212	31.3
Delaware	8	0	0.0	0	0.0	2	25.0	1	12.5	0	0.0	3	37.5	0	0.0	1	12.5	4	50.0
District of Columbia	13	2	15.4	1	7.7	3	23.1	1	7.7	2	15.4	11	84.6	3	23.1	3	23.1	5	38.5
Florida	142	6	4.2	7	4.9	16	11.3	6	4.2	3	2.1	43	30.3	13	9.2	38	26.8	33	23.2
Georgia	122	3	2.5	11	9.0	32	23.2	13	10.7	5	4.1	33	27.0	15	12.3	16	13.1	33	27.0
Maryland	59	2	3.4	5	8.5	15	25.4	4	6.8	2	3.4	40	67.8	7	11.9	15	25.4	16	27.1
North Carolina	121	7	5.8	7	5.8	48	39.7	13	10.7	11	9.1	54	44.6	16	13.2	30	24.8	34	28.1
South Carolina	80	2	2.5	36	45.0	39	43.8	9	11.3	28	35.0	24	30.0	13	16.3	16	20.0	57	71.3
Virginia	70	5	7.1	4	5.7	17	24.3	9	12.9	4	5.7	31	44.3	10	14.3	12	17.1	19	27.1
West Virginia	63	1	1.6	2	3.2	27	42.9	6	9.5	2	3.2	17	27.0	3	4.8	4	6.3	11	17.5
CENSUS DIVISION 4, EAST NORTH CENTRAL	753	42	5.6	58	7.7	193	25.6	59	7.8	49	6.5	296	39.6	104	13.8	200	26.6	281	37.3
Illinois	173	8	4.6	7	4.0	52	30.1	10	5.8	14	8.1	71	41.0	19	11.0	17	9.8	48	27.7
Indiana	121	4	3.3	9	7.4	28	23.1	10	8.3	4	3.3	41	33.9	9	7.4	19	15.7	40	33.1
Michigan	156	8	5.1	14	8.9	34	21.5	8	5.1	9	5.7	65	41.1	14	8.9	23	14.6	58	36.7
Ohio	159	12	7.5	11	6.9	48	30.2	14	8.8	16	10.1	76	47.8	24	15.1	31	19.5	63	39.6
Wisconsin	142	10	7.0	17	12.0	31	21.8	17	12.0	6	4.2	45	31.7	38	26.8	110	77.5	72	50.7
CENSUS DIVISION 5, EAST SOUTH CENTRAL	424	16	3.8	20	4.7	100	23.6	26	6.1	35	8.3	152	35.8	38	9.0	63	14.9	121	28.5
Alabama	104	5	4.8	2	1.9	10	9.6	7	6.7	4	3.8	35	33.7	5	4.8	14	13.5	19	18.3
Kentucky	100	5	5.0	10	10.0	31	31.0	8	8.0	4	4.0	35	35.0	8	8.0	11	11.0	24	24.0
Mississippi	109	2	1.8	1	0.9	27	24.8	0	0.0	21	19.3	44	40.4	15	13.8	16	14.7	51	46.8
Tennessee	111	4	3.6	7	6.3	32	28.8	11	9.9	6	5.4	38	34.2	10	9.0	22	19.8	27	24.3
CENSUS DIVISION 6, WEST NORTH CENTRAL	693	30	4.3	36	5.2	388	56.0	130	18.8	71	10.2	187	27.0	58	8.4	81	11.7	203	29.3
Iowa	125	7	5.6	7	5.6	75	60.0	42	33.6	17	13.6	39	31.2	15	12.0	12	9.6	31	24.8
Kansas	153	4	2.6	10	6.5	72	47.1	41	26.8	17	11.1	26	17.0	3	2.0	11	7.2	33	21.6
Minnesota	116	5	4.3	5	4.3	55	47.4	6	5.2	4	3.4	38	32.8	13	11.2	12	10.3	26	22.4
Missouri	149	8	5.4	8	5.4	70	47.0	14	9.4	10	5.7	60	40.3	17	11.4	29	19.5	84	56.4
Nebraska	65	2	3.1	1	1.5	48	73.8	12	18.5	10	15.4	9	13.8	3	4.6	7	10.8	11	16.9
North Dakota	31	2	6.5	2	6.5	26	83.9	5	16.1	4	12.9	9	29.0	5	16.1	5	16.1	8	25.8
South Dakota	54	2	3.7	3	5.6	30	55.6	10	18.5	9	15.7	6	11.1	2	3.7	5	9.3	10	18.5
CENSUS DIVISION 7, WEST SOUTH CENTRAL	852	21	2.5	112	13.1	109	12.8	33	3.9	11	1.3	206	24.2	47	5.5	84	9.9	233	27.3
Arkansas	98	1	1.0	9	9.2	22	22.4	4	4.1	0	2.0	34	34.7	3	3.1	7	7.1	32	32.7
Louisiana	96	4	4.2	11	11.5	18	18.8	5	5.2	3	3.1	41	42.7	5	5.2	8	8.3	31	32.3
Oklahoma	116	2	1.7	10	8.6	20	17.2	5	4.3	2	1.7	31	26.7	3	2.6	7	6.0	34	29.3
Texas	542	14	2.6	82	15.1	49	9.0	19	3.5	6	1.1	100	18.5	36	6.6	62	11.4	136	25.1
CENSUS DIVISION 8, MOUNTAIN	347	15	4.3	16	4.6	108	31.1	45	13.0	25	7.2	82	23.6	27	7.8	29	8.4	91	26.2
Arizona	59	3	5.1	1	1.7	2	3.4	4	6.8	1	1.7	17	28.8	2	3.4	1	1.7	20	33.9
Colorado	66	3	4.5	2	3.0	17	25.8	4	6.1	6	3.1	15	22.7	8	12.1	10	15.2	23	34.8
Idaho	34	1	2.9	1	2.9	14	41.2	3	8.8	2	5.9	8	23.5	1	2.9	3	8.8	6	17.6
Montana	59	2	3.4	5	8.5	38	64.4	10	16.9	7	11.9	9	15.3	3	5.1	5	8.5	10	16.9
Nevada	29	1	3.4	2	6.9	4	13.8	2	3.4	0	0.0	6	20.7	1	3.4	2	6.9	10	34.5
New Mexico	36	2	5.6	3	8.3	6	16.7	3	8.3	2	5.6	6	16.7	4	11.1	1	2.8	9	25.0
Utah	33	3	9.1	2	6.1	11	33.3	11	33.3	2	5.1	14	42.4	5	15.2	5	15.2	9	27.3
Wyoming	31	0	0.0	0	0.0	16	51.6	9	29.0	5	13.1	7	22.6	3	9.7	2	6.5	4	12.9
CENSUS DIVISION 9, PACIFIC	507	25	4.9	35	6.9	50	9.9	41	8.1	20	3.9	154	30.4	41	8.1	68	13.4	127	25.0
Alaska	14	0	0.0	0	0.0	2	14.3	3	21.4	1	7.1	5	35.7	2	14.3	1	7.1	3	21.4
California	334	20	6.0	28	8.4	17	5.1	18	5.4	14	4.2	100	29.9	27	8.1	42	12.6	85	25.4
Hawaii	20	1	5.0	1	5.0	10	50.0	8	40.0	0	0.0	6	30.0	0	0.0	1	5.0	1	5.0
Oregon	57	2	3.5	2	3.5	7	12.3	8	14.0	1	1.8	16	28.1	3	5.3	7	12.3	12	21.1
Washington	82	2	2.4	4	4.9	14	17.1	4	4.9	4	4.9	27	32.9	9	11.0	17	20.7	26	31.7

Table 7 (Continued)

These data include only hospital-based facilities and services as reported by responding hospitals in Section C of the 2008 AHA Annual Survey, beginning on page 215. All hospitals are represented with Community Hospitals listed separately under United States. No estimates have been made for nonresponding hospitals. Definitions of facilities and services are listed in the Glossary, page 201.

CLASSIFICATION	HOSPITALS REPORTING	ADULT DAY CARE PROGRAM Number	Percent	AIRBORNE INFECTION ISOLATION ROOM Number	Percent	ALCOHOL/DRUG ABUSE OR DEPENDENCY OUTPATIENT SERVICES Number	Percent	ALZHEIMER CENTER Number	Percent	AMBULANCE SERVICES Number	Percent	AMBULATORY SURGERY CENTERS Number	Percent	ARTHRITIS TREATMENT CENTER Number	Percent	ASSISTED LIVING Number	Percent	AUXILIARY Number	Percent	BARIATRIC/WEIGHT CONTROL SERVICES Number	Percent
UNITED STATES	4,862	290	6.0	3,419	70.3	750	15.4	213	4.4	780	16.0	1,106	22.7	272	5.6	216	4.4	2,905	59.7	1,062	21.8
COMMUNITY HOSPITALS	4,186	248	5.9	3,151	75.3	586	14.0	189	4.5	747	17.8	1,051	25.1	259	6.2	199	4.8	2,828	67.6	994	23.7
CENSUS DIVISION 1, NEW ENGLAND	210	21	10.0	157	74.8	66	31.4	16	7.6	27	12.9	73	34.8	17	8.1	10	4.8	124	59.0	58	27.6
Connecticut	33	4	12.1	26	78.8	15	45.5	3	9.1	3	9.1	16	48.5	4	12.1	2	6.1	21	63.6	14	42.4
Maine	38	3	7.9	28	73.7	14	36.8	4	10.5	8	21.1	11	28.9	0	0.0	3	7.9	25	65.8	5	13.2
Massachusetts	81	6	7.4	56	69.1	28	34.6	7	8.6	8	9.9	25	30.9	10	12.3	1	1.2	41	50.6	25	30.9
New Hampshire	30	7	23.3	27	90.0	2	6.7	1	3.3	6	20.0	8	26.7	2	6.7	2	6.7	19	63.3	7	23.3
Rhode Island	13	0	0.0	7	53.8	4	30.8	0	0.0	1	7.7	6	46.2	0	0.0	1	7.7	7	53.8	4	30.8
Vermont	15	1	6.7	13	86.7	3	20.0	1	6.7	1	6.7	7	46.7	1	6.7	1	6.7	11	73.3	3	20.0
CENSUS DIVISION 2, MIDDLE ATLANTIC	398	38	9.5	290	72.9	111	27.9	30	7.5	72	18.1	139	34.9	52	13.1	15	3.8	269	67.6	148	37.2
New Jersey	73	10	13.7	53	72.6	27	37.0	7	9.6	16	21.9	17	23.3	7	9.6	2	2.7	56	76.7	37	50.7
New York	157	21	13.4	110	70.1	60	38.2	12	7.6	30	19.1	80	51.0	26	16.6	4	2.5	98	62.4	60	38.2
Pennsylvania	168	7	4.2	127	75.6	24	14.3	11	6.5	26	15.5	42	25.0	19	11.3	9	5.4	115	68.5	51	30.4
CENSUS DIVISION 3, SOUTH ATLANTIC	678	29	4.3	527	77.7	109	16.1	32	4.7	107	15.8	164	24.2	36	5.3	21	3.1	442	65.2	171	25.2
Delaware	8	2	25.0	5	62.5	0	0.0	1	12.5	0	0.0	3	37.5	0	0.0	0	0.0	5	62.5	3	37.5
District of Columbia	13	0	0.0	8	61.5	5	38.5	3	23.1	2	15.4	6	46.2	2	15.4	2	15.4	4	30.8	5	38.5
Florida	142	7	4.9	123	86.6	13	9.2	11	7.7	18	12.7	44	31.0	5	3.5	0	0.0	93	65.5	52	36.6
Georgia	122	4	3.3	88	72.1	19	15.6	4	3.3	23	18.9	23	18.9	4	3.3	6	4.9	83	68.0	26	21.3
Maryland	59	6	10.2	48	81.4	21	35.6	4	6.8	6	10.2	17	28.8	7	11.9	5	8.5	46	78.0	17	28.8
North Carolina	121	5	4.1	97	80.2	21	17.4	4	3.3	24	19.8	36	29.8	7	5.8	3	2.5	80	66.1	29	24.0
South Carolina	80	2	2.5	59	73.8	8	10.0	2	2.5	18	22.5	10	12.5	3	3.8	0	0.0	41	51.3	13	16.3
Virginia	70	3	4.3	59	84.3	15	21.4	3	4.3	9	12.9	19	27.1	5	7.1	5	7.1	52	74.3	18	25.7
West Virginia	63	0	0.0	40	63.5	7	11.1	0	0.0	7	11.1	6	9.5	3	4.8	0	0.0	38	60.3	8	12.7
CENSUS DIVISION 4, EAST NORTH CENTRAL	753	57	7.6	554	73.6	166	22.0	63	8.4	130	17.3	196	26.0	70	9.3	35	4.6	500	66.4	189	25.1
Illinois	173	21	12.1	136	78.6	39	22.5	9	5.2	26	15.0	40	23.1	18	10.4	5	2.9	119	68.8	49	28.3
Indiana	121	5	4.1	97	80.2	21	17.4	1	0.8	35	28.9	33	27.3	5	4.1	4	3.3	65	53.7	26	21.5
Michigan	158	9	5.7	120	75.9	33	20.9	10	6.3	24	15.2	37	23.4	9	5.7	10	6.3	112	70.9	38	24.1
Ohio	159	9	5.7	123	77.4	37	23.3	13	8.2	25	15.7	52	32.7	19	11.9	7	4.4	118	74.2	42	26.4
Wisconsin	142	13	9.2	78	54.9	36	25.4	30	21.1	20	14.1	34	23.9	19	13.4	9	6.3	86	60.6	34	23.9
CENSUS DIVISION 5, EAST SOUTH CENTRAL	424	10	2.4	240	56.6	41	9.7	3	0.7	54	12.7	59	13.9	6	1.4	7	1.7	188	44.3	65	15.3
Alabama	104	2	1.9	58	55.8	7	6.7	1	1.0	13	12.5	17	16.3	2	1.9	3	2.9	54	51.9	23	22.1
Kentucky	100	4	4.0	74	74.0	14	14.0	1	1.0	11	11.0	14	14.0	2	2.0	0	0.0	63	63.0	20	20.0
Mississippi	109	4	3.7	33	30.3	8	7.3	1	0.9	12	11.0	12	11.0	0	0.0	2	1.8	24	22.0	5	4.6
Tennessee	111	0	0.0	75	67.6	12	10.8	0	0.0	18	16.2	16	14.4	2	1.8	2	1.8	47	42.3	17	15.3
CENSUS DIVISION 6, WEST NORTH CENTRAL	693	57	8.2	444	64.1	86	12.4	32	4.6	174	25.1	117	16.9	31	4.5	73	10.5	456	65.8	103	14.9
Iowa	125	5	4.0	68	54.4	22	17.6	5	4.0	54	43.2	23	18.4	3	2.4	11	8.8	110	88.0	17	13.6
Kansas	153	10	6.5	96	62.7	5	3.3	4	2.6	22	14.4	12	7.8	3	2.0	13	8.5	79	51.6	17	11.1
Minnesota	116	20	17.2	77	66.4	21	18.1	9	7.8	37	31.9	28	24.1	8	6.9	15	12.9	79	68.1	27	23.3
Missouri	149	5	3.4	112	75.2	23	15.4	7	4.7	31	20.8	26	17.4	12	8.1	3	2.0	101	67.8	24	16.1
Nebraska	65	7	10.8	42	64.6	7	10.8	4	6.2	12	18.5	11	16.9	1	1.5	13	20.0	36	55.4	8	12.3
North Dakota	31	2	6.5	22	71.0	4	12.9	0	0.0	7	22.6	10	32.3	3	9.7	3	9.7	23	74.2	5	16.1
South Dakota	54	8	14.8	27	50.0	4	7.4	3	5.6	11	20.4	7	13.0	1	1.9	15	27.8	28	51.9	5	9.3
CENSUS DIVISION 7, WEST SOUTH CENTRAL	852	17	2.0	617	72.4	57	6.7	4	0.5	110	12.9	124	14.6	23	2.7	24	2.8	432	50.7	152	17.8
Arkansas	98	5	5.1	80	81.6	3	3.1	2	2.0	14	14.3	18	18.4	4	4.1	1	1.0	63	64.3	11	11.2
Louisiana	96	5	5.2	60	62.5	6	6.3	0	0.0	12	12.5	22	22.9	4	4.2	4	4.2	48	50.0	20	20.8
Oklahoma	116	1	0.9	69	59.5	5	4.3	0	0.0	16	13.8	17	14.7	2	1.7	4	3.4	59	50.9	11	9.5
Texas	542	6	1.1	408	75.3	43	7.9	2	0.4	68	12.5	67	12.4	13	2.4	15	2.8	262	48.3	110	20.3
CENSUS DIVISION 8, MOUNTAIN	347	28	8.1	238	68.6	48	13.8	15	4.3	61	17.6	87	25.1	12	3.5	18	5.2	197	56.8	60	17.3
Arizona	59	0	0.0	47	79.7	11	18.6	1	1.7	2	3.4	18	30.5	0	0.0	1	1.7	36	61.0	11	18.6
Colorado	66	3	4.5	48	72.7	9	13.6	2	3.0	11	16.7	16	24.2	5	7.6	2	3.0	42	63.6	16	24.2
Idaho	34	5	14.7	24	70.6	2	5.9	0	0.0	7	20.6	9	26.5	1	2.9	7	20.3	23	67.6	8	23.5
Montana	59	16	27.1	34	57.6	3	5.1	5	8.5	16	27.1	11	18.6	1	1.7	2	3.4	31	52.5	3	5.1
Nevada	29	1	3.4	16	55.2	4	13.8	0	0.0	2	6.9	6	20.7	2	6.9	0	0.0	9	31.0	7	24.1
New Mexico	36	0	0.0	25	69.4	5	13.9	0	0.0	7	19.4	11	30.6	2	5.6	0	0.0	21	58.3	2	5.6
Utah	33	2	6.1	24	72.7	8	24.2	2	6.1	6	18.2	11	33.3	1	3.0	2	6.5	16	48.5	10	30.3
Wyoming	31	1	3.2	20	64.5	6	19.4	5	16.1	10	32.3	5	16.1	0	0.0	4	12.9	19	61.3	3	9.7
CENSUS DIVISION 9, PACIFIC	507	33	6.5	352	69.4	66	13.0	18	3.6	45	8.9	147	29.0	25	4.9	13	2.6	297	58.6	116	22.9
Alaska	14	0	0.0	11	78.6	4	28.6	0	0.0	1	7.1	3	21.4	0	0.0	0	0.0	7	50.0	2	14.3
California	334	22	6.6	230	68.9	41	12.3	15	4.5	24	7.2	95	28.4	16	4.8	6	1.8	189	56.6	78	23.4
Hawaii	20	2	10.0	13	65.0	1	5.0	0	0.0	0	0.0	4	20.0	1	5.0	0	0.0	7	35.0	3	15.0
Oregon	57	5	8.8	51	89.5	5	8.8	1	1.8	7	12.3	15	26.3	3	5.3	2	3.5	47	82.5	16	28.1
Washington	82	4	4.9	47	57.3	15	18.3	2	2.4	13	15.9	30	36.6	5	6.1	5	6.1	47	57.3	17	20.7

Table 7 (Continued)

These data include only hospital-based facilities and services as reported by responding hospitals in Section C of the 2008 AHA Annual Survey, beginning on page 215. All hospitals are represented with Community Hospitals listed separately under United States. No estimates have been made for nonresponding hospitals. Definitions of facilities and services are listed in the Glossary, page 201.

CARDIOLOGY AND CARDIAC SERVICES

Classification	Hospitals Reporting	Birthing/LDR/LDRP Room No.	%	Breast Cancer Screening No.	%	Adult Diag./Invasive Cath. No.	%	Pediatric Diag./Invasive Cath. No.	%	Adult Interv. Cardiac Cath. No.	%	Pediatric Interv. Cardiac Cath. No.	%	Adult Cardiac Surgery No.	%	Pediatric Cardiac Surgery No.	%	Adult Cardiac Electrophys. No.	%	Pediatric Cardiac Electrophys. No.	%	Cardiac Rehabilitation No.	%
UNITED STATES	4,862	2,708	55.7	3,407	70.1	1,815	37.3	218	4.5	1,449	29.8	195	4.0	1,127	23.2	188	3.9	1,073	22.1	191	3.9	2,464	50.7
COMMUNITY HOSPITALS	4,186	2,677	64.0	3,317	79.2	1,750	41.8	215	5.1	1,391	33.2	193	4.6	1,087	26.0	186	4.4	1,026	24.5	185	4.4	2,403	57.4
CENSUS DIVISION 1, NEW ENGLAND	210	133	63.3	163	77.6	91	43.3	10	4.8	59	28.1	9	4.3	42	20.0	8	3.8	52	24.8	10	4.8	141	67.1
Connecticut	33	26	78.8	26	78.8	21	63.6	2	6.1	16	48.5	2	6.1	13	39.4	2	6.1	11	33.3	2	6.1	25	75.8
Maine	38	27	71.1	31	81.6	11	28.9			4	10.5	1	2.6	3	7.9	1	2.6	6	15.8	2	5.3	28	73.7
Massachusetts	81	42	51.9	60	74.1	36	44.4	3	3.7	24	29.6	3	3.7	18	22.2	3	3.7	22	27.2	4	4.9	46	56.8
New Hampshire	30	22	73.3	24	80.0	13	43.3	2	6.7	9	30.0	1	3.3	4	13.3	1	3.3	8	26.7	1	3.3	23	76.7
Rhode Island	13	6	46.2	10	76.9	6	46.2	1	7.7	4	30.8	1	7.7	2	15.4	0	0.0	3	23.1	1	7.7	7	53.8
Vermont	15	10	66.7	12	80.0	4	26.7			2	13.3	1	6.7	2	13.3	1	6.7	2	13.3	0	0.0	12	80.0
CENSUS DIVISION 2, MIDDLE ATLANTIC	398	240	60.3	310	77.9	208	52.3	26	6.5	153	38.4	24	6.0	110	27.6	25	6.3	117	29.4	23	5.8	242	60.8
New Jersey	73	48	65.8	53	72.6	54	74.0	4	5.5	38	52.1	3	4.1	17	23.3	2	2.7	23	31.5	6	8.2	47	64.4
New York	157	100	63.7	126	80.3	70	44.6	17	10.8	50	31.8	16	10.2	37	23.6	16	10.2	47	29.9	12	7.6	84	53.5
Pennsylvania	168	92	54.8	131	78.0	84	50.0	5	3.0	65	38.7	5	3.0	56	33.3	7	4.2	47	28.0	5	3.0	111	66.1
CENSUS DIVISION 3, SOUTH ATLANTIC	678	395	58.3	523	77.1	339	50.0	30	4.4	222	32.7	27	4.0	164	24.2	25	3.7	191	28.2	31	4.6	351	51.8
Delaware	8	5	62.5	5	62.5	5	62.5			4	50.0	1	12.5	4	50.0	1	12.5	2	25.0	1	12.5	6	75.0
District of Columbia	13	7	53.8	7	53.8	9	69.2	2	15.4	7	53.8	2	15.4	6	46.2	1	7.7	6	46.2	3	23.1	5	38.5
Florida	142	79	55.6	117	82.4	93	65.5	11	7.7	65	45.8	8	5.5	56	39.4	9	6.3	49	34.5	8	5.6	67	47.2
Georgia	122	67	54.9	92	75.4	47	38.5	2	1.6	28	23.0	3	1.5	19	15.6	2	1.6	30	24.6	2	1.6	50	41.0
Maryland	59	35	59.3	42	71.2	38	64.4	3	5.1	31	52.5	3	5.1	11	18.6	2	3.4	26	44.1	4	6.8	33	55.9
North Carolina	121	83	68.6	96	79.3	61	50.4	6	5.0	34	28.1	6	5.0	27	22.3	5	4.1	35	28.9	7	5.8	74	61.2
South Carolina	80	42	52.5	55	68.8	32	40.0	1	1.3	18	22.5	1	1.3	19	23.8	1	1.3	12	15.0	1	1.3	38	47.5
Virginia	70	46	65.7	60	85.7	33	47.1	3	4.3	26	37.1	3	4.3	16	22.9	3	4.3	23	32.9	3	4.3	49	70.0
West Virginia	63	31	49.2	49	77.8	21	33.3	1	1.6	9	14.3	1	1.5	6	9.5	1	1.6	8	12.7	2	3.2	29	46.0
CENSUS DIVISION 4, EAST NORTH CENTRAL	753	481	63.9	607	80.6	326	43.3	33	4.4	274	36.4	31	4.1	216	28.7	30	4.0	210	27.9	32	4.2	516	68.5
Illinois	173	110	63.6	146	84.4	86	49.7	10	5.8	79	45.7	10	5.3	61	35.3	8	4.6	60	34.7	9	5.2	126	72.8
Indiana	121	84	69.4	94	77.7	51	42.1	4	3.3	44	36.4	3	2.5	30	24.8	5	4.1	28	23.1	5	4.1	80	66.1
Michigan	158	88	55.7	128	81.0	58	36.7	4	2.5	46	29.1	4	2.5	38	24.1	6	3.8	46	29.1	7	4.4	95	60.1
Ohio	159	103	64.8	131	82.4	83	52.2	9	5.7	65	40.9	8	5.0	56	35.2	7	4.4	47	29.6	6	3.8	109	68.6
Wisconsin	142	96	67.6	108	76.1	48	33.8	6	4.2	40	28.2	6	4.2	31	21.8	4	2.8	29	20.4	5	3.5	106	74.6
CENSUS DIVISION 5, EAST SOUTH CENTRAL	424	180	42.5	292	68.9	131	30.9	11	2.6	99	23.3	10	2.4	80	18.9	9	2.1	62	14.6	9	2.1	147	34.7
Alabama	104	45	43.3	70	67.3	37	35.6	4	3.8	29	27.9	3	2.9	24	23.1	2	1.9	18	17.3	2	1.9	36	34.6
Kentucky	100	46	46.0	78	78.0	37	37.0	2	2.0	25	25.0	2	2.0	20	20.0	2	2.0	15	15.0	2	2.0	48	48.0
Mississippi	109	41	37.6	60	55.0	16	14.7	1	0.9	12	11.0	1	0.9	12	11.0	1	0.9	9	8.3	1	0.9	18	16.5
Tennessee	111	48	43.2	84	75.7	41	36.9	4	3.6	33	29.7	4	3.6	24	21.6	4	3.6	20	18.0	4	3.6	45	40.5
CENSUS DIVISION 6, WEST NORTH CENTRAL	693	388	56.0	484	69.8	143	20.6	17	2.5	137	19.8	16	2.3	95	13.7	16	2.3	99	14.3	16	2.3	473	68.3
Iowa	125	82	65.6	112	89.6	24	19.2	2	1.6	24	19.2	2	1.6	12	9.6	0	0.0	19	15.2	4	2.6	106	84.8
Kansas	153	70	45.8	81	52.9	23	15.0	1	0.7	22	14.4	1	0.7	16	10.5	3	2.6	15	9.8	4	2.6	74	48.4
Minnesota	116	84	72.4	90	77.6	17	14.7	3	2.6	17	14.7	3	2.6	15	12.9	7	4.7	17	14.7	4	3.4	91	78.4
Missouri	149	74	49.7	104	69.8	54	36.2	6	4.0	50	33.6	5	3.4	35	23.5	2	1.5	35	23.5	7	4.7	87	58.4
Nebraska	65	42	64.6	48	73.8	13	20.0	2	1.5	12	18.5	2	1.5	8	12.3	2	6.5	7	10.8	0	0.0	48	73.8
North Dakota	31	16	51.6	19	61.3	5	16.1	2	6.5	5	16.1	2	6.5	5	16.1			3	9.7	1	3.2	25	80.6
South Dakota	54	20	37.0	30	55.6	7	13.0	2	3.7	7	13.0	2	3.7	4	7.4			3	5.6	1	1.9	42	77.8
CENSUS DIVISION 7, WEST SOUTH CENTRAL	852	359	42.1	429	50.4	254	29.8	32	3.8	254	26.3	28	3.3	194	22.8	29	3.4	156	18.3	25	2.9	272	31.9
Arkansas	98	44	44.9	59	60.2	25	25.5	1	1.0	24	24.5	1	1.0	20	20.4	1	1.0	15	15.3	1	1.0	39	39.8
Louisiana	96	44	45.8	65	67.7	41	42.7	8	8.3	36	37.5	7	7.3	31	32.3	7	7.3	26	27.1	5	5.2	32	33.3
Oklahoma	116	50	43.1	60	51.7	28	24.1	2	1.7	23	19.8	2	1.7	18	15.5	2	1.7	11	9.5	3	2.6	26	22.4
Texas	542	221	40.8	245	45.2	160	29.5	21	3.9	141	26.0	19	3.3	125	23.1	19	3.5	104	19.2	16	3.0	175	32.3
CENSUS DIVISION 8, MOUNTAIN	347	213	61.4	244	70.3	116	33.4	21	6.1	103	29.7	19	5.5	77	22.2	14	4.0	63	18.2	14	4.0	154	44.4
Arizona	59	35	59.3	40	67.8	33	55.9	5	8.5	31	52.5	4	6.8	24	40.7	3	5.1	19	32.2	2	3.4	32	54.2
Colorado	66	48	72.7	53	80.3	30	45.5	3	4.5	29	43.9	3	4.5	17	25.8	3	3.0	16	24.2	3	4.5	36	54.5
Idaho	34	23	67.6	20	58.8	7	20.6	2	5.9	6	17.6	2	5.9	5	14.7	1	2.9	2	5.9	1	2.9	11	32.4
Montana	59	28	47.5	39	66.1	8	13.6	1	1.7	7	11.9			5	10.2	2	3.4	5	8.5	2	3.4	26	44.1
Nevada	29	14	48.3	20	69.0	12	41.4	4	13.8	10	34.5	3	10.3	7	27.6	2	6.9	8	27.6	3	10.3	10	34.5
New Mexico	36	20	55.6	25	69.4	10	27.8	2	5.6	8	22.2	2	5.6	6	16.7	3	5.6	6	16.7	2	5.6	10	27.8
Utah	33	25	75.8	26	78.8	14	42.4	4	12.1	10	30.3	4	12.1	9	27.3	3	9.1	7	21.2	1	3.0	16	48.5
Wyoming	31	20	64.5	21	67.7	2	6.5	0	0.0	2	6.5	0	0.0	2	6.5	0	0.0	0	0.0	0	0.0	13	41.9
CENSUS DIVISION 9, PACIFIC	507	319	62.9	355	70.0	207	40.8	38	7.5	178	35.1	31	6.1	143	29.4	32	6.3	123	24.3	31	6.1	168	33.1
Alaska	14	10	71.4	12	85.7	3	21.4	2	14.3	3	21.4			3	21.4			2	14.3	2	14.3	5	35.7
California	334	197	59.0	222	66.5	143	42.8	26	7.8	123	36.8	22	6.6	111	33.2	22	6.6	84	25.1	17	5.1	107	32.0
Hawaii	20	9	45.0	12	60.0	7	35.0	1	5.0	5	25.0	1	5.0	4	20.0	0	0.0	4	20.0	1	5.0	2	10.0
Oregon	57	51	89.5	51	89.5	21	36.8	4	7.0	17	29.8	3	5.3	13	22.8	3	5.3	13	22.8	5	8.8	23	40.4
Washington	82	52	63.4	58	70.7	33	40.2	5	6.1	30	36.6	3	2.9	19	23.2	7	8.5	20	24.4	6	7.3	31	37.8

Table 7 (Continued)

These data include only hospital-based facilities and services as reported by responding hospitals in Section C of the 2008 AHA Annual Survey, beginning on page 215. All hospitals are represented with Community Hospitals listed separately under United States. No estimates have been made for nonresponding hospitals. Definitions of facilities and services are listed in the Glossary, page 201.

CLASSIFICATION	HOSPITALS REPORTING	CASE MANAGEMENT Number	Percent	CHAPLAINCY/ PASTORAL CARE SERVICES Number	Percent	CHEMOTHERAPY Number	Percent	CHILDREN'S WELLNESS PROGRAM Number	Percent	CHIROPRACTIC SERVICES Number	Percent	COMMUNITY OUTREACH Number	Percent	COMPLEMENTARY AND ALTERNATIVE MEDICINE SERVICES Number	Percent	CRISIS PREVENTION Number	Percent	DENTAL SERVICES Number	Percent
UNITED STATES	4,862	4,010	82.5	3,136	64.5	2,478	51.0	925	19.0	110	2.3	3,191	65.6	927	19.1	1,003	20.6	1,074	22.1
COMMUNITY HOSPITALS	4,186	3,593	85.8	2,858	68.3	2,393	57.2	897	21.4	87	2.1	2,991	71.5	876	20.9	878	21.0	910	21.7
CENSUS DIVISION 1, NEW ENGLAND	210	191	91.0	167	79.5	152	72.4	66	31.4	11	5.2	170	81.0	87	41.4	69	32.9	67	31.9
Connecticut	33	30	90.9	29	87.9	24	72.7	14	42.4	3	9.1	29	87.9	20	60.6	21	63.6	17	51.5
Maine	38	37	97.4	25	65.8	26	68.4	8	21.1	1	2.6	29	76.3	12	31.6	5	13.2	9	23.7
Massachusetts	81	72	88.9	66	81.5	59	72.8	23	28.4	4	4.9	64	79.0	30	37.0	23	28.4	20	24.7
New Hampshire	30	27	90.0	23	76.7	21	70.0	13	43.3	1	3.3	25	83.3	14	46.7	12	40.0	12	40.0
Rhode Island	13	11	84.6	11	84.6	11	84.6	4	30.8	0	0.0	10	76.9	3	23.1	5	38.5	5	38.5
Vermont	15	14	93.3	13	86.7	11	73.3	4	26.7	2	13.3	13	86.7	8	53.3	3	20.0	4	26.7
CENSUS DIVISION 2, MIDDLE ATLANTIC	398	360	90.5	324	81.4	269	67.6	140	35.2	19	4.8	315	79.1	129	32.4	163	41.0	151	37.9
New Jersey	73	66	90.4	61	83.6	56	76.7	32	43.8	4	5.5	62	84.9	26	35.6	39	53.4	21	28.8
New York	157	145	92.4	131	83.4	108	68.8	58	36.9	12	7.6	131	83.4	61	38.9	74	47.1	72	45.9
Pennsylvania	168	149	88.7	132	78.6	105	62.5	50	29.8	3	1.8	122	72.6	42	25.0	50	29.8	58	34.5
CENSUS DIVISION 3, SOUTH ATLANTIC	678	609	89.8	526	77.6	379	55.9	126	18.6	17	2.5	496	73.2	129	19.0	153	22.6	163	24.0
Delaware	8	6	75.0	6	75.0	6	75.0	5	62.5	0	0.0	6	75.0	3	37.5	3	37.5	2	25.0
District of Columbia	13	10	76.9	11	84.6	9	69.2	5	38.5	2	15.4	9	69.2	4	30.8	4	30.8	8	61.5
Florida	142	134	94.4	108	76.1	95	66.9	16	11.3	3	2.1	99	69.7	27	19.0	25	17.6	19	13.4
Georgia	122	109	89.3	90	73.8	57	46.7	10	8.2	3	2.5	82	67.2	13	10.7	28	23.0	23	18.9
Maryland	59	53	89.8	53	89.8	42	71.2	17	28.8	3	5.1	47	79.7	22	37.3	26	44.1	21	35.6
North Carolina	121	110	90.9	102	84.3	70	57.9	24	19.8	3	2.5	88	72.7	24	19.8	23	19.0	34	28.1
South Carolina	80	68	85.0	50	62.5	31	38.8	18	22.5	1	1.3	67	83.8	3	3.8	7	8.8	18	22.5
Virginia	70	66	94.3	62	88.6	44	62.9	15	21.4	2	2.9	56	80.0	25	35.7	25	35.7	23	32.9
West Virginia	63	53	84.1	44	69.8	25	39.7	16	25.4	0	0.0	42	66.7	8	12.7	12	19.0	15	23.8
CENSUS DIVISION 4, EAST NORTH CENTRAL	753	645	85.7	533	70.8	455	60.4	191	25.4	22	2.9	542	72.0	234	31.1	208	27.6	194	25.8
Illinois	173	150	86.7	138	79.8	117	67.6	53	30.6	6	3.5	129	74.6	44	25.4	60	34.7	44	25.4
Indiana	121	108	89.3	91	75.2	76	62.8	33	27.3	1	0.8	95	78.5	32	26.4	26	21.5	32	26.4
Michigan	158	131	82.9	118	74.7	95	60.1	39	24.7	4	2.5	117	74.1	57	36.1	48	30.4	41	25.9
Ohio	159	144	90.6	123	77.4	111	69.8	43	27.0	10	6.3	130	81.8	49	30.8	40	25.2	53	33.3
Wisconsin	142	112	78.9	63	44.4	56	39.4	23	16.2	1	0.7	71	50.0	52	36.6	34	23.9	24	16.9
CENSUS DIVISION 5, EAST SOUTH CENTRAL	424	343	80.9	242	57.1	131	30.9	34	8.0	2	0.5	250	59.0	26	6.1	53	12.5	80	18.9
Alabama	104	89	85.6	56	53.8	36	34.6	10	9.6	1	1.0	51	49.0	5	4.8	11	10.6	9	8.7
Kentucky	100	91	91.0	78	78.0	40	40.0	13	13.0	1	1.0	66	66.0	16	16.0	15	15.0	20	20.0
Mississippi	109	62	56.9	26	23.9	15	13.8	4	3.7	0	0.0	60	55.0	1	0.9	9	8.3	32	29.4
Tennessee	111	101	91.0	82	73.9	40	36.0	7	6.3	0	0.0	73	65.8	4	3.6	18	16.2	19	17.1
CENSUS DIVISION 6, WEST NORTH CENTRAL	693	460	66.4	362	52.2	376	54.3	118	17.0	15	2.2	421	60.8	118	17.0	118	17.0	124	17.9
Iowa	125	94	75.2	60	48.0	89	71.2	26	20.8	2	1.6	94	75.2	35	28.0	28	22.4	23	18.4
Kansas	153	77	50.3	67	43.8	51	33.3	13	8.5	0	0.0	51	33.3	7	5.9	7	4.6	15	9.8
Minnesota	116	74	63.8	59	50.9	75	64.7	23	19.8	6	5.2	80	69.0	33	28.4	26	22.4	19	16.4
Missouri	149	125	83.9	106	71.1	73	49.0	27	18.1	6	4.0	101	67.8	27	18.1	35	23.5	47	31.5
Nebraska	65	39	60.0	32	49.2	43	66.2	15	23.1	0	0.0	45	69.2	6	9.2	13	20.0	9	13.8
North Dakota	31	20	64.5	20	64.5	17	54.8	8	25.8	1	3.2	17	54.8	4	12.9	5	16.1	3	9.7
South Dakota	54	31	57.4	18	33.3	28	51.9	6	11.1	0	0.0	33	61.1	4	7.4	4	7.4	8	14.8
CENSUS DIVISION 7, WEST SOUTH CENTRAL	852	702	82.4	435	51.1	261	30.6	98	11.5	5	0.6	408	47.9	46	5.4	74	8.7	139	16.3
Arkansas	98	85	86.7	50	51.0	40	40.8	9	9.2	0	0.0	55	56.1	4	4.1	9	9.2	12	12.2
Louisiana	96	79	82.3	50	52.1	42	43.8	20	20.8	0	0.0	56	58.3	7	7.3	14	14.6	20	20.8
Oklahoma	116	86	74.1	59	50.9	29	25.0	7	6.0	3	2.6	48	41.4	1	0.9	6	5.2	19	16.4
Texas	542	452	83.4	276	50.9	150	27.7	62	11.4	2	0.4	249	45.9	34	6.3	45	8.3	88	16.2
CENSUS DIVISION 8, MOUNTAIN	347	272	78.4	200	57.6	171	49.3	60	17.3	6	1.7	230	66.3	66	19.0	69	19.9	66	19.0
Arizona	59	57	96.6	46	78.0	33	55.9	13	22.0	1	1.7	41	69.5	16	27.1	13	22.0	13	22.0
Colorado	66	53	80.3	48	72.7	46	69.7	9	13.6	1	1.5	51	77.3	25	37.9	13	19.7	11	16.7
Idaho	34	22	64.7	19	55.9	14	41.2	7	20.6	2	5.9	24	70.6	6	17.6	3	8.8	9	26.5
Montana	59	32	54.2	23	39.0	21	35.6	12	20.3	0	0.0	36	61.0	9	15.3	9	15.3	5	8.5
Nevada	29	28	96.6	17	58.6	14	48.3	6	20.7	1	3.4	16	55.2	1	3.4	6	20.7	5	17.2
New Mexico	36	32	88.9	22	61.1	13	36.1	4	11.1	1	2.8	27	75.0	2	5.6	5	13.9	8	22.2
Utah	33	26	78.8	11	33.3	15	45.5	6	18.2	0	0.0	20	60.6	4	12.1	15	45.5	9	27.3
Wyoming	31	22	71.0	14	45.2	15	48.4	3	9.7	0	0.0	15	48.4	3	9.7	5	16.1	6	19.4
CENSUS DIVISION 9, PACIFIC	507	428	84.4	347	68.4	284	56.0	92	18.1	13	2.6	359	70.8	92	18.1	96	18.9	90	17.8
Alaska	14	11	78.6	10	71.4	9	64.3	2	14.3	0	0.0	8	57.1	1	7.1	3	21.4	1	7.1
California	334	291	87.1	225	67.4	187	56.0	66	19.8	10	3.0	240	71.9	61	18.3	57	17.1	73	21.9
Hawaii	20	13	65.0	9	45.0	13	65.0	0	0.0	0	0.0	11	55.0	1	5.0	1	5.0	2	10.0
Oregon	57	48	84.2	46	80.7	33	57.9	11	19.3	2	3.5	45	78.9	12	21.1	10	17.5	5	8.8
Washington	82	65	79.3	57	69.5	42	51.2	13	15.9	1	1.2	55	67.1	17	20.7	25	30.5	9	11.0

Table 7 (Continued)

These data include only hospital-based facilities and services as reported by responding hospitals in Section C of the 2008 AHA Annual Survey, beginning on page 215. All hospitals are represented with Community Hospitals listed separately under United States. No estimates have been made for nonresponding hospitals. Definitions of facilities and services are listed in the Glossary, page 201.

RADIOLOGY, DIAGNOSTIC

CLASSIFICATION	HOSPITALS REPORTING	CT SCANNER Number	CT SCANNER Percent	DIAGNOSTIC RADIOISOTOPE FACILITY Number	Percent	ELECTRON BEAM COMPUTED TOMOGRAPHY (EBCT) Number	Percent	FULL-FIELD DIGITAL MAMMOGRAPHY (FFDM) Number	Percent	MAGNETIC RESONANCE IMAGING (MRI) Number	Percent	INTRAOPERATIVE MAGNETIC IMAGING Number	Percent	MULTI-SLICE SPIRAL COMPUTED TOMOGRAPHY (<64 SLICE CT) Number	Percent	MULTI-SLICE SPIRAL COMPUTED TOMOGRAPHY (64+ SLICE CT) Number	Percent	POSITRON EMISSION TOMOGRAPHY (PET) Number	Percent	POSITRON EMISSION TOMOGRAPHY/CT (PET/CT) Number	Percent	SINGLE PHOTON EMISSION COMPUTERIZED TOMOGRAPHY (SPECT) Number	Percent
UNITED STATES	4,862	4,016	82.6	2,634	54.2	301	6.2	1,495	30.7	2,999	61.5	198	4.1	2,739	56.3	1,549	31.9	694	14.3	809	16.6	1,784	36.7
COMMUNITY HOSPITALS	4,186	3,806	90.9	2,550	60.9	284	6.8	1,457	34.8	2,852	68.1	181	4.3	2,639	63.0	1,475	35.2	673	16.1	788	18.8	1,737	41.5
CENSUS DIVISION 1, NEW ENGLAND	210	177	84.3	143	68.1	8	3.8	100	47.6	130	61.9	10	4.8	124	59.0	88	41.9	45	21.4	57	27.1	111	52.9
Connecticut	33	27	81.8	25	75.8	3	9.1	17	51.5	23	69.7	3	9.1	22	66.7	16	48.5	14	42.4	17	51.5	22	66.7
Maine	38	33	86.8	28	73.7	0	0.0	14	36.8	21	55.3	3	5.3	19	50.0	14	36.8	5	13.2	6	15.8	17	44.7
Massachusetts	81	66	81.5	55	67.9	3	3.7	36	44.4	49	60.5	5	6.2	49	60.5	36	44.4	16	19.8	21	25.9	44	54.3
New Hampshire	30	26	86.7	15	50.0	0	0.0	18	60.0	15	50.0	0	0.0	17	56.7	13	43.3	5	16.7	8	26.7	14	46.7
Rhode Island	13	11	84.6	9	69.2	1	7.7	8	61.5	11	84.6	0	0.0	7	53.8	5	38.5	1	7.7	1	7.7	8	61.5
Vermont	15	14	93.3	11	73.3	1	6.7	7	46.7	11	73.3	0	0.0	10	66.7	4	26.7	4	26.7	4	26.7	6	40.0
CENSUS DIVISION 2, MIDDLE ATLANTIC	398	345	86.7	292	73.4	44	11.1	170	42.7	292	70.9	29	7.3	253	63.6	174	43.7	85	21.4	95	23.9	217	54.5
New Jersey	73	60	82.2	55	75.3	12	16.4	34	46.6	52	71.2	6	8.2	49	67.1	33	45.2	18	24.7	25	34.2	40	54.8
New York	157	142	90.4	116	73.9	16	10.2	76	48.4	112	71.3	13	8.3	97	61.8	66	42.0	37	23.6	34	21.7	79	50.3
Pennsylvania	168	143	85.1	121	72.0	16	9.5	60	35.7	118	70.2	10	6.0	107	63.7	75	44.6	30	17.9	36	21.4	98	58.3
CENSUS DIVISION 3, SOUTH ATLANTIC	678	576	85.0	448	66.1	57	8.4	243	35.8	483	71.2	22	3.2	460	67.8	254	37.5	125	18.4	140	20.6	321	47.3
Delaware	8	6	75.0	6	75.0	2	25.0	3	37.5	6	75.0	0	0.0	5	62.5	3	37.5	3	37.5	3	37.5	4	50.0
District of Columbia	13	9	69.2	9	69.2	3	23.1	7	53.8	9	69.2	2	15.4	8	61.5	7	53.8	4	30.8	6	46.2	8	61.5
Florida	142	130	91.5	106	74.6	20	14.1	66	46.5	124	87.3	8	5.6	114	80.3	61	43.0	35	24.6	45	31.7	67	47.2
Georgia	122	105	86.1	73	59.8	3	2.5	38	31.1	86	70.5	4	3.3	74	60.7	31	25.4	17	13.9	18	14.8	43	35.2
Maryland	59	48	81.4	43	72.9	5	8.5	16	27.1	39	66.1	3	5.1	41	69.5	33	55.9	12	20.3	11	18.6	36	61.0
North Carolina	121	108	89.3	75	62.0	10	8.3	43	35.5	90	72.7	3	2.5	90	74.4	48	39.7	20	16.5	20	16.5	64	52.9
South Carolina	80	59	73.8	50	62.5	6	7.5	27	33.8	46	57.5	1	1.3	43	53.8	21	26.3	8	10.0	8	10.0	27	33.8
Virginia	70	60	85.7	50	71.4	5	7.1	29	41.4	55	78.6	1	1.4	51	72.9	28	40.0	15	21.4	17	24.3	43	61.4
West Virginia	63	51	81.0	36	57.1	3	4.8	14	22.2	30	47.6	0	0.0	34	54.0	22	34.9	11	17.5	12	19.0	29	46.0
CENSUS DIVISION 4, EAST NORTH CENTRAL	753	660	87.6	458	60.8	57	7.6	271	36.0	504	66.9	44	5.8	455	60.4	301	40.0	154	20.5	186	24.7	376	49.9
Illinois	173	155	89.6	111	64.2	12	6.9	72	41.6	109	63.0	6	3.5	112	64.7	82	47.4	31	17.9	33	19.1	78	45.1
Indiana	121	108	89.3	72	59.5	6	5.0	48	39.7	92	76.0	5	4.1	83	68.6	47	38.8	17	14.0	27	22.3	49	40.5
Michigan	158	133	84.2	111	70.3	8	5.1	57	36.1	90	57.0	8	5.1	96	60.8	76	48.1	24	15.2	38	24.1	82	51.9
Ohio	159	147	92.5	120	75.5	18	11.3	58	36.5	130	81.8	13	8.2	107	67.3	65	40.9	49	30.8	54	34.0	98	61.6
Wisconsin	142	117	82.4	44	31.0	13	9.2	36	25.4	83	58.5	12	8.5	57	40.1	31	21.8	33	23.2	34	23.9	69	48.6
CENSUS DIVISION 5, EAST SOUTH CENTRAL	424	350	82.5	219	51.7	14	3.3	105	24.8	261	61.6	14	3.3	196	46.2	105	24.8	49	11.6	55	13.0	127	30.0
Alabama	104	91	87.5	65	62.5	2	1.9	24	23.1	69	66.3	2	1.9	51	49.0	27	26.0	14	13.5	16	15.4	28	26.9
Kentucky	100	84	84.0	53	53.0	5	5.0	30	30.0	66	66.0	5	5.0	61	61.0	30	30.0	8	8.0	13	13.0	35	35.0
Mississippi	109	83	76.1	49	45.0	3	2.8	18	16.5	51	46.8	5	4.6	24	22.0	20	18.3	15	13.8	12	11.0	29	26.6
Tennessee	111	92	82.9	52	46.8	4	3.6	33	29.7	75	67.6	2	1.8	60	54.1	28	25.2	12	10.8	14	12.6	35	31.5
CENSUS DIVISION 6, WEST NORTH CENTRAL	693	584	84.3	257	37.1	26	3.8	151	21.8	358	51.7	16	2.3	378	54.5	136	19.6	61	8.8	81	11.7	173	25.0
Iowa	125	115	92.0	48	38.4	3	2.4	31	24.8	57	45.6	2	1.6	88	70.4	22	17.6	11	8.8	16	12.8	39	31.2
Kansas	153	121	79.1	49	32.0	1	0.7	21	13.7	56	36.6	2	1.3	66	43.1	21	13.7	5	3.3	9	5.9	25	16.3
Minnesota	116	101	87.1	42	36.2	9	7.8	31	26.7	65	56.0	5	4.3	68	58.6	26	22.4	7	6.0	11	9.5	25	21.6
Missouri	149	120	80.5	72	48.3	6	4.0	37	24.8	111	74.5	4	2.7	84	56.4	37	24.8	24	16.1	24	16.1	52	34.9
Nebraska	65	58	89.2	24	36.9	4	6.2	17	26.2	34	52.3	2	3.1	34	52.3	18	27.7	6	9.2	13	20.0	16	24.6
North Dakota	31	28	90.3	9	29.0	3	9.7	6	19.4	13	41.9	1	3.2	17	54.8	4	12.9	3	9.7	4	12.9	7	22.6
South Dakota	54	41	75.9	13	24.1	0	0.0	8	14.8	22	40.7	0	0.0	21	38.9	8	14.8	5	9.3	4	7.4	9	16.7
CENSUS DIVISION 7, WEST SOUTH CENTRAL	852	607	71.2	343	40.3	34	4.0	184	21.6	431	50.6	27	3.2	394	46.2	214	25.1	52	6.1	69	8.1	179	21.0
Arkansas	98	72	73.5	38	38.8	6	6.1	14	14.3	55	56.1	1	1.0	47	48.0	21	21.4	5	5.1	6	6.1	20	20.4
Louisiana	96	73	76.0	51	53.1	8	8.3	40	41.7	50	52.1	3	3.1	50	52.1	32	33.3	8	8.3	13	13.5	26	27.1
Oklahoma	116	88	75.9	35	30.2	4	3.4	25	21.6	63	54.3	6	5.2	47	40.5	30	25.9	12	10.3	12	10.3	13	11.2
Texas	542	374	69.0	219	40.4	16	3.0	105	19.4	263	48.5	17	3.1	250	46.1	131	24.2	27	5.0	38	7.0	120	22.1
CENSUS DIVISION 8, MOUNTAIN	347	284	81.8	171	49.3	24	6.9	96	27.7	214	61.7	13	3.7	196	56.5	122	35.2	39	11.2	44	12.7	91	26.2
Arizona	59	48	81.4	37	62.7	6	10.2	19	22.2	45	76.3	6	10.2	37	62.7	28	47.5	12	20.3	13	22.0	27	45.8
Colorado	66	61	92.4	41	62.1	3	4.5	24	36.4	51	77.3	3	4.5	45	68.2	31	47.0	10	15.2	10	15.2	23	34.8
Idaho	34	27	79.4	12	35.3	2	5.9	8	23.5	17	50.0	1	2.9	17	50.0	10	29.4	3	8.8	4	11.8	7	20.6
Montana	59	41	69.5	19	32.2	2	3.4	14	23.7	18	30.5	1	1.7	26	44.1	12	20.3	2	3.4	4	6.8	9	15.3
Nevada	29	21	72.4	16	55.2	2	6.9	10	34.5	21	72.4	1	3.4	16	55.2	11	37.9	4	13.8	2	6.9	9	31.0
New Mexico	36	30	83.3	15	41.7	2	5.6	3	8.3	20	55.6	1	2.8	21	66.7	9	25.0	4	11.1	5	13.9	9	25.0
Utah	33	28	84.8	17	51.5	5	15.2	13	39.4	24	72.7	0	0.0	17	51.5	13	39.4	5	15.2	8	24.2	7	21.2
Wyoming	31	28	90.3	14	45.2	2	6.5	5	16.1	18	58.1	0	0.0	14	45.2	8	25.8	1	3.2	0	0.0	5	16.1
CENSUS DIVISION 9, PACIFIC	507	433	85.4	303	59.8	37	7.3	175	34.5	326	64.3	23	4.5	283	55.8	155	30.6	84	16.6	82	16.2	189	37.3
Alaska	14	12	85.7	6	42.9	0	0.0	4	28.6	9	64.3	1	7.1	7	50.0	5	35.7	0	0.0	0	0.0	2	14.3
California	334	280	83.8	204	61.1	25	7.5	102	30.5	219	65.6	16	4.8	177	53.0	101	30.2	60	18.0	54	16.2	134	40.1
Hawaii	20	13	65.0	10	50.0	1	5.0	8	40.0	10	50.0	0	0.0	9	45.0	4	20.0	1	5.0	1	5.0	3	15.0
Oregon	57	57	100.0	37	64.9	3	5.3	30	52.6	35	61.4	2	3.5	43	75.4	21	36.8	7	12.3	7	12.3	27	47.4
Washington	82	71	86.6	46	56.1	8	9.8	31	37.8	53	64.6	4	4.9	47	57.3	24	29.3	16	19.5	20	24.4	23	28.0

Table 7 (Continued)

These data include only hospital-based facilities and services as reported by responding hospitals in Section C of the 2008 AHA Annual Survey, beginning on page 215. All hospitals are represented with Community Hospitals listed separately under United States. No estimates have been made for nonresponding hospitals. Definitions of facilities and services are listed in the Glossary, page 201.

CLASSIFICATION	HOSPITALS REPORTING	Radiology, Diagnostic Ultrasound No.	%	Enabling Services No.	%	Enrollment Assistance Services No.	%	Extracorporeal Shock Wave Lithotripter (ESWL) No.	%	Emergency Department No.	%	Freestanding/Satellite Emergency Dept No.	%	Trauma Center (Certified) No.	%	Fitness Center No.	%	Fertility Clinic No.	%	Genetic Testing/Counseling No.	%	Geriatric Services No.	%
UNITED STATES	4,862	3,911	80.4	1,046	21.5	2,125	43.7	1,191	24.5	4,086	84.0	200	4.1	1,538	31.6	1,355	27.9	287	5.9	536	11.0	1,858	38.2
COMMUNITY HOSPITALS	4,186	3,714	88.7	977	23.3	1,988	47.5	1,150	27.5	3,867	92.4	188	4.5	1,504	35.9	1,263	30.2	281	6.7	525	12.5	1,679	40.1
CENSUS DIVISION 1, NEW ENGLAND	210	174	82.9	67	31.9	143	68.1	99	47.1	170	81.0	17	8.1	69	32.9	58	27.6	31	14.8	44	21.0	105	50.0
Connecticut	33	28	84.8	12	36.4	23	69.7	19	57.6	26	78.8	6	18.2	15	45.5	16	48.5	5	14.8	11	33.3	19	57.6
Maine	38	32	84.2	7	18.4	23	60.5	14	36.8	33	86.8	1	2.6	10	26.3	13	34.2	4	10.5	5	13.2	13	34.2
Massachusetts	81	64	79.0	29	35.8	61	75.3	35	43.2	59	72.8	5	6.2	22	27.2	10	12.3	13	16.0	19	23.5	41	50.6
New Hampshire	30	26	86.7	11	36.7	22	73.3	16	53.3	26	86.7	5	16.7	14	46.7	11	36.7	5	16.7	5	16.7	16	53.3
Rhode Island	13	11	84.6	2	15.4	4	30.8	8	61.5	12	92.3	0	0.0	2	15.4	3	23.1	1	7.7	2	15.4	10	76.9
Vermont	15	13	86.7	6	40.0	10	66.7	7	46.7	14	93.3	0	0.0	6	40.0	5	33.3	3	20.0	2	13.3	6	40.0
CENSUS DIVISION 2, MIDDLE ATLANTIC	398	343	86.2	129	32.4	233	58.5	135	33.9	333	83.7	16	4.0	97	24.4	129	32.4	54	13.6	108	27.1	230	57.8
New Jersey	73	58	79.5	33	45.2	43	58.9	24	32.9	59	80.8	5	6.8	15	20.5	23	31.5	9	12.3	29	39.7	53	72.6
New York	157	143	91.1	45	28.7	93	59.2	52	33.1	134	85.4	6	3.8	53	33.8	44	28.0	29	18.5	47	29.9	93	59.2
Pennsylvania	168	142	84.5	51	30.4	97	57.7	59	35.1	140	83.3	5	3.0	29	17.3	62	36.9	16	9.5	32	19.0	84	50.0
CENSUS DIVISION 3, SOUTH ATLANTIC	678	575	84.8	197	29.1	348	51.3	213	31.4	570	84.1	31	4.6	148	21.8	204	30.1	37	5.5	79	11.7	269	39.7
Delaware	8	6	75.0	2	25.0	4	50.0	4	50.0	6	75.0	1	12.5	4	50.0	3	37.5	0	0.0	2	25.0	4	50.0
District of Columbia	13	10	76.9	6	46.2	7	53.8	5	38.5	9	69.2	1	7.7	6	46.2	5	38.5	2	15.4	5	38.5	7	53.8
Florida	142	131	92.3	42	29.6	71	50.0	64	45.1	129	90.8	8	5.6	21	14.8	51	35.9	10	7.0	24	16.9	58	40.8
Georgia	122	100	82.0	35	28.7	62	50.8	31	25.4	101	82.8	2	1.6	15	12.3	26	21.3	3	2.5	7	5.7	38	31.1
Maryland	59	47	79.7	29	49.2	37	62.7	26	44.1	46	78.0	3	5.1	11	18.6	15	25.4	6	10.2	19	32.2	30	50.8
North Carolina	121	107	88.4	33	27.3	59	48.8	19	15.7	108	89.3	6	5.0	18	14.9	44	36.4	8	6.6	10	8.3	47	38.8
South Carolina	80	61	76.3	8	10.0	32	40.0	16	20.0	58	72.5	3	3.8	21	26.3	19	23.8	2	2.5	4	5.0	40	50.0
Virginia	70	63	90.0	29	41.4	49	70.0	30	42.9	61	87.1	7	10.0	19	27.1	21	30.0	4	5.7	4	5.7	26	37.1
West Virginia	63	50	79.4	13	20.6	27	42.9	18	28.6	52	82.5	0	0.0	33	52.4	21	31.7	2	3.2	4	6.3	19	30.2
CENSUS DIVISION 4, EAST NORTH CENTRAL	753	649	86.2	229	30.4	397	52.7	202	26.8	655	87.0	51	6.8	271	36.0	261	34.7	53	7.0	98	13.0	383	50.9
Illinois	173	151	87.3	51	29.5	90	52.0	33	19.1	159	91.9	7	4.0	68	39.3	49	28.3	14	8.1	24	13.9	89	51.4
Indiana	121	106	87.6	27	22.3	69	57.0	29	24.0	102	84.3	2	1.7	21	17.4	40	33.1	11	9.1	11	9.1	49	40.5
Michigan	158	135	85.4	58	36.7	96	60.8	52	32.9	133	84.2	15	9.5	47	29.7	55	34.8	16	10.1	19	12.0	76	48.1
Ohio	159	145	91.2	57	35.8	84	52.8	51	32.1	142	89.3	21	13.2	45	28.3	58	36.5	13	8.2	24	15.1	66	41.5
Wisconsin	142	112	78.9	36	25.4	58	40.8	37	26.1	119	83.8	6	4.2	90	63.4	59	41.5	5	3.5	20	14.1	103	72.5
CENSUS DIVISION 5, EAST SOUTH CENTRAL	424	345	81.4	48	11.3	124	29.2	91	21.5	355	83.7	14	3.3	130	30.7	106	25.0	12	2.8	18	4.2	107	25.2
Alabama	104	90	86.5	13	12.5	35	33.7	23	22.1	92	88.5	2	1.9	28	26.9	30	28.8	4	3.8	4	3.8	27	26.0
Kentucky	100	83	83.0	15	15.0	42	42.0	24	24.0	85	85.0	3	3.0	24	24.0	23	23.0	6	6.0	6	6.0	23	23.0
Mississippi	109	82	75.2	3	2.8	11	10.1	17	15.6	87	79.8	5	4.6	65	59.6	29	26.6	1	0.9	2	1.8	17	15.6
Tennessee	111	90	81.1	17	15.3	36	32.4	27	24.3	91	82.0	4	3.6	13	11.7	24	21.6	1	0.9	6	5.4	40	36.0
CENSUS DIVISION 6, WEST NORTH CENTRAL	693	529	76.3	130	18.8	236	34.1	107	15.4	609	87.9	18	2.6	224	32.3	235	33.9	28	4.0	49	7.1	258	37.2
Iowa	125	112	89.6	33	26.4	53	42.4	12	9.6	119	95.2	0	0.0	89	71.2	52	41.6	5	4.0	6	4.8	56	44.8
Kansas	153	97	63.4	14	9.2	33	21.6	18	11.8	128	83.7	3	2.0	10	6.5	39	25.5	2	1.3	6	3.9	46	30.1
Minnesota	116	91	78.4	21	18.1	38	32.8	17	14.7	101	87.1	2	1.7	39	33.6	32	27.6	5	4.3	12	10.3	51	44.0
Missouri	149	121	81.2	43	28.9	72	48.3	39	26.2	121	81.2	10	6.7	29	19.5	52	34.9	10	6.7	19	12.8	58	38.9
Nebraska	65	54	83.1	9	13.8	17	26.2	11	16.9	60	92.3	2	3.1	28	43.1	28	43.1	3	4.6	3	4.6	18	27.7
North Dakota	36	29	80.6	6	16.7	13	36.1	7	19.4	29	80.6	1	2.8	18	50.0	13	36.1	1	2.8	2	5.6	12	33.3
South Dakota	33	24	72.7	4	12.1	10	30.3	3	9.1	30	90.9	0	0.0	11	33.3	19	57.6	2	6.1	1	3.0	17	51.5
CENSUS DIVISION 7, WEST SOUTH CENTRAL	852	582	68.3	97	11.4	291	34.2	158	18.5	657	77.1	25	2.9	288	33.8	178	20.9	27	3.2	45	5.3	243	28.5
Arkansas	98	73	74.5	7	7.1	35	35.7	16	16.3	75	76.5	2	2.0	12	12.2	21	21.4	1	1.0	3	3.1	31	31.6
Louisiana	96	75	78.1	8	8.3	44	45.8	15	15.6	73	76.0	5	5.2	16	16.7	18	18.8	5	5.2	9	9.4	31	32.3
Oklahoma	116	87	75.0	6	5.2	19	16.4	20	17.2	103	88.8	0	0.0	39	33.6	17	14.7	2	1.7	4	3.4	25	21.6
Texas	542	347	64.0	76	14.0	193	35.6	107	19.7	406	74.9	18	3.3	221	40.8	122	22.5	19	3.5	29	5.4	156	28.8
CENSUS DIVISION 8, MOUNTAIN	347	274	79.0	53	15.3	145	41.8	69	19.9	299	86.2	19	5.5	140	40.3	83	23.9	16	4.6	28	8.1	117	33.7
Arizona	59	49	83.1	10	16.9	28	47.5	17	28.8	48	81.4	3	5.1	16	27.1	18	30.5	3	5.1	5	8.5	18	30.5
Colorado	66	58	87.9	13	19.7	32	48.5	15	22.7	62	93.9	8	12.1	52	78.8	23	34.8	5	7.6	10	15.2	23	34.8
Idaho	34	26	76.5	5	14.7	13	38.2	5	14.7	28	82.4	1	2.9	6	17.6	8	23.5	1	2.9	2	5.9	10	29.4
Montana	59	40	67.8	5	8.5	27	45.8	5	8.5	56	94.9	1	1.7	21	35.6	8	13.6	1	1.7	3	5.1	26	44.1
Nevada	29	21	72.4	5	17.2	10	34.5	4	13.8	19	65.5	1	3.4	5	17.2	2	6.9	0	0.0	0	0.0	8	27.6
New Mexico	36	29	80.6	5	13.9	13	36.1	11	30.6	30	83.3	2	5.6	8	22.2	9	25.0	2	5.6	2	5.6	9	25.0
Utah	33	24	72.7	10	30.3	17	51.5	7	21.2	29	87.9	1	3.0	13	39.4	11	33.3	6	18.2	6	18.2	12	36.4
Wyoming	31	27	87.1	0	0.0	5	16.1	5	16.1	27	87.1	2	6.5	19	61.3	4	12.9	0	0.0	0	0.0	11	35.5
CENSUS DIVISION 9, PACIFIC	507	440	86.8	96	18.9	208	41.0	117	23.1	438	86.4	9	1.8	171	33.7	101	19.9	29	5.7	67	13.2	146	28.8
Alaska	14	12	85.7	0	0.0	5	35.7	3	21.4	13	92.9	1	7.1	4	28.6	1	7.1	0	0.0	2	14.3	2	14.3
California	334	286	85.6	60	18.0	136	40.7	77	23.1	278	83.2	5	1.5	66	19.8	64	19.2	25	7.5	50	15.0	100	29.9
Hawaii	20	14	70.0	2	10.0	3	15.0	3	15.0	16	80.0	0	0.0	3	15.0	1	5.0	0	0.0	1	5.0	6	30.0
Oregon	57	57	100.0	16	28.1	36	63.2	15	26.3	57	100.0	1	1.8	41	71.9	19	33.3	2	3.5	3	5.3	19	33.3
Washington	82	71	86.6	18	22.0	28	34.1	19	23.2	74	90.2	2	2.4	57	69.5	16	19.5	2	2.4	11	13.4	19	23.2

Table 7 (Continued)

These data include only hospital-based facilities and services as reported by responding hospitals in Section C of the 2008 AHA Annual Survey, beginning on page 215. All hospitals are represented with Community Hospitals listed separately under United States. No estimates have been made for nonresponding hospitals. Definitions of facilities and services are listed in the Glossary, page 201.

The last five paired columns (IMAGE-GUIDED RADIATION THERAPY through STEREOTACTIC RADIOSURGERY) fall under the heading **RADIOLOGY, THERAPEUTIC**.

CLASSIFICATION	HOSPITALS REPORTING	HEALTH FAIR		COMMUNITY HEALTH EDUCATION		HEALTH SCREENINGS		HEMODIALYSIS		HIV/AIDS SERVICES		HOME HEALTH SERVICES		IMAGE-GUIDED RADIATION THERAPY (IGRT)		INTENSITY-MODULATED RADIATION THERAPY (IMRT)		PROTON BEAM THERAPY		SHAPED BEAM RADIATION SYSTEM		STEREOTACTIC RADIOSURGERY	
		Number	Percent	Number	Percent	Number	Percent	Number	Percent	Number	Percent	Number	Percent	Number	Percent	Number	Percent	Number	Percent	Number	Percent	Number	Percent
UNITED STATES	4,862	3,501	72.0	3,180	65.4	3,572	73.5	1,393	28.7	1,162	23.9	1,513	31.1	720	14.8	1,016	20.9	90	1.9	820	16.9	738	15.2
COMMUNITY HOSPITALS	4,186	3,308	79.0	2,982	71.2	3,372	80.6	1,312	31.3	1,065	25.4	1,443	34.5	703	16.8	997	23.8	85	2.0	805	19.2	725	17.3
CENSUS DIVISION 1, NEW ENGLAND	210	167	79.5	172	81.9	180	85.7	62	29.5	95	45.2	46	21.9	43	20.5	61	29.0	4	1.9	47	22.4	50	23.8
Connecticut	33	24	72.7	28	84.8	29	87.9	11	33.3	20	60.6	7	21.2	13	39.4	18	54.5	2	6.1	13	39.4	12	36.4
Maine	38	29	76.3	31	81.6	33	86.8	6	15.8	13	34.2	9	23.7	2	5.3	6	15.8	1	2.6	5	13.2	5	13.2
Massachusetts	81	64	79.0	62	76.5	66	81.5	32	39.5	38	46.9	20	24.7	21	25.9	27	33.3	1	1.2	22	27.2	23	28.4
New Hampshire	30	27	90.0	26	86.7	27	90.0	5	16.7	13	43.3	6	20.0	4	13.3	6	20.0	0	0.0	4	13.3	6	20.0
Rhode Island	13	11	84.6	11	84.6	12	92.3	6	46.2	6	46.2	3	23.1	1	7.7	1	7.7	0	0.0	1	7.7	2	15.4
Vermont	15	12	80.0	14	93.3	13	86.7	2	13.3	5	33.3	1	6.7	2	13.3	3	20.0	0	0.0	2	13.3	2	13.3
CENSUS DIVISION 2, MIDDLE ATLANTIC	398	332	83.4	309	77.6	333	83.7	190	47.7	178	44.7	125	31.4	109	27.4	152	38.2	12	3.0	125	31.4	107	26.9
New Jersey	73	59	80.8	58	79.5	58	79.5	44	60.3	39	53.4	19	26.0	27	37.0	38	52.1	1	1.4	35	47.9	23	31.5
New York	157	138	87.9	129	82.2	131	83.4	95	60.5	79	50.3	40	25.5	39	24.8	55	35.0	7	4.5	43	27.4	40	25.5
Pennsylvania	168	135	80.4	122	72.6	144	85.7	51	30.4	60	35.7	66	39.3	43	25.6	59	35.1	4	2.4	47	28.0	44	26.2
CENSUS DIVISION 3, SOUTH ATLANTIC	678	544	80.2	478	70.5	544	80.2	261	38.5	220	32.4	167	27.6	125	18.4	177	26.1	8	1.2	144	21.2	127	18.7
Delaware	8	4	50.0	5	62.5	4	50.0	4	50.0	4	50.0	2	25.0	1	12.5	4	50.0	0	0.0	4	50.0	1	12.5
District of Columbia	13	10	76.9	8	61.5	9	69.2	7	53.8	8	61.5	2	15.4	6	46.2	6	46.2	1	7.7	7	53.8	7	53.8
Florida	142	112	78.9	105	73.9	122	85.9	72	50.7	50	35.2	32	22.5	32	22.5	40	28.2	3	2.1	35	24.6	43	30.3
Georgia	122	94	77.0	86	70.5	93	76.2	40	32.8	33	27.0	18	14.8	14	11.5	21	17.2	0	0.0	17	13.9	19	15.6
Maryland	59	49	83.1	46	78.0	50	84.7	32	54.2	25	42.4	14	23.7	14	23.7	20	33.9	0	0.0	17	28.8	12	20.3
North Carolina	121	97	80.2	86	71.1	96	79.3	41	33.9	31	25.6	46	38.0	27	22.3	39	32.2	4	3.3	30	24.8	21	17.4
South Carolina	80	64	80.0	45	56.3	58	72.5	26	32.5	31	38.8	17	21.3	6	7.5	13	16.3	0	0.0	9	11.3	5	6.3
Virginia	70	60	85.7	52	74.3	60	85.7	25	35.7	27	38.6	33	47.1	20	28.6	25	35.7	0	0.0	16	22.9	13	18.6
West Virginia	63	54	85.7	45	71.4	52	82.5	14	22.2	11	17.5	21	33.3	5	7.9	9	14.3	0	0.0	9	14.3	6	9.5
CENSUS DIVISION 4, EAST NORTH CENTRAL	753	559	74.2	603	80.1	598	79.4	234	31.1	181	24.0	266	35.3	149	19.8	208	27.6	16	2.1	170	22.6	131	17.4
Illinois	173	143	82.7	142	82.1	153	88.4	53	30.6	54	31.2	67	38.7	34	19.7	54	31.2	4	2.3	41	23.7	31	17.9
Indiana	121	98	81.0	90	74.4	99	81.8	31	25.6	21	17.4	49	40.5	32	26.4	42	34.7	2	1.7	33	27.3	22	18.2
Michigan	158	119	75.3	119	75.3	131	82.9	49	31.0	46	29.1	60	38.0	31	19.6	42	26.6	3	1.9	36	22.8	29	18.4
Ohio	159	136	85.5	131	82.4	143	89.9	66	41.5	53	33.3	63	39.6	30	18.9	41	25.8	2	1.3	36	22.6	28	17.6
Wisconsin	142	63	44.4	121	85.2	72	50.7	35	24.6	7	4.9	27	19.0	22	15.5	29	20.4	5	3.5	24	16.9	21	14.8
CENSUS DIVISION 5, EAST SOUTH CENTRAL	424	270	63.7	222	52.4	259	61.1	78	18.4	75	17.7	124	29.2	35	8.3	64	15.1	6	1.4	46	10.8	49	11.6
Alabama	104	77	74.0	56	53.8	73	70.2	28	26.9	15	14.4	39	37.5	9	8.7	14	13.5	1	1.0	12	11.5	10	9.6
Kentucky	100	84	84.0	71	71.0	80	80.0	19	19.0	14	14.0	38	38.0	8	8.0	16	16.0	2	2.0	9	9.0	14	14.0
Mississippi	109	35	32.1	36	33.0	27	24.8	0	0.0	28	25.7	13	11.9	8	7.3	11	10.1	1	0.9	7	6.4	10	9.2
Tennessee	111	74	66.7	59	53.2	79	71.2	31	27.9	18	16.2	34	30.6	10	9.0	23	20.7	2	1.8	18	16.2	15	13.5
CENSUS DIVISION 6, WEST NORTH CENTRAL	693	475	68.5	419	60.5	517	74.6	142	20.5	119	17.2	303	43.7	67	9.7	102	14.7	9	1.3	80	11.5	64	9.2
Iowa	125	102	81.6	91	72.8	118	94.4	27	21.6	25	20.0	69	55.2	8	6.4	13	10.4	0	0.0	11	8.8	10	8.0
Kansas	153	79	51.6	56	36.6	76	49.7	13	8.5	17	11.1	56	36.6	8	5.2	15	9.8	3	2.0	14	9.2	7	4.6
Minnesota	116	81	69.8	80	69.0	86	74.1	18	15.5	20	17.2	50	43.1	12	10.3	16	13.8	3	2.6	10	8.6	11	9.5
Missouri	149	109	73.2	92	61.7	115	77.2	52	34.9	40	26.8	58	38.9	19	12.8	33	22.1	2	1.3	22	14.8	21	14.1
Nebraska	65	48	73.8	44	67.7	50	76.9	14	21.5	9	13.8	34	52.3	14	21.5	14	21.5	1	1.5	14	21.5	12	18.5
North Dakota	31	22	71.0	23	74.2	26	83.9	8	25.8	5	16.1	12	38.7	3	9.7	4	12.9	0	0.0	4	12.9	1	3.2
South Dakota	54	34	63.0	33	61.1	46	85.2	10	18.5	3	5.6	24	44.4	3	5.6	7	13.0	0	0.0	5	9.3	2	3.7
CENSUS DIVISION 7, WEST SOUTH CENTRAL	852	542	63.6	428	50.2	529	62.1	177	20.8	108	12.7	206	24.2	55	6.5	69	8.1	9	1.2	61	7.2	76	8.9
Arkansas	98	68	69.4	46	46.9	71	72.4	16	16.3	14	14.3	45	45.9	5	5.1	7	7.1	1	1.0	5	5.1	7	7.1
Louisiana	96	70	72.9	60	62.5	70	72.9	24	25.0	19	19.8	16	16.7	14	14.6	17	17.7	2	2.1	12	12.5	15	15.6
Oklahoma	116	67	57.8	55	47.4	65	56.0	20	17.2	11	9.5	45	38.8	11	9.5	0	0.0	1	0.9	12	10.3	7	6.0
Texas	542	337	62.2	267	49.3	323	59.6	117	21.6	64	11.8	100	18.5	25	4.6	45	8.3	6	1.1	32	5.9	47	8.7
CENSUS DIVISION 8, MOUNTAIN	347	260	74.9	226	65.1	253	72.9	83	23.9	64	18.4	105	30.5	47	13.5	64	18.4	8	2.3	49	14.1	40	11.5
Arizona	59	40	67.8	38	64.4	40	67.8	28	47.5	16	27.1	13	22.0	12	20.3	13	22.0	2	3.4	9	15.3	10	16.9
Colorado	66	51	77.3	48	72.7	48	72.7	15	22.7	17	25.8	17	25.8	11	16.7	18	27.3	2	3.0	13	19.7	11	16.7
Idaho	34	25	73.5	23	67.6	25	73.5	4	11.8	4	11.8	9	26.5	4	11.8	6	17.6	0	0.0	4	11.8	1	2.9
Montana	59	47	79.7	39	66.1	48	81.4	6	10.2	9	15.3	26	44.1	4	6.8	5	8.5	2	3.4	4	6.8	5	8.5
Nevada	29	19	65.5	18	62.1	17	58.6	7	24.1	4	13.8	5	17.2	3	10.3	3	10.3	1	3.4	3	10.3	4	13.8
New Mexico	36	28	77.8	17	47.2	26	72.2	7	19.4	4	11.1	13	36.1	2	5.6	6	16.7	1	2.8	5	13.9	3	8.3
Utah	33	26	78.8	24	72.7	27	81.8	10	30.3	7	21.2	12	36.4	6	18.2	8	24.2	1	3.0	7	21.2	4	12.1
Wyoming	31	24	77.4	19	61.3	22	71.0	6	19.4	3	9.7	11	35.5	5	16.1	5	16.1	0	0.0	4	12.9	2	6.5
CENSUS DIVISION 9, PACIFIC	507	352	69.4	323	63.7	359	70.8	166	32.7	122	24.1	150	29.6	90	17.8	119	23.5	17	3.4	98	19.3	94	18.5
Alaska	14	10	71.4	12	85.7	10	71.4	1	7.1	1	7.1	5	35.7	0	0.0	1	7.1	0	0.0	1	7.1	3	21.4
California	334	230	68.9	208	62.3	228	68.3	126	37.7	92	27.5	83	24.9	57	17.1	77	23.1	12	3.6	65	19.5	66	19.8
Hawaii	20	10	50.0	7	35.0	14	70.0	3	15.0	3	15.0	5	25.0	1	5.0	3	15.0	0	0.0	1	5.0	2	10.0
Oregon	57	46	80.7	46	80.7	49	86.0	14	24.6	10	17.5	33	57.9	12	21.1	16	28.1	2	3.5	12	21.1	9	15.8
Washington	82	56	68.3	50	61.0	58	70.7	21	25.6	16	19.5	24	29.3	20	24.4	22	26.8	3	3.7	19	23.2	14	17.1

Table 7 (Continued)

These data include only hospital-based facilities and services as reported by responding hospitals in Section C of the 2008 AHA Annual Survey, beginning on page 215. All hospitals are represented with Community Hospitals listed separately under United States. No estimates have been made for nonresponding hospitals. Definitions of facilities and services are listed in the Glossary, page 201.

CLASSIFICATION	HOSPITALS REPORTING	MEALS ON WHEELS Number	MEALS ON WHEELS Percent	NEUROLOGICAL SERVICES Number	NEUROLOGICAL SERVICES Percent	NUTRITION PROGRAMS CENTER Number	NUTRITION PROGRAMS CENTER Percent	OCCUPATIONAL HEALTH SERVICES Number	OCCUPATIONAL HEALTH SERVICES Percent	ONCOLOGY SERVICES Number	ONCOLOGY SERVICES Percent	ORTHOPEDIC SERVICES Number	ORTHOPEDIC SERVICES Percent	FREESTANDING OUTPATIENT CARE CENTER Number	FREESTANDING OUTPATIENT CARE CENTER Percent	HOSPITAL-BASED OUTPATIENT CARE CENTER SERVICES Number	HOSPITAL-BASED OUTPATIENT CARE CENTER SERVICES Percent	OUTPATIENT SURGERY Number	OUTPATIENT SURGERY Percent	PATIENT CONTROLLED ANALGESIA (PCA) Number	PATIENT CONTROLLED ANALGESIA (PCA) Percent
UNITED STATES	4,862	494	10.2	2,231	45.9	3,542	72.9	3,059	62.9	2,509	51.6	3,234	66.5	1,376	28.3	3,460	71.2	3,942	81.1	3,130	64.4
COMMUNITY HOSPITALS	4,186	486	11.6	2,080	49.7	3,228	77.1	2,857	68.3	2,420	57.8	3,050	72.9	1,274	30.4	3,234	77.3	3,741	89.4	2,914	69.6
CENSUS DIVISION 1, NEW ENGLAND	210	10	4.8	145	69.0	190	90.5	169	80.5	159	75.7	173	82.4	84	40.0	179	85.2	173	82.4	160	76.2
Connecticut	33	2	6.1	28	84.8	28	84.8	22	66.7	25	75.8	26	78.8	14	42.4	29	87.9	26	78.8	24	72.7
Maine	38	3	7.9	19	50.0	36	94.7	29	76.3	28	73.7	34	89.5	16	42.1	29	76.3	33	86.8	29	76.3
Massachusetts	81	2	2.5	59	72.8	73	90.1	69	85.2	62	76.5	65	80.2	33	40.7	71	87.7	63	77.8	63	77.8
New Hampshire	30	1	3.3	20	66.7	29	96.7	26	86.7	23	76.7	26	86.7	12	40.0	26	86.7	26	86.7	25	83.3
Rhode Island	13	1	7.7	11	84.6	11	84.6	10	76.9	11	84.6	10	76.9	4	30.8	11	84.6	12	92.3	7	53.8
Vermont	15	1	6.7	8	53.3	13	86.7	13	86.7	10	66.7	12	80.0	5	33.3	13	86.7	13	86.7	12	80.0
CENSUS DIVISION 2, MIDDLE ATLANTIC	398	46	11.6	278	69.8	338	84.9	299	75.1	284	71.4	330	82.9	198	49.7	321	80.7	338	84.9	284	71.4
New Jersey	73	12	16.4	57	78.1	64	87.7	46	63.0	55	75.3	55	75.3	27	37.0	57	78.1	59	80.8	48	65.8
New York	157	18	11.5	116	73.9	130	82.8	120	76.4	117	74.5	138	87.9	94	59.9	132	84.1	139	88.5	117	74.5
Pennsylvania	168	16	9.5	105	62.5	144	85.7	133	79.2	112	66.7	137	81.5	77	45.8	132	78.6	140	83.3	119	70.8
CENSUS DIVISION 3, SOUTH ATLANTIC	678	35	5.2	397	58.6	541	79.8	478	70.5	386	56.9	524	77.3	249	36.7	505	74.5	564	83.2	488	72.0
Delaware	13	0	0.0	10	75.0	5	62.5	4	50.0	5	62.5	6	75.0	5	37.5	5	62.5	8	75.0	6	75.0
District of Columbia	13	1	7.7	10	76.9	11	84.6	10	76.9	9	69.2	10	76.9	5	38.5	10	76.9	9	69.2	9	69.2
Florida	142	5	3.5	110	77.5	122	85.9	106	74.6	102	71.8	122	85.9	57	40.1	112	78.9	129	90.8	113	79.6
Georgia	122	2	1.6	58	47.5	88	72.1	81	66.4	57	46.7	87	71.3	42	34.4	78	63.9	99	81.1	75	61.5
Maryland	59	3	5.1	44	74.6	48	81.4	45	76.3	41	69.5	47	79.7	25	42.4	45	76.3	48	81.4	47	79.7
North Carolina	121	6	5.0	60	49.6	97	80.2	91	75.2	71	58.7	95	78.5	45	37.2	94	77.7	108	89.3	96	79.3
South Carolina	80	5	6.3	35	43.8	64	80.0	54	67.5	31	38.8	59	73.8	25	31.3	58	72.5	57	71.3	51	63.8
Virginia	70	9	12.9	44	62.9	61	87.1	54	77.1	46	65.7	59	84.3	31	44.3	56	80.0	60	85.7	55	78.6
West Virginia	63	4	6.3	30	47.6	45	71.4	33	52.4	24	38.1	39	61.9	16	25.4	47	74.6	48	76.2	36	57.1
CENSUS DIVISION 4, EAST NORTH CENTRAL	753	152	20.2	404	53.7	633	84.1	528	70.1	500	66.4	565	75.0	284	37.7	597	79.3	665	88.3	545	72.4
Illinois	173	30	17.3	101	58.4	138	79.8	107	61.8	116	67.1	132	76.3	59	34.1	136	78.6	157	90.8	132	76.3
Indiana	121	32	26.4	65	53.7	104	86.0	81	66.9	78	64.5	95	78.5	44	36.4	89	73.6	106	87.6	99	81.8
Michigan	158	16	10.1	88	55.7	133	84.2	123	77.8	97	61.4	125	79.1	66	41.8	126	79.7	134	84.8	113	71.5
Ohio	159	32	20.1	105	66.0	138	86.8	125	78.6	121	76.1	147	92.5	65	40.9	130	81.8	148	93.1	128	80.5
Wisconsin	142	42	29.6	45	31.7	120	84.5	92	64.8	88	62.0	66	46.5	50	35.2	116	81.7	120	84.5	73	51.4
CENSUS DIVISION 5, EAST SOUTH CENTRAL	424	13	3.1	141	33.3	229	54.0	202	47.6	151	35.6	215	50.7	75	17.7	227	53.5	321	75.7	199	46.9
Alabama	104	4	3.8	41	39.4	54	51.9	47	45.2	41	39.4	61	58.7	17	16.3	70	67.3	83	79.8	47	45.2
Kentucky	100	6	6.0	44	44.0	69	69.0	61	61.0	42	42.0	64	64.0	25	25.0	71	71.0	82	82.0	62	62.0
Mississippi	109	0	0.0	17	15.6	36	33.0	31	28.4	28	25.7	26	23.9	7	6.4	26	23.9	68	62.4	27	24.8
Tennessee	111	3	2.7	39	35.1	70	63.1	63	56.8	40	36.0	64	57.7	26	23.4	60	54.1	88	79.3	63	56.8
CENSUS DIVISION 6, WEST NORTH CENTRAL	693	139	20.1	198	28.6	466	67.2	437	63.1	312	45.0	385	55.6	97	14.0	509	73.4	587	84.7	420	60.6
Iowa	125	39	31.2	34	27.2	110	88.0	90	72.0	79	63.2	84	67.2	15	12.0	110	88.0	118	94.4	87	69.6
Kansas	153	33	21.6	30	19.6	77	50.3	78	51.0	47	30.7	61	39.9	12	7.8	102	66.7	119	77.8	77	50.3
Minnesota	116	26	22.4	28	24.1	79	68.1	86	74.1	51	44.0	65	56.0	21	18.1	84	72.4	100	86.2	71	61.2
Missouri	149	18	12.1	74	49.7	114	76.5	100	67.1	74	49.7	103	69.1	36	24.2	113	75.8	114	76.5	106	71.1
Nebraska	65	10	15.4	18	27.7	40	61.5	39	60.0	35	53.8	42	64.6	8	12.3	44	67.7	61	93.8	42	64.6
North Dakota	31	4	12.9	6	19.4	20	64.5	15	48.4	12	38.7	9	29.0	2	6.5	24	77.4	29	93.5	17	54.8
South Dakota	54	9	16.7	8	14.8	26	48.1	29	53.7	14	25.9	21	38.9	3	5.6	32	59.3	46	85.2	20	37.0
CENSUS DIVISION 7, WEST SOUTH CENTRAL	852	42	4.9	293	34.4	540	63.4	419	49.2	267	31.3	453	53.2	150	17.6	515	60.4	585	68.7	487	57.2
Arkansas	98	5	5.1	28	28.6	60	61.2	51	52.0	36	36.7	50	51.0	14	14.3	71	72.4	71	72.4	57	58.2
Louisiana	96	1	1.0	38	39.6	68	70.8	48	50.0	45	46.9	52	54.2	23	24.0	57	59.4	75	78.1	55	57.3
Oklahoma	116	16	13.8	29	25.0	55	47.4	45	38.8	27	23.3	60	51.7	12	10.3	48	41.4	86	74.1	62	53.4
Texas	542	20	3.7	198	36.5	357	65.9	275	50.7	159	29.3	291	53.7	101	18.6	339	62.5	353	65.1	313	57.7
CENSUS DIVISION 8, MOUNTAIN	347	26	7.5	138	39.8	241	69.5	199	57.3	157	45.2	219	63.1	84	24.2	299	68.9	277	79.8	211	60.8
Arizona	59	6	10.2	38	64.4	46	78.0	35	59.3	35	59.3	43	72.9	21	35.6	45	76.3	49	83.1	38	64.4
Colorado	66	6	9.1	32	48.5	52	78.8	49	74.2	40	60.6	51	77.3	22	33.3	50	75.8	60	90.9	49	74.2
Idaho	34	2	5.9	10	29.4	20	58.8	17	50.0	9	26.5	24	70.6	9	26.5	24	70.6	28	82.4	23	67.6
Montana	59	9	15.3	13	22.0	35	59.3	30	50.8	19	32.2	24	40.7	4	6.8	42	71.2	37	62.7	25	42.4
Nevada	29	0	0.0	15	51.7	23	69.0	19	65.5	14	48.3	19	65.5	8	27.6	16	55.2	20	69.0	18	62.1
New Mexico	36	1	2.8	10	27.8	23	63.9	12	33.3	15	41.7	16	44.4	9	25.0	26	72.2	29	80.6	20	55.6
Utah	33	1	3.0	13	39.4	25	75.8	20	60.6	13	39.4	21	63.6	10	30.3	21	63.6	29	87.9	19	57.6
Wyoming	31	1	3.2	7	22.6	20	64.5	17	54.8	12	38.7	21	67.7	1	3.2	15	48.4	25	80.6	19	61.3
CENSUS DIVISION 9, PACIFIC	507	31	6.1	237	46.7	364	71.8	328	64.7	293	57.8	370	73.0	155	30.6	368	72.6	432	85.2	336	66.3
Alaska	14	1	7.1	4	28.6	11	78.6	9	64.3	8	57.1	8	57.1	2	14.3	9	64.3	10	71.4	12	85.7
California	334	25	7.5	170	50.9	231	69.2	216	64.7	199	59.6	242	72.5	108	32.3	237	71.0	284	85.0	224	67.1
Hawaii	20	1	5.0	6	30.0	14	70.0	17	85.0	10	50.0	12	60.0	3	15.0	12	60.0	13	65.0	7	35.0
Oregon	57	1	1.8	21	36.8	51	89.5	36	63.2	30	52.6	46	80.7	19	33.3	50	87.7	55	96.5	42	73.7
Washington	82	3	3.7	36	43.9	57	69.5	50	61.0	46	56.1	62	75.6	23	28.0	60	73.2	70	85.4	51	62.2

Table 7 (Continued)

These data include only hospital-based facilities and services as reported by responding hospitals in Section C of the 2008 AHA Annual Survey, beginning on page 215. All hospitals are represented with Community Hospitals listed separately under United States. No estimates have been made for nonresponding hospitals. Definitions of facilities and services are listed in the Glossary, page 201.

| | | END OF LIFE SERVICE | | | | | | | | | | | | PHYSICAL REHABILITATION SERVICES | | | | | | | |
| | | HOSPICE | | PAIN MANAGEMENT PROGRAM | | PALLIATIVE CARE PROGRAM | | INPATIENT PALLIATIVE CARE UNIT | | PATIENT EDUCATION CENTER | | PATIENT REPRESENTATIVE SERVICES | | PHYSICAL REHABILITATION OUTPATIENT SERVICES | | ROBOT ASSISTED WALKING THERAPY | | SIMULATED REHABILITATION ENVIRONMENT | | PRIMARY CARE DEPARTMENT | |
CLASSIFICATION	HOSPITALS REPORTING	Number	Percent	Number	Percent	Number	Percent	Number	Percent	Number	Percent	Number	Percent	Number	Percent	Number	Percent	Number	Percent	Number	Percent
UNITED STATES	4,862	1,126	23.2	2,296	47.2	1,455	29.9	428	8.8	2,699	55.5	3,185	65.5	3,670	75.5	123	2.5	801	16.5	1,795	36.9
COMMUNITY HOSPITALS	4,186	1,051	25.1	2,131	50.9	1,351	32.3	374	8.9	2,471	59.0	2,876	68.7	3,478	83.1	114	2.7	753	18.0	1,664	39.8
CENSUS DIVISION 1, NEW ENGLAND	210	64	30.5	144	68.6	96	45.7	37	17.6	148	70.5	166	79.0	179	85.2	6	2.9	49	23.3	120	57.1
Connecticut	33	17	51.5	24	72.7	19	57.6	9	27.3	22	66.7	25	75.8	25	75.8	0	0.0	11	33.3	17	51.5
Maine	38	9	23.7	17	63.2	17	44.7	10	26.3	24	63.2	27	71.1	33	86.8	1	2.6	7	18.4	28	73.7
Massachusetts	81	19	23.5	60	74.1	26	32.1	12	14.8	60	74.1	69	85.2	70	86.4	4	4.9	17	21.0	39	48.1
New Hampshire	30	9	30.0	20	66.7	15	50.0	4	13.3	19	63.3	25	83.3	28	93.3	1	3.3	6	20.0	19	63.3
Rhode Island	13	2	15.4	7	53.8	7	53.8	0	0.0	11	84.6	9	69.2	9	69.2	0	0.0	4	30.8	9	69.2
Vermont	15	8	53.3	9	60.0	12	80.0	2	13.3	12	80.0	11	73.3	14	93.3	0	0.0	4	26.7	8	53.3
CENSUS DIVISION 2, MIDDLE ATLANTIC	398	129	32.4	285	71.6	178	44.7	61	15.3	272	68.3	312	73.4	328	82.4	17	4.3	100	25.1	221	55.5
New Jersey	73	21	28.8	60	82.2	39	53.4	12	16.4	50	68.5	63	86.3	59	80.8	3	4.1	19	26.0	47	64.4
New York	157	54	34.4	115	73.2	73	46.5	29	18.5	109	69.4	127	80.9	132	84.1	5	3.2	37	23.6	107	68.2
Pennsylvania	168	54	32.1	110	65.5	66	39.3	20	11.9	113	67.3	122	72.6	137	81.5	9	5.4	44	26.2	67	39.9
CENSUS DIVISION 3, SOUTH ATLANTIC	678	128	18.9	370	54.6	238	35.1	71	10.5	423	62.4	491	72.4	535	78.9	30	4.4	135	19.9	227	33.5
Delaware	8	0	0.0	3	37.5	2	25.0	0	0.0	3	37.5	6	75.0	5	62.5	0	0.0	1	12.5	4	50.0
District of Columbia	13	2	15.4	10	76.9	9	69.2	3	23.1	11	84.6	12	92.3	11	84.6	3	23.1	6	46.2	7	53.8
Florida	142	23	16.2	87	61.3	42	29.6	15	10.6	91	64.1	105	73.9	120	84.5	5	3.5	31	21.8	43	30.3
Georgia	122	16	13.1	55	45.1	24	19.7	9	7.4	67	54.9	86	70.5	94	77.0	3	2.5	20	16.4	29	23.8
Maryland	59	12	20.3	43	72.9	32	54.2	7	11.9	38	64.4	47	79.7	41	69.5	3	5.1	17	28.8	24	40.7
North Carolina	121	28	23.1	77	63.6	53	43.8	15	12.4	70	57.9	84	69.4	104	86.0	6	5.0	31	25.6	47	38.8
South Carolina	80	11	13.8	32	40.0	19	23.8	3	3.8	56	70.0	52	65.0	56	70.0	5	6.3	5	6.3	22	27.5
Virginia	70	27	38.6	41	58.6	35	50.0	13	18.6	48	68.6	57	81.4	59	84.3	2	2.9	12	17.1	26	37.1
West Virginia	63	9	14.3	22	34.9	22	34.9	6	9.5	39	61.9	42	66.7	45	71.4	3	4.8	12	19.0	25	39.7
CENSUS DIVISION 4, EAST NORTH CENTRAL	753	226	30.0	447	59.4	269	35.7	80	10.6	525	69.7	559	74.2	634	84.2	16	2.1	182	24.2	351	46.6
Illinois	173	52	30.1	98	56.6	59	34.1	14	8.1	104	60.1	124	71.7	149	86.1	5	2.9	43	24.9	80	46.2
Indiana	121	37	30.6	55	45.5	37	30.6	9	7.4	76	62.8	91	75.2	99	81.8	2	1.7	27	22.3	51	42.1
Michigan	158	65	41.1	86	54.4	61	38.6	18	11.4	98	62.0	116	73.4	131	82.9	5	3.2	38	24.1	97	61.4
Ohio	159	54	34.0	110	69.2	65	40.9	21	13.2	112	70.4	124	78.0	139	87.4	4	2.5	46	28.9	84	52.8
Wisconsin	142	18	12.7	98	69.0	47	33.1	18	12.7	135	95.1	104	73.2	116	81.7	0	0.0	28	19.7	39	27.5
CENSUS DIVISION 5, EAST SOUTH CENTRAL	424	61	14.4	109	25.7	63	14.9	22	5.2	194	45.8	258	60.8	290	68.4	9	2.1	39	9.2	107	25.2
Alabama	104	14	13.5	41	39.4	16	15.4	6	5.8	47	45.2	56	53.8	70	67.3	4	3.8	9	8.7	21	20.2
Kentucky	100	18	18.0	40	40.0	22	22.0	6	6.0	56	56.0	67	67.0	74	74.0	2	2.0	5	5.0	36	36.0
Mississippi	109	10	9.2	0	0.0	7	6.4	2	1.8	43	39.4	67	61.5	57	52.3	1	0.9	7	6.4	25	22.9
Tennessee	111	19	17.1	28	25.2	18	16.2	8	7.2	48	43.2	68	61.3	89	80.2	2	1.8	18	16.2	25	22.5
CENSUS DIVISION 6, WEST NORTH CENTRAL	693	203	29.3	277	40.0	192	27.7	55	7.9	340	49.1	389	56.1	549	79.2	10	1.4	89	12.8	265	38.2
Iowa	125	59	47.2	52	41.6	32	25.6	7	5.6	70	56.0	68	54.4	107	85.6	0	0.0	20	16.0	57	45.6
Kansas	153	19	12.4	45	29.4	27	17.6	10	6.5	52	34.0	67	43.8	118	77.1	2	1.3	12	7.8	48	31.4
Minnesota	116	43	37.1	49	42.2	40	34.5	14	12.1	56	48.3	69	59.5	97	83.6	2	1.7	20	17.2	45	38.8
Missouri	149	28	18.8	71	47.7	50	33.6	11	7.4	88	59.1	109	73.2	111	74.5	3	2.0	20	13.4	58	38.9
Nebraska	65	24	36.9	35	53.8	21	32.3	9	13.8	35	53.8	37	56.9	52	80.0	1	1.5	9	13.8	24	36.9
North Dakota	31	12	38.7	11	35.5	13	41.9	2	6.5	17	54.8	18	58.1	29	93.5	1	3.2	3	9.7	17	54.8
South Dakota	54	18	33.3	14	25.9	9	16.7	2	3.7	22	40.7	21	38.9	35	64.8	1	1.9	5	9.3	16	29.6
CENSUS DIVISION 7, WEST SOUTH CENTRAL	862	97	11.4	276	32.4	123	14.4	25	2.9	372	43.7	485	56.9	534	62.7	22	2.6	117	13.7	192	22.5
Arkansas	98	15	15.3	24	24.5	13	13.3	3	3.1	40	40.8	51	52.0	68	69.4	4	4.1	11	11.2	24	24.5
Louisiana	96	14	14.6	30	31.3	18	8.8	2	2.1	42	43.8	57	59.4	55	57.3	1	1.0	15	15.6	33	34.4
Oklahoma	116	17	14.7	39	33.6	12	10.3	0	0.0	31	26.7	53	45.7	76	65.5	0	0.0	12	10.3	17	14.7
Texas	542	51	9.4	183	33.8	80	14.8	20	3.7	259	47.8	324	59.8	335	61.8	17	3.1	79	14.6	118	21.8
CENSUS DIVISION 8, MOUNTAIN	347	88	25.4	147	42.4	99	28.5	30	8.6	154	44.4	213	61.4	259	74.6	5	1.4	34	9.8	142	40.9
Arizona	59	13	22.0	30	50.8	22	37.3	8	13.6	27	45.8	40	67.8	44	74.6	0	0.0	3	5.1	17	28.8
Colorado	66	10	15.2	30	45.5	23	34.8	4	6.1	34	51.5	49	74.2	59	89.4	1	1.5	10	15.2	37	56.1
Idaho	34	12	35.3	18	52.9	9	26.5	6	17.6	18	52.9	18	52.9	22	64.7	0	0.0	4	11.8	10	29.4
Montana	59	23	39.0	20	33.9	15	25.4	6	10.2	21	35.6	27	45.8	45	76.3	0	0.0	3	5.1	31	52.5
Nevada	29	3	10.3	10	34.5	7	24.1	2	6.9	14	48.3	16	55.2	22	75.9	2	6.9	3	10.3	6	20.7
New Mexico	36	7	19.4	12	33.3	7	19.4	2	5.6	11	30.6	23	63.9	26	72.2	1	2.8	5	13.9	17	47.2
Utah	33	10	30.3	16	48.5	11	33.3	1	3.0	19	57.6	23	69.7	23	69.7	1	3.0	5	15.2	12	36.4
Wyoming	31	10	32.3	11	35.5	5	16.1	1	3.2	10	32.3	17	54.8	18	58.1	0	0.0	1	3.2	12	38.7
CENSUS DIVISION 9, PACIFIC	507	130	25.6	241	47.5	197	38.9	47	9.3	271	53.5	312	61.5	362	71.4	8	1.6	56	11.0	170	33.5
Alaska	14	2	14.3	5	21.4	2	14.3	1	7.1	6	42.9	10	71.4	11	78.6	0	0.0	0	0.0	6	42.9
California	334	78	23.4	164	49.1	135	40.4	34	10.2	179	53.6	199	59.6	228	68.3	5	1.5	40	12.0	95	28.4
Hawaii	20	3	15.0	4	20.0	4	20.0	0	0.0	9	45.0	9	45.0	15	75.0	0	0.0	2	10.0	2	10.0
Oregon	57	26	45.6	27	47.4	24	42.1	7	12.3	33	57.9	42	73.7	49	86.0	2	3.5	5	8.8	28	49.1
Washington	82	21	25.6	40	43.8	32	39.0	5	6.1	48	58.5	52	63.4	59	72.0	1	1.2	9	11.0	39	47.6

Table 7 (Continued)

These data include only hospital-based facilities and services as reported by responding hospitals in Section C of the 2008 AHA Annual Survey, beginning on page 215. All hospitals are represented with Community Hospitals listed separately under United States. No estimates have been made for nonresponding hospitals. Definitions of facilities and services are listed in the Glossary, page 201.

CLASSIFICATION	HOSPITALS REPORTING	PSYCHIATRIC SERVICES — CHILD/ADOLESCENT SERVICES Number	Percent	CONSULTATION/LIAISON SERVICES Number	Percent	EDUCATION SERVICES Number	Percent	EMERGENCY SERVICES Number	Percent	GERIATRIC SERVICES Number	Percent	OUTPATIENT SERVICES Number	Percent	PARTIAL HOSPITILIZATION PROGRAM Number	Percent	RETIREMENT HOUSING Number	Percent	SLEEP CENTER Number	Percent	SOCIAL WORK SERVICES Number	Percent	SPORTS MEDICINE Number	Percent
UNITED STATES	4,862	870	17.9	1,535	31.6	1,155	23.8	1,580	32.5	1,429	29.4	1,308	26.9	807	16.6	165	3.4	2,205	45.4	4,101	84.3	1,755	36.1
COMMUNITY HOSPITALS	4,186	662	15.8	1,289	30.8	906	21.6	1,367	32.7	1,177	28.1	1,072	25.6	633	15.1	159	3.8	2,121	50.7	3,618	86.4	1,705	40.7
CENSUS DIVISION 1, NEW ENGLAND	210	66	31.4	105	50.0	84	40.0	104	49.5	101	48.1	111	52.9	75	35.7	8	3.8	116	55.2	199	94.8	114	54.3
Connecticut	33	17	51.5	23	69.7	20	60.6	25	75.8	21	63.6	25	75.8	19	57.6	2	6.1	21	63.6	31	93.9	20	60.6
Maine	38	9	23.7	13	34.2	10	26.3	13	34.2	11	28.9	15	39.5	7	18.4	3	7.9	21	55.3	36	94.7	17	44.7
Massachusetts	81	26	32.1	40	49.4	33	40.7	39	48.1	42	51.9	41	50.6	30	37.0	0	0.0	43	53.1	76	93.8	44	54.3
New Hampshire	30	9	30.0	13	43.3	9	30.0	12	40.0	13	43.3	12	40.0	9	30.0	1	3.3	17	56.7	29	96.7	18	60.0
Rhode Island	13	1	7.7	9	69.2	6	46.2	9	69.2	8	61.5	9	69.2	6	46.2	1	7.7	8	61.5	12	92.3	5	38.5
Vermont	15	4	26.7	7	46.7	6	40.0	6	40.0	6	40.0	9	60.0	4	26.7	1	6.7	6	40.0	15	100.0	10	66.7
CENSUS DIVISION 2, MIDDLE ATLANTIC	398	138	34.7	232	58.3	158	39.7	211	53.0	201	50.5	162	40.7	98	24.6	7	1.8	225	56.5	377	94.7	190	47.7
New Jersey	73	31	42.5	48	65.8	36	49.3	48	65.8	41	56.2	32	43.8	30	41.1	2	2.7	46	63.0	68	93.2	31	42.5
New York	157	61	38.9	101	64.3	66	42.0	88	56.1	83	52.9	80	51.0	40	25.5	3	1.9	75	47.8	149	94.9	85	54.1
Pennsylvania	168	46	27.4	83	49.4	56	33.3	75	44.6	77	45.8	50	29.8	28	16.7	2	1.2	104	61.9	160	95.2	74	44.0
CENSUS DIVISION 3, SOUTH ATLANTIC	678	133	19.6	247	36.4	191	28.2	267	39.4	202	29.8	185	27.3	135	19.9	8	1.2	356	52.5	599	88.3	264	38.9
Delaware	8	3	37.5	3	37.5	1	12.5	2	25.0	2	25.0	3	37.5	3	37.5	0	0.0	6	75.0	7	87.5	3	37.5
District of Columbia	13	5	38.5	9	69.2	9	69.2	10	76.9	8	61.5	9	69.2	8	61.5	1	7.7	9	69.2	12	92.3	10	76.9
Florida	142	22	15.5	47	33.1	35	24.6	48	33.8	38	26.8	31	21.8	21	14.8	0	0.0	70	49.3	117	82.4	64	45.1
Georgia	122	19	15.6	36	29.5	27	22.1	33	27.0	27	22.1	29	23.8	21	17.2	4	3.3	62	50.8	101	82.8	37	30.3
Maryland	59	21	35.6	40	67.8	26	44.1	43	72.9	29	49.2	27	45.8	27	45.8	0	0.0	42	71.2	57	96.6	21	35.6
North Carolina	121	23	19.0	37	30.6	36	29.8	50	41.3	42	34.7	38	31.4	20	16.5	2	1.7	71	58.7	110	90.9	44	36.4
South Carolina	80	14	17.5	24	30.0	19	23.8	24	30.0	19	23.8	17	21.3	11	13.8	0	0.0	32	40.0	71	88.8	27	33.8
Virginia	70	14	20.0	33	47.1	21	30.0	41	58.6	23	32.9	22	31.4	17	24.3	1	1.4	34	48.6	67	95.7	35	50.0
West Virginia	63	12	19.0	18	28.6	17	27.0	16	25.4	14	22.2	9	14.3	7	11.1	0	0.0	30	47.6	57	90.5	23	36.5
CENSUS DIVISION 4, EAST NORTH CENTRAL	753	162	21.5	300	39.8	250	33.2	295	39.2	268	35.6	264	35.1	176	23.4	31	4.1	449	59.6	678	90.0	391	51.9
Illinois	173	47	27.2	70	40.5	61	35.3	73	42.2	62	35.8	70	40.5	52	30.1	9	5.2	114	65.9	156	90.2	82	47.4
Indiana	121	18	14.9	35	28.9	30	24.8	37	30.6	41	33.9	32	26.4	21	17.4	1	0.8	86	71.1	105	86.8	53	43.8
Michigan	158	28	17.7	70	44.3	61	38.6	70	44.3	56	35.4	54	34.2	31	19.6	4	2.5	96	60.8	145	91.8	86	54.4
Ohio	159	31	19.5	70	44.0	57	35.8	66	41.5	61	38.4	58	36.5	45	28.3	9	5.7	103	64.8	143	89.9	94	59.1
Wisconsin	142	38	26.8	55	38.7	41	28.9	49	34.5	48	33.8	50	35.2	27	19.0	8	5.6	50	35.2	129	90.8	76	53.5
CENSUS DIVISION 5, EAST SOUTH CENTRAL	424	46	10.8	92	21.7	69	16.3	100	23.6	129	30.4	77	18.2	45	10.6	3	0.7	171	40.3	341	80.4	121	28.5
Alabama	104	11	10.6	22	21.2	16	15.4	25	24.0	28	26.9	22	21.2	10	9.6	2	1.9	46	44.2	76	73.1	40	38.5
Kentucky	100	13	13.0	29	29.0	18	18.0	31	31.0	25	25.0	16	16.0	11	11.0	1	1.0	51	51.0	84	84.0	26	26.0
Mississippi	109	11	10.1	21	19.3	18	16.5	16	14.7	40	36.7	20	18.3	9	8.3	0	0.0	18	16.5	98	89.9	21	19.3
Tennessee	111	11	9.9	20	18.0	17	15.3	28	25.2	36	32.4	19	17.1	15	13.5	0	0.0	56	50.5	83	74.8	34	30.6
CENSUS DIVISION 6, WEST NORTH CENTRAL	693	113	16.3	174	25.1	132	19.0	187	27.0	163	23.5	164	23.7	73	10.5	79	11.4	307	44.3	557	80.4	266	38.4
Iowa	125	29	23.2	32	25.6	30	24.0	45	36.0	32	25.6	32	25.6	17	13.6	19	15.2	67	53.6	104	83.2	55	44.0
Kansas	153	10	6.5	15	9.8	10	6.5	24	15.7	25	16.3	15	9.8	5	3.3	5	3.3	41	26.8	102	66.7	36	23.5
Minnesota	116	20	17.2	43	37.1	29	25.0	34	29.3	34	29.3	33	28.4	17	14.7	22	19.0	55	47.4	103	88.8	41	35.3
Missouri	149	30	20.1	58	38.9	45	30.2	57	38.3	50	33.6	50	33.6	17	11.4	2	1.3	86	57.7	139	93.3	68	45.6
Nebraska	65	12	18.5	14	21.5	8	12.3	12	18.5	13	20.0	20	30.8	9	13.8	6	9.2	30	46.2	48	73.8	31	47.7
North Dakota	31	8	25.8	8	25.8	7	22.6	9	29.0	7	22.6	9	29.0	6	19.4	7	22.6	11	35.5	30	96.8	16	51.6
South Dakota	54	4	7.4	4	7.4	3	5.6	6	11.1	2	3.7	5	9.3	2	3.7	13	24.1	17	31.5	31	57.4	19	35.2
CENSUS DIVISION 7, WEST SOUTH CENTRAL	852	77	9.0	145	17.0	111	13.0	159	18.7	183	21.5	146	17.1	75	8.8	12	1.4	293	34.4	639	75.0	185	21.7
Arkansas	98	14	14.3	23	23.5	14	14.3	18	18.4	27	27.6	20	20.4	6	6.1	2	2.0	42	42.9	73	74.5	24	24.5
Louisiana	96	9	9.4	17	17.7	12	12.5	27	28.1	30	31.3	19	19.8	11	11.5	3	3.1	35	36.5	72	75.0	21	21.9
Oklahoma	116	0	0.0	18	15.5	16	13.8	25	21.6	25	21.6	21	18.1	8	6.9	2	1.7	49	42.2	70	60.3	23	19.8
Texas	542	54	10.0	87	16.1	69	12.7	89	16.4	101	18.6	86	15.9	50	9.2	5	0.9	167	30.8	424	78.2	117	21.6
CENSUS DIVISION 8, MOUNTAIN	347	57	16.4	86	24.8	62	17.9	103	29.7	72	20.7	75	21.6	44	12.7	7	2.0	150	43.2	280	80.7	106	30.5
Arizona	59	12	20.3	19	32.2	13	22.0	21	35.6	14	23.7	17	28.8	6	10.2	0	0.0	20	33.9	50	84.7	10	16.9
Colorado	66	10	15.2	16	24.2	13	19.7	21	31.8	13	19.7	15	22.7	8	12.1	2	3.0	45	68.2	49	74.2	29	43.9
Idaho	34	6	17.6	7	20.6	5	14.7	7	20.6	4	11.8	7	20.6	2	5.9	0	0.0	15	44.1	26	76.5	17	50.0
Montana	59	6	10.2	11	18.6	7	11.9	16	27.1	8	13.6	7	11.9	8	13.6	4	6.8	14	23.7	49	83.1	22	37.3
Nevada	29	5	17.2	7	24.1	5	17.2	6	20.7	6	20.7	5	17.2	4	13.8	0	0.0	10	34.5	23	79.3	6	20.7
New Mexico	36	6	16.7	9	25.0	5	13.9	10	27.8	10	27.8	7	19.4	3	8.3	0	0.0	13	36.1	28	77.8	4	11.1
Utah	33	7	21.2	11	33.3	8	24.2	13	39.4	9	27.3	9	27.3	8	24.2	0	0.0	18	54.5	27	81.8	12	36.4
Wyoming	31	5	16.1	6	19.4	6	19.4	9	29.0	8	25.8	8	25.8	5	16.1	1	3.2	15	48.4	28	90.3	6	19.4
CENSUS DIVISION 9, PACIFIC	507	78	15.4	154	30.4	98	19.3	154	30.4	110	21.7	124	24.5	86	17.0	10	2.0	138	27.2	431	85.0	118	23.3
Alaska	14	6	42.9	6	42.9	6	42.9	6	42.9	3	21.4	5	35.7	3	21.4	0	0.0	6	42.9	12	85.7	3	21.4
California	334	53	15.9	102	30.5	61	18.3	94	28.1	75	22.5	83	24.9	60	18.0	6	1.8	68	20.4	292	87.4	69	20.7
Hawaii	20	2	10.0	4	20.0	4	20.0	4	20.0	4	20.0	3	15.0	2	10.0	0	0.0	4	20.0	17	85.0	3	15.0
Oregon	57	7	12.3	18	31.6	10	17.5	23	40.4	8	14.0	11	19.3	6	10.5	3	5.3	22	38.6	48	84.2	18	31.6
Washington	82	10	12.2	24	29.3	17	20.7	27	32.9	20	24.4	22	26.8	15	18.3	1	1.2	38	46.3	62	75.6	24	29.3

Table 7 (Continued)

These data include only hospital-based facilities and services as reported by responding hospitals in Section C of the 2008 AHA Annual Survey, beginning on page 215. All hospitals are represented with Community Hospitals listed separately under United States. No estimates have been made for nonresponding hospitals. Definitions of facilities and services are listed in the Glossary, page 201.

CLASSIFICATION	HOSPITALS REPORTING	SUPPORT GROUPS Number	SUPPORT GROUPS Percent	SWING BED SERVICES Number	SWING BED SERVICES Percent	TEEN OUTREACH SERVICES Number	TEEN OUTREACH SERVICES Percent	TOBACCO TREATMENT/CESSATION PROGRAM Number	TOBACCO TREATMENT/CESSATION PROGRAM Percent	BONE MARROW Number	BONE MARROW Percent	HEART Number	HEART Percent	KIDNEY Number	KIDNEY Percent	LIVER Number	LIVER Percent	LUNG Number	LUNG Percent	TISSUE Number	TISSUE Percent	OTHER Number	OTHER Percent
UNITED STATES	4,862	3,016	62.0	1,529	31.4	652	13.4	2,363	48.6	208	4.3	137	2.8	234	4.8	132	2.7	80	1.6	272	5.6	222	4.6
COMMUNITY HOSPITALS	4,186	2,767	66.1	1,483	35.4	632	15.1	2,182	52.1	199	4.8	133	3.2	229	5.5	129	3.1	78	1.9	261	6.2	214	5.1
CENSUS DIVISION 1, NEW ENGLAND	210	186	88.6	45	21.4	59	28.1	154	73.3	13	6.2	6	2.9	15	7.1	8	3.8	4	1.9	12	5.7	14	6.7
Connecticut	33	31	93.9	3	9.1	12	36.4	25	75.8	2	6.1	2	5.1	2	6.1	2	6.1	1	3.0	2	6.1	3	9.1
Maine	38	34	89.5	11	28.9	10	26.3	31	81.6	1	2.6	0	0.0	1	2.6	0	0.0	0	0.0	0	0.0	1	2.6
Massachusetts	81	71	87.7	6	7.4	23	28.4	47	58.0	7	8.6	4	4.9	9	11.1	6	7.4	3	3.7	8	9.9	7	8.6
New Hampshire	30	25	83.3	15	50.0	9	30.0	25	83.3	1	3.3	0	0.0	1	3.3	0	0.0	0	0.0	1	3.3	1	3.3
Rhode Island	13	12	92.3	1	7.7	3	23.1	11	84.6	1	7.7	0	0.0	1	7.7	0	0.0	0	0.0	0	0.0	1	7.7
Vermont	15	13	86.7	9	60.0	2	13.3	15	100.0	1	6.7	0	0.0	1	6.7	0	0.0	0	0.0	1	6.7	1	6.7
CENSUS DIVISION 2, MIDDLE ATLANTIC	398	323	81.2	65	16.3	119	29.9	277	67.8	29	7.3	17	4.3	34	8.5	18	4.5	9	2.3	30	7.5	34	8.5
New Jersey	73	57	78.1	10	13.7	27	37.0	42	57.5	2	2.7	2	2.7	5	6.8	2	2.7	1	1.4	4	5.5	6	8.2
New York	157	130	82.8	21	13.4	47	29.9	123	75.4	15	9.6	6	3.3	13	8.3	6	3.8	2	1.3	13	8.3	13	8.3
Pennsylvania	168	136	81.0	34	20.2	45	26.8	103	64.3	12	7.1	9	5.4	16	9.5	10	6.0	6	3.6	13	7.7	15	8.9
CENSUS DIVISION 3, SOUTH ATLANTIC	678	466	68.7	132	19.5	94	13.9	377	55.6	36	5.3	26	3.8	33	4.9	23	3.4	14	2.1	45	6.6	44	6.5
Delaware	8	5	62.5	0	0.0	3	37.5	5	62.5	2	25.0	1	12.5	2	25.0	1	12.5	0	0.0	0	0.0	0	0.0
District of Columbia	13	10	76.9	2	15.4	5	38.5	8	61.5	4	30.8	2	15.4	5	38.5	2	15.4	0	0.0	4	30.8	3	23.1
Florida	142	101	71.1	12	8.5	16	11.3	75	52.8	9	6.3	6	4.2	8	5.6	8	5.6	5	3.5	11	7.7	7	4.9
Georgia	122	72	59.0	33	27.0	20	16.4	60	49.2	6	4.9	5	4.1	5	4.1	4	3.4	2	1.6	6	4.9	7	5.7
Maryland	59	49	83.1	1	1.7	12	20.3	39	66.1	3	5.1	3	5.1	2	3.4	2	3.4	2	3.4	4	6.8	5	8.5
North Carolina	121	84	69.4	36	29.8	14	11.6	74	61.2	3	3.3	4	3.3	5	4.1	3	2.5	2	1.7	7	5.8	11	9.1
South Carolina	80	48	60.0	8	10.0	9	11.3	39	48.8	3	3.8	1	1.3	4	1.3	1	1.3	2	2.9	3	3.8	3	3.8
Virginia	70	56	80.0	17	24.3	8	11.4	42	60.0	3	4.3	4	5.7	4	5.7	2	2.9	3	4.3	8	11.4	7	10.0
West Virginia	63	41	65.1	23	36.5	7	11.1	35	55.6	2	3.2	0	0.0	1	1.6	0	0.0	2	2.8	2	3.2	1	1.6
CENSUS DIVISION 4, EAST NORTH CENTRAL	753	563	74.8	203	27.0	142	18.9	481	63.9	34	4.5	24	3.2	35	4.6	22	2.9	16	2.1	57	7.6	29	3.9
Illinois	173	141	81.5	59	34.1	36	20.8	102	59.0	10	5.8	5	2.9	8	4.6	6	3.5	2	1.2	15	8.7	12	6.9
Indiana	121	92	76.0	36	29.8	20	16.5	94	77.7	2	1.7	1	2.5	2	1.7	1	0.8	1	0.8	7	5.8	0	0.0
Michigan	158	129	81.6	36	22.8	31	19.6	103	65.2	6	5.1	5	3.2	10	6.3	4	2.5	4	2.5	14	8.9	7	4.4
Ohio	159	129	81.1	37	23.3	37	23.3	121	76.1	6	5.7	7	4.4	11	6.9	6	3.8	5	3.1	16	10.1	6	3.8
Wisconsin	142	72	50.7	35	24.6	18	12.7	61	43.0	5	3.5	4	2.8	4	2.8	5	3.5	4	2.8	5	3.5	4	2.8
CENSUS DIVISION 5, EAST SOUTH CENTRAL	424	204	48.1	160	37.7	34	8.0	158	37.3	11	2.6	8	1.9	12	2.8	5	1.2	5	1.2	13	3.1	10	2.4
Alabama	104	48	46.2	24	23.1	7	6.7	37	35.6	2	1.9	1	1.0	3	1.0	1	1.0	1	1.0	3	2.9	2	1.9
Kentucky	100	59	59.0	42	42.0	10	10.0	60	60.0	3	3.0	3	3.0	3	3.0	2	2.0	2	2.0	2	2.0	3	3.0
Mississippi	109	38	34.9	54	49.5	8	7.3	19	17.4	1	0.9	1	0.9	1	0.9	0	0.0	0	0.0	1	0.9	0	0.0
Tennessee	111	59	53.2	40	36.0	9	8.1	42	37.8	5	4.5	3	2.7	5	6.3	2	1.8	2	1.8	7	6.3	5	4.5
CENSUS DIVISION 6, WEST NORTH CENTRAL	693	404	58.3	420	60.6	64	9.2	316	45.6	19	2.6	10	1.4	23	3.3	11	1.6	6	0.9	26	3.8	20	2.9
Iowa	125	98	78.4	90	72.0	20	16.0	81	64.8	2	0.8	1	0.8	4	3.2	1	0.8	1	0.8	5	4.0	3	2.4
Kansas	153	56	36.6	101	66.0	4	2.6	40	26.1	2	1.3	1	0.7	4	1.3	1	0.7	0	0.0	2	1.3	2	1.3
Minnesota	116	81	69.8	63	54.3	12	10.3	52	44.8	5	4.3	3	2.6	8	3.4	3	2.6	3	2.6	5	4.3	2	1.7
Missouri	149	96	64.4	55	36.9	18	12.1	84	56.4	9	4.0	4	2.7	8	5.4	5	3.4	2	1.3	9	6.0	9	6.0
Nebraska	65	34	52.3	43	66.2	7	10.8	29	44.6	3	4.6	0	0.0	2	1.5	1	1.5	0	0.0	2	3.1	2	3.1
North Dakota	31	16	51.6	24	77.4	1	3.2	14	45.2	3	9.1	0	0.0	2	6.5	0	0.0	0	0.0	0	0.0	1	3.2
South Dakota	54	23	42.6	44	81.5	2	3.7	16	29.6	0	0.0	0	0.0	2	3.7	0	0.0	0	0.0	3	5.6	1	1.9
CENSUS DIVISION 7, WEST SOUTH CENTRAL	852	386	45.3	247	29.0	43	5.0	256	30.0	19	2.2	17	2.0	37	4.3	18	2.1	10	1.2	31	3.6	28	3.3
Arkansas	98	52	53.1	40	40.8	5	5.1	37	37.8	2	2.0	2	2.0	3	3.1	1	1.0	1	1.0	1	1.0	1	1.0
Louisiana	96	41	42.7	25	26.0	8	8.3	48	50.0	3	3.1	2	2.1	5	5.2	4	4.2	1	1.0	6	6.3	6	6.3
Oklahoma	116	39	33.6	51	44.0	3	2.6	32	27.6	2	1.7	2	1.7	5	4.3	1	0.9	1	0.9	3	2.6	1	0.9
Texas	542	254	46.9	131	24.2	27	5.0	139	25.6	12	2.2	11	2.0	24	4.4	12	2.2	8	1.5	21	3.9	20	3.7
CENSUS DIVISION 8, MOUNTAIN	347	169	48.7	149	42.9	38	11.0	165	47.0	16	4.6	9	2.6	16	4.0	10	2.9	5	1.7	19	5.5	13	3.7
Arizona	59	32	54.2	10	16.9	8	13.6	32	54.2	4	6.8	2	3.4	4	6.8	3	5.1	3	5.1	5	8.5	3	5.1
Colorado	66	36	54.5	26	39.4	7	10.6	29	43.9	5	7.6	2	3.0	5	4.5	3	4.5	1	1.5	5	7.6	2	3.0
Idaho	34	16	47.1	18	52.9	7	20.6	19	55.9	1	2.9	0	0.0	0	0.0	0	0.0	0	0.0	2	5.9	2	5.9
Montana	59	23	39.0	48	81.4	3	5.1	24	40.7	2	3.4	1	1.7	2	1.7	0	0.0	1	1.7	3	5.1	1	1.7
Nevada	29	11	37.9	3	10.3	4	13.8	11	37.9	0	0.0	0	0.0	2	6.9	0	0.0	0	0.0	0	0.0	1	3.4
New Mexico	36	18	50.0	11	30.6	3	8.3	18	50.0	1	2.8	0	0.0	2	5.6	0	0.0	0	0.0	0	0.0	1	2.8
Utah	33	17	51.5	11	33.3	4	12.1	13	39.4	3	9.1	4	12.1	2	6.1	3	9.1	1	3.0	4	12.1	3	9.1
Wyoming	31	16	51.6	22	71.0	2	6.5	17	54.8	0	0.0	0	0.0	0	0.0	0	0.0	0	0.0	0	0.0	0	0.0
CENSUS DIVISION 9, PACIFIC	507	315	62.1	108	21.3	59	11.6	188	37.1	32	6.3	20	3.9	31	6.1	17	3.4	10	2.0	39	7.7	30	5.9
Alaska	14	3	21.4	7	50.0	1	7.1	7	50.0	0	0.0	0	0.0	0	0.0	0	0.0	0	0.0	1	7.1	1	7.1
California	334	206	61.7	42	12.6	41	12.3	104	31.1	20	6.0	12	3.6	22	6.6	12	3.6	8	2.4	30	9.0	24	7.2
Hawaii	20	9	45.0	5	25.0	1	5.0	5	25.0	2	10.0	3	15.0	1	5.0	1	5.0	0	0.0	0	0.0	0	0.0
Oregon	57	51	89.5	27	47.4	5	8.8	37	64.9	3	5.3	1	1.7	2	3.5	1	1.8	0	0.0	2	3.5	1	1.8
Washington	82	46	56.1	27	32.9	11	13.4	35	42.7	7	8.5	4	4.9	6	7.3	3	3.7	2	2.4	7	8.5	4	4.9

Table 7 (Continued)

These data include only hospital-based facilities and services as reported by responding hospitals in Section C of the 2008 AHA Annual Survey, beginning on page 215. All hospitals are represented with Community Hospitals listed separately under United States. No estimates have been made for nonresponding hospitals. Definitions of facilities and services are listed in the Glossary, page 201.

CLASSIFICATION	HOSPITALS REPORTING	TRANSPORTATION TO HEALTH FACILITIES Number	Percent	URGENT CARE CENTER Number	Percent	VOLUNTEER SERVICES DEPARTMENT Number	Percent	WOMEN'S HEALTH SERVICES Number	Percent	WOUND MANAGEMENT SERVICES Number	Percent	BLOOD DONOR CENTER Number	Percent	COMPUTER ASSISTED ORTHOPEDIC SURGERY (CAOS) Number	Percent	MOBILE HEALTH SERVICES Number	Percent	ROBOTIC SURGERY Number	Percent
UNITED STATES	4,862	1,192	24.5	1,029	21.2	3,565	73.3	2,254	46.4	2,812	57.8	351	7.2	599	12.3	480	9.9	574	11.8
COMMUNITY HOSPITALS	4,186	1,029	24.6	974	23.3	3,320	79.3	2,146	51.3	2,595	62.0	339	8.1	584	14.0	454	10.8	559	13.4
CENSUS DIVISION 1, NEW ENGLAND	210	68	32.4	80	38.1	194	92.4	147	70.0	140	66.7	28	13.3	34	16.2	23	11.0	37	17.6
Connecticut	33	5	15.2	18	54.5	31	93.9	21	63.6	26	78.8	3	9.1	5	15.2	9	27.3	11	33.3
Maine	38	11	28.9	10	26.3	35	92.1	28	73.7	24	63.2	0	0.0	4	10.5	1	2.6	3	7.9
Massachusetts	81	31	38.3	33	40.7	73	90.1	55	67.9	53	65.4	20	24.7	14	17.3	5	6.2	14	17.3
New Hampshire	30	8	26.7	11	36.7	29	96.7	25	83.3	20	66.7	4	13.3	6	20.0	6	20.0	7	23.3
Rhode Island	13	6	46.2	4	30.8	12	92.3	10	76.9	8	61.5	0	0.0	1	7.7	1	7.7	1	7.7
Vermont	15	7	46.7	4	26.7	14	93.3	8	53.3	9	60.0	1	6.7	4	26.7	1	6.7	1	6.7
CENSUS DIVISION 2, MIDDLE ATLANTIC	398	144	36.2	79	19.8	352	88.4	252	63.3	258	64.8	72	18.1	71	17.8	61	15.3	78	19.6
New Jersey	73	36	49.3	13	17.8	65	89.0	49	67.1	54	74.0	13	17.8	14	19.2	16	21.9	17	23.3
New York	157	60	38.2	39	24.8	138	87.9	111	70.7	93	59.2	38	24.2	30	19.1	31	19.7	36	22.9
Pennsylvania	168	48	28.6	27	16.1	149	88.7	92	54.8	111	66.1	21	12.5	27	16.1	14	8.3	25	14.9
CENSUS DIVISION 3, SOUTH ATLANTIC	678	171	25.2	149	22.0	569	83.9	379	55.9	434	64.0	49	7.2	112	16.5	91	13.4	107	15.8
Delaware	8	2	25.0	1	12.5	5	62.5	5	62.5	6	75.0	0	0.0	1	12.5	1	12.5	2	25.0
District of Columbia	13	9	69.2	6	46.2	11	84.6	9	69.2	10	76.9	3	23.1	5	38.5	4	30.8	6	46.2
Florida	142	39	27.5	32	22.5	127	89.4	87	61.3	94	66.2	9	6.3	32	22.5	16	11.3	34	23.9
Georgia	122	24	19.7	23	18.9	92	75.4	59	48.4	70	57.4	4	3.3	21	17.2	14	11.5	11	9.0
Maryland	59	17	28.8	21	35.6	53	89.8	32	54.2	41	69.5	13	22.0	13	22.0	12	20.3	8	13.6
North Carolina	121	37	30.6	31	25.6	109	90.1	66	54.5	82	67.8	8	6.6	16	13.2	20	16.5	22	18.2
South Carolina	80	11	13.8	9	11.3	59	73.8	45	56.3	46	57.5	5	6.3	6	7.5	8	10.0	8	10.0
Virginia	70	18	25.7	15	21.4	65	92.9	41	58.6	51	72.9	7	10.0	16	22.9	14	20.0	12	17.1
West Virginia	63	14	22.2	11	17.5	48	76.2	35	55.6	34	54.0	0	0.0	2	3.2	2	3.2	4	6.3
CENSUS DIVISION 4, EAST NORTH CENTRAL	753	217	28.8	286	38.0	605	80.3	414	55.0	473	62.8	52	6.9	128	17.0	75	10.0	107	14.2
Illinois	173	50	28.9	46	26.6	141	81.5	93	53.8	113	65.3	16	9.2	37	21.4	16	9.2	23	13.3
Indiana	121	26	21.5	35	28.9	105	86.8	67	55.4	83	68.6	6	5.0	7	5.8	11	9.1	12	9.9
Michigan	158	46	29.1	69	43.7	137	86.7	87	55.1	107	67.7	9	5.7	22	13.9	15	9.5	31	19.6
Ohio	159	65	40.9	54	34.0	148	93.1	103	64.8	106	66.7	17	10.7	37	23.3	21	13.2	26	16.4
Wisconsin	142	30	21.1	82	57.7	74	52.1	64	45.1	64	45.1	4	2.8	25	17.6	12	8.5	15	16.6
CENSUS DIVISION 5, EAST SOUTH CENTRAL	424	61	14.4	34	8.0	264	62.3	160	37.7	169	39.9	20	4.7	30	7.1	26	6.1	31	7.3
Alabama	104	14	13.5	9	8.7	75	72.1	39	37.5	43	41.3	8	7.7	8	7.7	2	1.9	8	7.7
Kentucky	100	12	12.0	12	12.0	79	79.0	45	45.0	47	47.0	4	4.0	9	9.0	15	15.0	5	5.0
Mississippi	109	17	15.6	5	4.6	31	28.4	31	28.4	23	21.1	2	1.8	4	3.7	1	0.9	6	5.5
Tennessee	111	18	16.2	8	7.2	79	71.2	45	40.5	56	50.5	6	5.4	9	8.1	8	7.2	12	10.8
CENSUS DIVISION 6, WEST NORTH CENTRAL	693	174	25.1	107	15.4	440	63.5	225	32.5	348	50.2	27	3.9	45	6.5	62	8.9	45	6.5
Iowa	125	28	22.4	19	15.2	99	79.2	46	36.8	72	57.6	5	4.0	11	8.8	12	9.6	8	6.4
Kansas	153	36	23.5	13	8.5	72	47.1	35	22.9	73	47.7	1	0.7	6	3.9	7	4.6	5	3.3
Minnesota	116	24	20.7	31	26.7	87	75.0	44	37.9	59	50.9	7	6.0	7	6.0	11	9.5	10	8.6
Missouri	149	53	35.6	31	20.8	107	71.8	60	40.3	82	55.0	10	6.7	9	6.0	18	12.1	13	8.7
Nebraska	65	15	23.1	5	7.7	38	58.5	16	24.6	28	43.1	1	1.5	10	15.4	3	4.6	6	9.2
North Dakota	31	8	25.8	5	16.1	16	51.6	11	35.5	11	35.5	1	3.2	2	6.5	1	3.2	1	3.2
South Dakota	54	10	18.5	3	5.6	21	38.9	13	24.1	23	42.6	2	3.7	0	0.0	8	14.8	2	3.7
CENSUS DIVISION 7, WEST SOUTH CENTRAL	852	138	16.2	94	11.0	482	56.6	284	33.3	479	56.2	32	3.8	65	7.6	56	6.6	64	7.5
Arkansas	98	20	20.4	12	12.2	59	60.2	32	32.7	53	54.1	3	3.1	4	4.1	7	7.1	8	8.2
Louisiana	96	20	20.8	16	16.7	63	65.6	40	41.7	54	56.3	7	7.3	13	13.5	8	8.3	13	13.5
Oklahoma	116	19	16.4	13	11.2	63	54.3	37	31.9	51	44.0	4	3.4	5	4.3	7	6.0	3	2.6
Texas	542	79	14.6	53	9.8	297	54.8	175	32.3	321	59.2	18	3.3	43	7.9	34	6.3	40	7.4
CENSUS DIVISION 8, MOUNTAIN	347	83	23.9	74	21.3	243	70.0	156	45.0	205	59.1	30	8.6	47	13.5	28	8.1	40	11.5
Arizona	59	15	25.4	15	25.4	46	78.0	23	39.0	43	72.9	5	8.5	12	20.3	5	8.5	18	30.5
Colorado	66	13	19.7	12	18.2	52	78.8	41	62.1	49	74.2	12	18.2	15	22.7	6	9.1	10	15.2
Idaho	34	7	20.6	7	20.6	24	70.6	13	38.2	16	47.1	2	5.9	6	17.6	4	11.8	2	5.9
Montana	59	28	47.5	17	28.8	37	62.7	18	30.5	24	40.7	2	3.4	4	6.8	6	10.2	1	1.7
Nevada	29	4	13.8	4	13.8	19	65.5	12	41.4	18	62.1	1	3.4	2	6.9	4	13.8	4	13.8
New Mexico	36	4	11.1	7	19.4	16	44.4	15	41.7	23	63.9	4	11.1	4	11.1	1	2.8	2	5.6
Utah	33	3	9.1	7	21.2	28	84.8	22	66.7	20	60.6	5	15.2	4	12.1	1	3.0	3	9.1
Wyoming	31	6	19.4	5	16.1	21	67.7	12	38.7	12	38.7	0	0.0	0	0.0	1	3.2	0	0.0
CENSUS DIVISION 9, PACIFIC	507	136	26.8	126	24.9	416	82.1	237	46.7	306	60.4	41	8.1	67	13.2	58	11.4	65	12.8
Alaska	14	3	21.4	2	14.3	8	57.1	6	42.9	9	64.3	0	0.0	1	7.1	1	7.1	2	14.3
California	334	98	29.3	87	26.0	280	83.8	150	44.9	190	56.9	41	12.3	44	13.2	40	12.0	46	13.8
Hawaii	20	4	20.0	0	0.0	17	85.0	9	45.0	15	75.0	0	0.0	0	0.0	1	5.0	1	5.0
Oregon	57	17	29.8	12	21.1	50	87.7	35	61.4	44	77.2	0	0.0	10	17.5	5	8.8	5	8.8
Washington	82	14	17.1	25	30.5	61	74.4	37	45.1	48	58.5	0	0.0	12	14.6	11	13.4	11	13.4

Table 7 (Continued)

These data include only hospital-based facilities and services as reported by responding hospitals in Section C of the 2008 AHA Annual Survey, beginning on page 215. All hospitals are represented with Community Hospitals listed separately under United States. No estimates have been made for nonresponding hospitals. Definitions of facilities and services are listed in the Glossary, page 201.

CLASSIFICATION	HOSPITALS REPORTING	Virtual Colonoscopy No.	Virtual Colonoscopy %	Linguistic Translation Services No.	Linguistic Translation Services %	Endoscopic Ultrasound No.	Endoscopic Ultrasound %	Ablation of Barrett's Esophagus No.	Ablation of Barrett's Esophagus %	Esophageal Impedance Study No.	Esophageal Impedance Study %	ERCP No.	ERCP %	Optical Colonoscopy No.	Optical Colonoscopy %	Health Research No.	Health Research %	Immunization Program No.	Immunization Program %	Indigent Care Clinic No.	Indigent Care Clinic %
UNITED STATES	4,862	692	14.2	2,558	52.6	1,272	26.2	739	15.2	755	15.5	1,720	35.4	2,076	42.7	955	19.6	1,588	32.7	706	14.5
COMMUNITY HOSPITALS	4,186	671	16.0	2,359	56.4	1,213	29.0	712	17.0	726	17.3	1,665	39.8	1,973	47.1	877	21.0	1,464	35.0	681	16.3
CENSUS DIVISION 1, NEW ENGLAND	210	44	21.0	141	67.1	66	31.4	39	18.6	38	18.1	95	45.2	97	46.2	70	33.3	97	46.2	45	21.4
Connecticut	33	14	42.4	23	69.7	15	45.5	11	33.3	9	27.3	23	69.7	19	57.6	18	54.5	17	51.5	14	42.4
Maine	38	6	15.8	16	42.1	7	18.4	4	10.5	5	13.2	5	13.2	18	47.4	8	21.1	21	55.3	5	13.2
Massachusetts	81	19	23.5	65	80.2	23	28.4	13	16.0	15	18.5	35	43.2	30	37.0	27	33.3	33	40.7	11	13.6
New Hampshire	30	3	10.0	19	63.3	12	40.0	8	26.7	6	20.0	15	50.0	17	56.7	6	20.0	14	46.7	7	23.3
Rhode Island	13	0	0.0	9	69.2	5	38.5	1	7.7	1	7.7	8	61.5	4	30.8	7	53.8	7	53.8	5	38.5
Vermont	15	2	13.3	9	60.0	4	26.7	2	13.3	2	13.3	6	40.0	9	60.0	4	26.7	5	33.3	3	20.0
CENSUS DIVISION 2, MIDDLE ATLANTIC	398	94	23.6	269	67.6	164	41.2	84	21.1	89	22.4	233	58.5	210	52.8	141	35.4	202	50.8	140	35.2
New Jersey	73	12	16.4	57	78.1	41	56.2	25	34.2	23	31.5	49	67.1	37	50.7	33	45.2	37	50.7	44	60.3
New York	157	51	32.5	116	73.9	73	46.5	36	22.9	35	22.3	94	59.9	81	51.6	64	40.8	86	54.8	59	37.6
Pennsylvania	168	31	18.5	96	57.1	50	29.8	23	13.7	31	18.5	90	53.6	92	54.8	44	26.2	79	47.0	37	22.0
CENSUS DIVISION 3, SOUTH ATLANTIC	678	111	16.4	385	56.8	226	33.3	140	20.6	154	22.7	309	45.6	325	47.9	172	25.4	214	31.6	99	14.6
Delaware	8	1	12.5	6	75.0	2	25.0	2	25.0	2	25.0	4	50.0	4	50.0	3	37.5	3	37.5	2	25.0
District of Columbia	13	4	30.8	11	84.6	9	69.2	4	30.8	3	23.1	5	38.5	7	53.8	9	69.2	8	61.5	5	38.5
Florida	142	28	19.7	88	62.0	59	41.5	32	22.5	37	26.1	79	55.6	71	50.0	46	32.4	43	30.3	19	13.4
Georgia	122	9	7.4	67	54.9	43	35.2	21	17.2	27	22.1	46	37.7	49	40.2	24	19.7	26	21.3	13	10.7
Maryland	59	10	16.9	36	61.0	26	44.1	16	27.1	14	23.7	34	57.6	29	49.2	25	42.4	31	52.5	18	30.5
North Carolina	121	25	20.7	74	61.2	38	31.4	29	24.0	30	24.3	57	47.1	74	61.2	25	20.7	41	33.9	21	17.4
South Carolina	80	9	11.3	33	41.3	14	17.5	16	20.0	15	18.3	26	32.5	20	25.0	13	16.3	13	16.3	6	7.5
Virginia	70	14	20.0	46	65.7	22	31.4	13	18.6	18	25.7	37	52.9	40	57.1	18	25.7	23	32.9	8	11.4
West Virginia	63	11	17.5	24	38.1	13	20.6	7	11.1	8	12.7	21	33.3	31	49.2	9	14.3	26	41.3	7	11.1
CENSUS DIVISION 4, EAST NORTH CENTRAL	753	134	17.8	443	58.8	229	30.4	134	17.8	140	18.6	311	41.3	331	44.0	197	26.2	279	37.1	159	21.1
Illinois	173	43	24.9	107	61.8	55	31.8	41	23.7	35	20.2	94	54.3	82	47.4	53	30.6	61	35.3	33	19.1
Indiana	121	21	17.4	71	58.7	34	28.1	18	14.9	23	19.0	47	38.8	53	43.8	24	19.8	37	30.6	23	19.0
Michigan	158	22	13.9	102	64.6	57	36.1	23	14.6	23	14.6	60	38.0	80	50.6	50	31.6	80	50.6	37	23.4
Ohio	159	27	17.0	103	64.8	56	35.2	34	21.4	38	23.9	72	45.3	73	45.9	53	33.3	61	38.4	50	31.4
Wisconsin	142	21	14.8	60	42.3	27	19.0	18	12.7	21	14.8	38	26.8	43	30.3	17	12.0	40	28.2	16	11.3
CENSUS DIVISION 5, EAST SOUTH CENTRAL	424	36	8.5	154	36.3	71	16.7	43	10.1	55	13.0	115	27.1	131	30.9	47	11.1	63	14.9	26	6.1
Alabama	104	8	7.7	36	34.6	17	16.3	9	7.7	8	7.7	29	27.9	33	31.7	12	11.5	16	15.4	9	8.7
Kentucky	100	8	8.0	47	47.0	21	21.0	9	9.0	21	21.0	39	39.0	44	44.0	14	14.0	15	15.0	8	8.0
Mississippi	109	10	9.2	21	19.3	8	7.3	9	8.3	11	10.1	16	14.7	17	15.6	4	3.7	10	9.2	4	3.7
Tennessee	111	10	9.0	50	45.0	25	22.5	17	15.3	15	13.5	31	27.9	37	33.3	17	15.3	22	19.8	5	4.5
CENSUS DIVISION 6, WEST NORTH CENTRAL	693	87	12.6	311	44.9	105	15.2	54	7.8	65	9.4	135	19.5	305	44.0	81	11.7	246	35.5	52	7.5
Iowa	125	16	12.8	68	54.4	23	18.4	8	6.4	12	9.6	20	16.0	67	53.6	12	9.6	56	44.8	13	10.4
Kansas	153	16	10.5	50	32.7	15	9.8	10	6.5	11	7.2	21	13.7	60	39.2	8	5.2	31	20.3	5	3.3
Minnesota	116	23	19.8	53	45.7	22	19.0	9	7.8	12	10.3	23	19.8	53	45.7	17	14.7	44	37.9	9	7.8
Missouri	149	16	10.7	85	57.0	24	16.1	20	13.4	16	10.7	52	34.9	52	34.9	25	16.8	56	37.6	16	10.7
Nebraska	65	9	13.8	30	46.2	13	20.0	5	7.7	6	9.2	10	15.4	30	46.2	10	15.4	24	36.9	3	4.6
North Dakota	31	3	9.7	11	35.5	2	6.5	2	6.5	3	9.7	5	16.1	16	51.6	5	16.1	14	45.2	4	12.9
South Dakota	54	4	7.4	14	25.9	6	11.1	0	0.0	5	9.3	4	7.4	27	50.0	4	7.4	21	38.9	2	3.7
CENSUS DIVISION 7, WEST SOUTH CENTRAL	852	70	8.2	353	41.4	169	19.8	101	11.9	84	9.9	235	27.6	325	38.1	91	10.7	208	24.4	73	8.6
Arkansas	98	5	5.1	43	43.9	16	16.3	10	10.2	12	12.2	21	21.4	41	41.8	8	8.2	14	14.3	0	0.0
Louisiana	96	7	7.3	33	34.4	27	28.1	20	20.8	16	16.7	37	38.5	45	46.9	19	19.8	29	30.2	16	16.7
Oklahoma	116	8	6.9	33	28.4	15	12.9	9	7.8	8	6.9	25	21.6	33	28.4	10	8.6	24	20.7	9	7.8
Texas	542	50	9.2	244	45.2	111	20.5	32	11.4	48	8.9	152	28.0	206	38.0	54	10.0	141	26.0	48	8.9
CENSUS DIVISION 8, MOUNTAIN	347	43	12.4	192	55.3	92	26.5	45	13.0	57	16.4	105	30.3	168	48.4	55	15.9	108	31.1	37	10.7
Arizona	59	8	13.6	42	71.2	22	37.3	14	23.7	10	16.9	29	49.2	27	45.8	18	30.5	18	30.5	8	13.6
Colorado	66	7	10.6	40	60.5	22	33.3	10	15.2	13	19.7	28	42.4	37	56.1	12	18.2	14	21.2	10	15.2
Idaho	34	2	5.9	18	52.9	8	23.5	4	11.8	7	20.6	8	23.5	17	50.0	3	8.8	11	32.4	1	2.9
Montana	59	10	16.9	16	27.1	7	11.9	2	3.4	5	8.5	7	11.9	24	40.7	5	8.5	24	40.7	5	8.5
Nevada	29	3	10.3	17	58.5	6	20.7	3	10.3	3	10.3	11	37.9	11	37.9	7	24.1	11	37.9	3	10.3
New Mexico	36	2	5.6	24	66.7	8	22.2	4	11.1	4	11.1	6	16.7	19	52.8	3	8.3	14	38.9	4	11.1
Utah	33	4	12.1	19	57.3	9	27.3	6	18.2	10	30.3	13	39.4	20	60.6	7	21.2	9	27.3	4	12.1
Wyoming	31	7	22.6	16	51.5	10	32.3	2	6.5	5	16.1	3	9.7	13	41.9	0	0.0	7	22.6	2	6.5
CENSUS DIVISION 9, PACIFIC	507	73	14.4	310	61.1	150	29.6	99	19.5	73	14.4	182	35.9	184	36.3	101	19.9	171	33.7	75	14.8
Alaska	14	3	21.4	10	71.4	4	28.6	1	7.1	0	0.0	2	14.3	4	28.6	3	21.4	5	35.7	1	7.1
California	334	48	14.4	203	60.3	96	28.7	69	20.7	55	16.5	128	38.3	112	33.5	74	22.2	117	35.0	53	15.9
Hawaii	20	2	10.0	9	45.0	3	15.0	2	10.0	0	0.0	6	30.0	3	15.0	0	0.0	1	5.0	1	5.0
Oregon	57	10	17.5	40	70.2	25	43.9	12	21.1	6	10.5	18	31.6	38	66.7	8	14.0	21	36.8	9	15.8
Washington	82	10	12.2	48	58.5	22	26.8	15	18.3	12	14.6	28	34.1	27	32.9	16	19.5	27	32.9	11	13.4

Facilities and Services

Table 8

Table		Page

MSAs

Metropolitan Statistical Areas

Metropolitan Statistical Areas (MSAs) definitions announced by the U.S. Office of Management and Budget (OMB) effective June 6, 2003 were recently added with the 2006 edition.

According to the OMB, an MSA is a geographical designation that represents an integrated social and economic unit with a large population nucleus. Under these standards, an area qualifies for recognition as an MSA if there is a city within the area of at least 50,000 with a total metropolitan population of at least 100,000. MSAs are defined as entire counties. In addition to the county containing the main city, an MSA also includes additional counties having strong economic and social ties to the central county. Such counties must have a specified level of commuting to the central counties and must meet certain standards regarding metropolitan character, such as population density.

When an MSA encompasses two or more central cities, up to three cities may be specified in the MSA title. They will be listed in order of population size. When a single central city exists, the MSA is named for that particular city. A MSA may extend beyond a single state.

An MSA containing a single core with a population of 2.5 million or more may be subdivided to form smaller groupings of counties referred to as Metropolitan Divisions. Where they exist the Metropolitan Divisions are shown in this table rather than the entire MSA.

TABLE 8

U.S. CENSUS DIVISION 1, NEW ENGLAND

U.S. Community Hospitals
(Nonfederal, short-term general and other special hospitals)

2008 Utilization, Personnel and Finances

| | | | | | | | | | | NEWBORNS | | OUTPATIENT VISITS | |
CLASSIFICATION	Hospitals	Beds	Admissions	Inpatient Days	Adjusted Patient Days	Average Daily Census	Adjusted Average Daily Census	Average Stay (days)	Surgical Operations	Bassinets	Births	Emergency	Total
UNITED STATES	5,010	808,069	35,760,750	196,078,468	351,559,836	536,215	961,620	5.5	27,459,438	57,301	4,073,724	123,024,024	624,098,296
Nonmetropolitan	1,998	143,524	4,592,673	29,262,322	70,831,752	80,001	193,693	6.4	4,175,758	11,324	491,044	23,469,370	119,205,443
Metropolitan	3,012	664,545	31,168,077	166,816,146	280,728,084	456,214	767,927	5.4	23,283,680	45,977	3,582,680	99,554,654	504,892,853
CENSUS DIVISION 1, NEW ENGLAND	200	33,743	1,660,654	8,992,337	18,977,091	24,567	51,854	5.4	1,453,639	2,652	163,857	6,848,347	44,036,614
Nonmetropolitan	58	3,957	158,086	947,530	2,697,940	2,589	7,369	6.0	189,808	435	15,242	1,044,800	7,448,951
Metropolitan	142	29,786	1,502,568	8,044,807	16,279,151	21,978	44,485	5.4	1,263,831	2,217	148,615	5,803,547	36,587,663
Connecticut	35	7,906	400,632	2,296,558	3,903,365	6,277	10,668	5.7	300,155	525	40,963	1,524,545	8,074,634
Nonmetropolitan	5	387	22,429	94,921	216,561	260	592	4.2	19,159	56	1,962	143,058	902,914
Metropolitan	30	7,519	378,203	2,201,637	3,686,804	6,017	10,076	5.8	280,996	469	39,001	1,381,487	7,171,720
Bridgeport-Stamford-Norwalk	6	1,717	94,019	471,048	828,673	1,287	2,264	5.0	68,707	146	12,450	279,991	1,768,344
Hartford-West Hartford-East Hartford	12	2,720	137,225	813,809	1,391,392	2,223	3,804	5.9	103,555	136	13,155	503,339	3,454,118
New Haven-Milford	10	2,646	122,528	801,001	1,194,989	2,190	3,266	6.5	84,809	145	10,645	455,976	1,372,661
Norwich-New London	2	436	24,431	115,779	271,750	317	742	4.7	23,925	42	2,751	142,181	576,597
Maine	37	3,504	148,635	845,428	1,923,863	2,310	5,258	5.7	175,520	312	13,489	780,874	5,093,378
Nonmetropolitan	22	1,320	47,618	299,425	831,882	818	2,272	6.3	68,935	153	4,498	370,457	2,394,805
Metropolitan	15	2,184	101,017	546,003	1,091,981	1,492	2,986	5.4	106,585	159	8,991	410,417	2,698,573
Bangor	4	483	25,791	125,631	238,634	343	653	4.9	29,594	26	1,875	79,671	691,766
Lewiston-Auburn	2	361	15,531	79,023	164,976	216	450	5.1	11,286	46	1,504	78,516	606,879
Portland-South Portland-Biddeford	9	1,340	59,695	341,349	688,371	933	1,883	5.7	65,705	87	5,612	252,230	1,399,928
Massachusetts	75	15,710	808,489	4,190,441	9,059,795	11,449	24,755	5.2	668,494	1,242	77,002	3,119,580	20,459,758
Nonmetropolitan	2	44	1,751	7,007	32,605	20	89	4.0	1,937	10	329	35,560	84,686
Metropolitan	73	15,666	806,738	4,183,434	9,027,190	11,429	24,666	5.2	666,557	1,232	76,673	3,084,020	20,375,072
Barnstable Town	2	338	22,284	91,636	211,901	251	579	4.1	14,121	18	1,563	123,658	821,721
Boston-Cambridge-Quincy.	45	10,467	548,042	2,836,825	6,091,548	7,751	16,645	5.2	454,139	819	51,944	1,824,847	12,953,810
Pittsfield.	3	365	16,833	88,330	224,139	242	612	5.2	20,167	30	1,163	93,344	585,307
Providence-New Bedford-Fall River.	4	1,153	55,250	304,974	717,010	833	1,959	5.5	46,648	109	5,174	311,212	1,397,865
Springfield	10	1,673	78,881	427,996	885,366	1,168	2,419	5.4	60,289	116	7,842	353,998	2,382,115
Worcester.	9	1,670	85,448	433,673	897,226	1,184	2,452	5.1	71,193	140	8,987	376,961	2,234,254
New Hampshire	28	2,858	124,184	664,659	1,732,317	1,813	4,732	5.4	126,342	305	13,636	623,814	4,468,523
Nonmetropolitan	17	1,379	57,698	342,098	960,757	934	2,624	5.9	63,345	130	5,181	277,122	2,410,237
Metropolitan	11	1,479	66,486	322,561	771,560	879	2,108	4.9	62,997	175	8,455	346,692	2,058,286
Manchester-Nashua	5	851	38,603	185,517	446,174	506	1,219	4.8	27,892	105	5,501	180,669	1,148,176
Rockingham County-Strafford County	6	628	27,883	137,044	325,386	373	889	4.9	35,105	70	2,954	166,023	910,110
Rhode Island	11	2,463	127,413	666,745	1,285,438	1,821	3,512	5.2	121,567	147	12,785	494,817	2,634,226
Metropolitan	11	2,463	127,413	666,745	1,285,438	1,821	3,512	5.2	121,567	147	12,785	494,817	2,634,226
Providence-New Bedford-Fall River.	11	2,463	127,413	666,745	1,285,438	1,821	3,512	5.2	121,567	147	12,785	494,817	2,634,226
Vermont	14	1,302	51,301	328,506	1,072,313	897	2,929	6.4	61,561	121	5,982	304,717	3,306,095
Nonmetropolitan	12	827	28,590	204,079	656,135	557	1,792	7.1	36,432	86	3,272	218,603	1,656,309
Metropolitan	2	475	22,711	124,427	416,178	340	1,137	5.5	25,129	35	2,710	86,114	1,649,786
Burlington-South Burlington.	2	475	22,711	124,427	416,178	340	1,137	5.5	25,129	35	2,710	86,114	1,649,786

TABLE 8

U.S. CENSUS DIVISION 1, NEW ENGLAND

U.S. Community Hospitals
(Nonfederal, short-term general and other special hospitals)

2008 Utilization, Personnel and Finances

FULL-TIME EQUIVALENT PERSONNEL					FULL-TIME EQUIV. TRAINEES			EXPENSES						
								LABOR				TOTAL		
Physicians and Dentists	Registered Nurses	Licensed Practical Nurses	Other Salaried Personnel	Total Personnel	Medical and Dental Residents	Other Trainees	Total Trainees	Payroll (in thousands)	Employee Benefits (in thousands)	Total (in thousands)	Percent of Total	Amount (in thousands)	Adjusted per Admission	Adjusted per Inpatient Day
95,400	1,228,383	104,562	3,121,215	4,549,560	90,543	9,573	100,116	$256,559,486	$65,376,486	$321,935,957	51.4	$626,576,958	$9,788.25	$1,782.28
12,071	149,214	30,278	467,807	659,370	1,535	394	1,929	30,769,205	8,096,158	38,865,353	53.4	72,719,071	6,539.38	1,026.65
83,329	1,079,169	74,284	2,653,408	3,890,190	89,008	9,179	98,187	225,790,281	57,280,329	283,070,604	51.1	553,857,887	10,471.29	1,972.93
11,188	63,279	2,861	191,965	269,293	8,182	1,187	9,369	16,735,405	4,151,740	20,887,149	52.6	39,734,569	11,038.15	2,093.82
1,481	7,104	641	24,386	33,612	389	18	407	1,960,694	542,688	2,503,383	57.2	4,379,408	9,739.44	1,623.24
9,707	56,175	2,220	167,579	235,681	7,793	1,169	8,962	14,774,711	3,609,051	18,383,766	52.0	35,355,161	11,223.53	2,171.81
1,278	13,498	533	37,114	52,423	1,459	248	1,707	3,498,449	920,446	4,418,894	55.9	7,906,959	10,900.18	2,025.68
59	682	78	1,874	2,693	3	2	5	179,588	49,019	228,607	53.8	424,735	8,135.13	1,961.27
1,219	12,816	455	35,240	49,730	1,456	246	1,702	3,318,861	871,427	4,190,287	56.0	7,482,224	11,114.63	2,029.46
303	2,606	52	8,002	10,963	372	11	383	828,661	214,079	1,042,741	54.1	1,927,008	11,468.44	2,325.41
447	4,637	183	14,505	19,772	140	179	319	1,232,765	334,902	1,567,667	57.6	2,722,724	10,859.32	1,956.83
409	4,914	175	10,259	15,757	944	55	999	1,035,000	266,149	1,301,148	55.2	2,356,134	11,956.61	1,971.68
60	659	45	2,474	3,238	0	1	1	222,434	56,296	278,731	58.5	476,358	8,302.38	1,752.93
1,283	6,397	315	20,418	28,413	283	3	286	1,519,474	371,516	1,890,989	53.8	3,516,496	10,315.97	1,827.83
453	2,161	158	8,394	11,166	1	2	3	559,655	137,280	696,935	54.7	1,273,572	9,278.06	1,530.95
830	4,236	157	12,024	17,247	282	1	283	959,819	234,237	1,194,054	53.2	2,242,925	11,015.68	2,054.00
229	1,247	44	2,832	4,352	26	0	26	257,797	65,747	323,544	51.1	632,629	12,269.52	2,651.04
219	738	44	2,159	3,160	21	0	21	149,142	31,248	180,390	48.6	371,257	11,464.91	2,250.37
382	2,251	69	7,033	9,735	235	1	236	552,879	137,242	690,120	55.7	1,239,039	10,353.89	1,799.96
6,445	31,469	1,263	95,954	135,131	4,938	849	5,787	8,299,209	1,932,802	10,232,015	49.3	20,772,340	11,574.41	2,292.81
7	78	10	281	376	0	1	1	31,416	8,121	39,537	51.0	77,573	7,549.66	2,379.17
6,438	31,391	1,253	95,673	134,755	4,938	848	5,786	8,267,793	1,924,681	10,192,478	49.3	20,694,775	11,597.59	2,292.49
51	539	12	1,426	2,028	0	3	3	194,731	56,438	251,169	51.9	483,910	9,377.56	2,203.00
5,320	22,918	787	68,084	97,109	4,006	835	4,841	5,080,054	1,965,400	7,045,400	40.0	15,287,391	12,650.39	2,509.61
63	636	47	1,956	2,702	64	0	64	179,234	47,137	226,371	57.6	392,929	9,051.78	1,753.06
66	1,663	93	5,226	7,048	5	0	5	471,649	115,481	587,132	61.1	960,420	7,330.89	1,339.48
92	2,391	100	8,208	10,791	306	5	311	672,711	154,259	826,972	53.4	1,547,470	9,235.92	1,747.83
846	3,244	214	10,773	15,077	557	5	562	769,413	185,935	955,348	47.2	2,022,656	11,090.34	2,254.34
885	5,731	301	18,763	25,680	387	12	399	1,483,970	426,943	1,910,911	57.4	3,330,628	10,332.85	1,922.64
678	3,004	182	9,562	13,426	384	12	396	848,458	250,417	1,098,874	59.6	1,842,875	11,612.98	1,918.15
207	2,727	119	9,201	12,254	3	0	3	635,512	176,526	812,037	54.6	1,487,753	9,091.45	1,928.24
146	1,505	65	5,589	7,305	0	0	0	350,856	102,915	453,770	56.8	798,625	8,509.96	1,789.94
61	1,222	54	3,612	4,949	3	0	3	284,656	73,611	358,267	52.0	689,128	9,873.31	2,117.88
566	3,874	152	11,914	16,506	831	6	837	1,197,426	308,554	1,505,982	56.8	2,649,566	10,670.09	2,061.22
566	3,874	152	11,914	16,506	831	6	837	1,197,426	308,554	1,505,982	56.8	2,649,566	10,670.09	2,061.22
566	3,874	152	11,914	16,506	831	6	837	1,197,426	308,554	1,505,982	56.8	2,649,566	10,670.09	2,061.22
731	2,310	297	7,802	11,140	284	69	353	736,878	191,479	928,358	59.6	1,558,573	9,269.22	1,453.47
284	1,179	213	4,275	5,951	1	1	2	341,576	97,853	439,430	57.8	760,653	8,339.22	1,159.29
447	1,131	84	3,527	5,189	283	68	351	395,302	93,626	488,928	61.3	797,920	10,371.89	1,917.26
447	1,131	84	3,527	5,189	283	68	351	395,302	93,626	488,928	61.3	797,920	10,371.89	1,917.26

MSAs

TABLE **8**

U.S. CENSUS DIVISION 2, MIDDLE ATLANTIC

U.S. Community Hospitals
(Nonfederal, short-term general and other special hospitals)

2008 Utilization, Personnel and Finances

CLASSIFICATION	Hospitals	Beds	Admissions	Inpatient Days	Adjusted Patient Days	Average Daily Census	Adjusted Average Daily Census	Average Stay (days)	Surgical Operations	NEWBORNS Bassinets	Births	OUTPATIENT VISITS Emergency	Total
UNITED STATES	5,010	808,069	35,760,750	196,078,468	351,559,836	536,215	961,620	5.5	27,459,438	57,301	4,073,724	123,024,024	624,098,296
Nonmetropolitan	1,998	143,524	4,592,673	29,262,322	70,831,752	80,001	193,693	6.4	4,175,758	11,324	491,044	23,469,370	119,205,443
Metropolitan	3,012	664,545	31,168,077	166,816,146	280,728,084	456,214	767,927	5.4	23,283,680	45,977	3,582,680	99,554,654	504,892,853
CENSUS DIVISION 2, MIDDLE ATLANTIC.	468	122,511	5,516,053	33,922,806	56,116,097	92,722	153,401	6.1	4,142,531	6,847	493,580	17,471,705	109,165,950
Nonmetropolitan	89	12,267	372,685	2,828,829	6,414,734	7,732	17,535	7.6	406,384	702	30,159	1,887,947	12,725,215
Metropolitan	379	110,244	5,143,368	31,093,977	49,701,363	84,990	135,866	6.0	3,736,147	6,145	463,421	15,583,758	96,440,735
New Jersey	73	20,867	1,086,445	5,595,966	7,946,820	15,285	21,718	5.2	633,652	1,455	107,580	3,350,786	18,139,915
Metropolitan	73	20,867	1,086,445	5,595,966	7,946,820	15,285	21,718	5.2	633,652	1,455	107,580	3,350,786	18,139,915
Allentown-Bethlehem-Easton	2	261	11,792	49,914	91,768	136	251	4.2	16,193	12	1,037	52,720	204,870
Atlantic City	3	855	43,830	213,408	319,299	582	872	4.9	15,556	56	3,811	125,744	384,003
Camden.	10	2,799	146,629	712,402	1,000,804	1,946	2,736	4.9	87,669	134	14,148	502,343	1,459,255
Edison.	17	5,047	266,701	1,391,884	1,872,623	3,802	5,116	5.2	145,136	392	27,602	792,089	2,489,517
New York-White Plains-Wayne. . .	13	4,215	246,548	1,142,285	1,606,533	3,122	4,393	4.6	127,229	344	24,272	646,418	7,460,707
Newark-Union	18	5,541	272,619	1,555,425	2,182,925	4,248	5,964	5.7	169,509	345	27,231	860,847	4,345,412
Ocean City	1	208	10,493	41,871	62,079	114	170	4.0	4,795	16	523	44,442	141,775
Trenton-Ewing	6	1,376	61,280	360,432	585,384	984	1,600	5.9	44,854	108	5,973	203,143	1,324,366
Vineland-Millville-Bridgeton	2	455	21,083	108,318	193,575	296	529	5.1	18,765	32	2,585	97,433	266,244
Wilmington	1	110	5,470	20,027	31,830	55	87	3.7	3,946	16	398	25,607	63,766
New York	194	61,237	2,528,191	17,973,047	29,896,760	49,137	81,736	7.1	2,001,109	3,317	242,326	8,114,078	52,569,640
Nonmetropolitan	40	6,315	149,427	1,542,750	3,437,103	4,218	9,397	10.3	190,045	317	13,730	749,884	5,830,590
Metropolitan	154	54,922	2,378,764	16,430,297	26,459,657	44,919	72,339	6.9	1,811,064	3,000	228,596	7,364,194	46,739,050
Albany-Schenectady-Troy	9	2,719	107,209	673,730	1,142,169	1,842	3,122	6.3	74,988	67	9,568	313,004	2,130,614
Binghamton	2	610	27,072	153,026	393,187	418	1,074	5.7	35,970	41	2,745	95,223	1,710,667
Buffalo-Niagara Falls.	12	4,923	151,305	1,603,505	2,591,611	4,384	7,088	10.6	158,093	269	13,191	532,795	3,158,433
Elmira	2	496	17,024	136,604	285,430	374	781	8.0	12,681	20	1,343	69,802	470,283
Glens Falls.	1	335	14,676	91,969	146,308	252	401	6.3	13,716	20	1,230	124,787	667,292
Ithaca	1	209	6,960	33,907	87,701	93	240	4.9	6,718	19	823	28,022	221,937
Kingston	3	354	14,237	81,283	134,728	222	368	5.7	7,589	31	756	51,773	264,562
Nassau-Suffolk	25	8,549	415,931	2,690,800	4,030,455	7,356	11,022	6.5	322,098	502	36,708	1,027,983	5,570,825
New York-White Plains-Wayne. . .	69	29,247	1,312,922	8,883,538	13,802,127	24,285	37,732	6.8	918,882	1,530	131,211	4,000,615	23,133,908
Poughkeepsie-Newburgh-Middletown	7	1,616	75,158	407,693	660,055	1,116	1,803	5.4	54,671	87	6,930	258,209	956,809
Rochester.	11	3,129	118,617	899,992	1,743,323	2,460	4,764	7.6	115,199	217	12,720	514,927	5,884,789
Syracuse	7	1,773	79,196	493,694	858,991	1,350	2,350	6.2	60,156	125	7,938	231,844	1,543,628
Utica-Rome.	5	962	38,457	280,556	583,572	767	1,594	7.3	30,303	72	3,433	115,210	1,025,303
Pennsylvania	201	40,407	1,901,417	10,353,793	18,272,517	28,300	49,947	5.4	1,507,770	2,075	143,674	6,006,841	38,456,395
Nonmetropolitan	49	5,952	223,258	1,286,079	2,977,631	3,514	8,138	5.8	216,339	385	16,429	1,138,063	6,894,625
Metropolitan	152	34,455	1,678,159	9,067,714	15,294,886	24,786	41,809	5.4	1,291,431	1,690	127,245	4,868,778	31,561,770
Allentown-Bethlehem-Easton	8	2,157	111,459	600,567	1,012,504	1,641	2,766	5.4	77,198	93	9,089	371,357	1,805,562
Altoona	4	573	24,835	128,361	248,016	351	678	5.2	23,758	30	1,883	78,233	568,312
Erie	7	1,159	44,412	226,086	370,702	618	1,013	5.1	29,443	57	3,700	149,094	607,308
Harrisburg-Carlisle	9	1,764	86,516	464,691	754,723	1,271	2,064	5.4	71,201	74	7,830	240,988	1,550,508
Johnstown	4	783	34,312	193,036	336,409	529	921	5.6	34,386	30	1,874	119,417	630,276
Lancaster.	4	1,113	53,280	277,983	496,751	760	1,358	5.2	61,726	67	6,368	180,402	2,014,331
Lebanon	1	180	10,405	49,603	84,940	136	232	4.8	11,460	19	988	54,263	256,246
Philadelphia	46	12,626	665,417	3,512,858	5,440,454	9,600	14,872	5.3	471,078	690	51,234	1,747,938	9,792,495
Pittsburgh.	40	9,227	426,866	2,415,643	4,040,942	6,601	11,046	5.7	340,313	377	25,209	1,160,900	8,260,197
Reading.	3	960	40,242	224,795	394,805	615	1,079	5.6	30,016	55	4,463	144,658	1,255,306
Scranton--Wilkes-Barre	13	1,816	85,762	469,140	888,943	1,283	2,430	5.5	49,474	70	6,230	266,248	1,984,381
State College	2	288	16,365	66,268	113,618	182	310	4.0	9,472	5	1,347	47,926	207,800
Williamsport	4	434	13,914	109,967	383,425	301	1,048	7.9	32,035	22	1,184	80,364	709,297
York-Hanover	4	837	42,486	213,262	444,615	583	1,215	5.0	32,457	72	4,573	143,141	1,241,208
Youngstown-Warren-Boardman . .	3	538	21,888	115,454	284,039	315	777	5.3	17,414	29	1,273	83,849	678,543

TABLE 8

U.S. CENSUS DIVISION 2, MIDDLE ATLANTIC

U.S. Community Hospitals
(Nonfederal, short-term general and other special hospitals)

2008 Utilization, Personnel and Finances

FULL-TIME EQUIVALENT PERSONNEL					FULL-TIME EQUIV. TRAINEES			EXPENSES						
								LABOR				TOTAL		
Physicians and Dentists	Registered Nurses	Licensed Practical Nurses	Other Salaried Personnel	Total Personnel	Medical and Dental Residents	Other Trainees	Total Trainees	Payroll (in thousands)	Employee Benefits (in thousands)	Total (in thousands)	Percent of Total	Amount (in thousands)	Adjusted per Admission	Adjusted per Inpatient Day
95,400	1,228,383	104,562	3,121,215	4,549,560	90,543	9,573	100,116	$256,559,486	$65,376,486	$321,935,957	51.4	$626,576,958	$9,788.25	$1,782.28
12,071	149,214	30,278	467,807	659,370	1,535	394	1,929	30,769,205	8,096,158	38,865,353	53.4	72,719,071	6,539.38	1,026.65
83,329	1,079,169	74,284	2,653,408	3,890,190	89,008	9,179	98,187	225,790,281	57,280,329	283,070,604	51.1	553,857,887	10,471.29	1,972.93
22,295	184,400	13,095	499,301	719,091	25,644	1,268	26,912	43,068,318	11,252,955	54,321,267	53.6	101,341,326	11,146.70	1,805.92
1,428	12,114	2,418	38,455	54,415	496	32	528	2,532,982	647,012	3,179,988	53.1	5,991,641	6,877.28	934.04
20,867	172,286	10,677	460,846	664,676	25,148	1,236	26,384	40,535,336	10,605,942	51,141,279	53.6	95,349,685	11,599.19	1,918.45
2,103	32,111	1,160	81,416	116,790	2,551	31	2,582	7,516,747	1,768,929	9,285,675	54.3	17,087,597	11,107.05	2,150.24
2,103	32,111	1,160	81,416	116,790	2,551	31	2,582	7,516,747	1,768,929	9,285,675	54.3	17,087,597	11,107.05	2,150.24
12	399	33	1,476	1,920	21	0	21	82,612	18,934	101,546	51.9	195,755	9,116.75	2,133.15
81	1,367	45	3,700	5,193	40	0	40	315,483	94,822	410,305	57.0	720,146	11,168.01	2,255.40
505	4,288	108	10,752	15,653	305	1	306	909,333	226,665	1,135,998	48.7	2,333,075	11,347.75	2,331.20
250	7,311	258	16,641	24,460	538	3	541	1,676,163	392,024	2,068,187	52.5	3,941,712	11,064.05	2,104.91
484	6,706	154	18,960	26,304	480	7	487	1,692,084	364,733	2,056,817	56.7	3,630,129	10,409.42	2,259.60
607	9,124	322	21,780	31,833	1,098	14	1,112	2,165,606	504,942	2,670,547	56.5	4,727,612	12,314.66	2,165.72
0	248	5	624	877	0	6	6	43,846	16,802	60,648	55.2	109,954	7,067.82	1,771.19
152	1,993	107	5,351	7,603	68	0	68	466,872	100,475	567,347	54.2	1,047,631	10,779.09	1,789.65
11	546	112	1,866	2,535	0	0	0	142,520	44,628	187,148	57.7	324,476	8,877.11	1,676.23
1	120	16	266	412	1	0	1	22,228	4,904	27,132	47.5	57,108	6,568.65	1,794.15
13,502	87,952	6,739	253,225	361,418	15,635	484	16,119	23,186,662	6,420,174	29,606,835	55.9	52,930,512	12,597.81	1,770.44
704	4,980	1,055	17,715	24,454	142	11	153	1,186,787	283,023	1,469,808	57.6	2,551,060	7,153.86	742.21
12,798	82,972	5,684	235,510	336,964	15,493	473	15,966	21,999,875	6,137,151	28,137,027	55.9	50,379,452	13,102.70	1,904.01
383	3,916	285	10,518	15,102	360	27	387	727,630	150,217	877,846	51.0	1,721,239	9,436.87	1,506.99
88	972	87	3,172	4,319	78	0	78	233,498	71,903	305,401	53.0	576,127	7,865.76	1,465.28
378	5,940	454	15,974	22,746	355	64	419	1,199,629	362,542	1,562,171	54.6	2,859,793	11,781.20	1,103.48
101	686	73	1,747	2,607	10	1	11	132,386	36,290	168,677	57.0	296,116	7,962.89	1,037.44
57	733	48	1,867	2,705	33	3	36	107,172	26,761	133,933	51.0	262,466	11,241.94	1,793.92
5	277	5	666	953	0	0	0	45,161	15,390	60,550	51.4	117,748	6,540.81	1,342.60
3	442	44	1,090	1,579	6	0	6	70,720	16,202	87,000	50.7	102,247	7,034.99	1,352.70
3,465	13,591	574	32,690	50,320	2,140	22	2,162	3,627,084	989,349	4,616,434	58.3	7,923,921	12,690.84	1,966.01
7,125	44,984	2,736	136,485	191,330	11,327	299	11,626	13,436,459	3,805,343	17,241,802	66.8	30,010,707	14,973.26	2,240.22
61	2,288	104	5,739	8,192	4	0	4	458,501	134,189	592,691	54.9	1,080,200	8,827.55	1,636.53
935	5,192	682	14,279	21,088	749	46	795	1,092,414	286,415	1,378,829	57.5	2,399,659	10,751.02	1,376.49
125	2,618	334	7,396	10,473	400	11	411	605,313	174,877	780,191	53.3	1,463,795	10,952.20	1,704.09
72	1,333	258	3,887	5,550	32	0	32	254,901	65,672	320,572	55.6	576,345	7,626.34	987.62
6,690	64,337	5,196	164,660	240,883	7,458	753	8,211	12,364,909	3,063,852	15,428,757	49.3	31,323,217	9,345.79	1,714.23
724	7,134	1,363	20,740	29,961	354	21	375	1,346,195	363,989	1,710,180	49.7	3,440,581	6,685.62	1,155.48
5,966	57,203	3,833	143,920	210,922	7,104	732	7,836	11,018,714	2,699,863	13,718,577	49.2	27,882,636	9,828.34	1,823.00
455	4,439	179	9,459	14,532	396	26	422	696,601	181,332	877,933	47.1	1,862,611	10,424.81	1,839.61
35	833	102	1,778	2,748	19	0	19	141,947	37,702	179,648	50.5	355,943	7,026.54	1,435.16
107	1,672	108	3,631	5,518	60	8	68	238,428	63,495	301,923	47.5	635,663	8,692.47	1,714.75
650	3,080	338	9,385	13,453	646	275	921	641,183	163,128	804,310	52.8	1,522,697	10,900.15	2,017.56
34	1,130	137	3,293	4,594	89	1	90	195,283	49,677	244,960	49.7	492,504	8,179.37	1,464.00
141	2,025	224	5,664	8,054	55	2	57	429,388	104,679	534,067	52.1	1,024,427	10,473.32	2,062.25
8	196	60	907	1,171	0	0	0	52,962	14,377	67,340	47.5	141,657	7,950.21	1,667.73
2,838	22,493	882	52,586	78,799	4,380	315	4,695	4,920,257	1,158,692	6,078,950	51.0	11,909,773	11,461.86	2,189.11
1,162	14,454	716	37,591	53,923	1,198	98	1,296	2,338,397	552,080	2,890,480	44.8	6,451,953	8,848.15	1,596.65
239	1,468	222	4,233	6,162	78	0	78	307,478	88,804	396,282	52.3	758,287	10,662.37	1,920.66
173	2,268	427	6,789	9,657	21	0	21	439,645	117,180	556,824	47.2	1,178,668	7,237.66	1,325.92
4	353	38	959	1,354	0	0	0	69,692	17,125	86,817	52.8	164,376	5,887.60	1,446.74
31	613	114	1,647	2,405	0	0	0	110,208	26,838	137,046	49.2	278,626	6,152.03	726.68
57	1,460	197	4,045	5,759	158	0	158	321,120	87,117	408,238	50.6	806,745	9,015.83	1,814.48
32	719	89	1,953	2,793	4	7	11	116,125	37,635	153,759	51.5	298,707	5,527.31	1,051.64

MSAs

TABLE 8   U.S. CENSUS DIVISION 3, SOUTH ATLANTIC

U.S. Community Hospitals
(Nonfederal, short-term general and other special hospitals)

2008 Utilization, Personnel and Finances

CLASSIFICATION	Hospitals	Beds	Admissions	Inpatient Days	Adjusted Patient Days	Average Daily Census	Adjusted Average Daily Census	Average Stay (days)	Surgical Operations	NEWBORNS Bassinets	Births	OUTPATIENT VISITS Emergency	Total
UNITED STATES	5,010	808,069	35,760,750	196,078,468	351,559,836	536,215	961,620	5.5	27,459,438	57,301	4,073,724	123,024,024	624,098,296
Nonmetropolitan	1,998	143,524	4,592,673	29,262,322	70,831,752	80,001	193,693	6.4	4,175,758	11,324	491,044	23,469,370	119,205,443
Metropolitan	3,012	664,545	31,168,077	166,816,146	280,728,084	456,214	767,927	5.4	23,283,680	45,977	3,582,680	99,554,654	504,892,853
CENSUS DIVISION 3, SOUTH ATLANTIC	762	156,622	6,958,360	38,331,279	66,729,193	105,023	182,752	5.5	5,350,751	10,267	764,298	24,482,937	94,321,097
Nonmetropolitan	246	25,484	860,988	5,396,517	11,846,016	14,766	32,431	6.3	739,150	1,805	85,550	4,603,025	16,871,099
Metropolitan	516	131,138	6,097,372	32,934,762	54,883,177	90,257	150,321	5.4	4,611,601	8,462	678,748	19,879,912	77,449,998
Delaware	7	2,071	103,726	613,049	1,037,854	1,674	2,835	5.9	91,188	97	12,536	363,979	1,681,076
Nonmetropolitan	2	382	14,994	100,930	208,385	275	569	6.7	10,469	28	2,007	78,479	478,400
Metropolitan	5	1,689	88,732	512,119	829,469	1,399	2,266	5.8	80,719	69	10,529	285,500	1,202,676
Dover	1	331	17,629	95,291	172,549	260	471	5.4	14,278	20	2,454	63,668	412,089
Wilmington	4	1,358	71,103	416,828	656,920	1,139	1,795	5.9	66,441	49	8,075	221,832	790,587
District of Columbia	10	3,358	137,260	954,416	1,442,552	2,608	3,943	7.0	108,915	199	14,901	436,918	2,356,063
Metropolitan	10	3,358	137,260	954,416	1,442,552	2,608	3,943	7.0	108,915	199	14,901	436,918	2,356,063
Washington-Arlington-Alexandria	10	3,358	137,260	954,416	1,442,552	2,608	3,943	7.0	108,915	199	14,901	436,918	2,356,063
Florida	211	52,836	2,396,691	12,192,327	19,236,080	33,563	52,888	5.1	1,505,788	2,736	218,035	7,161,108	24,429,940
Nonmetropolitan	30	2,009	89,986	379,588	785,270	1,040	2,146	4.2	64,116	118	5,576	443,943	1,531,092
Metropolitan	181	50,827	2,306,705	11,812,739	18,450,810	32,523	50,742	5.1	1,441,672	2,618	212,459	6,717,165	22,898,848
Cape Coral-Fort Myers	5	2,310	104,760	527,004	848,239	1,444	2,324	5.0	65,971	119	9,237	259,524	1,638,356
Deltona-Daytona Beach-Ormond Beach	5	1,363	61,803	292,655	480,296	800	1,313	4.7	37,126	46	4,456	275,401	705,437
Fort Lauderdale-Pompano Beach-Deerfield Beach	17	4,943	238,586	1,171,054	1,866,773	3,201	5,101	4.9	134,701	265	24,193	782,509	2,156,539
Fort Walton Beach-Crestview-Destin	3	432	20,202	93,057	138,560	254	378	4.6	13,218	32	2,012	75,905	193,266
Gainesville	3	1,057	53,751	321,503	450,183	878	1,230	6.0	44,291	38	5,296	91,412	763,798
Jacksonville	12	3,317	159,181	867,560	1,408,007	2,430	3,943	5.5	127,370	267	15,110	497,074	1,707,726
Lakeland	5	1,693	74,142	346,525	527,736	946	1,443	4.7	41,090	51	6,613	258,437	651,557
Miami-Miami Beach-Kendall	26	8,235	321,845	1,804,811	2,715,449	5,100	7,625	5.6	172,683	283	26,995	808,696	2,988,283
Naples-Marco Island	2	751	35,239	166,760	226,522	455	619	4.7	14,220	36	3,793	101,752	345,946
Ocala	3	671	37,997	176,506	276,829	483	757	4.6	21,248	26	2,939	117,731	243,476
Orlando-Kissimmee	11	5,522	282,647	1,429,955	2,213,146	3,908	6,048	5.1	169,453	387	33,217	880,041	2,060,752
Palm Bay-Melbourne-Titusville	6	1,365	62,808	315,524	517,427	861	1,413	5.0	33,350	122	5,579	180,657	875,093
Palm Coast	1	99	5,690	24,492	51,303	67	140	4.3	4,053	0	0	34,090	80,435
Panama City-Lynn Haven	4	649	29,770	158,173	252,068	432	689	5.3	19,706	28	2,887	104,026	307,540
Pensacola-Ferry Pass-Brent	7	1,530	61,036	300,226	529,528	822	1,449	4.9	48,656	68	5,889	282,987	1,002,528
Port St. Lucie-Fort Pierce	3	841	44,056	208,604	326,146	570	892	4.7	42,145	66	4,533	110,839	205,950
Punta Gorda	3	742	27,636	129,560	186,725	355	511	4.7	22,528	10	1,247	95,849	241,904
Sarasota-Bradenton-Venice	8	2,004	74,989	385,817	589,214	1,055	1,612	5.1	45,769	67	6,467	241,569	863,953
Sebastian-Vero Beach	3	429	21,072	111,580	182,931	304	500	5.3	10,711	22	1,235	61,535	190,479
Tallahassee	4	747	35,867	187,536	330,785	513	904	5.2	26,076	65	5,277	102,938	487,009
Tampa-St. Petersburg-Clearwater	34	8,421	375,681	1,925,516	2,976,328	5,269	8,141	5.1	252,754	443	30,947	916,779	3,799,637
West Palm Beach-Boca Raton-Boynton Beach	16	3,706	177,947	868,321	1,356,615	2,376	3,710	4.9	94,553	177	14,537	437,414	1,389,184
Georgia	153	25,583	959,375	6,172,510	11,496,846	16,910	31,507	6.4	756,836	1,935	142,382	3,843,244	14,184,092
Nonmetropolitan	66	6,843	155,015	1,516,312	3,399,306	4,165	9,354	9.8	144,249	406	19,881	860,723	3,096,568
Metropolitan	87	18,740	804,360	4,656,198	8,097,540	12,745	22,153	5.8	612,587	1,529	122,501	2,982,521	11,087,524
Albany	3	634	25,672	135,859	292,002	372	798	5.3	18,096	42	3,426	89,744	898,167
Athens-Clarke County	2	503	27,377	124,652	226,589	341	620	4.6	21,282	29	3,586	85,803	324,644
Atlanta-Sandy Springs-Marietta	44	10,088	453,466	2,660,813	4,518,032	7,273	12,346	5.9	331,607	868	79,114	1,673,611	5,654,819
Augusta-Richmond County	8	1,485	61,101	342,754	567,252	938	1,551	5.6	53,595	128	6,741	273,872	1,111,750
Brunswick	1	273	10,102	61,075	106,397	167	291	6.0	5,617	30	1,059	40,755	167,975
Chattanooga	2	307	6,662	67,466	149,255	184	408	10.1	8,655	15	870	29,341	92,193
Columbus	5	1,067	33,655	205,698	372,236	578	1,037	6.1	23,023	31	4,231	132,670	343,100
Dalton	2	292	12,509	50,369	90,842	137	249	4.0	8,131	44	2,253	70,354	241,629
Gainesville	1	471	24,533	115,178	184,201	316	505	4.7	14,479	45	3,225	48,177	269,117
Hinesville-Fort Stewart	1	133	2,045	38,388	77,090	105	211	18.8	1,453	4	471	7,220	30,143
Macon	5	1,010	43,364	248,085	379,170	678	1,036	5.7	36,663	96	4,502	108,238	540,257
Rome	2	552	24,528	119,325	218,126	327	596	4.9	20,632	28	2,666	98,772	331,234
Savannah	5	1,212	46,033	307,018	558,553	839	1,527	6.7	44,481	71	5,887	182,004	589,278
Valdosta	4	488	19,484	116,159	221,611	317	606	6.0	13,296	64	2,439	73,692	250,806
Warner Robins	2	225	13,829	63,359	136,184	173	372	4.6	11,577	34	2,031	68,268	242,412

TABLE 8

U.S. CENSUS DIVISION 3, SOUTH ATLANTIC

U.S. Community Hospitals
(Nonfederal, short-term general and other special hospitals)

2008 Utilization, Personnel and Finances

| FULL-TIME EQUIVALENT PERSONNEL | | | | | FULL-TIME EQUIV. TRAINEES | | | EXPENSES | | | | | | |
| | | | | | | | | LABOR | | | | TOTAL | | |
Physicians and Dentists	Registered Nurses	Licensed Practical Nurses	Other Salaried Personnel	Total Personnel	Medical and Dental Residents	Other Trainees	Total Trainees	Payroll (in thousands)	Employee Benefits (in thousands)	Total (in thousands)	Percent of Total	Amount (in thousands)	Adjusted per Admission	Adjusted per Inpatient Day
95,400	1,228,383	104,562	3,121,215	4,549,560	90,543	9,573	100,116	$256,559,486	$65,376,486	$321,935,957	51.4	$626,576,958	$9,788.25	$1,782.28
12,071	149,214	30,278	467,807	659,370	1,535	394	1,929	30,769,205	8,096,158	38,865,353	53.4	72,719,071	6,539.38	1,026.65
83,329	1,079,169	74,284	2,653,408	3,890,190	89,008	9,179	98,187	225,790,281	57,280,329	283,070,604	51.1	553,857,887	10,471.29	1,972.93
11,436	235,377	18,716	560,619	826,148	13,532	1,810	15,342	44,008,134	10,595,519	54,603,647	49.7	109,762,269	9,103.81	1,644.89
1,320	27,406	5,012	76,794	110,532	166	52	218	4,857,883	1,272,377	6,130,256	52.4	11,703,675	6,207.59	987.98
10,116	207,971	13,704	483,825	715,616	13,366	1,758	15,124	39,150,251	9,323,142	48,473,391	49.4	98,058,594	9,640.66	1,786.68
495	4,495	241	11,584	16,815	308	2	310	927,863	277,986	1,205,848	56.9	2,119,860	12,337.68	2,042.54
22	599	46	1,727	2,394	0	0	0	113,907	40,732	154,639	53.1	291,322	9,877.66	1,398.00
473	3,896	195	9,857	14,421	308	2	310	813,956	237,254	1,051,209	57.5	1,828,538	12,847.44	2,204.47
23	693	59	1,747	2,522	0	0	0	133,483	39,266	172,748	56.0	308,356	9,659.68	1,787.07
450	3,203	136	8,110	11,899	308	2	310	680,473	197,988	878,461	57.8	1,520,182	13,769.14	2,314.11
1,169	5,346	235	15,252	22,002	1,433	43	1,476	1,520,100	295,298	1,816,307	53.5	3,002,001	16,402.40	2,351.94
1,169	5,346	235	15,252	22,002	1,433	43	1,476	1,520,100	295,298	1,815,397	53.5	3,392,801	16,402.46	2,351.94
1,169	5,346	235	15,252	22,002	1,433	43	1,476	1,520,100	295,298	1,815,397	53.5	3,392,801	16,402.46	2,351.94
2,796	72,727	5,137	161,873	242,533	3,676	1,126	4,802	13,117,105	3,167,664	16,284,768	49.2	33,117,894	8,721.21	1,721.66
119	2,432	413	6,004	8,968	8	4	12	412,341	97,994	510,335	49.0	1,042,533	5,816.25	1,327.61
2,677	70,295	4,724	155,869	233,565	3,668	1,122	4,790	12,704,765	3,069,669	15,774,433	49.2	32,075,361	8,865.12	1,738.43
224	2,672	192	6,771	9,859	404	54	458	549,368	142,771	692,140	52.9	1,307,760	7,748.54	1,541.74
129	2,204	194	4,956	7,483	61	2	63	348,273	86,944	435,216	58.1	749,571	7,326.18	1,560.64
415	6,497	330	13,046	20,288	350	31	381	1,268,894	268,220	1,537,114	52.9	2,905,329	7,585.38	1,556.34
6	478	56	949	1,489	7	1	8	72,007	16,300	88,307	40.9	190,445	8,264.03	1,374.46
10	2,040	97	4,982	7,129	12	18	30	356,653	85,972	442,625	44.9	985,066	13,127.39	2,188.15
70	5,748	175	12,346	18,339	61	20	81	828,813	250,724	1,079,536	44.8	2,408,082	9,370.95	1,710.28
80	2,105	198	5,261	7,644	99	6	105	350,914	82,280	433,194	51.0	848,740	7,488.71	1,608.27
426	11,394	769	25,132	37,721	1,376	768	2,144	2,284,526	543,467	2,827,992	50.2	5,635,359	11,437.27	2,075.30
6	1,040	77	2,291	3,414	0	0	0	184,008	39,276	223,284	57.8	386,317	8,076.88	1,705.43
16	989	65	2,234	3,304	9	2	11	173,927	41,494	215,421	52.5	410,597	6,835.99	1,483.22
261	9,272	490	21,058	31,081	342	109	451	1,645,121	438,550	2,083,671	47.2	4,415,979	10,167.22	1,995.34
25	1,712	109	3,866	5,712	8	24	32	353,914	81,669	435,583	49.7	876,700	8,440.20	1,694.35
19	218	16	427	680	0	0	0	35,544	9,372	44,916	49.3	91,127	7,645.52	1,776.25
11	637	150	1,721	2,519	0	0	0	130,796	31,054	161,851	54.7	296,092	6,165.12	1,174.65
28	2,109	154	3,809	6,100	8	39	47	286,988	56,397	343,386	42.8	803,022	7,402.83	1,516.49
12	1,007	62	2,295	3,376	9	2	11	204,555	51,838	256,393	50.3	510,208	7,348.00	1,564.36
11	853	73	1,496	2,433	18	2	20	126,913	29,253	156,166	46.4	336,326	8,444.03	1,801.18
30	2,054	198	4,618	6,900	18	1	19	352,099	88,944	441,043	47.9	920,701	8,063.31	1,562.59
34	617	46	1,399	2,096	1	2	3	112,563	21,736	134,299	51.1	262,578	7,607.00	1,435.40
63	1,044	146	2,722	3,975	32	0	32	211,365	36,742	248,107	49.3	503,572	7,976.24	1,522.35
711	11,302	749	25,860	38,622	787	36	823	2,022,256	477,668	2,499,922	48.4	5,163,081	8,874.35	1,734.72
90	4,303	378	8,630	13,401	66	5	71	804,367	188,970	993,337	48.0	2,068,708	7,437.22	1,524.90
921	33,808	4,167	85,272	124,168	560	228	788	6,107,217	1,491,083	7,598,304	50.3	15,098,640	8,544.26	1,313.29
225	5,062	1,591	16,059	22,937	45	3	48	912,116	237,597	1,149,714	52.6	2,185,061	5,965.16	642.80
696	28,746	2,576	69,213	101,231	515	225	740	5,195,102	1,253,486	6,448,590	49.9	12,913,579	9,218.68	1,594.75
87	779	145	2,615	3,626	18	0	18	169,159	50,122	219,281	44.3	494,546	9,056.47	1,693.64
23	881	45	2,625	3,574	6	1	7	186,399	46,802	233,201	51.5	452,656	9,117.31	1,997.70
358	16,443	1,082	38,456	56,339	109	26	135	2,920,318	685,111	3,605,432	49.6	7,274,331	9,319.53	1,610.07
16	2,487	292	5,312	8,107	10	2	12	427,281	114,375	541,656	51.5	1,050,927	10,377.48	1,852.66
12	314	43	906	1,275	11	1	12	61,881	17,445	79,325	53.0	149,549	8,498.04	1,405.57
6	243	79	769	1,097	0	0	0	51,143	11,263	62,406	61.6	101,341	6,899.61	678.98
53	994	151	2,405	3,603	40	10	50	206,913	45,258	252,171	48.9	515,684	8,416.45	1,385.37
5	395	75	986	1,461	0	0	0	78,637	20,515	99,152	52.0	190,732	8,362.85	2,099.60
51	683	39	1,782	2,555	63	9	72	115,489	28,935	144,424	51.4	280,985	7,161.59	1,525.43
9	95	14	284	402	6	0	6	6,589	1,968	8,557	55.2	15,496	3,773.18	201.02
14	1,662	118	4,020	5,814	102	135	237	311,392	87,637	399,030	52.5	759,466	11,285.29	2,002.97
48	805	181	1,797	2,831	29	37	66	148,751	29,899	178,650	49.8	358,510	8,037.98	1,643.59
5	1,770	120	4,306	6,201	121	4	125	334,141	67,711	401,853	48.9	820,985	10,791.22	1,469.84
6	722	110	1,856	2,694	0	0	0	107,776	28,657	136,433	48.9	279,284	7,486.50	1,260.24
3	473	82	1,094	1,652	0	0	0	69,231	17,788	87,019	51.5	169,086	5,684.71	1,241.60

Table continues

MSAs

TABLE 8

U.S. CENSUS DIVISION 3, SOUTH ATLANTIC
CONTINUED

U.S. Community Hospitals
(Nonfederal, short-term general and other special hospitals)

2008 Utilization, Personnel and Finances

MSAs

CLASSIFICATION	Hospitals	Beds	Admissions	Inpatient Days	Adjusted Patient Days	Average Daily Census	Adjusted Average Daily Census	Average Stay (days)	Surgical Operations	NEWBORNS Bassinets	NEWBORNS Births	OUTPATIENT VISITS Emergency	OUTPATIENT VISITS Total
Maryland	50	12,018	711,267	3,298,930	5,217,030	9,012	14,255	4.6	552,130	948	73,595	2,282,417	8,083,115
Nonmetropolitan	6	541	33,048	116,760	220,784	318	603	3.5	37,316	50	2,870	168,507	795,509
Metropolitan	44	11,477	678,219	3,182,170	4,996,246	8,694	13,652	4.7	514,814	898	70,725	2,113,910	7,287,606
Baltimore-Towson	23	7,171	429,710	2,013,762	3,108,275	5,502	8,493	4.7	340,304	452	38,765	1,314,199	4,485,032
Bethesda-Gaithersburg-Frederick	7	1,677	110,427	494,395	751,601	1,351	2,054	4.5	70,274	233	19,109	348,332	964,446
Cumberland	2	385	17,210	102,779	195,782	281	535	6.0	10,923	12	1,027	54,675	385,068
Hagerstown-Martinsburg	1	300	16,456	71,938	127,072	197	347	4.4	8,781	41	2,050	66,884	225,696
Salisbury	3	539	26,446	144,731	252,673	395	691	5.5	16,858	28	2,246	82,069	537,089
Washington-Arlington-Alexandria	7	1,290	69,364	324,075	503,719	885	1,376	4.7	60,039	120	6,806	206,041	539,898
Wilmington	1	115	8,606	30,490	57,124	83	156	3.5	7,635	12	722	41,710	150,377
North Carolina	116	23,140	1,041,918	6,019,401	11,655,349	16,444	31,841	5.8	853,885	1,634	126,934	4,166,718	17,733,068
Nonmetropolitan	58	6,780	266,228	1,495,862	3,307,698	4,087	9,035	5.6	212,921	591	28,967	1,480,571	4,951,998
Metropolitan	58	16,360	775,690	4,523,539	8,347,651	12,357	22,806	5.8	640,964	1,043	97,967	2,686,147	12,781,070
Asheville	6	1,232	58,944	336,355	607,613	918	1,659	5.7	58,022	58	5,503	169,398	1,046,532
Burlington	1	210	11,764	50,051	119,099	137	325	4.3	9,417	20	1,482	53,712	106,157
Charlotte-Gastonia-Concord	13	3,380	171,263	930,517	1,762,427	2,542	4,815	5.4	128,717	283	26,183	651,830	2,792,563
Durham	6	1,880	95,126	586,381	1,055,488	1,602	2,884	6.2	82,323	69	9,331	215,815	2,451,958
Fayetteville	1	614	32,169	189,612	313,678	518	857	5.9	16,120	48	4,782	108,307	597,287
Goldsboro	1	269	13,423	66,372	124,441	181	340	4.9	12,066	30	1,504	51,298	149,712
Greensboro-High Point	4	1,699	78,470	447,120	904,401	1,221	2,471	5.7	51,722	111	9,855	285,022	1,116,927
Greenville	1	739	38,554	231,463	322,380	632	881	6.0	32,306	42	3,939	95,230	348,679
Hickory-Lenoir-Morganton	5	1,083	35,832	258,824	530,384	707	1,449	7.2	34,121	70	4,580	174,458	766,172
Jacksonville	1	133	8,544	32,714	70,167	89	192	3.8	5,887	23	1,467	44,400	161,582
Raleigh-Cary	6	1,832	94,482	522,252	1,027,441	1,427	2,808	5.5	91,967	136	15,923	365,424	1,705,686
Rocky Mount	3	477	20,958	106,438	176,529	291	482	5.1	11,808	34	1,925	86,004	242,701
Wilmington	4	856	37,268	213,583	438,960	583	1,199	5.7	36,525	50	4,445	164,331	605,701
Winston-Salem	6	1,956	78,893	551,857	894,643	1,509	2,444	7.0	69,963	69	7,048	220,938	689,413
South Carolina	69	12,498	528,872	2,962,830	5,040,278	8,090	13,771	5.6	490,584	858	56,068	1,954,264	5,924,215
Nonmetropolitan	25	3,161	105,603	584,114	1,133,918	1,594	3,099	5.5	91,606	242	11,507	485,812	1,053,913
Metropolitan	44	9,337	423,269	2,378,716	3,906,360	6,496	10,672	5.6	398,978	616	44,561	1,468,452	4,870,302
Anderson	2	412	19,622	106,843	155,290	292	424	5.4	19,302	28	2,179	80,124	526,497
Augusta-Richmond County	2	281	12,701	58,720	88,118	160	240	4.6	9,802	18	1,310	65,913	144,782
Charleston-North Charleston	7	1,706	85,164	439,428	839,185	1,201	2,292	5.2	79,998	134	10,413	282,059	1,429,865
Charlotte-Gastonia-Concord	2	318	15,143	78,987	122,965	215	336	5.2	17,245	32	2,378	50,623	157,218
Columbia	7	2,105	97,389	544,745	862,448	1,488	2,356	5.6	73,545	141	10,618	282,087	736,449
Florence	6	1,159	49,153	278,862	427,603	761	1,168	5.7	51,089	40	2,736	126,488	191,378
Greenville	11	1,561	71,505	414,076	654,402	1,131	1,789	5.8	67,567	88	6,756	244,733	761,237
Myrtle Beach-Conway-North Myrtle Beach	3	668	26,735	172,708	315,511	472	862	6.5	24,065	54	2,916	149,552	318,055
Spartanburg	3	835	36,156	209,315	315,838	571	863	5.8	39,849	57	4,041	134,609	458,292
Sumter	1	292	9,701	75,032	125,000	205	342	7.7	16,516	24	1,214	52,264	146,529
Virginia	90	17,648	795,578	4,452,740	8,129,197	12,175	22,222	5.6	699,020	1,392	98,991	3,091,131	13,314,419
Nonmetropolitan	30	2,919	99,822	597,492	1,249,123	1,634	3,413	6.0	93,206	180	7,649	543,060	2,358,894
Metropolitan	60	14,729	695,756	3,855,248	6,880,074	10,541	18,809	5.5	605,814	1,212	91,342	2,548,071	10,955,525
Blacksburg-Christiansburg-Radford	4	312	15,895	65,119	150,343	178	411	4.1	18,881	34	1,741	90,707	253,685
Charlottesville	3	788	41,487	221,148	402,689	604	1,101	5.3	71,999	45	3,534	96,608	1,897,926
Danville	1	186	9,963	57,034	100,575	156	275	5.7	6,950	20	957	38,861	148,062
Harrisonburg	1	244	14,221	55,047	133,524	150	365	3.9	18,985	28	1,713	72,030	447,244
Kingsport-Bristol-Bristol	1	135	4,864	19,191	36,472	53	100	3.9	5,239	12	700	23,139	115,470
Lynchburg	2	1,229	32,656	346,443	555,687	947	1,519	10.6	18,052	52	3,051	92,564	129,993
Richmond	15	3,597	149,285	848,040	1,380,963	2,322	3,777	5.7	131,514	196	16,000	447,644	1,576,057
Roanoke	3	1,143	56,696	329,218	530,040	901	1,450	5.8	44,991	58	5,393	213,625	536,226
Virginia Beach-Norfolk-Newport News	15	3,166	155,899	880,061	1,719,639	2,405	4,700	5.6	136,471	328	19,130	766,895	3,359,100
Washington-Arlington-Alexandria	14	3,518	191,254	931,660	1,706,557	2,545	4,663	4.9	142,380	415	37,196	647,764	2,166,470
Winchester	1	411	23,536	102,287	163,585	280	448	4.3	10,352	24	1,927	58,234	325,292
West Virginia	56	7,470	283,673	1,665,076	3,474,007	4,547	9,490	5.9	292,405	468	20,856	1,183,158	6,615,109
Nonmetropolitan	29	2,849	96,292	605,459	1,541,532	1,653	4,212	6.3	85,267	190	7,093	541,930	2,604,725
Metropolitan	27	4,621	187,381	1,059,617	1,932,475	2,894	5,278	5.7	207,138	278	13,763	641,228	4,010,384
Charleston	7	1,289	52,902	293,846	532,402	802	1,454	5.6	87,547	62	4,013	166,155	1,001,843
Cumberland	1	25	1,085	3,590	12,401	10	34	3.3	1,461	0	0	12,647	45,835
Hagerstown-Martinsburg	2	200	7,644	42,751	106,208	117	290	5.6	8,288	24	962	45,067	201,167
Huntington-Ashland	3	703	40,265	186,882	343,830	511	939	4.6	26,889	55	2,765	117,069	667,249
Morgantown	4	799	34,881	213,230	309,707	582	846	6.1	31,583	24	2,314	79,958	756,062
Parkersburg-Marietta-Vienna	3	526	18,008	93,589	162,681	255	445	5.2	17,327	38	1,719	74,163	378,048
Washington-Arlington-Alexandria	1	45	1,964	8,356	28,312	23	77	4.3	3,048	10	169	18,902	64,167
Weirton-Steubenville	1	238	7,899	43,457	98,234	119	268	5.5	6,547	21	370	41,800	208,662
Wheeling	4	752	22,251	161,456	288,502	441	788	7.3	24,174	44	1,451	78,831	662,503
Winchester	1	44	482	12,460	50,198	34	137	25.9	274	0	0	6,636	24,848

TABLE 8

U.S. CENSUS DIVISION 3, SOUTH ATLANTIC CONTINUED

U.S. Community Hospitals
(Nonfederal, short-term general and other special hospitals)

2008 Utilization, Personnel and Finances

	FULL-TIME EQUIVALENT PERSONNEL				FULL-TIME EQUIV. TRAINEES			EXPENSES						
								LABOR				TOTAL		
Physicians and Dentists	Registered Nurses	Licensed Practical Nurses	Other Salaried Personnel	Total Personnel	Medical and Dental Residents	Other Trainees	Total Trainees	Payroll (in thousands)	Employee Benefits (in thousands)	Total (in thousands)	Percent of Total	Amount (in thousands)	Adjusted per Admission	Adjusted per Inpatient Day
1,941	20,647	690	55,273	78,551	1,345	99	1,444	4,569,259	1,028,788	5,598,046	49.1	11,389,973	10,097.90	2,183.23
53	874	42	2,635	3,604	6	0	6	185,950	46,406	232,355	55.1	421,709	6,770.53	1,910.05
1,888	19,773	648	52,638	74,947	1,339	99	1,438	4,383,310	982,382	5,365,691	48.9	10,968,264	10,292.37	2,195.30
1,742	13,370	353	36,440	51,905	1,289	89	1,378	3,007,534	685,421	3,692,955	48.2	7,666,616	11,536.66	2,466.52
28	2,669	29	6,725	9,451	0	4	4	608,426	120,853	729,278	49.7	1,466,001	8,674.05	1,950.50
25	533	27	1,322	1,907	0	0	0	94,169	30,463	124,633	50.7	245,609	7,561.61	1,254.50
5	471	35	1,205	1,716	0	0	0	96,230	25,459	121,689	55.6	218,840	7,528.54	1,722.17
29	783	86	2,081	2,979	0	0	0	151,572	35,730	187,301	49.9	375,522	8,555.01	1,486.20
47	1,768	106	4,263	6,184	50	4	54	381,039	74,879	455,917	51.1	891,622	8,065.54	1,770.08
12	179	12	602	805	0	2	2	44,341	9,577	53,918	51.8	104,055	6,453.44	1,821.57
1,344	41,036	2,202	99,662	144,244	2,566	134	2,700	7,429,646	1,785,071	9,214,717	52.2	17,662,605	8,736.81	1,515.41
200	9,100	904	24,791	35,244	6	33	39	1,553,364	398,289	1,951,653	54.1	3,606,064	6,102.04	1,090.20
1,048	31,843	1,238	74,871	109,000	2,560	101	2,661	5,876,282	1,386,782	7,263,064	51.7	14,056,541	9,825.13	1,683.89
117	2,210	102	6,122	8,551	0	14	14	419,654	102,168	521,822	52.9	986,420	9,310.68	1,623.43
7	431	5	1,333	1,776	0	0	0	72,698	16,446	89,144	48.0	182,166	8,617.02	1,531.07
324	7,431	170	15,798	23,723	272	17	289	1,296,749	309,000	1,605,750	46.4	3,460,601	10,435.16	1,963.54
20	5,009	96	10,740	15,865	1,200	2	1,202	985,669	194,517	1,180,187	53.6	2,201,354	13,020.14	2,085.63
97	993	213	2,871	4,174	0	0	0	247,241	55,679	302,920	57.3	528,991	9,940.07	1,686.41
0	299	17	1,061	1,377	0	0	0	74,777	18,700	93,478	55.1	169,557	6,737.28	1,362.55
194	2,734	126	6,782	9,836	78	2	80	483,613	146,233	629,846	55.1	1,143,599	7,323.11	1,264.48
20	1,597	33	4,365	6,015	332	0	332	307,166	86,704	393,869	52.0	758,147	14,118.71	2,351.72
79	1,258	45	3,319	4,701	0	0	0	243,876	58,779	302,656	52.8	573,565	8,083.27	1,081.41
0	304	28	697	1,029	0	0	0	45,278	10,660	55,938	68.6	81,488	4,446.60	1,161.35
173	4,216	146	9,125	13,660	0	13	13	718,408	158,846	877,253	55.6	1,577,071	8,483.76	1,534.95
6	639	41	1,566	2,252	0	0	0	116,174	31,945	148,119	56.1	264,255	7,241.05	1,496.95
4	1,334	48	3,145	4,531	63	0	63	254,390	70,942	325,331	50.3	646,739	9,151.27	1,473.34
7	3,388	168	7,947	11,510	615	53	668	610,588	126,164	736,751	49.7	1,482,299	11,816.42	1,656.86
1,113	19,123	1,547	43,616	65,399	1,123	2	1,125	3,219,820	846,800	4,066,621	45.7	8,890,466	9,974.68	1,763.88
157	3,212	420	8,822	12,611	35	1	36	614,400	171,395	785,795	49.3	1,592,556	7,836.03	1,404.47
956	15,911	1,127	34,794	52,788	1,088	1	1,089	2,605,420	675,405	3,280,826	45.0	7,297,910	10,606.38	1,868.21
52	553	45	2,311	2,961	32	0	32	140,107	49,794	189,901	43.9	433,017	14,848.67	2,788.44
3	293	36	581	913	0	0	0	63,115	14,572	77,687	47.2	164,540	8,386.32	1,867.26
60	3,667	156	6,974	10,857	571	0	571	599,250	148,215	747,465	45.4	1,647,661	10,901.91	1,963.41
0	591	27	853	1,471	0	0	0	72,386	17,015	89,401	40.8	219,232	8,978.29	1,782.88
60	3,534	243	7,773	11,610	234	0	234	602,248	148,921	751,169	44.5	1,687,157	10,974.17	1,956.24
46	1,599	220	4,050	5,915	23	0	23	253,029	66,918	319,947	41.6	768,210	9,711.14	1,796.55
518	2,985	131	5,517	9,151	170	1	171	397,790	99,785	497,575	41.6	1,194,686	10,522.25	1,825.62
8	837	101	1,782	2,728	0	0	0	135,172	36,334	171,506	49.5	346,412	7,644.70	1,097.94
209	1,513	149	3,982	5,853	58	0	58	266,209	74,228	340,437	52.5	648,924	11,614.06	2,054.61
0	339	19	971	1,329	0	0	0	76,114	19,624	95,738	50.9	188,072	11,637.40	1,504.58
1,162	28,415	2,890	62,975	95,442	1,963	148	2,111	5,448,146	1,217,576	6,665,714	48.3	13,800,772	9,341.21	1,697.68
198	3,332	743	8,681	12,954	37	3	40	554,536	133,454	687,987	50.7	1,358,186	6,294.16	1,087.31
964	25,083	2,147	54,294	82,488	1,926	145	2,071	4,893,610	1,084,122	5,977,727	48.0	12,442,587	9,862.37	1,808.50
2	639	91	1,102	1,834	13	0	13	98,460	19,967	118,426	47.4	249,999	6,791.96	1,662.86
44	2,116	156	4,806	7,122	763	6	769	413,292	100,861	514,153	47.1	1,091,168	13,917.96	2,709.70
16	178	43	827	1,064	0	0	0	49,363	10,001	59,364	41.7	142,241	8,096.13	1,414.28
54	467	83	1,360	1,964	0	0	0	103,878	24,130	128,008	52.0	246,067	7,133.40	1,842.86
14	177	17	500	708	4	0	4	31,403	7,976	39,380	52.6	74,904	8,102.96	2,053.73
80	950	114	3,252	4,396	21	9	30	231,814	52,417	284,231	55.2	514,518	9,953.34	925.91
118	5,463	542	11,010	17,133	701	95	796	1,020,272	251,367	1,271,637	47.2	2,692,250	10,991.92	1,949.55
318	2,296	191	4,407	7,212	179	5	184	434,708	87,831	522,539	47.1	1,110,066	11,808.33	2,094.31
87	5,359	572	12,202	18,220	69	7	76	1,083,218	229,743	1,312,960	46.5	2,822,799	9,119.13	1,641.51
168	6,590	290	12,657	19,705	101	13	114	1,267,283	259,762	1,527,043	49.1	3,109,493	8,953.64	1,822.09
63	848	48	2,171	3,130	75	10	85	159,919	40,067	199,986	51.4	389,083	10,336.68	2,378.48
495	9,780	1,607	25,112	36,994	558	28	586	1,668,977	485,254	2,154,232	50.2	4,289,258	7,205.64	1,234.67
250	2,702	793	8,075	11,820	29	8	37	511,270	146,509	657,778	54.5	1,206,245	5,066.72	782.50
245	7,078	814	17,037	25,174	529	20	549	1,157,707	338,745	1,496,454	48.5	3,083,013	8,631.25	1,595.37
93	2,315	229	5,015	7,652	152	1	153	360,211	105,162	465,373	48.0	969,487	9,785.98	1,820.97
0	34	8	148	190	0	0	0	6,071	1,442	7,513	49.2	15,259	4,071.36	1,230.50
5	359	34	833	1,231	0	0	0	47,598	14,705	62,303	53.5	116,453	6,649.14	1,096.46
32	1,217	147	2,836	4,232	0	0	0	213,242	80,159	293,401	50.6	579,768	7,581.94	1,686.21
31	1,530	122	3,566	5,249	319	18	337	246,052	65,209	311,261	45.0	691,448	12,890.05	2,232.59
13	511	86	1,430	2,040	0	0	0	90,123	24,411	114,535	46.3	247,627	7,674.31	1,522.16
0	57	11	193	261	0	0	0	14,513	4,851	19,365	52.8	36,711	5,517.12	1,296.66
11	243	32	630	916	0	0	0	40,286	11,216	51,502	57.6	89,357	5,004.29	909.63
60	797	135	2,288	3,280	58	1	59	135,187	30,609	165,796	50.9	325,910	6,785.12	1,129.66
0	15	10	98	123	0	0	0	4,425	981	5,405	49.2	10,993	5,660.76	219.00

MSAs

TABLE 8

U.S. CENSUS DIVISION 4, EAST NORTH CENTRAL

U.S. Community Hospitals
(Nonfederal, short-term general and other special hospitals)

2008 Utilization, Personnel and Finances

CLASSIFICATION	Hospitals	Beds	Admissions	Inpatient Days	Adjusted Patient Days	Average Daily Census	Adjusted Average Daily Census	Average Stay (days)	Surgical Operations	NEWBORNS Bassinets	NEWBORNS Births	OUTPATIENT VISITS Emergency	OUTPATIENT VISITS Total
UNITED STATES	5,010	808,069	35,760,750	196,078,468	351,559,836	536,215	961,620	5.5	27,459,438	57,301	4,073,724	123,024,024	624,098,296
Nonmetropolitan	1,998	143,524	4,592,673	29,262,322	70,831,752	80,001	193,693	6.4	4,175,758	11,324	491,044	23,469,370	119,205,443
Metropolitan	3,012	664,545	31,168,077	166,816,146	280,728,084	456,214	767,927	5.4	23,283,680	45,977	3,582,680	99,554,654	504,892,853
CENSUS DIVISION 4, EAST NORTH CENTRAL	774	124,957	5,730,456	29,237,134	57,644,511	79,993	157,738	5.1	4,789,140	9,913	590,869	20,682,680	123,102,656
Nonmetropolitan	275	19,389	719,804	3,913,070	11,291,471	10,694	30,878	5.4	727,249	1,930	77,039	3,919,469	22,943,195
Metropolitan	499	105,568	5,010,652	25,324,064	46,353,040	69,299	126,860	5.1	4,061,891	7,983	513,830	16,763,211	100,159,461
Illinois	191	34,506	1,610,844	8,069,859	15,078,143	22,065	41,226	5.0	1,134,509	2,762	176,458	5,123,091	30,986,757
Nonmetropolitan	64	4,568	166,626	917,392	2,460,325	2,505	6,726	5.5	147,787	332	14,383	799,374	4,671,798
Metropolitan	127	29,938	1,444,218	7,152,467	12,617,818	19,560	34,500	5.0	986,722	2,430	162,075	4,323,717	26,314,959
Bloomington-Normal	2	355	15,881	64,204	118,957	176	325	4.0	11,654	33	2,448	68,018	472,920
Champaign-Urbana	4	564	27,537	135,349	273,391	369	748	4.9	21,907	52	3,447	106,982	619,072
Chicago-Naperville-Joliet	78	21,086	1,050,287	5,152,575	8,760,363	14,091	23,956	4.9	640,510	1,707	119,201	2,918,553	17,482,435
Danville	2	258	7,827	56,530	128,648	155	352	7.2	3,965	26	815	44,658	240,865
Davenport-Moline-Rock Island	5	583	24,960	124,047	294,667	339	806	5.0	19,268	85	2,470	100,988	549,372
Decatur	2	484	21,449	107,881	199,256	296	545	5.0	14,446	36	1,915	103,041	453,752
Kankakee-Bradley	2	464	21,458	98,432	191,038	269	522	4.6	18,704	26	1,631	70,229	534,704
Lake County-Kenosha County	5	941	52,600	223,877	418,589	613	1,144	4.3	41,478	117	8,025	160,205	1,155,391
Peoria	6	1,250	57,011	314,799	587,596	861	1,606	5.5	67,862	81	5,527	187,168	1,609,131
Rockford	5	927	44,912	231,864	389,963	634	1,066	5.2	44,598	68	5,342	151,136	1,027,024
Springfield	2	897	45,270	229,679	368,315	627	1,006	5.1	33,549	56	3,735	123,772	712,088
St. Louis	14	2,129	75,026	413,230	887,035	1,130	2,424	5.5	68,781	143	7,519	288,967	1,458,205
Indiana	123	17,612	732,627	3,829,835	7,516,301	10,513	20,652	5.2	651,384	1,512	82,040	3,041,160	17,022,314
Nonmetropolitan	40	2,238	92,661	372,618	1,150,956	1,014	3,146	4.0	111,578	297	12,460	659,960	3,449,859
Metropolitan	83	15,374	639,966	3,457,217	6,365,345	9,499	17,506	5.4	539,806	1,215	69,580	2,381,200	13,572,455
Anderson	2	210	8,543	50,233	137,502	138	375	5.9	12,921	10	463	45,915	383,346
Bloomington	2	322	14,207	63,283	132,295	173	362	4.5	13,000	19	2,116	65,921	374,816
Cincinnati-Middletown	1	88	4,911	21,849	52,863	60	144	4.4	6,375	11	562	19,464	148,118
Columbus	1	222	6,282	25,603	61,594	114	274	4.1	6,905	20	799	33,622	197,464
Elkhart-Goshen	2	420	18,842	80,130	159,303	219	436	4.3	13,921	51	2,857	88,439	686,469
Evansville	7	1,310	50,053	300,172	558,768	821	1,526	6.0	37,860	63	4,573	161,741	706,764
Fort Wayne	8	1,694	64,383	370,984	624,972	1,014	1,707	5.8	61,948	144	7,432	190,855	840,332
Gary	12	2,615	110,072	614,264	1,052,336	1,680	2,877	5.6	72,534	239	10,015	360,815	1,817,795
Indianapolis	24	4,816	196,312	1,139,010	2,102,751	3,114	5,749	5.8	166,413	356	22,674	787,617	5,272,604
Kokomo	4	305	12,577	63,107	143,629	173	393	5.0	14,934	35	1,291	90,965	469,635
Lafayette	3	583	25,128	120,494	198,843	330	545	4.8	15,958	24	2,736	95,994	518,661
Louisville	6	615	30,805	142,087	283,810	388	776	4.6	29,709	54	2,915	114,831	601,831
Michigan City-La Porte	2	375	12,831	71,602	150,114	196	410	5.6	13,869	35	1,438	50,756	253,238
Muncie	1	363	16,203	76,408	139,656	209	382	4.7	14,132	24	1,765	56,054	294,499
South Bend-Mishawaka	3	850	42,896	196,542	306,471	538	838	4.6	30,451	77	5,304	111,119	400,767
Terre Haute	5	586	25,921	121,449	260,438	332	712	4.7	28,876	53	2,640	107,092	606,116
Michigan	153	25,272	1,221,970	6,350,025	12,707,477	17,351	34,724	5.2	1,077,354	1,753	118,965	4,428,070	27,998,296
Nonmetropolitan	59	4,483	159,851	937,457	2,737,397	2,562	7,483	5.9	178,613	395	15,624	812,137	5,977,652
Metropolitan	94	20,789	1,062,119	5,412,568	9,970,080	14,789	27,241	5.1	898,741	1,358	103,341	3,615,933	22,020,644
Ann Arbor	6	1,581	81,834	456,885	840,120	1,249	2,295	5.6	76,058	52	6,488	195,073	2,736,181
Battle Creek	3	331	16,801	73,937	170,100	202	464	4.4	16,066	24	1,776	66,811	338,606
Bay City	2	364	17,927	88,779	137,545	243	376	5.0	11,310	10	908	43,098	337,505
Detroit-Livonia-Dearborn	20	5,191	265,959	1,402,188	2,508,992	3,832	6,856	5.3	191,435	320	24,582	983,987	4,838,083
Flint	4	1,203	72,815	334,653	546,830	914	1,493	4.6	45,537	89	6,227	222,708	1,575,528
Grand Rapids-Wyoming	8	1,827	94,670	458,247	806,637	1,252	2,203	4.8	89,006	152	13,267	320,149	1,594,229
Holland-Grand Haven	3	221	11,688	39,054	93,323	107	256	3.3	14,752	49	2,743	77,474	560,371
Jackson	2	441	19,398	89,080	197,341	244	539	4.6	9,304	24	1,885	61,111	416,240
Kalamazoo-Portage	5	979	47,726	266,190	509,923	727	1,393	5.6	33,918	70	5,163	181,970	1,116,627
Lansing-East Lansing	5	989	54,022	246,105	496,346	672	1,357	4.6	45,714	62	5,947	189,451	1,128,241
Monroe	1	169	9,524	37,495	90,863	102	248	3.9	9,131	13	878	39,691	223,497
Muskegon-Norton Shores	3	443	21,627	88,520	233,530	242	638	4.1	31,288	46	2,417	110,928	744,255
Niles-Benton Harbor	2	284	16,411	59,683	119,439	163	326	3.6	10,558	44	1,946	74,709	304,075
Saginaw-Saginaw Township North	4	1,111	42,086	285,301	435,172	779	1,190	6.8	24,978	31	3,291	130,746	664,080
South Bend-Mishawaka	1	25	889	3,178	14,214	9	39	3.6	1,148	0	0	7,818	84,919
Warren-Farmington Hills-Troy	25	5,630	288,742	1,483,273	2,769,705	4,052	7,568	5.1	288,538	372	25,823	910,209	5,358,207

TABLE 8

U.S. CENSUS DIVISION 4, EAST NORTH CENTRAL

U.S. Community Hospitals
(Nonfederal, short-term general and other special hospitals)

2008 Utilization, Personnel and Finances

FULL-TIME EQUIVALENT PERSONNEL					FULL-TIME EQUIV. TRAINEES			EXPENSES						
								LABOR				TOTAL		
Physicians and Dentists	Registered Nurses	Licensed Practical Nurses	Other Salaried Personnel	Total Personnel	Medical and Dental Residents	Other Trainees	Total Trainees	Payroll (in thousands)	Employee Benefits (in thousands)	Total (in thousands)	Percent of Total	Amount (in thousands)	Adjusted per Admission	Adjusted per Inpatient Day
95,400	1,228,383	104,562	3,121,215	4,549,560	90,543	9,573	100,116	$256,559,486	$65,376,486	$321,935,957	51.4	$626,576,958	$9,788.25	$1,782.28
12,071	149,214	30,278	467,807	659,370	1,535	394	1,929	30,769,205	8,096,158	38,865,353	53.4	72,719,071	6,539.38	1,026.65
83,329	1,079,169	74,284	2,653,408	3,890,190	89,008	9,179	98,187	225,790,281	57,280,329	283,070,604	51.1	553,857,887	10,471.29	1,972.93
19,624	202,395	13,714	543,284	779,017	19,316	2,065	21,381	43,496,919	11,305,767	54,802,694	50.7	108,029,057	9,639.77	1,874.06
2,182	25,314	3,867	82,006	113,369	154	73	227	5,611,123	1,610,820	7,221,941	53.5	13,496,699	6,634.42	1,195.30
17,442	177,081	9,847	461,278	665,648	19,162	1,992	21,154	37,885,796	9,694,947	47,580,753	50.3	94,532,358	10,306.34	2,039.40
4,240	51,501	2,686	137,493	195,900	5,637	286	5,923	11,041,705	2,844,203	13,885,912	49.6	27,982,802	9,427.88	1,855.85
398	5,360	973	17,080	23,811	40	13	53	1,100,231	314,119	1,414,351	53.1	2,665,069	6,137.26	1,083.22
3,842	46,141	1,693	120,413	172,089	5,597	273	5,870	9,941,474	2,500,004	12,471,501	49.0	25,317,733	9,991.82	2,006.51
46	482	27	1,511	2,066	14	0	14	105,390	25,598	130,988	47.2	277,807	9,428.04	2,335.35
9	975	25	2,149	3,158	27	1	28	171,702	46,588	218,291	40.1	544,157	11,357.19	1,990.40
3,242	33,607	1,017	85,939	123,805	5,103	181	5,284	7,389,374	1,852,424	9,241,799	49.8	18,556,615	10,329.76	2,118.25
6	192	31	659	888	0	0	0	42,054	14,193	56,248	46.1	122,110	7,232.30	949.18
37	708	54	2,072	2,871	0	0	0	133,034	36,159	169,194	45.4	372,671	6,927.35	1,264.72
38	752	75	1,974	2,839	23	2	25	144,375	40,454	184,828	51.1	361,985	9,135.26	1,816.68
44	731	36	1,515	2,326	0	3	3	119,444	28,703	148,147	46.1	321,701	7,712.61	1,683.96
29	1,553	35	4,159	5,776	0	0	0	349,954	82,623	432,577	46.8	924,596	9,611.08	2,208.84
289	2,278	63	5,948	8,578	203	62	265	469,586	125,718	595,305	51.0	1,167,265	11,056.79	1,986.51
63	1,642	62	4,275	6,042	0	15	15	333,895	90,487	424,382	48.6	873,688	11,495.60	2,240.44
4	1,222	115	3,946	5,287	225	0	225	284,948	75,841	360,789	44.9	804,320	11,058.53	2,183.78
35	1,999	153	6,266	8,453	2	9	11	307,718	111,296	509,013	51.4	990,818	6,290.11	1,117.00
1,562	27,438	2,730	72,338	104,068	1,139	191	1,330	5,741,852	1,535,117	7,276,970	49.7	14,654,457	9,896.34	1,949.69
377	3,719	692	12,044	16,832	10	33	43	803,825	226,368	1,030,193	54.0	1,906,976	6,505.34	1,656.86
1,185	23,719	2,038	60,294	87,236	1,129	158	1,287	4,938,027	1,308,749	6,246,777	49.0	12,747,481	10,733.32	2,002.64
43	313	52	1,098	1,506	0	0	0	83,485	24,406	107,892	58.4	184,690	7,749.02	1,343.18
13	661	71	1,818	2,563	0	0	0	122,576	33,232	155,808	55.3	281,922	9,368.97	2,131.01
4	121	27	492	644	0	0	0	32,028	10,838	42,865	57.8	74,219	6,246.30	1,403.98
0	287	33	1,175	1,495	0	0	0	74,407	22,480	96,887	50.2	193,008	12,770.97	3,133.55
67	794	41	1,957	2,859	0	0	0	142,386	52,730	195,115	49.4	395,265	10,339.68	2,481.22
141	1,599	92	4,421	6,253	17	6	23	326,143	85,575	411,719	47.3	870,051	9,816.78	1,557.09
22	2,244	151	4,734	7,151	0	51	51	396,696	114,443	511,139	50.2	1,018,449	9,560.66	1,629.59
194	3,162	229	8,130	11,715	81	10	91	666,296	163,866	830,161	47.7	1,741,812	9,187.93	1,655.19
402	9,044	793	21,873	32,112	791	49	840	1,991,238	515,107	2,506,348	48.6	5,161,091	14,011.53	2,454.45
51	536	70	1,769	2,426	17	1	18	121,155	34,214	155,370	54.1	287,447	9,936.28	2,001.31
67	928	68	2,320	3,383	57	8	65	185,398	46,457	231,854	52.0	446,264	10,617.24	2,244.30
41	839	141	2,751	3,772	0	0	0	168,437	38,720	207,157	55.2	375,608	5,895.13	1,323.45
51	384	27	1,345	1,807	4	1	5	120,932	33,251	154,182	51.5	299,582	11,225.78	1,995.70
8	471	24	1,258	1,761	65	30	95	88,392	24,482	112,874	45.6	247,685	8,363.48	1,773.53
45	1,457	39	3,233	4,774	72	2	74	263,658	67,993	331,651	46.7	709,504	10,611.94	2,315.08
36	879	180	1,920	3,015	25	0	25	154,801	40,954	195,755	42.5	460,885	8,002.30	1,769.65
5,867	43,027	2,345	116,371	167,610	4,727	253	4,980	9,788,987	2,408,473	12,197,459	52.1	23,392,921	9,622.89	1,840.88
594	5,485	932	18,874	25,885	72	15	87	1,328,104	368,932	1,697,035	53.0	3,202,723	7,113.91	1,169.99
5,273	37,542	1,413	97,497	141,725	4,655	238	4,893	8,460,884	2,039,541	10,500,424	52.0	20,190,198	10,193.16	2,025.08
1,834	5,007	166	11,465	18,472	1,160	17	1,177	977,981	297,845	1,275,826	53.1	2,403,271	15,605.25	2,860.63
23	574	8	1,321	1,926	0	0	0	122,789	31,107	153,896	51.1	301,218	7,603.26	1,770.83
14	394	64	1,198	1,670	8	0	8	99,802	24,268	124,069	51.3	241,973	8,462.36	1,759.23
1,320	8,521	143	22,631	32,615	1,581	67	1,648	2,239,687	476,516	2,716,202	49.8	5,458,980	11,548.12	2,175.77
101	2,411	146	4,516	7,174	315	0	315	441,472	151,985	593,456	57.1	1,039,639	8,670.66	1,901.21
268	3,362	176	9,877	13,683	70	0	70	734,244	198,318	932,562	50.7	1,840,440	10,865.49	2,281.62
48	477	54	1,547	2,126	9	1	10	108,229	32,380	140,609	57.9	242,915	8,734.48	2,602.95
55	634	79	2,330	3,098	0	0	0	147,374	30,415	177,788	54.0	329,113	7,379.04	1,667.74
149	1,627	32	4,579	6,387	0	0	0	410,143	107,055	517,198	54.3	953,170	11,537.78	1,869.24
189	2,090	62	5,876	8,217	227	3	230	444,680	123,016	567,697	55.3	1,026,800	9,096.55	2,068.72
13	297	24	941	1,275	0	0	0	59,583	14,669	74,252	51.9	143,038	6,197.49	1,574.22
100	579	12	2,046	2,737	19	6	25	170,165	46,952	217,117	53.7	404,394	6,898.21	1,731.66
7	519	46	2,183	2,755	0	0	0	115,845	37,466	153,310	53.1	288,971	8,835.15	2,419.41
125	1,469	159	4,471	6,224	0	40	40	287,757	68,613	356,370	50.4	706,431	9,943.57	1,623.34
6	39	1	158	204	0	2	2	11,280	3,439	14,719	60.5	24,329	6,118.96	1,711.62
1,021	9,542	241	22,358	33,162	1,266	102	1,368	2,089,855	395,498	2,485,353	51.9	4,785,516	8,875.07	1,727.81

Table continues

MSAs

TABLE 8

U.S. CENSUS DIVISION 4, EAST NORTH CENTRAL CONTINUED

U.S. Community Hospitals
(Nonfederal, short-term general and other special hospitals)

2008 Utilization, Personnel and Finances

CLASSIFICATION	Hospitals	Beds	Admissions	Inpatient Days	Adjusted Patient Days	Average Daily Census	Adjusted Average Daily Census	Average Stay (days)	Surgical Operations	NEWBORNS		OUTPATIENT VISITS	
										Bassinets	Births	Emergency	Total
Ohio	181	33,860	1,547,720	7,814,849	14,975,504	21,377	40,959	5.0	1,201,809	2,603	143,941	6,023,705	32,891,862
Nonmetropolitan	55	4,537	185,972	809,367	2,148,100	2,213	5,869	4.4	170,661	594	21,653	1,142,886	5,493,718
Metropolitan	126	29,323	1,361,748	7,005,482	12,827,404	19,164	35,090	5.1	1,031,148	2,009	122,288	4,880,819	27,398,144
Akron	10	2,034	96,984	505,032	935,325	1,381	2,557	5.2	74,091	92	7,753	351,500	2,018,126
Canton-Massillon	5	1,297	56,053	307,470	576,608	840	1,575	5.5	44,763	85	4,821	218,113	1,277,028
Cincinnati-Middletown	20	4,370	210,727	1,046,705	1,764,201	2,861	4,824	5.0	149,599	340	23,147	748,906	3,284,631
Cleveland-Elyria-Mentor	30	7,652	350,361	1,896,790	3,619,488	5,185	9,890	5.4	302,201	445	26,433	1,069,941	8,305,421
Columbus	19	5,121	247,131	1,195,823	2,157,612	3,283	5,930	4.8	171,471	398	27,892	964,023	4,791,115
Dayton	8	2,580	115,559	595,813	1,055,008	1,629	2,882	5.2	92,766	166	11,080	435,699	1,920,230
Lima	4	676	28,792	133,725	245,575	366	670	4.6	14,440	61	2,518	98,884	631,890
Mansfield	1	295	16,122	74,480	141,166	203	386	4.6	7,777	38	1,395	65,551	362,472
Parkersburg-Marietta-Vienna	2	181	9,483	44,367	86,821	122	237	4.7	12,670	16	679	41,541	273,740
Sandusky	1	221	9,570	43,845	93,103	120	254	4.6	9,579	15	676	47,131	237,359
Springfield	1	277	16,531	77,172	139,378	211	381	4.7	12,140	31	1,550	73,956	303,882
Toledo	13	2,526	110,878	575,217	1,089,758	1,571	2,979	5.2	85,619	174	9,211	419,995	2,348,368
Weirton-Steubenville	1	319	11,723	70,586	137,919	193	377	6.0	5,042	19	627	45,937	234,242
Wheeling	3	263	8,211	62,171	136,922	170	374	7.6	6,982	10	396	37,338	282,321
Youngstown-Warren-Boardman	8	1,511	73,623	376,286	648,520	1,029	1,774	5.1	42,008	119	4,110	262,304	1,127,319
Wisconsin	126	13,707	617,295	3,172,566	7,367,086	8,687	20,177	5.1	724,084	1,283	69,465	2,066,654	14,203,427
Nonmetropolitan	57	3,563	114,694	876,236	2,794,693	2,400	7,654	7.6	118,610	312	12,919	505,112	3,350,168
Metropolitan	69	10,144	502,601	2,296,330	4,572,393	6,287	12,523	4.6	605,474	971	56,546	1,561,542	10,853,259
Appleton	4	393	18,955	79,900	176,948	217	484	4.2	32,203	48	2,434	67,883	402,926
Duluth	1	25	603	4,460	36,174	12	99	7.4	1,443	0	0	13,351	48,390
Eau Claire	5	551	24,740	122,071	262,955	334	721	4.9	16,926	40	2,473	70,281	410,442
Fond du Lac	3	216	10,633	39,070	128,016	107	350	3.7	12,907	23	1,079	44,597	282,108
Green Bay	5	710	34,052	141,767	295,522	388	809	4.2	54,901	106	4,760	141,106	930,925
Janesville	3	352	15,096	68,039	140,980	186	386	4.5	13,368	33	1,972	68,886	1,091,250
La Crosse	2	444	22,046	91,936	172,714	252	473	4.2	24,204	46	2,439	46,087	270,161
Lake County-Kenosha County	3	477	25,020	101,610	240,617	277	659	4.1	22,099	66	2,967	127,834	811,093
Madison	8	1,469	70,895	380,151	755,801	1,042	2,071	5.4	116,107	96	7,891	163,186	1,308,047
Milwaukee-Waukesha-West Allis	21	3,989	208,322	957,639	1,674,024	2,624	4,586	4.6	242,183	318	23,175	601,331	4,101,872
Minneapolis-St. Paul-Bloomington	4	92	5,471	16,779	51,291	46	140	3.1	6,306	25	895	24,825	90,311
Oshkosh-Neenah	4	443	18,604	78,427	156,264	214	427	4.2	28,989	67	2,697	54,310	264,732
Racine	2	454	19,849	105,386	286,951	289	787	5.3	3,662	47	300	69,314	548,025
Sheboygan	2	213	9,812	34,293	75,997	94	208	3.5	17,004	28	1,535	31,233	177,249
Wausau	2	316	18,503	74,802	118,139	205	323	4.0	13,172	28	1,929	37,318	115,728

TABLE 8

U.S. CENSUS DIVISION 4, EAST NORTH CENTRAL CONTINUED

U.S. Community Hospitals
(Nonfederal, short-term general and other special hospitals)

2008 Utilization, Personnel and Finances

FULL-TIME EQUIVALENT PERSONNEL					FULL-TIME EQUIV. TRAINEES			EXPENSES						
								LABOR				TOTAL		
Physicians and Dentists	Registered Nurses	Licensed Practical Nurses	Other Salaried Personnel	Total Personnel	Medical and Dental Residents	Other Trainees	Total Trainees	Payroll (in thousands)	Employee Benefits (in thousands)	Total (in thousands)	Percent of Total	Amount (in thousands)	Adjusted per Admission	Adjusted per Inpatient Day
6,851	58,208	4,803	155,435	225,297	6,803	841	7,644	12,029,084	3,046,606	15,075,693	51.9	29,074,987	9,687.71	1,941.50
444	6,746	894	19,882	27,966	32	1	33	1,310,645	385,319	1,695,964	52.7	3,217,696	6,339.48	1,497.93
6,407	51,462	3,909	135,553	197,331	6,771	840	7,611	10,718,438	2,661,287	13,379,729	51.7	25,857,291	10,369.21	2,015.79
435	3,766	444	9,390	14,035	469	67	536	747,986	180,161	928,147	53.1	1,747,433	9,744.56	1,868.26
74	2,101	214	5,667	8,056	65	2	67	336,581	93,878	430,458	57.1	754,172	7,212.88	1,307.95
643	8,557	374	21,871	31,445	952	355	1,307	1,518,106	381,499	1,899,606	49.3	3,854,357	10,573.47	2,184.76
2,610	13,210	1,478	41,912	59,210	2,502	365	2,867	3,508,859	809,230	4,318,091	55.2	7,829,402	11,819.02	2,163.12
2,154	9,630	206	21,514	33,504	1,763	6	1,769	1,822,668	466,483	2,289,151	48.5	4,721,460	10,344.78	2,188.28
80	4,263	172	11,342	15,857	407	2	409	876,844	210,236	1,087,080	51.3	2,120,227	10,356.46	2,009.68
20	984	88	2,314	3,406	0	0	0	180,138	56,478	236,616	50.7	467,060	8,847.52	1,901.91
1	502	101	1,511	2,115	0	0	0	107,930	37,493	145,422	56.7	256,320	8,388.25	1,815.73
23	313	54	867	1,257	6	2	8	78,930	27,489	106,418	57.2	186,107	10,058.23	2,143.58
3	305	84	1,085	1,477	18	0	18	74,532	19,668	94,200	53.0	177,812	8,749.74	1,909.84
2	414	13	1,029	1,458	0	0	0	82,133	17,469	99,602	45.1	221,083	7,404.98	1,586.21
183	4,401	360	9,515	14,459	457	19	476	845,164	223,417	1,068,583	50.0	2,136,635	10,564.38	1,960.65
10	451	26	1,065	1,552	0	0	0	60,636	19,126	79,762	53.7	148,410	6,479.07	1,076.06
29	251	73	811	1,164	0	0	0	49,531	13,256	62,787	53.0	118,576	6,362.39	866.01
140	2,314	222	5,660	8,336	132	22	154	428,300	105,406	533,006	47.7	1,118,237	8,885.47	1,724.29
1,104	22,221	1,170	61,647	86,142	1,010	494	1,504	4,895,291	1,471,369	6,366,660	49.3	12,923,890	9,750.00	1,754.27
369	4,004	376	14,126	18,875	0	11	11	1,068,318	316,082	1,384,398	55.3	2,504,235	7,171.55	896.07
735	18,217	794	47,521	67,267	1,010	483	1,493	3,826,973	1,155,287	4,982,262	47.8	10,419,655	10,672.19	2,278.82
13	599	63	1,559	2,234	0	7	7	128,937	35,945	164,883	50.8	324,295	7,613.46	1,832.72
0	31	10	148	189	0	0	0	15,602	4,884	20,486	67.6	30,318	6,198.74	838.12
11	684	91	2,259	3,045	265	12	277	167,098	50,434	217,532	52.3	416,237	9,365.01	1,582.92
35	330	53	967	1,385	1	0	1	99,798	25,816	125,614	43.8	286,876	8,251.62	2,240.94
71	1,449	111	3,819	5,450	0	6	6	313,037	89,453	402,491	51.1	787,439	10,928.31	2,664.57
228	595	41	2,354	3,218	19	0	19	126,743	40,053	166,796	38.0	438,372	14,231.00	3,109.46
13	822	69	2,058	2,962	16	0	16	152,291	55,504	207,795	51.1	406,681	9,873.06	2,354.65
88	787	48	2,771	3,094	0	8	8	205,142	50,677	255,819	54.4	470,468	7,900.92	1,955.26
25	2,855	69	7,314	10,263	504	125	629	640,169	215,906	856,076	54.1	1,582,512	13,134.95	2,093.82
185	7,375	141	17,473	25,174	177	295	472	1,443,572	435,358	1,878,929	43.8	4,287,772	11,692.67	2,561.36
0	185	7	592	784	0	0	0	43,822	10,863	54,685	49.0	111,574	6,647.63	2,175.31
10	656	23	1,477	2,166	0	11	11	123,069	36,272	159,342	48.4	329,420	8,716.19	2,108.10
52	860	53	2,222	3,187	28	11	39	195,422	54,422	249,843	55.8	447,488	8,329.07	1,559.46
0	290	5	751	1,046	0	8	8	53,038	17,103	70,142	46.1	152,028	7,017.88	2,000.45
4	699	10	1,757	2,470	0	0	0	119,293	32,537	151,829	43.6	348,174	12,052.14	2,947.16

MSAs

TABLE 8

U.S. CENSUS DIVISION 5, EAST SOUTH CENTRAL

U.S. Community Hospitals
(Nonfederal, short-term general and other special hospitals)

2008 Utilization, Personnel and Finances

CLASSIFICATION	Hospitals	Beds	Admissions	Inpatient Days	Adjusted Patient Days	Average Daily Census	Adjusted Average Daily Census	Average Stay (days)	Surgical Operations	NEWBORNS Bassinets	Births	OUTPATIENT VISITS Emergency	Total
UNITED STATES	5,010	808,069	35,760,750	196,078,468	351,559,836	536,215	961,620	5.5	27,459,438	57,301	4,073,724	123,024,024	624,098,296
Nonmetropolitan	1,998	143,524	4,592,673	29,262,322	70,831,752	80,001	193,693	6.4	4,175,758	11,324	491,044	23,469,370	119,205,443
Metropolitan	3,012	664,545	31,168,077	166,816,146	280,728,084	456,214	767,927	5.4	23,283,680	45,977	3,582,680	99,554,654	504,892,853
CENSUS DIVISION 5, EAST SOUTH CENTRAL.	449	63,626	2,587,919	14,460,015	26,213,650	39,520	71,661	5.6	2,045,964	4,431	245,061	9,557,382	34,939,921
Nonmetropolitan	238	22,019	733,085	4,548,098	9,672,299	12,423	26,440	6.2	584,728	1,483	64,665	3,565,152	12,114,324
Metropolitan	211	41,607	1,854,834	9,911,917	16,541,351	27,097	45,221	5.3	1,461,236	2,948	180,396	5,992,230	22,825,597
Alabama.	109	15,250	687,446	3,524,687	6,130,292	9,634	16,755	5.1	567,548	1,411	62,436	2,271,755	9,018,521
Nonmetropolitan	49	3,507	138,662	660,633	1,436,928	1,806	3,927	4.8	114,895	315	12,120	658,603	2,538,937
Metropolitan	60	11,743	548,784	2,864,054	4,693,364	7,828	12,828	5.2	452,653	1,096	50,316	1,613,152	6,479,584
Anniston-Oxford	3	425	21,664	98,880	156,333	270	427	4.6	11,567	37	1,978	89,458	186,473
Auburn-Opelika	1	375	16,073	107,672	204,112	294	558	6.7	12,398	38	1,825	42,496	103,894
Birmingham-Hoover.	19	4,330	188,780	1,050,397	1,658,450	2,870	4,534	5.6	179,434	444	16,635	530,022	2,687,288
Columbus.	1	38	781	11,978	12,670	33	35	15.3	0	0	0	0	4,298
Decatur	4	514	18,851	86,710	166,805	238	457	4.6	11,051	42	1,989	82,643	275,060
Dothan	4	711	34,506	161,865	303,912	442	831	4.7	29,515	47	2,719	101,964	338,350
Florence-Muscle Shoals	3	533	22,441	108,392	195,257	296	534	4.8	15,507	46	1,733	93,663	229,035
Gadsden	3	507	20,511	118,331	179,858	323	491	5.8	20,856	32	1,043	51,374	186,750
Huntsville	4	1,127	60,758	293,146	506,515	802	1,384	4.8	50,446	78	6,141	179,377	840,368
Mobile.	6	1,442	72,288	382,986	607,494	1,047	1,658	5.3	58,193	183	6,466	181,263	643,152
Montgomery	8	1,067	53,786	251,215	409,796	687	1,121	4.7	42,257	106	6,290	138,076	423,306
Tuscaloosa	4	674	38,345	192,482	292,162	526	798	5.0	21,429	43	3,497	122,816	561,610
Kentucky.	105	14,180	610,449	3,216,149	6,189,065	8,789	16,919	5.3	561,606	987	54,872	2,339,390	9,658,798
Nonmetropolitan	64	5,888	226,744	1,177,038	2,567,638	3,213	7,019	5.2	193,710	435	17,248	1,107,513	3,855,296
Metropolitan	41	8,292	383,705	2,039,111	3,621,427	5,576	9,900	5.3	367,896	552	37,624	1,231,877	5,803,502
Bowling Green.	3	542	21,306	112,875	188,569	308	515	5.3	21,893	19	2,320	61,245	148,143
Cincinnati-Middletown	5	982	49,881	237,305	429,543	647	1,174	4.8	32,020	80	5,183	209,564	916,557
Clarksville.	2	164	7,581	32,974	66,313	91	182	4.3	2,567	18	892	36,812	167,376
Elizabethtown	2	308	12,634	66,837	159,100	183	434	5.3	8,820	26	1,624	49,706	262,519
Evansville.	1	216	6,308	27,635	64,867	76	177	4.4	4,200	16	664	27,406	316,712
Huntington-Ashland.	2	687	31,958	195,364	330,992	535	907	6.1	53,014	34	1,422	90,481	695,235
Lexington-Fayette	14	2,022	92,234	488,169	838,220	1,336	2,291	5.3	77,325	155	9,089	255,817	1,271,236
Louisville	11	3,013	144,001	793,926	1,382,586	2,170	3,779	5.5	148,897	170	14,674	435,661	1,728,502
Owensboro	1	358	17,802	84,026	161,237	230	441	4.7	19,160	34	1,756	65,185	297,222
Mississippi.	98	13,094	430,680	2,807,964	5,067,738	7,669	13,856	6.5	287,646	761	43,775	1,694,645	5,015,607
Nonmetropolitan	69	7,739	222,884	1,709,483	3,279,162	4,668	8,966	7.7	149,665	445	21,509	956,687	3,057,236
Metropolitan	29	5,355	207,796	1,098,481	1,788,576	3,001	4,890	5.3	137,981	316	22,266	737,958	1,958,371
Gulfport-Biloxi	6	906	30,604	165,190	258,548	451	707	5.4	33,020	65	3,060	141,772	452,237
Hattiesburg.	3	756	36,427	177,353	283,797	485	776	4.9	17,465	45	4,198	111,004	202,278
Jackson.	15	2,941	104,189	585,147	973,698	1,600	2,662	5.6	70,907	143	11,051	302,205	779,371
Memphis	3	318	17,592	84,470	127,395	230	348	4.8	5,108	23	2,132	64,620	122,616
Pascagoula.	2	434	18,984	86,321	145,138	235	397	4.5	11,481	40	1,825	118,357	401,869
Tennessee	137	21,102	859,344	4,911,215	8,826,555	13,428	24,131	5.7	629,164	1,272	83,978	3,251,592	11,246,995
Nonmetropolitan	56	4,885	144,795	1,000,944	2,388,571	2,736	6,528	6.9	126,458	288	13,788	842,349	2,662,855
Metropolitan	81	16,217	714,549	3,910,271	6,437,984	10,692	17,603	5.5	502,706	984	70,190	2,409,243	8,584,140
Chattanooga	6	1,605	73,760	406,970	633,476	1,112	1,731	5.5	65,250	60	7,422	241,651	785,428
Clarksville.	1	240	11,245	42,492	73,898	116	202	3.8	9,298	30	1,817	47,841	131,202
Cleveland.	2	234	10,414	41,528	94,187	113	257	4.0	13,499	22	1,085	57,868	135,812
Jackson.	2	755	34,306	190,926	364,368	521	995	5.6	31,248	47	3,711	104,923	208,763
Johnson City.	6	841	36,813	212,167	368,855	580	1,008	5.8	21,419	79	2,706	114,403	412,835
Kingsport-Bristol-Bristol	6	1,054	45,026	217,851	383,995	595	1,050	4.8	23,076	78	2,938	209,579	501,478
Knoxville	12	2,802	114,815	676,407	1,157,381	1,851	3,166	5.9	77,894	136	10,233	385,970	1,680,446
Memphis	15	3,524	151,836	924,870	1,377,099	2,530	3,765	6.1	86,187	218	18,713	518,147	1,360,585
Morristown	3	273	10,140	40,179	80,045	110	219	4.0	12,487	33	1,323	48,189	207,384
Nashville-Davidson--Murfreesboro .	28	4,889	226,194	1,156,881	1,904,680	3,164	5,210	5.1	162,348	281	20,242	680,672	3,160,207

MSAs

TABLE 8

U.S. CENSUS DIVISION 5, EAST SOUTH CENTRAL

U.S. Community Hospitals
(Nonfederal, short-term general and other special hospitals)

2008 Utilization, Personnel and Finances

FULL-TIME EQUIVALENT PERSONNEL					FULL-TIME EQUIV. TRAINEES			EXPENSES						
								LABOR				TOTAL		
Physicians and Dentists	Registered Nurses	Licensed Practical Nurses	Other Salaried Personnel	Total Personnel	Medical and Dental Residents	Other Trainees	Total Trainees	Payroll (in thousands)	Employee Benefits (in thousands)	Total (in thousands)	Percent of Total	Amount (in thousands)	Adjusted per Admission	Adjusted per Inpatient Day
95,400	1,228,383	104,562	3,121,215	4,549,560	90,543	9,573	100,116	$256,559,486	$65,376,486	$321,935,957	51.4	$626,576,958	$9,788.25	$1,782.28
12,071	149,214	30,278	467,807	659,370	1,535	394	1,929	30,769,205	8,096,158	38,865,353	53.4	72,719,071	6,539.38	1,026.65
83,329	1,079,169	74,284	2,653,408	3,890,190	89,008	9,179	98,187	225,790,281	57,280,329	283,070,604	51.1	553,857,887	10,471.29	1,972.93
3,451	82,790	9,917	200,709	296,867	3,404	554	3,958	13,811,167	3,450,454	17,261,619	49.4	34,933,935	7,372.05	1,332.66
1,119	20,061	4,440	58,692	84,312	155	130	285	3,479,415	885,916	4,365,332	52.4	8,337,184	5,238.93	861.97
2,332	62,729	5,477	142,017	212,555	3,249	424	3,673	10,331,753	2,564,538	12,896,287	48.5	26,596,751	8,450.64	1,607.89
1,368	21,284	2,176	47,796	72,624	1,187	59	1,246	3,308,792	820,237	4,129,028	49.8	8,288,703	6,735.62	1,352.09
150	3,370	640	9,336	13,496	25	6	31	502,492	124,365	626,855	51.8	1,209,494	3,947.14	841.72
1,218	17,914	1,536	38,460	59,128	1,162	53	1,215	2,806,300	695,872	3,502,173	10.5	7,070,200	7,000.00	1,500.04
4	541	88	1,223	1,856	1	0	1	78,166	18,827	96,993	56.0	173,346	5,052.79	1,108.83
12	559	48	1,799	2,418	0	0	0	97,920	20,593	118,513	50.7	233,689	7,669.73	1,144.91
920	6,636	408	14,084	22,048	838	17	855	1,135,277	275,325	1,410,602	47.0	2,905,099	9,506.72	1,787.87
0	16	14	101	131	0	0	0	8,376	1,069	9,445	91.9	10,275	12,439.39	810.97
12	476	45	995	1,528	1	0	1	80,741	19,816	100,558	54.2	185,624	5,045.24	1,112.82
35	974	183	2,663	3,855	1	1	2	162,245	37,184	199,429	47.7	418,199	6,347.50	1,376.05
6	837	39	1,348	2,230	0	0	0	88,174	24,034	112,207	47.1	238,378	5,848.61	1,220.84
5	619	73	1,050	1,747	4	1	5	84,798	21,514	106,313	49.2	216,146	6,925.76	1,201.76
64	2,274	177	3,991	6,506	0	0	0	301,375	98,590	399,965	51.8	772,581	7,227.67	1,525.29
78	2,392	126	5,703	8,299	284	10	294	371,068	99,534	471,402	52.1	904,700	7,700.30	1,489.23
69	1,516	139	2,976	4,700	33	1	34	209,934	41,633	251,566	43.7	575,520	6,516.96	1,404.41
13	1,074	196	2,527	3,810	0	23	23	187,426	37,754	225,180	68.4	385,652	6,500.88	1,319.99
696	19,301	2,034	48,200	70,231	621	45	666	3,372,033	883,937	4,255,971	48.2	8,831,618	7,319.55	1,426.97
407	6,265	1,289	18,101	26,062	68	15	83	1,093,822	297,580	1,391,402	51.6	2,693,991	5,258.59	1,049.21
289	13,036	745	30,099	44,169	553	30	583	2,278,211	586,357	2,864,569	46.7	6,137,627	8,840.31	1,694.81
2	600	34	1,494	2,130	0	0	0	110,405	27,614	138,020	49.5	278,864	7,877.74	1,478.84
71	1,488	150	3,324	5,033	24	17	41	288,853	86,330	375,183	56.1	668,747	7,357.92	1,556.88
17	225	25	890	905	6	1	7	40,593	10,307	50,900	52.9	96,168	6,372.53	1,450.21
9	399	19	1,053	1,480	0	0	0	72,736	20,503	93,239	50.9	183,278	5,992.42	1,151.97
13	283	25	722	1,043	3	0	3	43,704	14,753	58,458	59.4	98,455	6,649.25	1,517.80
124	999	59	2,659	3,841	128	6	134	203,122	54,266	257,387	49.0	525,204	9,215.56	1,586.76
41	3,094	173	7,781	11,089	384	6	390	574,848	143,877	718,726	45.4	1,583,832	9,782.90	1,889.52
7	5,349	216	10,724	16,296	8	0	8	844,902	198,117	1,043,019	43.0	2,426,795	9,537.11	1,755.26
5	599	44	1,644	2,292	0	0	0	99,047	30,590	129,637	46.9	276,283	8,087.92	1,713.52
649	13,029	1,977	36,271	51,926	435	139	574	2,449,224	580,418	3,029,641	52.1	5,817,368	7,518.96	1,147.02
393	6,327	1,396	18,647	26,763	29	99	128	1,183,541	287,324	1,470,865	52.2	2,817,098	6,488.20	859.09
256	6,702	581	17,624	25,163	406	40	446	1,265,683	293,095	1,558,776	52.0	3,000,270	8,837.19	1,677.46
112	1,328	87	2,782	4,309	0	0	0	217,468	46,651	264,119	53.4	494,522	9,947.93	1,912.69
36	904	104	2,516	3,560	0	0	0	188,873	46,448	235,322	57.7	407,606	7,031.94	1,436.26
51	3,229	297	9,423	13,000	406	0	406	663,247	145,251	808,497	49.2	1,642,969	9,491.01	1,687.35
0	541	56	1,080	1,677	0	40	40	75,422	20,539	95,960	56.9	168,718	6,358.79	1,324.37
57	700	37	1,823	2,617	0	0	0	120,673	34,205	154,878	54.1	286,455	8,899.44	1,973.67
738	29,176	3,730	68,442	102,086	1,161	311	1,472	4,681,118	1,165,862	5,846,979	48.7	11,996,246	7,851.74	1,359.11
169	4,099	1,115	12,608	17,991	33	10	43	699,560	176,647	876,210	54.2	1,616,601	4,776.10	676.81
569	25,077	2,615	55,834	84,095	1,128	301	1,429	3,981,559	989,214	4,970,769	47.9	10,379,645	8,727.02	1,612.25
83	2,604	201	5,187	8,075	154	0	154	440,521	118,551	559,072	49.7	1,124,678	9,607.87	1,775.41
17	275	40	667	999	0	0	0	41,618	10,683	52,301	47.8	109,519	5,600.29	1,482.03
8	331	45	659	1,043	0	1	1	42,128	8,091	50,219	48.7	103,055	4,367.68	1,094.16
17	1,086	195	3,286	4,584	0	2	2	201,996	54,623	256,619	55.9	459,267	7,104.67	1,260.45
1	1,031	185	2,037	3,254	0	0	0	156,900	34,047	190,947	41.1	465,022	7,756.97	1,260.72
4	1,270	158	3,284	4,716	0	0	0	217,275	57,036	274,310	46.7	587,112	7,285.62	1,528.96
110	4,336	424	9,608	14,478	152	90	242	620,903	152,701	773,605	48.1	1,609,375	8,046.39	1,390.53
73	6,192	511	13,911	20,687	262	197	459	878,052	214,499	1,092,551	49.4	2,210,355	9,596.76	1,605.08
20	302	37	793	1,152	5	1	6	47,193	11,626	58,818	51.1	115,033	5,634.17	1,437.10
236	7,650	819	16,402	25,107	555	10	565	1,334,972	327,358	1,662,327	46.2	3,596,228	9,635.39	1,888.10

MSAs

TABLE 8

U.S. CENSUS DIVISION 6, WEST NORTH CENTRAL

U.S. Community Hospitals
(Nonfederal, short-term general and other special hospitals)

2008 Utilization, Personnel and Finances

CLASSIFICATION	Hospitals	Beds	Admissions	Inpatient Days	Adjusted Patient Days	Average Daily Census	Adjusted Average Daily Census	Average Stay (days)	Surgical Operations	NEWBORNS Bassinets	NEWBORNS Births	OUTPATIENT VISITS Emergency	OUTPATIENT VISITS Total
UNITED STATES	5,010	808,069	35,760,750	196,078,468	351,559,836	536,215	961,620	5.5	27,459,438	57,301	4,073,724	123,024,024	624,098,296
Nonmetropolitan	1,998	143,524	4,592,673	29,262,322	70,831,752	80,001	193,693	6.4	4,175,758	11,324	491,044	23,469,370	119,205,443
Metropolitan	3,012	664,545	31,168,077	166,816,146	280,728,084	456,214	767,927	5.4	23,283,680	45,977	3,582,680	99,554,654	504,892,853
CENSUS DIVISION 6, WEST NORTH CENTRAL	683	70,208	2,589,852	15,912,612	32,911,569	43,490	89,966	6.1	2,143,789	4,874	279,320	8,056,684	53,922,090
Nonmetropolitan	463	27,707	652,908	5,673,400	14,552,476	15,505	39,791	8.7	606,085	2,074	74,807	2,602,737	20,460,522
Metropolitan	220	42,501	1,936,944	10,239,212	18,359,093	27,985	50,175	5.3	1,537,704	2,800	204,513	5,453,947	33,461,568
Iowa	118	10,531	373,330	2,248,874	5,475,135	6,140	14,959	6.0	438,975	754	39,060	1,226,568	10,380,628
Nonmetropolitan	84	4,600	118,629	951,272	2,901,730	2,596	7,928	8.0	137,809	347	11,699	505,501	4,308,950
Metropolitan	34	5,931	254,701	1,297,602	2,573,405	3,544	7,031	5.1	301,166	407	27,361	721,067	6,071,678
Ames	2	276	10,367	67,833	144,920	185	397	6.5	10,156	17	1,269	27,347	175,369
Cedar Rapids	4	803	28,880	173,730	440,168	475	1,202	6.0	34,887	54	3,510	109,806	865,022
Davenport-Moline-Rock Island . . .	3	534	25,985	112,960	186,602	309	510	4.3	13,252	33	2,779	87,026	240,287
Des Moines	8	1,470	73,952	331,374	566,589	904	1,548	4.5	49,386	129	8,461	189,479	1,597,148
Dubuque	3	465	14,615	79,622	142,708	217	390	5.4	13,643	34	1,636	51,844	139,056
Iowa City	3	978	39,593	249,231	472,376	681	1,291	6.3	111,158	48	3,133	73,804	1,344,350
Omaha-Council Bluffs	3	294	15,123	63,096	121,034	172	330	4.2	12,599	22	1,189	53,440	211,028
Sioux City	2	406	20,675	92,607	144,572	253	395	4.5	12,941	32	2,541	54,779	367,031
Waterloo-Cedar Falls.	6	705	25,511	127,149	354,436	348	968	5.0	43,144	38	2,843	73,542	1,132,387
Kansas.	132	10,269	328,279	2,079,667	4,318,037	5,687	11,808	6.3	245,691	725	41,592	1,028,706	6,526,203
Nonmetropolitan	99	5,214	117,802	998,013	2,500,205	2,730	6,843	8.5	101,350	363	12,527	405,497	3,244,485
Metropolitan	33	5,055	210,477	1,081,654	1,817,832	2,957	4,965	5.1	144,341	362	29,065	623,209	3,281,718
Kansas City	15	2,299	98,140	497,025	837,348	1,360	2,287	5.1	74,204	193	14,226	269,958	1,614,475
Lawrence	1	152	6,740	24,097	73,882	66	202	3.6	4,404	13	1,113	35,428	217,100
Topeka	6	839	29,329	164,608	319,600	450	873	5.6	19,498	40	3,204	95,075	567,004
Wichita	11	1,765	76,268	395,924	587,002	1,081	1,603	5.2	46,235	116	10,522	222,748	883,139
Minnesota	130	15,621	640,976	3,873,690	7,747,360	10,595	21,183	6.0	481,403	1,245	69,360	1,772,982	10,006,069
Nonmetropolitan	81	5,668	125,209	1,264,879	3,133,115	3,460	8,567	10.1	127,137	445	17,435	521,253	3,448,667
Metropolitan	49	9,953	515,767	2,608,811	4,614,245	7,135	12,616	5.1	354,266	800	51,925	1,251,729	6,557,402
Duluth	10	1,501	47,515	361,897	768,240	989	2,098	7.6	48,288	96	3,883	128,394	582,173
Grand Forks	2	124	1,929	24,407	103,553	66	283	12.7	4,335	8	225	3,048	78,759
Minneapolis-St. Paul-Bloomington .	29	6,302	360,531	1,628,047	2,708,918	4,453	7,406	4.5	252,933	607	43,068	960,591	4,856,783
Rochester.	4	1,337	75,828	411,314	665,006	1,126	1,822	5.4	33,682	49	1,766	102,752	613,594
St. Cloud	4	689	29,964	183,146	368,528	501	1,007	6.1	15,028	40	2,983	56,944	426,093
Missouri	123	18,968	841,118	4,396,779	8,387,008	12,011	22,914	5.2	599,970	1,188	80,282	2,860,410	18,828,585
Nonmetropolitan	53	3,864	146,943	688,244	1,730,988	1,877	4,730	4.7	108,903	359	15,775	671,590	5,162,631
Metropolitan	70	15,104	694,175	3,708,535	6,656,020	10,134	18,184	5.3	491,067	829	64,507	2,188,820	13,665,954
Columbia	4	869	37,705	202,511	304,965	553	834	5.4	31,675	41	3,859	75,408	831,967
Jefferson City	3	316	18,786	71,989	150,078	196	410	3.8	11,706	30	1,652	74,258	619,082
Joplin	4	775	36,743	184,117	349,229	504	953	5.0	22,216	51	3,552	170,986	1,027,607
Kansas City	23	3,742	160,641	880,947	1,648,538	2,407	4,505	5.5	123,884	222	15,967	657,595	3,213,635
Springfield	5	1,395	69,279	345,840	738,911	945	2,019	5.0	60,825	82	7,167	251,720	2,387,567
St. Joseph	1	353	19,449	87,177	148,753	238	406	4.5	10,417	20	1,887	51,243	619,539
St. Louis	30	7,654	351,572	1,935,954	3,315,546	5,291	9,057	5.5	230,344	383	30,423	907,610	4,966,557
Nebraska	86	7,264	214,808	1,562,960	3,132,407	4,271	8,570	7.3	201,688	544	26,802	639,756	4,627,089
Nonmetropolitan	70	3,758	81,108	742,876	1,834,979	2,030	5,020	9.2	73,993	326	9,484	252,919	2,516,072
Metropolitan	16	3,506	133,700	820,084	1,297,428	2,241	3,550	6.1	127,695	218	17,318	386,837	2,111,017
Lincoln	4	1,091	38,482	276,883	401,176	756	1,098	7.2	24,331	59	5,119	100,657	406,354
Omaha-Council Bluffs	12	2,415	95,218	543,201	896,252	1,485	2,452	5.7	103,364	159	12,199	286,180	1,704,663
North Dakota	41	3,442	89,225	744,876	1,785,094	2,037	4,881	8.3	73,185	182	9,966	289,070	1,695,560
Nonmetropolitan	34	2,031	27,715	428,110	1,105,709	1,171	3,022	15.4	23,941	89	2,958	133,750	736,034
Metropolitan	7	1,411	61,510	316,766	679,385	866	1,859	5.1	49,244	93	7,008	155,320	959,526
Bismarck	2	505	19,771	88,893	200,320	243	549	4.5	16,896	27	1,951	43,407	595,833
Fargo	3	568	27,913	144,537	266,507	395	729	5.2	21,959	43	3,488	54,483	238,270
Grand Forks	2	338	13,826	83,336	212,558	228	581	6.0	10,389	23	1,569	57,430	125,423
South Dakota	53	4,113	102,116	1,005,766	2,066,528	2,749	5,651	9.8	102,877	236	12,258	239,192	1,857,956
Nonmetropolitan	42	2,572	35,502	600,006	1,345,750	1,641	3,681	16.9	32,952	145	4,929	112,227	1,043,683
Metropolitan	11	1,541	66,614	405,760	720,778	1,108	1,970	6.1	69,925	91	7,329	126,965	814,273
Rapid City	3	496	17,264	121,862	207,703	333	567	7.1	12,911	52	2,338	57,664	204,049
Sioux Falls	8	1,045	49,350	283,898	513,075	775	1,403	5.8	57,014	39	4,991	69,301	610,224

MSAs

TABLE 8

U.S. CENSUS DIVISION 6, WEST NORTH CENTRAL

U.S. Community Hospitals
(Nonfederal, short-term general and other special hospitals)

2008 Utilization, Personnel and Finances

	FULL-TIME EQUIVALENT PERSONNEL				FULL-TIME EQUIV. TRAINEES			EXPENSES						
								LABOR				TOTAL		
Physicians and Dentists	Registered Nurses	Licensed Practical Nurses	Other Salaried Personnel	Total Personnel	Medical and Dental Residents	Other Trainees	Total Trainees	Payroll (in thousands)	Employee Benefits (in thousands)	Total (in thousands)	Percent of Total	Amount (in thousands)	Adjusted per Admission	Adjusted per Inpatient Day
95,400	1,228,383	104,562	3,121,215	4,549,560	90,543	9,573	100,116	$256,559,486	$65,376,486	$321,935,957	51.4	$626,576,958	$9,788.25	$1,782.28
12,071	149,214	30,278	467,807	659,370	1,535	394	1,929	30,769,205	8,096,158	38,865,353	53.4	72,719,071	6,539.38	1,026.65
83,329	1,079,169	74,284	2,653,408	3,890,190	89,008	9,179	98,187	225,790,281	57,280,329	283,070,604	51.1	553,857,887	10,471.29	1,972.93
7,451	94,754	10,298	255,471	367,974	3,198	410	3,608	19,746,669	4,917,215	24,663,885	51.1	48,227,547	9,385.41	1,465.37
2,164	24,382	5,383	79,841	111,770	85	56	141	5,092,173	1,271,157	6,363,337	54.3	11,719,684	6,908.93	805.34
5,287	70,372	4,915	175,630	256,204	3,113	354	3,467	14,654,496	3,646,059	18,300,548	50.1	36,507,863	10,605.79	1,988.54
1,067	14,377	1,270	40,846	57,560	621	23	644	2,686,050	726,940	3,412,993	52.4	6,518,050	7,704.49	1,190.48
359	4,989	760	15,564	21,672	26	6	32	950,163	245,158	1,195,323	54.2	2,203,791	6,194.11	759.47
708	9,388	510	25,282	35,888	595	17	612	1,735,887	491,792	2,217,670	51.4	4,311,260	8,000.68	1,670.40
4	308	9	900	1,221	0	0	0	61,478	19,364	80,842	50.9	158,914	7,919.58	1,096.57
26	1,117	84	3,010	4,237	0	0	0	190,905	54,060	244,965	51.4	476,259	7,196.42	1,081.99
10	734	13	1,351	2,108	5	0	5	111,184	27,213	138,397	30.0	350,904	8,027.89	1,912.43
320	2,852	85	7,790	11,047	154	5	159	478,026	120,447	598,473	52.3	1,144,636	9,028.23	2,020.22
9	510	13	1,248	1,780	0	0	0	76,713	17,437	94,150	44.8	210,240	7,897.81	1,473.22
129	1,935	26	6,394	7,484	433	12	445	397,938	142,163	540,101	55.2	979,261	13,222.71	2,073.05
24	435	22	1,040	1,521	0	0	0	76,935	19,817	96,752	49.2	196,653	6,828.95	1,624.78
63	670	38	1,672	2,443	0	0	0	128,198	29,857	158,055	52.4	301,825	9,341.52	2,087.71
123	827	220	2,877	4,047	3	0	3	214,510	51,425	265,935	54.3	489,608	6,900.74	1,381.37
805	12,144	1,355	30,838	45,142	3	94	97	2,250,372	520,996	2,771,372	52.0	5,330,136	8,121.51	1,234.39
265	4,198	754	13,776	18,993	3	16	19	811,341	184,433	995,777	55.7	1,787,077	6,347.35	714.77
540	7,946	601	17,062	26,149	0	78	78	1,439,031	336,563	1,775,595	50.1	3,543,058	9,454.41	1,949.06
223	3,913	113	8,039	12,288	0	18	18	681,813	171,801	853,615	47.5	1,795,724	10,027.83	2,144.54
20	271	23	702	1,016	0	0	0	53,775	11,554	65,329	50.0	130,771	6,328.12	1,769.99
213	1,183	348	3,278	5,022	0	8	8	294,153	60,878	355,032	58.3	608,504	9,982.18	1,903.95
84	2,579	117	5,043	7,823	0	52	52	409,290	92,330	501,619	49.8	1,008,061	8,838.45	1,717.30
1,782	20,910	2,373	58,026	83,091	583	149	732	5,434,123	1,422,642	6,856,763	55.3	12,401,407	10,422.65	1,600.73
509	4,638	1,302	16,088	22,537	13	9	22	1,127,878	285,848	1,413,726	55.5	2,548,210	8,002.84	813.32
1,273	16,272	1,071	41,938	60,554	570	140	710	4,306,245	1,136,794	5,443,037	55.2	9,853,197	11,306.81	2,135.39
175	1,254	214	4,654	6,297	0	61	61	405,612	118,039	523,651	59.3	882,616	10,102.05	1,148.88
9	150	37	493	689	0	0	0	22,917	4,925	27,841	58.3	47,726	6,307.19	460.89
909	11,954	486	29,801	43,150	449	55	504	3,185,910	832,338	4,018,249	55.4	7,251,450	11,996.58	2,676.88
158	1,863	118	4,115	6,254	108	24	132	470,486	118,815	589,301	50.6	1,164,473	9,643.90	1,751.07
22	1,051	216	2,875	4,164	13	0	13	221,319	62,676	283,995	56.0	506,932	9,882.67	1,375.56
2,307	30,275	3,132	77,137	112,851	1,912	128	2,040	5,913,700	1,439,159	7,352,856	46.5	15,824,163	9,823.80	1,886.75
548	4,773	1,287	14,820	21,428	33	20	53	987,321	262,243	1,249,567	51.1	2,444,852	6,668.86	1,412.40
1,759	25,502	1,845	62,317	91,423	1,879	108	1,987	4,926,379	1,176,915	6,103,289	45.6	13,379,310	10,753.41	2,010.11
16	872	196	4,229	5,313	311	0	311	276,214	76,829	353,043	43.9	803,307	13,889.63	2,634.09
86	516	128	1,530	2,260	8	0	8	115,643	27,268	142,909	46.9	304,886	7,784.05	2,031.52
224	1,312	131	3,558	5,225	19	0	19	272,692	54,613	327,304	50.2	652,475	9,333.07	1,868.33
379	6,388	399	14,323	21,489	193	108	301	1,251,533	282,817	1,534,349	49.1	3,126,532	11,028.53	1,896.55
231	2,768	305	9,483	12,787	26	0	26	577,906	151,758	729,663	45.7	1,597,759	10,748.10	2,162.32
104	645	162	1,695	2,606	0	0	0	167,973	42,015	209,988	54.6	384,324	11,580.90	2,583.64
719	13,001	524	27,499	41,743	1,322	0	1,322	2,264,419	541,616	2,806,033	43.1	6,510,028	10,638.29	1,963.49
544	9,338	1,174	23,906	34,962	42	14	56	1,765,625	441,828	2,207,454	50.4	4,380,338	10,470.79	1,398.39
211	3,086	743	10,260	14,300	10	3	13	647,196	168,689	815,885	54.1	1,508,421	7,404.64	822.04
333	6,252	431	13,646	20,662	32	11	43	1,118,429	273,139	1,391,569	48.5	2,871,916	13,381.03	2,213.55
97	1,497	198	4,112	5,904	2	8	10	281,910	86,866	368,776	52.6	701,604	11,895.23	1,748.87
236	4,755	233	9,534	14,758	30	3	33	836,519	186,273	1,022,793	47.1	2,170,312	13,944.08	2,421.54
544	3,426	745	11,145	15,860	22	1	23	842,274	173,166	1,015,438	54.8	1,853,693	8,597.40	1,038.43
170	1,137	367	4,416	6,090	0	1	1	274,624	53,505	328,128	55.8	588,419	7,057.33	532.16
374	2,289	378	6,729	9,770	22	0	22	567,650	119,661	687,310	54.3	1,265,274	9,568.45	1,862.38
189	837	172	2,486	3,684	0	0	0	197,218	31,773	228,991	54.8	417,955	9,338.10	2,086.44
14	991	150	1,846	3,001	1	0	1	184,364	47,566	231,930	48.5	478,146	9,274.30	1,794.12
171	461	56	2,397	3,085	21	0	21	186,067	40,322	226,389	61.3	369,174	10,277.66	1,736.81
402	4,284	249	13,573	18,508	15	1	16	854,525	192,484	1,047,009	54.5	1,919,762	9,519.75	928.98
102	1,561	170	4,917	6,750	0	1	1	293,651	71,280	364,931	57.1	638,914	7,355.25	474.76
300	2,723	79	8,656	11,758	15	0	15	560,875	121,204	682,078	53.3	1,280,848	11,157.60	1,777.03
19	601	47	1,858	2,525	15	0	15	126,968	18,525	145,492	47.0	309,616	10,705.93	1,490.66
281	2,122	32	6,798	9,233	0	0	0	433,907	102,680	536,586	55.2	971,232	11,309.70	1,892.96

MSAs

TABLE 8

U.S. CENSUS DIVISION 7, WEST SOUTH CENTRAL

U.S. Community Hospitals
(Nonfederal, short-term general and other special hospitals)

2008 Utilization, Personnel and Finances

CLASSIFICATION	Hospitals	Beds	Admissions	Inpatient Days	Adjusted Patient Days	Average Daily Census	Adjusted Average Daily Census	Average Stay (days)	Surgical Operations	NEWBORNS Bassinets	Births	OUTPATIENT VISITS Emergency	Total
UNITED STATES	5,010	808,069	35,760,750	196,078,468	351,559,836	536,215	961,620	5.5	27,459,438	57,301	4,073,724	123,024,024	624,098,296
Nonmetropolitan	1,998	143,524	4,592,673	29,262,322	70,831,752	80,001	193,693	6.4	4,175,758	11,324	491,044	23,469,370	119,205,443
Metropolitan	3,012	664,545	31,168,077	166,816,146	280,728,084	456,214	767,927	5.4	23,283,680	45,977	3,582,680	99,554,654	504,892,853
CENSUS DIVISION 7, WEST SOUTH CENTRAL	757	97,720	4,061,559	21,234,945	35,635,593	58,078	97,441	5.2	2,812,036	7,072	546,219	14,148,116	56,384,809
Nonmetropolitan	315	16,903	616,851	2,843,946	6,362,063	7,789	17,401	4.6	424,401	1,405	65,996	2,979,939	11,568,915
Metropolitan	442	80,817	3,444,708	18,390,999	29,273,530	50,289	80,040	5.3	2,387,635	5,667	480,223	11,168,177	44,815,894
Arkansas	86	9,686	376,158	1,989,969	3,564,878	5,439	9,744	5.3	239,246	604	39,013	1,301,330	4,972,752
Nonmetropolitan	49	3,360	116,771	602,154	1,363,411	1,643	3,724	5.2	75,668	247	11,312	493,465	1,766,081
Metropolitan	37	6,326	259,387	1,387,815	2,201,467	3,796	6,020	5.4	163,578	357	27,701	807,865	3,206,671
Fayetteville-Springdale-Rogers	8	840	43,892	187,702	288,586	514	789	4.3	27,529	82	6,450	160,654	396,449
Fort Smith	7	947	31,412	184,830	273,095	505	747	5.9	21,296	53	3,624	115,157	261,814
Hot Springs	3	481	19,051	106,653	157,346	291	430	5.6	11,827	24	1,791	55,431	496,276
Jonesboro	3	542	25,926	126,475	213,837	347	586	4.9	13,364	32	2,165	63,210	253,729
Little Rock-North Little Rock	14	2,995	122,372	697,041	1,117,395	1,907	3,054	5.7	80,997	118	11,741	336,608	1,548,544
Memphis	1	142	4,207	21,704	39,756	59	109	5.2	3,490	12	551	23,903	57,724
Pine Bluff	1	379	12,527	63,410	111,452	173	305	5.1	5,075	36	1,379	52,902	192,135
Louisiana	130	16,007	636,767	3,378,368	6,073,833	9,241	16,603	5.3	462,895	1,095	67,081	2,381,889	11,161,368
Nonmetropolitan	50	3,160	119,469	572,988	1,206,489	1,571	3,302	4.8	89,295	226	10,906	562,669	1,929,313
Metropolitan	80	12,847	517,298	2,805,380	4,867,344	7,670	13,301	5.4	373,600	869	56,175	1,819,220	9,232,055
Alexandria	6	756	34,934	190,668	305,335	522	835	5.5	20,825	64	3,246	130,400	448,799
Baton Rouge	15	2,693	99,156	525,049	889,852	1,437	2,432	5.3	64,929	141	11,923	364,403	1,263,831
Houma-Bayou Cane-Thibodaux	5	693	24,193	111,648	216,254	305	591	4.6	22,729	69	3,881	121,446	482,874
Lafayette	7	1,028	41,657	230,625	365,014	629	997	5.5	25,727	91	5,593	167,331	538,729
Lake Charles	8	852	33,265	154,892	279,880	424	764	4.7	25,840	64	3,382	119,647	455,643
Monroe	10	973	37,230	211,552	559,976	577	1,531	5.7	23,237	66	3,981	104,412	504,267
New Orleans-Metairie-Kenner	19	3,705	161,863	878,581	1,476,872	2,402	4,036	5.4	120,677	276	17,404	531,482	4,311,848
Shreveport-Bossier City	10	2,147	85,000	502,365	774,161	1,374	2,115	5.9	69,636	98	6,765	280,099	1,226,064
Oklahoma	115	10,988	462,954	2,436,253	4,266,033	6,660	11,651	5.3	315,989	715	49,851	1,645,625	5,431,621
Nonmetropolitan	65	3,554	144,663	660,615	1,432,109	1,809	3,911	4.6	97,494	324	15,065	608,247	2,177,352
Metropolitan	50	7,434	318,291	1,775,638	2,833,924	4,851	7,740	5.6	218,495	391	34,786	1,037,378	3,254,269
Fort Smith	2	110	3,917	14,119	33,569	38	92	3.6	1,370	9	419	31,322	65,969
Lawton	2	400	15,568	93,261	167,681	255	458	6.0	10,929	32	1,808	62,190	152,145
Oklahoma City	23	3,885	163,189	974,517	1,505,509	2,663	4,112	6.0	109,194	211	18,693	593,393	1,691,594
Tulsa	23	3,039	135,617	693,741	1,127,165	1,895	3,078	5.1	97,002	139	13,866	350,473	1,344,561
Texas	426	61,039	2,585,680	13,430,355	21,730,849	36,738	59,443	5.2	1,793,906	4,658	390,274	8,819,272	34,819,068
Nonmetropolitan	151	6,829	235,948	1,008,189	2,360,054	2,766	6,464	4.3	161,944	608	28,713	1,315,558	5,696,169
Metropolitan	275	54,210	2,349,732	12,422,166	19,370,795	33,972	52,979	5.3	1,631,962	4,050	361,561	7,503,714	29,122,899
Abilene	5	655	25,371	128,180	208,541	350	570	5.1	14,658	46	2,839	86,010	372,866
Amarillo	5	1,062	41,025	216,151	298,709	590	815	5.3	22,464	54	4,808	93,388	317,692
Austin-Round Rock	21	2,603	126,232	588,830	964,961	1,609	2,636	4.7	94,901	262	25,485	564,835	1,450,320
Beaumont-Port Arthur	9	1,661	60,522	321,910	516,851	882	1,418	5.3	41,486	108	6,232	213,659	666,807
Brownsville-Harlingen	3	1,063	40,399	193,432	283,321	528	774	4.8	21,606	92	7,537	72,223	211,522
College Station-Bryan	4	449	24,039	101,162	184,615	276	505	4.2	18,938	52	3,718	99,811	419,502
Corpus Christi	6	1,471	61,837	349,727	520,659	957	1,423	5.7	42,269	100	7,397	198,518	570,295
Dallas-Plano-Irving	50	9,141	391,063	2,141,637	3,262,134	5,854	8,915	5.5	252,429	755	66,736	1,343,372	4,834,579
El Paso	6	1,635	75,444	358,395	557,225	989	1,542	4.8	46,929	179	15,765	240,229	1,020,358
Fort Worth-Arlington	28	4,540	210,069	1,128,953	1,732,365	3,085	4,734	5.4	159,154	383	33,360	776,989	2,528,083
Houston-Sugar Land-Baytown	57	12,486	536,677	3,028,090	4,830,550	8,278	13,206	5.6	379,424	870	85,317	1,491,766	7,899,283
Killeen-Temple-Fort Hood	5	934	40,321	186,277	349,560	509	956	4.6	39,694	46	4,851	162,359	1,283,856
Laredo	2	509	25,012	117,140	192,961	320	527	4.7	18,662	63	6,429	65,190	259,315
Longview	6	673	30,779	146,403	245,174	400	670	4.8	23,607	60	3,984	140,045	328,422
Lubbock	6	1,637	54,716	303,476	446,989	830	1,222	5.5	33,471	61	5,560	136,467	553,664
McAllen-Edinburg-Mission	8	2,732	126,935	579,854	828,557	1,586	2,265	4.6	90,825	219	22,327	179,681	471,435
Midland	4	390	14,932	79,082	133,627	216	366	5.3	12,393	34	2,476	66,576	171,346
Odessa	3	535	21,723	109,645	168,668	299	461	5.0	16,190	39	4,164	73,014	245,019
San Angelo	2	395	20,064	92,060	159,276	251	436	4.6	15,913	36	2,155	69,055	206,159
San Antonio	22	5,616	255,844	1,305,288	1,969,810	3,577	5,395	5.1	172,493	390	34,021	834,307	3,419,497
Sherman-Denison	2	420	18,267	93,493	150,550	255	411	5.1	18,813	37	1,508	59,061	124,589
Texarkana TX-Texarkana AR	5	621	29,635	151,433	219,999	413	602	5.1	13,711	25	2,733	96,673	298,518
Tyler	6	1,069	47,480	266,060	408,662	728	1,117	5.6	31,009	41	3,376	146,879	625,567
Victoria	3	545	22,560	104,517	178,220	285	486	4.6	19,323	31	2,486	74,772	202,074
Waco	2	866	29,043	236,529	412,774	646	1,128	8.1	15,943	51	3,969	132,620	452,974
Wichita Falls	5	502	19,743	94,442	146,037	259	399	4.8	15,657	16	2,328	86,215	189,157

MSAs

TABLE 8

U.S. CENSUS DIVISION 7, WEST SOUTH CENTRAL

U.S. Community Hospitals
(Nonfederal, short-term general and other special hospitals)

2008 Utilization, Personnel and Finances

FULL-TIME EQUIVALENT PERSONNEL					FULL-TIME EQUIV. TRAINEES			EXPENSES						
								LABOR				TOTAL		
Physicians and Dentists	Registered Nurses	Licensed Practical Nurses	Other Salaried Personnel	Total Personnel	Medical and Dental Residents	Other Trainees	Total Trainees	Payroll (in thousands)	Employee Benefits (in thousands)	Total (in thousands)	Percent of Total	Amount (in thousands)	Adjusted per Admission	Adjusted per Inpatient Day
95,400	1,228,383	104,562	3,121,215	4,549,560	90,543	9,573	100,116	$256,559,486	$65,376,486	$321,935,957	51.4	$626,576,958	$9,788.25	$1,782.28
12,071	149,214	30,278	467,807	659,370	1,535	394	1,929	30,769,205	8,096,158	38,865,353	53.4	72,719,071	6,539.38	1,026.65
83,329	1,079,169	74,284	2,653,408	3,890,190	89,008	9,179	98,187	225,790,281	57,280,329	283,070,604	51.1	553,857,887	10,471.29	1,972.93
5,199	127,511	19,995	312,591	465,296	3,927	1,169	5,096	24,216,227	5,564,412	29,780,624	49.1	60,693,799	8,626.87	1,703.18
822	15,022	6,039	49,712	71,595	29	6	35	3,012,304	709,475	3,721,769	52.2	7,131,759	5,130.15	1,120.98
4,377	112,489	13,956	262,879	393,701	3,090	1,163	5,061	21,203,923	4,854,937	26,058,855	48.7	53,562,040	9,487.95	1,829.71
435	11,492	2,861	29,467	44,255	2	5	7	1,951,530	449,073	2,400,602	48.8	4,921,858	7,175.45	1,380.65
140	3,106	1,313	9,161	13,720	0	0	0	527,258	119,859	647,118	51.5	1,256,357	4,714.16	921.48
295	8,386	1,548	20,306	30,535	2	5	7	1,424,272	329,214	1,753,484	47.8	3,665,501	8,700.00	1,000.00
71	1,222	166	2,566	4,025	2	0	2	193,522	42,054	235,575	49.1	480,058	6,900.26	1,663.48
96	845	289	2,941	4,171	0	0	0	149,131	33,835	182,966	46.2	395,674	8,228.29	1,448.85
63	598	196	1,489	2,346	0	0	0	94,456	25,722	120,177	52.9	227,371	7,916.00	1,446.04
5	744	199	1,538	2,486	0	0	0	88,756	21,461	110,217	41.3	267,102	6,100.32	1,249.09
41	4,469	554	10,607	15,671	0	5	5	810,782	184,557	995,338	47.9	2,077,190	10,410.26	1,858.96
10	148	42	317	517	0	0	0	21,375	7,120	28,495	51.2	55,629	7,218.91	1,399.26
9	360	102	848	1,319	0	0	0	66,251	14,465	80,716	49.7	162,476	7,379.25	1,457.81
1,548	19,709	3,419	52,920	77,596	926	25	951	3,615,880	837,954	4,453,831	49.4	9,014,213	7,566.49	1,484.11
188	3,043	966	9,917	14,114	17	1	18	580,695	140,881	721,573	55.4	1,302,596	5,090.30	1,079.66
1,360	16,666	2,453	43,003	63,482	909	24	933	3,035,185	697,073	3,732,258	48.4	7,711,616	8,243.88	1,584.36
43	963	179	2,660	3,845	8	0	8	179,097	42,290	221,385	46.0	480,831	8,662.53	1,574.77
181	2,860	380	8,050	11,471	39	5	44	573,701	107,906	681,607	50.1	1,360,772	8,033.89	1,529.21
26	752	119	2,361	3,258	0	10	10	158,099	40,191	198,291	48.4	409,978	8,493.25	1,895.82
91	1,202	357	3,183	4,833	74	0	74	220,978	55,238	276,216	46.1	599,430	9,229.52	1,642.21
12	880	206	2,472	3,570	1	1	2	156,943	40,541	197,486	43.8	451,124	7,228.85	1,611.85
91	1,066	160	2,791	4,108	83	8	91	210,115	52,660	262,774	49.9	526,899	4,056.22	940.93
227	6,311	603	14,347	21,488	283	0	283	1,099,873	225,072	1,324,945	46.4	2,856,836	10,503.15	1,934.38
689	2,632	449	7,139	10,909	421	0	421	436,380	133,175	569,554	55.5	1,025,747	7,710.76	1,324.98
542	12,432	2,241	33,961	49,176	105	59	164	2,482,453	609,249	3,091,698	48.6	6,361,690	7,639.01	1,491.24
226	3,257	1,031	10,860	15,374	12	3	15	703,266	160,155	863,419	52.1	1,658,484	5,422.57	1,158.07
316	9,175	1,210	23,101	33,802	93	56	149	1,779,187	449,095	2,228,279	47.4	4,703,206	8,925.47	1,659.61
8	90	41	342	481	0	0	0	13,786	2,923	16,709	67.4	24,792	2,560.10	738.54
79	316	208	1,416	2,019	0	11	11	100,540	17,867	118,407	49.4	239,875	8,387.81	1,430.54
193	4,999	500	10,927	16,619	85	42	127	961,312	216,318	1,177,626	47.1	2,501,033	9,505.26	1,661.25
36	3,770	461	10,416	14,683	8	3	11	703,550	211,987	915,537	47.3	1,937,507	8,590.56	1,718.92
2,674	83,878	11,474	196,243	294,269	2,894	1,080	3,974	16,166,364	3,668,136	19,834,493	49.1	40,396,037	9,339.30	1,858.93
268	5,616	2,729	19,774	28,387	0	2	2	1,201,085	288,581	1,489,659	51.1	2,914,322	5,186.42	1,234.85
2,406	78,262	8,745	176,469	265,882	2,894	1,078	3,972	14,965,278	3,379,556	18,344,834	48.9	37,481,716	9,959.35	1,934.96
1	811	252	1,882	2,946	0	19	19	123,307	23,965	147,272	47.1	312,619	7,558.11	1,499.08
25	1,427	192	2,869	4,513	0	2	2	213,611	43,192	256,804	43.9	584,885	9,955.49	1,958.04
22	4,364	315	7,884	12,585	6	20	26	777,453	146,119	923,572	49.0	1,884,972	8,710.59	1,953.42
19	1,849	270	3,588	5,726	10	2	12	295,612	65,848	361,459	49.0	737,180	7,384.21	1,426.29
0	915	197	1,738	2,850	0	29	29	178,548	36,770	215,318	49.1	438,311	7,389.80	1,547.05
5	718	129	1,795	2,647	0	1	1	137,502	32,606	170,108	50.0	340,304	7,848.70	1,843.32
1	1,928	262	4,877	7,068	130	0	130	339,989	75,242	415,231	47.7	869,805	9,276.34	1,670.59
291	14,868	673	29,562	45,394	833	81	914	2,799,800	583,979	3,383,778	50.5	6,701,767	10,850.62	2,054.41
9	1,862	141	4,245	6,257	0	0	0	333,430	68,537	401,968	40.6	990,844	8,384.55	1,778.18
22	7,445	864	15,526	23,857	202	11	213	1,349,701	316,546	1,666,246	47.1	3,541,101	10,559.51	2,044.09
1,047	20,505	1,727	52,915	76,194	951	774	1,725	4,715,398	1,159,749	5,875,147	52.5	11,196,118	12,717.62	2,317.77
749	1,208	285	3,006	5,248	364	0	364	281,736	66,849	348,586	49.4	705,075	9,166.82	2,017.04
0	510	54	1,184	1,748	0	0	0	83,979	16,215	100,194	42.0	238,740	5,767.49	1,237.24
0	940	84	1,687	2,711	0	0	0	128,553	27,595	156,147	42.4	368,265	7,003.90	1,502.06
1	2,030	292	4,385	6,708	0	0	0	292,541	86,305	378,845	49.9	758,733	9,309.26	1,697.43
10	3,238	278	5,670	9,196	14	2	16	455,020	92,998	548,018	46.9	1,168,414	6,241.66	1,410.18
1	429	85	1,246	1,761	0	0	0	95,787	26,788	122,576	49.1	249,679	9,085.51	1,868.48
6	661	109	1,489	2,265	0	0	0	114,586	35,282	149,869	46.7	320,587	9,371.41	1,900.70
0	503	138	1,401	2,042	0	0	0	86,572	19,542	106,114	47.2	224,952	6,513.94	1,412.34
75	7,349	1,227	16,347	24,998	360	69	429	1,295,631	261,890	1,557,523	43.0	3,624,367	9,275.89	1,839.96
0	487	89	1,185	1,761	0	0	0	88,666	22,974	111,640	49.7	224,654	7,650.67	1,492.22
0	758	231	1,757	2,746	0	0	0	123,662	27,627	151,289	45.8	330,409	7,393.69	1,501.87
90	1,524	321	5,239	7,174	24	52	76	293,429	66,827	360,256	45.1	798,263	10,537.85	1,953.36
5	655	155	1,375	2,190	0	16	16	103,167	22,911	126,078	51.9	243,155	6,283.39	1,364.35
23	749	199	2,151	3,122	0	0	0	144,318	30,259	174,577	48.8	358,007	6,885.69	867.32
4	529	176	1,466	2,175	0	0	0	113,281	22,938	136,219	50.4	270,507	8,420.20	1,852.32

MSAs

Table 8

U.S. CENSUS DIVISION 8, MOUNTAIN

U.S. Community Hospitals
(Nonfederal, short-term general and other special hospitals)

2008 Utilization, Personnel and Finances

CLASSIFICATION	Hospitals	Beds	Admissions	Inpatient Days	Adjusted Patient Days	Average Daily Census	Adjusted Average Daily Census	Average Stay (days)	Surgical Operations	NEWBORNS Bassinets	Births	OUTPATIENT VISITS Emergency	Total
UNITED STATES	5,010	808,069	35,760,750	196,078,468	351,559,836	536,215	961,620	5.5	27,459,438	57,301	4,073,724	123,024,024	624,098,296
Nonmetropolitan	1,998	143,524	4,592,673	29,262,322	70,831,752	80,001	193,693	6.4	4,175,758	11,324	491,044	23,469,370	119,205,443
Metropolitan	3,012	664,545	31,168,077	166,816,146	280,728,084	456,214	767,927	5.4	23,283,680	45,977	3,582,680	99,554,654	504,892,853
CENSUS DIVISION 8, MOUNTAIN . . .	374	46,293	2,098,239	10,533,261	18,924,909	28,798	51,727	5.0	1,574,622	4,185	314,340	7,302,452	35,699,318
Nonmetropolitan	191	9,743	265,721	1,864,573	4,890,297	5,095	13,366	7.0	259,062	898	45,501	1,532,931	8,017,609
Metropolitan	183	36,550	1,832,518	8,668,688	14,034,612	23,703	38,361	4.7	1,315,560	3,287	268,839	5,769,521	27,681,709
Arizona.	71	13,138	716,136	3,235,063	5,023,898	8,844	13,734	4.5	480,281	1,058	96,193	2,172,149	7,714,351
Nonmetropolitan	14	655	25,599	112,788	314,266	307	860	4.4	23,789	68	5,871	157,272	743,787
Metropolitan	57	12,483	690,537	3,122,275	4,709,632	8,537	12,874	4.5	456,492	990	90,322	2,014,877	6,970,564
Flagstaff.	3	369	18,500	78,645	133,247	216	365	4.3	12,171	43	2,286	88,758	803,621
Lake Havasu City-Kingman.	4	493	28,652	126,272	211,432	346	578	4.4	17,591	32	2,883	126,197	395,392
Phoenix-Mesa-Scottsdale	34	8,423	467,162	2,134,442	3,162,528	5,835	8,645	4.6	309,835	733	65,533	1,266,606	3,960,355
Prescott.	3	288	17,173	61,056	117,036	167	320	3.6	10,258	23	1,875	93,986	260,680
Tucson	11	2,536	139,436	634,426	937,292	1,734	2,561	4.5	95,061	140	14,215	371,240	1,394,891
Yuma	2	374	19,614	87,434	148,097	239	405	4.5	11,576	19	3,530	68,090	155,625
Colorado.	78	10,053	442,161	2,210,340	4,147,102	6,046	11,334	5.0	345,769	1,046	68,659	1,621,056	8,407,972
Nonmetropolitan	37	1,566	45,221	291,398	920,542	799	2,515	6.4	52,301	149	7,895	273,433	1,780,247
Metropolitan	41	8,487	396,940	1,918,942	3,226,560	5,247	8,819	4.8	293,468	897	60,764	1,347,623	6,627,725
Boulder	4	653	34,497	142,630	252,217	391	690	4.1	23,883	98	7,350	131,324	691,280
Colorado Springs	5	1,074	53,725	250,632	446,994	685	1,222	4.7	38,896	87	7,445	207,611	786,720
Denver-Aurora	21	4,886	224,152	1,106,886	1,803,960	3,026	4,930	4.9	169,950	566	35,000	714,537	2,938,146
Fort Collins-Loveland.	4	562	28,701	116,218	197,862	317	541	4.0	21,290	53	3,902	92,768	802,806
Grand Junction	3	456	16,354	110,630	198,264	303	542	6.8	10,826	18	2,415	60,154	522,105
Greeley	2	322	17,312	75,076	143,318	206	392	4.3	13,045	38	2,215	49,902	579,991
Pueblo.	2	534	22,199	116,870	183,945	319	502	5.3	15,578	37	2,437	91,327	306,677
Idaho.	39	3,311	135,697	643,039	1,369,357	1,759	3,741	4.7	111,388	275	23,014	520,941	2,940,411
Nonmetropolitan	25	1,070	36,623	197,515	537,200	541	1,468	5.4	34,501	103	7,056	166,313	878,244
Metropolitan	14	2,241	99,074	445,524	832,157	1,218	2,273	4.5	76,887	172	15,958	354,628	2,062,167
Boise City-Nampa.	7	1,290	61,406	248,719	481,981	680	1,317	4.1	49,370	104	10,143	213,397	1,327,273
Coeur d'Alene	1	246	13,047	56,956	100,313	156	274	4.4	6,127	18	1,695	48,521	157,692
Idaho Falls	2	304	11,322	66,262	97,725	181	267	5.9	11,845	10	1,495	36,471	170,290
Lewiston	1	136	4,957	22,748	42,893	62	117	4.6	4,409	12	738	13,231	99,891
Logan	1	65	547	14,554	29,701	40	81	26.6	425	5	106	3,343	4,053
Pocatello	2	200	7,795	36,285	79,544	99	217	4.7	4,711	23	1,781	39,665	302,968
Montana.	48	3,765	103,840	903,981	1,927,836	2,467	5,268	8.7	75,709	227	10,708	346,670	3,154,274
Nonmetropolitan	43	2,377	47,726	557,065	1,267,519	1,519	3,464	11.7	37,405	148	5,091	201,382	1,265,974
Metropolitan	5	1,388	56,114	346,916	660,317	948	1,804	6.2	38,304	79	5,617	145,288	1,888,300
Billings	2	582	28,495	169,110	377,807	462	1,032	5.9	19,248	34	2,581	60,138	1,438,206
Great Falls	1	478	13,526	111,857	163,478	306	447	8.3	8,455	24	1,414	38,468	135,548
Missoula	2	328	14,093	65,949	119,032	180	325	4.7	10,601	21	1,622	46,682	314,546
Nevada	35	5,144	247,232	1,300,514	1,966,238	3,555	5,377	5.3	168,891	317	29,248	780,500	2,916,309
Nonmetropolitan	11	404	9,527	65,094	159,889	178	438	6.8	12,588	35	1,562	100,024	479,493
Metropolitan	24	4,740	237,705	1,235,420	1,806,349	3,377	4,939	5.2	156,303	282	27,686	680,476	2,436,816
Carson City	1	172	9,777	38,993	58,804	107	161	4.0	2,857	12	994	33,720	166,191
Las Vegas-Paradise	16	3,471	181,751	955,647	1,363,499	2,612	3,728	5.3	113,338	203	19,959	468,594	1,542,269
Reno-Sparks	7	1,097	46,177	240,780	384,046	658	1,050	5.2	40,108	67	6,733	178,162	728,356
New Mexico.	36	3,935	174,169	809,916	1,593,513	2,217	4,357	4.7	133,294	471	24,127	770,475	4,251,559
Nonmetropolitan	22	1,348	53,958	209,663	495,489	573	1,355	3.9	48,483	168	8,076	366,969	1,425,147
Metropolitan	14	2,587	120,211	600,253	1,098,024	1,644	3,002	5.0	84,811	303	16,051	403,506	2,826,412
Albuquerque	9	1,830	80,326	425,992	796,586	1,167	2,178	5.3	55,969	211	10,534	265,038	2,265,643
Farmington	1	197	9,620	43,525	79,437	119	217	4.5	5,136	22	1,387	48,015	198,456
Las Cruces	3	380	19,407	89,154	142,976	244	390	4.6	18,213	46	2,828	66,281	241,687
Santa Fe	1	180	10,858	41,582	79,025	114	217	3.8	5,493	24	1,302	24,172	120,626

TABLE 8

U.S. CENSUS DIVISION 8, MOUNTAIN

U.S. Community Hospitals
(Nonfederal, short-term general and other special hospitals)

2008 Utilization, Personnel and Finances

FULL-TIME EQUIVALENT PERSONNEL					FULL-TIME EQUIV. TRAINEES			EXPENSES						
								LABOR				TOTAL		
Physicians and Dentists	Registered Nurses	Licensed Practical Nurses	Other Salaried Personnel	Total Personnel	Medical and Dental Residents	Other Trainees	Total Trainees	Payroll (in thousands)	Employee Benefits (in thousands)	Total (in thousands)	Percent of Total	Amount (in thousands)	Adjusted per Admission	Adjusted per Inpatient Day
95,400	1,228,383	104,562	3,121,215	4,549,560	90,543	9,573	100,116	$256,559,486	$65,376,486	$321,935,957	51.4	$626,576,958	$9,788.25	$1,782.28
12,071	149,214	30,278	467,807	659,370	1,535	394	1,929	30,769,205	8,096,158	38,865,353	53.4	72,719,071	6,539.38	1,026.65
83,329	1,079,169	74,284	2,653,408	3,890,190	89,008	9,179	98,187	225,790,281	57,280,329	283,070,604	51.1	553,857,887	10,471.29	1,972.93
4,364	74,892	4,807	174,522	258,585	2,912	418	3,330	14,884,148	3,426,809	18,310,966	51.1	35,816,821	9,767.67	1,892.58
944	9,355	1,425	31,761	43,485	29	12	41	2,157,336	528,657	2,685,998	52.7	5,092,936	7,386.25	1,041.44
3,420	65,537	3,382	142,761	215,100	2,883	406	3,289	12,726,812	2,898,152	15,624,968	50.9	30,723,885	10,319.17	2,189.15
1,084	24,133	1,084	47,042	73,343	1,256	106	1,362	4,368,586	953,844	5,322,430	50.9	10,461,228	9,363.19	2,082.29
67	813	116	2,647	3,643	1	2	3	186,439	45,811	232,250	53.6	432,947	6,098.19	1,377.65
1,017	23,320	968	44,395	69,700	1,255	104	1,359	4,182,147	908,033	5,090,180	50.8	10,028,280	9,584.74	2,129.31
28	769	24	1,537	2,358	2	14	16	153,579	36,837	190,416	51.0	373,335	11,362.77	2,801.83
37	852	80	2,076	3,045	5	8	13	146,033	35,498	181,531	49.7	365,546	7,592.61	1,728.91
799	15,800	618	28,773	45,990	1,157	59	1,216	2,878,776	632,191	3,510,967	51.1	6,876,638	9,909.36	2,174.41
33	564	54	1,417	2,068	18	22	40	129,960	35,401	165,361	56.1	294,004	8,842.12	2,517.72
118	4,732	164	9,157	14,171	73	1	74	764,266	140,091	905,157	49.3	1,835,234	8,956.95	1,958.02
2	603	28	1,435	2,068	0	0	0	109,533	27,215	136,748	48.3	282,864	8,545.47	1,909.99
1,087	17,860	891	40,622	60,460	636	51	687	3,624,178	825,582	4,449,763	50.1	8,889,584	11,183.15	2,143.57
166	1,855	268	6,192	8,481	16	4	20	458,899	117,206	576,106	51.4	1,120,538	8,831.34	1,217.26
921	16,005	623	34,430	51,979	620	47	667	3,165,279	708,377	3,873,657	49.9	7,769,046	11,629.84	2,407.84
73	1,308	105	3,526	5,012	22	2	24	272,909	62,177	335,086	51.8	647,226	10,622.97	2,566.15
68	1,888	55	4,350	6,361	43	6	49	361,617	94,823	456,439	50.6	901,991	9,355.78	2,017.90
628	9,213	310	18,822	28,973	404	38	442	1,893,457	392,856	2,286,314	49.0	4,665,047	12,701.82	2,586.00
35	1,504	16	2,448	4,003	10	0	18	240,614	66,807	307,420	51.8	593,115	11,928.39	2,997.62
50	640	41	1,749	2,480	23	0	23	136,703	30,464	167,167	51.2	326,390	11,428.24	1,646.24
36	611	32	1,374	2,053	94	0	94	127,016	28,861	155,877	47.4	328,954	10,883.16	2,295.28
31	841	64	2,161	3,097	16	1	17	132,964	32,390	165,354	54.0	306,322	8,775.38	1,665.29
356	5,058	527	14,214	20,155	40	6	46	1,022,756	244,867	1,267,624	52.7	2,406,259	8,518.09	1,757.22
113	1,267	207	4,218	5,805	6	3	9	271,474	68,139	339,613	54.1	627,194	6,675.97	1,167.52
243	3,791	320	9,996	14,350	34	3	37	751,282	176,729	928,011	52.2	1,779,065	9,436.01	2,137.90
199	2,433	148	6,887	9,667	34	3	37	511,133	111,501	622,634	52.8	1,179,523	9,623.02	2,447.24
7	409	11	1,065	1,492	0	0	0	78,925	19,983	98,908	51.1	193,459	8,418.96	1,928.56
4	461	68	650	1,183	0	0	0	60,578	16,796	77,374	50.2	154,200	8,826.04	1,577.89
17	182	6	463	668	0	0	0	38,895	10,376	49,271	49.0	100,556	10,758.08	2,344.34
2	20	20	144	186	0	0	0	5,036	1,375	6,412	58.3	11,006	9,862.26	370.57
14	286	67	787	1,154	0	0	0	56,714	16,698	73,412	52.3	140,322	9,321.21	1,764.07
568	3,467	660	12,959	17,654	0	0	0	906,079	199,753	1,105,836	53.2	2,077,754	9,342.25	1,077.76
196	1,594	295	6,514	8,599	0	0	0	387,885	92,304	480,192	53.8	892,354	7,640.22	704.02
372	1,873	365	6,445	9,055	0	0	0	518,194	107,449	625,644	52.8	1,185,400	11,224.63	1,795.20
288	923	235	3,468	4,914	0	0	0	306,899	62,351	369,251	55.3	668,043	11,034.92	1,768.21
17	454	55	1,318	1,844	0	0	0	84,200	19,134	103,335	50.5	204,715	10,355.88	1,252.25
67	496	75	1,659	2,297	0	0	0	127,094	25,963	153,058	49.0	312,641	12,357.36	2,626.53
131	7,217	493	15,675	23,516	32	8	40	1,536,818	380,374	1,917,193	49.0	3,912,576	10,540.46	1,989.88
39	419	51	1,293	1,802	0	0	0	102,195	24,835	127,031	54.4	233,468	9,685.45	1,460.19
92	6,798	442	14,382	21,714	32	8	40	1,434,624	355,538	1,790,162	48.7	3,679,108	10,599.84	2,036.76
0	276	9	692	977	0	5	5	59,641	14,278	73,919	48.4	152,818	10,364.77	2,598.77
89	5,152	374	9,605	15,220	32	3	35	1,074,914	263,833	1,338,748	50.3	2,659,011	10,298.70	1,950.14
3	1,370	59	4,085	5,517	0	0	0	300,068	77,427	377,495	43.5	867,279	11,695.02	2,258.27
731	6,153	474	14,972	22,330	37	136	173	1,404,585	307,387	1,711,973	55.6	3,078,570	8,783.24	1,931.94
203	1,542	225	4,898	6,868	4	3	7	361,289	82,277	443,566	50.2	883,419	6,727.37	1,782.92
528	4,611	249	10,074	15,462	33	133	166	1,043,296	225,110	1,268,407	57.8	2,195,151	10,014.92	1,999.18
440	3,444	181	7,101	11,166	9	112	121	775,582	160,170	935,752	59.0	1,584,696	10,566.19	1,989.36
43	367	3	963	1,376	0	0	0	78,011	22,373	100,385	56.8	176,627	10,060.22	2,223.49
19	460	33	1,056	1,568	16	19	35	104,816	21,007	125,823	54.4	231,357	7,458.78	1,618.15
26	340	32	954	1,352	8	2	10	84,886	21,560	106,447	52.6	202,471	9,812.02	2,562.11

Table continues

MSAs

TABLE **8**

U.S. CENSUS DIVISION 8, MOUNTAIN
CONTINUED

U.S. Community Hospitals
(Nonfederal, short-term general and other special hospitals)

2008 Utilization, Personnel and Finances

CLASSIFICATION	Hospitals	Beds	Admissions	Inpatient Days	Adjusted Patient Days	Average Daily Census	Adjusted Average Daily Census	Average Stay (days)	Surgical Operations	NEWBORNS Bassinets	NEWBORNS Births	OUTPATIENT VISITS Emergency	OUTPATIENT VISITS Total
Utah	43	4,874	226,376	1,015,945	1,989,825	2,777	5,439	4.5	219,945	616	55,088	856,277	5,305,448
Nonmetropolitan	17	674	15,859	107,616	421,922	294	1,154	6.8	22,409	92	5,038	105,550	632,081
Metropolitan	26	4,200	210,517	908,329	1,567,903	2,483	4,285	4.3	197,536	524	50,050	750,727	4,673,367
Logan	2	154	7,867	24,524	55,962	67	153	3.1	7,886	34	2,598	38,401	287,384
Ogden-Clearfield	4	718	35,765	142,604	249,780	390	682	4.0	26,271	103	9,346	177,401	494,582
Provo-Orem	6	722	35,096	140,563	241,315	383	659	4.0	33,763	136	12,202	133,584	715,880
Salt Lake City	13	2,345	117,161	546,614	929,325	1,495	2,541	4.7	118,417	235	23,182	360,630	2,768,385
St. George	1	261	14,628	54,024	91,521	148	250	3.7	11,199	16	2,722	40,711	407,136
Wyoming	24	2,073	52,628	414,463	907,140	1,133	2,477	7.9	39,345	175	7,303	234,384	1,008,994
Nonmetropolitan	22	1,649	31,208	323,434	773,470	884	2,112	10.4	27,586	135	4,912	161,988	812,636
Metropolitan	2	424	21,420	91,029	133,670	249	365	4.2	11,759	40	2,391	72,396	196,358
Casper	1	207	9,712	42,022	59,604	115	163	4.3	5,552	24	1,107	38,322	81,593
Cheyenne.	1	217	11,708	49,007	74,066	134	202	4.2	6,207	16	1,284	34,074	114,765

MSAs

TABLE 8

U.S. Community Hospitals
(Nonfederal, short-term general and other special hospitals)

2008 Utilization, Personnel and Finances

FULL-TIME EQUIVALENT PERSONNEL					FULL-TIME EQUIV. TRAINEES			EXPENSES						
								LABOR				TOTAL		
Physicians and Dentists	Registered Nurses	Licensed Practical Nurses	Other Salaried Personnel	Total Personnel	Medical and Dental Residents	Other Trainees	Total Trainees	Payroll (in thousands)	Employee Benefits (in thousands)	Total (in thousands)	Percent of Total	Amount (in thousands)	Adjusted per Admission	Adjusted per Inpatient Day
263	9,088	518	23,025	32,894	909	111	1,020	1,610,777	413,715	2,024,494	50.1	4,041,482	9,542.96	2,031.07
29	664	132	1,998	2,823	0	0	0	117,596	31,462	149,058	49.0	304,201	5,811.57	720.99
234	8,424	386	21,027	30,071	909	111	1,020	1,493,181	382,253	1,875,436	50.2	3,737,281	10,069.19	2,383.62
4	262	7	688	961	0	0	0	40,146	11,359	51,505	50.6	101,748	5,600.09	1,818.16
34	1,234	99	2,687	4,054	26	0	26	199,593	52,988	252,581	49.1	514,894	8,237.24	2,061.39
34	1,447	68	3,026	4,575	35	30	65	219,154	58,846	277,999	50.5	550,058	8,665.48	2,279.42
150	4,987	203	13,208	18,548	848	81	929	946,726	233,223	1,179,952	50.6	2,332,294	11,533.16	2,509.66
12	494	9	1,418	1,933	0	0	0	87,562	25,838	113,399	47.6	238,287	9,615.73	2,603.64
144	1,916	160	6,013	8,233	2	0	2	410,368	101,206	511,053	53.9	949,369	9,076.36	1,046.55
131	1,201	131	4,001	5,464	2	0	2	271,560	66,624	338,182	56.5	598,816	8,188.71	774.19
13	715	29	2,012	2,769	0	0	0	138,809	34,662	173,471	49.5	350,553	11,138.92	2,622.53
0	815	7	000	1,192	0	0	0	61,889	17,089	78,978	50.1	157,692	11,446.89	2,645.67
11	400	22	1,144	1,577	0	0	0	76,919	17,574	94,493	49.0	192,861	10,899.17	2,603.90

MSAs

TABLE 8

U.S. CENSUS DIVISION 9, PACIFIC

U.S. Community Hospitals
(Nonfederal, short-term general and other special hospitals)

2008 Utilization, Personnel and Finances

CLASSIFICATION	Hospitals	Beds	Admissions	Inpatient Days	Adjusted Patient Days	Average Daily Census	Adjusted Average Daily Census	Average Stay (days)	Surgical Operations	NEWBORNS		OUTPATIENT VISITS	
										Bassinets	Births	Emergency	Total
UNITED STATES	5,010	808,069	35,760,750	196,078,468	351,559,836	536,215	961,620	5.5	27,459,438	57,301	4,073,724	123,024,024	624,098,296
Nonmetropolitan	1,998	143,524	4,592,673	29,262,322	70,831,752	80,001	193,693	6.4	4,175,758	11,324	491,044	23,469,370	119,205,443
Metropolitan.	3,012	664,545	31,168,077	166,816,146	280,728,084	456,214	767,927	5.4	23,283,680	45,977	3,582,680	99,554,654	504,892,853
CENSUS DIVISION 9, PACIFIC	543	92,389	4,557,658	23,454,079	38,407,223	64,024	105,080	5.1	3,146,966	7,060	676,180	14,473,721	72,525,841
Nonmetropolitan	123	6,055	212,545	1,246,359	3,104,456	3,408	8,482	5.9	238,891	592	32,085	1,333,370	7,055,613
Metropolitan.	420	86,334	4,345,113	22,207,720	35,302,767	60,616	96,598	5.1	2,908,075	6,468	644,095	13,140,351	65,470,228
Alaska	22	1,553	58,204	346,837	704,190	947	1,925	6.0	64,089	154	8,882	328,164	1,693,342
Nonmetropolitan	17	624	15,575	131,664	356,510	359	975	8.5	20,906	62	2,700	98,710	566,658
Metropolitan.	5	929	42,629	215,173	347,680	588	950	5.0	43,183	92	6,182	229,454	1,126,684
Anchorage	4	722	36,779	163,806	262,105	447	716	4.5	38,979	76	5,258	167,961	830,515
Fairbanks.	1	207	5,850	51,367	85,575	141	234	8.8	4,204	16	924	61,493	296,169
California	352	69,587	3,460,688	18,044,888	28,277,342	49,241	77,398	5.2	2,214,586	5,079	526,946	10,068,613	48,877,149
Nonmetropolitan	31	1,467	54,887	320,727	762,412	876	2,081	5.8	65,513	136	8,411	439,555	2,323,489
Metropolitan.	321	68,120	3,405,801	17,724,161	27,514,930	48,365	75,317	5.2	2,149,073	4,943	518,535	9,629,058	46,553,660
Bakersfield	9	1,249	68,389	350,091	576,753	957	1,578	5.1	41,338	93	12,824	168,668	622,792
Chico	4	522	27,875	137,015	231,600	376	636	4.9	17,430	43	3,033	89,500	718,860
El Centro	2	272	11,213	45,159	91,053	123	248	4.0	8,971	25	3,200	78,938	263,707
Fresno	10	1,619	86,183	452,146	746,606	1,235	2,042	5.2	54,842	193	16,330	275,277	1,476,835
Hanford-Corcoran.	3	180	9,208	43,567	102,525	119	280	4.7	12,261	35	2,180	71,827	359,221
Los Angeles-Long Beach-Glendale	92	21,274	1,068,278	5,537,785	8,302,424	15,065	22,798	5.2	610,843	1,562	152,320	2,407,009	10,612,207
Madera	3	445	18,467	108,943	172,176	298	471	5.9	16,905	10	1,995	99,303	333,462
Merced	1	158	10,438	44,934	74,796	123	204	4.3	5,928	16	2,711	49,878	206,079
Modesto.	4	1,395	55,653	350,596	502,676	957	1,374	6.3	34,809	70	9,988	181,386	396,236
Napa.	2	331	15,051	84,383	149,364	231	409	5.6	11,807	12	1,399	48,037	332,144
Oakland-Fremont-Hayward	20	4,884	231,139	1,286,959	1,964,656	3,516	5,373	5.6	127,360	304	30,553	731,475	4,102,751
Oxnard-Thousand Oaks-Ventura. .	6	1,258	60,009	298,791	469,288	816	1,281	5.0	33,848	100	9,901	319,583	1,369,710
Redding.	3	579	23,270	130,442	220,046	356	602	5.6	13,282	13	2,166	75,725	191,690
Riverside-San Bernardino-Ontario .	33	6,453	360,388	1,674,247	2,631,022	4,575	7,192	4.6	198,013	440	53,857	1,047,365	3,351,652
Sacramento—Arden-Arcade— Roseville	15	3,538	194,798	970,696	1,530,277	2,652	4,182	5.0	156,106	311	27,738	464,752	2,989,976
Salinas	4	706	33,813	176,837	282,406	483	772	5.2	22,908	80	7,295	144,229	530,987
San Diego-Carlsbad-San Marcos .	20	5,151	279,696	1,501,641	2,174,923	4,103	5,942	5.4	204,041	359	45,842	725,389	2,999,344
San Francisco-San Mateo- Redwood City	18	4,953	180,075	1,251,922	2,052,751	3,421	5,611	7.0	141,767	166	20,418	549,639	4,648,221
San Jose-Sunnyvale-Santa Clara .	11	2,911	164,930	819,352	1,306,913	2,238	3,572	5.0	94,570	311	29,396	493,270	3,589,480
San Luis Obispo-Paso Robles . . .	4	455	19,372	85,389	132,157	233	362	4.4	12,999	37	2,756	88,533	308,461
Santa Ana-Anaheim-Irvine	28	5,418	275,721	1,306,474	2,010,311	3,572	5,493	4.7	187,510	380	42,459	673,439	3,036,288
Santa Barbara-Santa Maria.	5	875	34,003	216,390	349,984	591	956	6.4	27,545	86	7,412	114,203	390,757
Santa Cruz-Watsonville	3	410	21,874	97,502	171,289	267	469	4.5	21,353	47	3,628	56,230	282,390
Santa Rosa-Petaluma	7	741	36,736	164,086	290,117	447	793	4.5	28,569	41	5,941	104,225	477,300
Stockton	7	1,195	59,411	275,932	481,140	755	1,316	4.6	31,269	95	10,748	271,788	1,185,409
Vallejo-Fairfield	4	525	27,034	125,592	213,221	344	583	4.6	16,762	61	4,844	122,703	1,034,087
Visalia-Porterville	3	623	32,777	187,290	284,456	512	778	5.7	16,037	53	7,601	176,687	743,614
Hawaii	25	3,087	111,310	846,756	1,537,865	2,315	4,203	7.6	89,914	197	10,522	361,068	2,019,132
Nonmetropolitan	11	838	30,492	212,108	424,887	580	1,163	7.0	24,792	67	4,449	112,880	287,290
Metropolitan.	14	2,249	80,818	634,648	1,112,978	1,735	3,040	7.9	65,122	130	6,073	248,188	1,731,842
Honolulu	14	2,249	80,818	634,648	1,112,978	1,735	3,040	7.9	65,122	130	6,073	248,188	1,731,842
Oregon.	58	6,814	348,600	1,551,894	2,936,201	4,244	8,024	4.5	330,381	702	47,273	1,330,142	8,558,164
Nonmetropolitan	29	1,437	63,963	284,141	749,806	779	2,049	4.4	64,316	176	8,732	352,946	2,181,524
Metropolitan.	29	5,377	284,637	1,267,753	2,186,395	3,465	5,975	4.5	266,065	526	38,541	977,196	6,376,640
Bend.	2	309	16,673	69,114	118,794	189	324	4.1	15,599	33	2,093	53,706	214,351
Corvallis.	1	185	8,636	39,901	71,873	109	196	4.6	7,821	24	1,065	20,645	192,771
Eugene-Springfield	4	623	34,458	142,859	217,691	390	595	4.1	26,349	70	3,685	112,205	237,595
Medford.	3	461	22,747	100,645	163,610	275	448	4.4	20,543	40	2,563	77,303	678,061
Portland-Vancouver-Beaverton. . .	15	3,288	176,673	805,698	1,416,558	2,202	3,871	4.6	179,999	289	23,523	582,251	4,300,971
Salem	4	511	25,450	109,536	197,869	300	541	4.3	15,754	70	5,612	131,086	752,891

TABLE 8

U.S. CENSUS DIVISION 9, PACIFIC

U.S. Community Hospitals
(Nonfederal, short-term general and other special hospitals)

2008 Utilization, Personnel and Finances

FULL-TIME EQUIVALENT PERSONNEL					FULL-TIME EQUIV. TRAINEES			EXPENSES						
								LABOR				TOTAL		
Physicians and Dentists	Registered Nurses	Licensed Practical Nurses	Other Salaried Personnel	Total Personnel	Medical and Dental Residents	Other Trainees	Total Trainees	Payroll (in thousands)	Employee Benefits (in thousands)	Total (in thousands)	Percent of Total	Amount (in thousands)	Adjusted per Admission	Adjusted per Inpatient Day
95,400	1,228,383	104,562	3,121,215	4,549,560	90,543	9,573	100,116	$256,559,486	$65,376,486	$321,935,957	51.4	$626,576,958	$9,788.25	$1,782.28
12,071	149,214	30,278	467,807	659,370	1,535	394	1,929	30,769,205	8,096,158	38,865,353	53.4	72,719,071	6,539.38	1,026.65
83,329	1,079,169	74,284	2,653,408	3,890,190	89,008	9,179	98,187	225,790,281	57,280,329	283,070,604	51.1	553,857,887	10,471.29	1,972.93
10,392	162,985	11,159	382,753	567,289	10,428	692	11,120	36,592,498	10,711,615	47,304,106	53.7	88,037,636	11,771.44	2,292.22
611	8,456	1,053	26,160	36,280	32	15	47	2,065,295	628,055	2,693,349	55.3	4,866,085	9,500.62	1,567.45
9,781	154,529	10,106	356,593	531,009	10,396	677	11,073	34,527,203	10,083,559	44,610,757	53.6	83,171,551	11,938.38	2,355.95
262	2,514	186	6,997	9,959	56	12	68	629,409	177,434	806,842	51.4	1,570,874	14,282.49	2,230.75
87	764	106	2,572	3,529	4	2	6	222,892	67,723	290,615	55.5	523,514	12,783.30	1,468.44
175	1,750	80	4,425	6,430	52	10	62	406,517	109,711	516,227	49.3	1,047,359	15,171.87	3,012.42
153	1,420	56	3,582	5,211	39	8	47	337,360	91,880	429,240	49.0	876,479	14,783.66	3,344.00
22	330	24	843	1,219	13	2	15	69,156	17,921	86,087	50.0	170,001	17,533.41	1,990.85
6,632	122,756	9,178	276,858	415,424	8,139	560	8,699	20,034,672	8,004,033	34,638,702	53.8	64,441,143	11,851.62	2,278.90
61	2,329	326	6,552	9,207	10	2	12	542,021	181,121	723,142	54.0	1,338,632	10,888.06	1,755.79
6,571	120,427	8,853	270,306	406,157	8,129	558	8,687	26,092,651	7,822,912	33,915,560	53.7	63,102,511	11,873.91	2,293.39
87	1,901	190	4,755	6,933	45	7	52	399,639	105,604	505,244	53.5	944,902	8,478.64	1,638.31
6	1,060	126	2,604	3,796	0	1	1	207,631	89,317	296,948	56.8	522,386	11,540.36	2,255.55
2	334	26	946	1,308	0	0	0	67,072	16,102	83,174	62.1	133,961	5,939.03	1,471.24
376	2,514	162	7,507	10,559	215	18	233	514,099	124,714	638,813	51.2	1,247,454	8,526.51	1,670.83
26	340	63	967	1,396	4	3	7	90,757	23,218	113,974	52.5	217,246	9,426.63	2,118.96
2,250	35,845	3,343	84,414	125,852	2,884	212	3,096	7,296,893	2,037,651	9,334,545	52.4	17,819,178	11,071.63	2,146.26
1	672	74	2,231	2,978	0	0	0	172,877	65,880	238,757	61.7	386,980	13,797.56	2,247.58
20	237	24	711	992	7	1	8	65,672	16,127	81,799	53.5	152,780	8,793.07	2,042.62
11	2,453	140	3,657	6,261	3	21	24	405,715	126,226	531,942	56.8	937,195	12,205.76	1,864.41
13	551	29	1,369	1,962	3	0	3	145,810	55,753	201,564	56.3	358,063	13,511.82	2,397.25
1,297	7,732	617	18,307	27,953	525	58	583	2,149,345	734,180	2,883,525	56.5	5,107,871	14,399.48	2,599.88
47	1,886	179	4,009	6,121	31	2	33	460,347	140,975	601,321	54.3	1,106,663	11,492.55	2,358.18
13	929	69	1,820	2,831	16	1	17	164,740	51,841	216,580	53.6	403,834	11,551.66	1,835.23
970	11,965	989	23,060	36,984	907	49	956	2,027,878	580,399	2,608,276	52.3	4,984,917	8,681.09	1,894.67
480	7,664	351	16,531	25,026	618	24	642	1,718,299	492,390	2,210,688	53.9	4,102,585	12,960.92	2,680.94
28	1,165	72	3,137	4,402	24	0	24	372,623	180,618	553,240	62.1	891,044	17,584.20	3,155.19
116	10,177	574	19,681	30,548	708	48	756	1,931,038	486,452	2,417,490	51.5	4,692,483	11,639.20	2,157.54
297	8,022	441	20,578	29,338	529	59	588	2,253,717	639,442	2,893,159	53.6	5,396,799	17,833.94	2,629.06
205	6,766	280	14,231	21,482	1,270	18	1,288	2,139,385	785,640	2,925,026	59.1	4,951,776	18,864.70	3,788.91
0	694	14	1,045	1,753	0	0	0	124,865	31,882	156,747	54.1	289,543	9,673.67	2,190.90
91	9,833	490	22,043	32,457	117	9	126	1,801,420	567,179	2,368,597	50.5	4,687,881	10,994.07	2,331.92
24	1,287	106	2,908	4,325	58	1	60	260,828	67,099	328,527	53.3	616,250	12,062.52	1,760.80
43	693	49	1,749	2,534	24	1	25	158,478	43,694	202,172	50.9	397,405	10,127.55	2,320.09
32	1,167	91	3,184	4,474	41	2	43	311,494	99,976	411,470	54.6	753,413	11,643.45	2,596.93
136	1,897	128	4,587	6,748	100	16	116	410,726	127,632	538,357	56.0	962,206	9,293.99	1,999.85
0	1,526	91	1,407	3,024	0	0	0	210,054	60,248	270,302	50.9	531,538	11,542.63	2,492.90
0	1,117	135	2,868	4,120	0	7	7	231,252	72,072	303,323	59.9	506,154	9,925.96	1,779.38
377	4,403	338	11,191	16,309	65	32	97	979,818	241,582	1,221,401	52.6	2,321,588	11,664.98	1,509.62
55	1,043	127	2,680	3,905	10	2	12	207,357	65,495	272,852	55.7	489,683	8,272.51	1,152.50
322	3,360	211	8,511	12,404	55	30	85	772,461	176,087	948,549	51.8	1,831,905	13,101.13	1,645.95
322	3,360	211	8,511	12,404	55	30	85	772,461	176,087	948,549	51.8	1,831,905	13,101.13	1,645.95
1,592	13,374	301	31,574	46,841	942	16	958	2,997,417	895,953	3,893,368	52.8	7,376,298	11,111.88	2,512.19
253	2,319	101	7,446	10,119	0	5	5	573,177	175,696	748,873	55.9	1,340,262	8,317.84	1,787.48
1,339	11,055	200	24,128	36,722	942	11	953	2,424,240	720,256	3,144,495	52.1	6,036,037	12,007.47	2,760.73
7	582	6	1,773	2,368	0	0	0	151,656	46,054	197,710	53.3	370,812	12,664.34	3,121.47
68	293	16	868	1,245	0	5	5	97,034	27,146	124,180	53.2	233,242	14,993.73	3,245.20
56	1,205	28	2,937	4,226	0	0	0	253,528	70,030	323,558	57.0	568,000	10,454.82	2,609.20
32	897	24	2,139	3,092	0	0	0	173,743	69,058	242,801	51.4	472,812	12,639.67	2,889.87
1,120	7,065	93	13,648	21,926	942	6	948	1,513,079	454,904	1,967,982	50.7	3,883,093	12,269.71	2,741.22
56	1,013	33	2,763	3,865	0	0	0	235,200	53,064	288,264	56.7	508,077	10,235.24	2,567.75

Table continues

MSAs

TABLE **8**

U.S. CENSUS DIVISION 9, PACIFIC CONTINUED

U.S. Community Hospitals
(Nonfederal, short-term general and other special hospitals)

2008 Utilization, Personnel and Finances

CLASSIFICATION	Hospitals	Beds	Admissions	Inpatient Days	Adjusted Patient Days	Average Daily Census	Adjusted Average Daily Census	Average Stay (days)	Surgical Operations	NEWBORNS Bassinets	Births	OUTPATIENT VISITS Emergency	Total
Washington	86	11,348	578,856	2,663,704	4,951,625	7,277	13,530	4.6	447,996	928	82,557	2,385,734	11,378,054
Nonmetropolitan	35	1,689	47,628	297,719	810,841	814	2,214	6.3	63,364	151	7,793	329,279	1,696,652
Metropolitan	51	9,659	531,228	2,365,985	4,140,784	6,463	11,316	4.5	384,632	777	74,764	2,056,455	9,681,402
Bellingham	1	243	15,459	62,293	100,549	170	275	4.0	6,821	30	2,048	58,381	99,496
Bremerton-Silverdale	1	267	17,148	66,756	99,194	182	271	3.9	11,703	24	2,063	75,822	195,780
Kennewick-Richland-Pasco	4	399	19,886	85,210	178,846	233	489	4.3	14,608	39	4,430	119,591	341,199
Lewiston	1	25	1,685	6,891	18,305	19	50	4.1	2,192	0	0	16,147	73,172
Longview	1	202	10,221	42,253	70,391	116	193	4.1	3,561	27	1,056	55,685	268,199
Mount Vernon-Anacortes	3	215	13,359	47,764	114,187	130	312	3.6	12,057	32	1,829	63,270	420,272
Olympia	2	447	24,479	100,973	146,096	276	399	4.1	12,197	24	2,961	80,466	331,963
Portland-Vancouver-Beaverton . . .	2	499	29,394	120,529	214,200	329	585	4.1	17,796	65	5,568	126,776	407,541
Seattle-Bellevue-Everett	19	4,238	237,031	1,101,800	1,973,217	3,010	5,390	4.6	169,004	312	33,340	871,871	5,178,733
Spokane	6	1,325	59,961	315,625	477,095	863	1,306	5.3	53,905	71	6,415	194,782	619,439
Tacoma	5	1,096	67,336	280,029	493,331	765	1,348	4.2	46,893	81	8,801	228,438	1,180,185
Wenatchee	2	184	10,235	40,000	69,110	109	189	3.9	7,710	25	2,253	34,281	47,515
Yakima	4	519	25,034	95,862	186,263	261	509	3.8	26,185	47	4,000	130,945	517,908

MSAs

TABLE 8

U.S. CENSUS DIVISION 9, PACIFIC CONTINUED

U.S. Community Hospitals
(Nonfederal, short-term general and other special hospitals)

2008 Utilization, Personnel and Finances

FULL-TIME EQUIVALENT PERSONNEL					FULL-TIME EQUIV. TRAINEES			EXPENSES						
								LABOR				TOTAL		
Physicians and Dentists	Registered Nurses	Licensed Practical Nurses	Other Salaried Personnel	Total Personnel	Medical and Dental Residents	Other Trainees	Total Trainees	Payroll (in thousands)	Employee Benefits (in thousands)	Total (in thousands)	Percent of Total	Amount (in thousands)	Adjusted per Admission	Adjusted per Inpatient Day
1,529	19,938	1,156	56,133	78,756	1,226	72	1,298	5,351,182	1,392,613	6,743,793	54.7	12,327,733	11,534.59	2,489.63
155	2,001	394	6,910	9,460	8	4	12	519,849	138,019	657,867	56.0	1,173,993	9,174.48	1,447.87
1,374	17,937	762	49,223	69,296	1,218	68	1,286	4,831,333	1,254,594	6,085,926	54.6	11,153,740	11,855.60	2,693.63
32	595	41	1,430	2,098	0	0	0	121,305	33,246	154,552	54.9	281,338	11,274.71	2,798.02
0	0	0	1,471	1,471	0	0	0	108,658	28,665	137,324	55.3	248,495	9,752.18	2,505.14
32	723	48	1,944	2,747	10	0	10	156,662	35,684	192,346	49.8	386,609	9,585.67	2,161.69
0	104	8	227	339	0	0	0	15,144	3,744	18,888	39.7	47,607	10,635.97	2,600.74
22	325	24	832	1,203	14	1	15	80,895	20,857	101,753	50.9	199,887	11,738.71	2,830.66
8	416	7	1,188	1,619	0	0	0	95,789	22,573	118,362	51.9	228,126	7,185.52	1,997.83
47	738	62	1,527	2,374	19	0	19	153,201	53,481	206,683	53.4	387,242	10,863.85	2,650.60
28	1,136	30	2,172	3,366	37	0	37	224,214	62,021	286,235	53.2	538,081	10,321.70	2,512.05
920	9,026	315	25,928	36,189	1,080	51	1,131	2,616,078	669,137	3,285,215	55.8	5,892,044	13,678.03	2,986.01
47	1,911	53	4,747	6,758	32	12	44	461,831	122,696	584,526	51.4	1,136,594	12,350.12	2,382.32
190	1,673	96	4,693	6,652	20	2	22	558,496	132,524	691,020	57.0	1,212,435	10,222.80	2,457.65
21	374	7	968	1,370	0	0	0	84,566	20,443	105,009	58.1	180,730	10,514.28	2,615.11
27	916	71	2,096	3,110	6	2	8	154,492	49,521	204,013	49.2	414,553	8,346.48	2,225.03

MSAs

Statistics for Multihospital Health Care Systems and their Hospitals

The following tables describing multihospital health care systems refer to information in section B of the 2008 *AHA Guide*.

Table 1 shows the number of multihospital health care systems by type of control. Table 2 provides a breakdown of the number of systems that own, lease, sponsor or contract manage hospitals within each control category. Table 3 gives the number of hospitals and beds in each control category as well as total hospitals and beds. Finally, Table 4 shows the percentage of hospitals and beds in each control category.

For more information on multihospital health care systems, please write to the Section for Health Care Systems, One North Franklin, Chicago, Illinois 60606–3401 or call 312/422–3000.

Table 1. Multihospital Health Care Systems, by Type of Organizaton Control

Type of Control	Code	Number of Systems
Catholic (Roman) church related	CC	39
Other church-related	CO	12
Subtotal, church-related		51
Other not-for-profit	NP	264
Subtotal, not-for-profit		315
Investor Owned	IO	77
Federal Government	FG	5
Total		397

Table 2. Multihospital Health Care Systems, by Type of Ownership and Control

Type of Ownership	Catholic Church-Related (CC)	Other Church-Related (CO)	Total Church-Related (CC + CO)	Other Not-for-Profit (NP)	Total Not-for-Profit (CC, CO, + NP)	Investor-Owned (IO)	Federal Government (FG)	All Systems
Systems that only own, lease or sponsor	34	11	45	234	279	69	5	353
Systems that only contract-manage	0	0	0	0	0	0	0	0
Systems that manage, own, lease, or sponsor	5	1	6	30	36	8	0	44
Total	39	12	51	264	315	77	5	397

Table 3. Hospitals and Beds in Multihospital Health Care Systems, by Type of Ownership and Control

Type of Ownership	Catholic Church-Related (CC) H	B	Other Church-Related (CO) H	B	Total Church-Related (CC + CO) H	B	Other Not-for-Profit (NP) H	B	Total Not-for-Profit (CC, CO, + NP) H	B	Investor-Owned (IO) H	B	Federal Government (FG) H	B	All Systems H	B
Owned, leased or sponsored	521	103,086	101	21,722	622	124,808	1,225	277,511	1,847	402,319	1,183	139,571	212	46,311	3,242	588,201
Contract-managed	35	1,495	1	268	36	1,763	92	7,785	128	9,548	166	11,734	0	0	294	21,282
Total	556	104,581	102	21,990	658	126,571	1,317	285,296	1,975	411,867	1,349	151,305	212	46,311	3,536	609,483

H = hospitals; **B** = beds.

Table 4. Hospitals and Beds in Multihospital Health Care Systems, by Type of Ownership and Control as a Percentage of All Systems

Type of Ownership	Catholic Church-Related (CC) H	B	Other Church-Related (CO) H	B	Total Church-Related (CC + CO) H	B	Other Not-for-Profit (NP) H	B	Total Not-for-Profit (CC, CO, + NP) H	B	Investor-Owned (IO) H	B	Federal Government (FG) H	B	All Systems H	B
Owned, leased or sponsored	16.1	17.5	3.1	3.7	19.2	21.2	37.8	47.2	57.0	68.4	36.5	23.7	6.5	7.9	100.0	100.0
Contract-managed	11.9	7.0	0.3	1.3	12.2	8.3	31.3	36.6	43.5	44.9	56.5	55.1	0.0	0.0	100.0	100.0
Total	15.7	17.2	2.9	3.6	18.6	20.8	37.2	46.8	55.9	67.6	38.2	24.8	6.0	7.6	100.0	100.0

H = hospitals; **B** = beds.
*Please note that figures may not always equal the provided subtotal or total percentages due to rounding.

Glossary

This glossary explains specific terms as they are used in the tables and text of AHA Hospital Statistics

Ablation of Barrett's esophagus: Premalignant condition that can lead to adenocarcinoma of the esophagus. The non surgical ablation of the premalignant tissue in Barrett's esophagus by the application of thermal energy or light through an endoscope passed from the mouth into the esophagus.

Acute long term care: Providers specialized acute hospital care to medically complex patients who are critically ill, have multisystem complications and/or failure, and require hospitalization averaging 25 days, in a facility offering specialized treatment programs and therapeutic intervention on a 24 hour/7day a week basis.

Adjusted average daily census: An estimate of the average number of patients (both inpatients and outpatients) receiving care each day during the reporting period, which is usually 12 months. The figure is derived by dividing the number of inpatient day equivalents (also called adjusted inpatient days) by the number of days in the reporting period.

Adjusted inpatient days: An aggregate figure reflecting the number of days of inpatient care, plus an estimate of the volume of outpatient services, expressed in units equivalent to an inpatient day in terms of level of effort. The figure is derived by first multiplying the number of outpatient visits by the ratio of outpatient revenue per outpatient visit to inpatient revenue per inpatient day. The product (which represents the number of patient days attributable to outpatient services) is then added to the number of *inpatient days*. Originally, the purpose of this calculation was to summarize overall productivity and calculate a unit cost that would include both inpatient and outpatient activities.

Formula 1:

$$\frac{\text{total expenses}}{\text{inpatient days} + \text{outpatient visits}\left(\dfrac{\dfrac{\text{outpatient revenue}}{\text{per outpatient visit}}}{\dfrac{\text{inpatient revenue}}{\text{per inpatient day}}}\right)}$$

However, the value of this calculation has changed over the years as the outpatient share of total revenue has grown and third-party payers have exerted a greater influence on pricing.

Admissions: The number of patients, excluding newborns, accepted for inpatient service during the reporting period; the number includes patients who visit the emergency room and are later admitted for inpatient service.

Adult Cardiac Surgery: Includes minimally invasive procedures that include surgery done with only a small incision or no incision at all, such as through a laparoscope or an endoscope and more invasive major surgical procedures that include open chest and open heart surgery.

Adult day care program: Program providing supervision, medical and psychological care, and social activities for older adults who live at home or in another family setting, but cannot be alone or prefer to be with others during the day. May include intake assessment, health monitoring, occupational therapy, personal care, noon meal, and transportation services.

Adult Diagnostic/invasive catheterization: (also called coronary angiography or coronary arteriography) is used to assist in diagnosing complex heart conditions. Cardiac angiography involves the insertion of a tiny catheter into the artery in the groin then carefully threading the catheter up into the aorta where the coronary arteries originate. Once the catheter is in place, a dye is injected which allows the cardiologist to see the size, shape, and distribution of the coronary arteries. These images are used to diagnose heart disease and to determine, among other things, whether or not surgery is indicated.

Adult Interventional cardiac catheterization: Non surgical procedure that utilizes the same basic principles as diagnostic catheterization and then uses advanced techniques to improve the heart's function. It can be a less-invasive alternative to heart surgery.

Airborne infection isolation room:
A single-occupancy room for patient care where environmental factors are controlled in an effort to minimize the transmission of those infectious agents, usually spread person to person by droplet nuclei associated with coughing and inhalation. Such rooms typically have specific ventilation requirements for controlled ventilation, air pressure and filtration.

Alcoholism-drug abuse or dependency inpatient care: Provides diagnosis and therapeutic services to patients with alcoholism or other drug dependencies. Includes care for inpatient/residential treatment for patients whose course of treatment involves more intensive care than provided in an outpatient setting or where patient requires supervised withdrawal.

Alcoholism-drug abuse or dependency outpatient services: Organized hospital services that provide medical care and/or rehabilitative treatment services to outpatients for whom the primary diagnosis is alcoholism or other chemical dependency.

Alzheimer Center: Facility that offers care to persons with Alzheimer's disease and their families through an integrated program of clinical services, research, and education.

Ambulance services: Provision of ambulance services to the ill and injured who require medical attention on a scheduled or unscheduled basis.

Ambulatory Surgery Center: Facility that provides care to patients requiring surgery who are admitted and discharged on the same day. Ambulatory surgery centers are distinct from same day surgical units within the hospital outpatient departments for purposes of Medicare payments.

Arthritis treatment center: Specifically equipped and staffed center for the diagnosis and treatment of arthritis and other joint disorders.

Assisted living: A special combination of housing, supportive services, personalized assistance and health care designed to respond to the individual needs of those who need help in activities of daily living and instrumental activities of daily living. Supportive services are available, 24 hours a day, to meet scheduled and unscheduled needs, in a way that promotes maximum independence and dignity for each resident and encourages the involvement of a resident's family, neighbor and friends.

Auxiliary: A volunteer community organization formed to assist the hospital in carrying out its purpose and to serve as a link between the institution and the community.

Average daily census: The average number of people served on an inpatient basis on a single day during the reporting period; the figure is calculated by dividing the number of inpatient days by the number of days in the reporting period.

Bariatric/weight control services: Bariatrics is the medical practice of weight reduction.

Beds: Number of beds regularly maintained (set up and staffed for use) for inpatients as of the close of the reporting period. Excludes newborn bassinets.

Bed-size category: Hospitals are categorized by the number of beds set up and staffed for use at the end of the reporting period. The eight categories in Hospital Statistics are: 6 to 24 beds; 25 to 49; 50 to 99; 100 to 199; 200 to 299; 300 to 399; 400 to 499; and 500 or more.

Birthing room-LDR room-LDRP room:
A single-room type of maternity care with a more homelike setting for families than the traditional three-room unit(labor/delivery/recovery) with a separate postpartum area. A birthing room combines labor and delivery in one room. An LDR room accommodates three stages in the birthing process—labor, delivery, and recovery. An LDRP room accommodates all four stages of the birth process—labor, delivery, recovery, and postpartum.

Births: Total number of infants born in the hospital during the reporting period. Births do not include infants transferred from other institutions, and are excluded from admission and discharge figures.

Blood Donor Center: A facility that performs, or is responsible for the collection, processing, testing or distribution of blood and components.

Bone marrow transplant: See definition for Transplant on page 213.

Breast cancer screening/mammograms:
Mammography screening – The use of breast x-ray to detect unsuspected breast cancer in asymptomatic women. Diagnostic mammography – The x-ray imaging of breast tissue in symptomatic women who are considered to have a substantial likelihood of having breast cancer already.

Burn care: Provides care to severely burned patients. Severely burned patients are those with any of the following: (1) second-degree burns of more than 25% total body surface area for adults or 20% total body surface area for children: (2) third-degree burns of more than 10% total body surface area; (3) any severe burns of the hands, face, eyes, ears, or feet; or (4) all inhalation injuries, electrical burns, complicated burn injuries involving fractures and other major traumas, and all other poor risk factors.

Cardiac electrophysiology: Evaluation and management of patients with complex rhythm or conduction abnormalities, including diagnostic testing, treatment of arrhythmias by catheter ablation or drug therapy, and pacemaker/defibrillator implantation and follow-up.

Cardiac intensive care: Provides patient care of a more specialized nature than the usual medical and surgical care, on the basis of physicians' orders and approved nursing care plans. The unit is staffed with specially trained nursing personnel and contains monitoring and specialized support or treatment equipment for patients who, because of heart seizure, open-heart surgery, or other life-threatening conditions, require intensified, comprehensive observation and care. May include myocardial infarction, pulmonary care, and heart transplant units.

Cardiac Rehabilitation: A medically supervised program to help heart patients recover quickly and improve their overall physical and mental functioning. The goal is to reduce risk of another cardiac event or to keep an already present heart condition from getting worse. Cardiac rehabilitation programs include: counseling to patients, an exercise program, helping patients modify risk factors such as smoking and high blood pressure, providing vocational guidance to enable the patient to return to work, supplying information on physical limitations and lending emotional support.

Case management: A system of assessment, treatment planning, referral and follow-up that ensures the provision of comprehensive and continuous services and the coordination of payment and reimbursement for care.

Chaplaincy/pastoral care services: A service ministering religious activities and providing pastoral counseling to patients, their families, and staff of a health care organization.

Chemotherapy: An organized program for the treatment of cancer by the use of drugs or chemicals.

Children's wellness program: A program that encourages improved health status and a healthful lifestyle of children through health education, exercise, nutrition and health promotion.

Chiropractic services: An organized clinical service including spinal manipulation or adjustment and related diagnostic and therapeutic services.

Closed physician-hospital organization (Closed PHO): A joint venture between the hospital and physicians who have been selected on the basis of cost-effectiveness and/or high quality. The PHO can act as a unified agent in managed care contracting, own a managed care plan, own and operate ambulatory care centers or ancillary services projects, or provide administrative services to physician members.

Community health education: Education that provides health information to individuals and populations, as well as support for personal, family and community health decisions with the objective of improving health status.

Community hospitals: All nonfederal, short-term general, and special hospitals whose facilities and services are available to the public. (Special hospitals include obstetrics and gynecology; eye, ear, nose, and throat; rehabilitation; orthopedic; and other individually described specialty services.) Short-term general and special childrens hospitals are also considered to be community hospitals.

A hospital may include a nursing-home-type unit and still be classified as short-term, provided that the majority of its patients are admitted to units where the average length of stay is less than 30 days. Therefore, statistics for community hospitals often include some data about such nursing-home-type units. An example is furnished by Montana, where in 1995 63.6 percent of all hospitals classified as community hospitals include nursing-home-type units. Expense, revenue, utilization, and personnel data for these hospitals include data about their nursing-home-type units. Thus, total admissions to Montana community hospitals in 1995 were 96,154; total inpatient days, 997,759; total expenses, $791,806,393; and total payroll expenses, $352,583,331. If nursing-home-type unit data were excluded, these same items would be 94,034; 457,340; 752,567,865; and $328,911841, respectively.

Note that before 1972, hospital units of institutions such as prison and college infirmaries were included in the category of community hospitals. Including these units made this category equivalent to the short-term general and other special hospitals category. Although these hospital units are few in number and small in size, this change in definition should be taken into consideration when comparing data.

Community outreach: A program that systematically interacts with the community to identify those in need of services, alerting persons and their families to the availability of services, locating needed services, and enabling persons to enter the service delivery system.

Complementary and alternative medicine services: Organized hospital services or formal arrangements to providers that provide care or treatment not based solely on traditional western allopathic medical teachings as instructed in most U.S. medical schools. Includes any of the following: acupuncture, chiropractic, homeopathy, osteopathy, diet and lifestyle changes, herbal medicine, message therapy, etc.

Computer assisted orthopedic surgery (CAOS): Orthopedic surgery using computer technology, enabling three-dimensional graphic models to visualize a patient's anatomy.

Control: The type of organization responsible for establishing policy concerning the overall operation of hospitals. The three major categories are government (including federal, state, and local); nongovernment (nonprofit); and investor-owned (for-profit).

Crisis prevention: Services provided in order to promote physical and mental well being and the early identification of disease and ill health prior to the onset and recognition of symptoms so as to permit early treatment.

CT scanner: Computed tomographic scanner for head or whole body scans.

Deduction from revenue: The difference between revenue at full established rates (gross) and the payment actually received from payers (net).

Dental Services: An organized dental service or dentists on staff, not necessarily involving special facilities, providing dental or oral services to inpatients or outpatients.

Diagnostic radioisotope facility: The use of radioactive isotopes (Radiopharmaceuticals) as tracers or indicators to detect an abnormal condition or disease.

Electron beam computed tomography (EBCT): A high tech computed tomography scan used to detect coronary artery disease by measuring coronary calcifications. This imaging procedure uses electron beams which are magnetically steered to produce a visual of the coronary artery and the images are produced faster than conventional CT scans.

Emergency department: Hospital facilities for the provision of unscheduled outpatient services to patients whose conditions require immediate care.

Emergency room visits: The number of visits to the emergency unit. When emergency outpatients are admitted to the inpatient areas of the hospital, they are counted as emergency room visits and subsequently, as inpatient admissions.

Enabling services: A program that is designed to help the patient access health care services by offering any of the following: linguistic services, transportation services, and/or referrals to local social services agencies.

End of Life: Services offered to patients suffering from chronic, severe, and life-threatening diseases including comprehensive services that give patients and caregivers the resources and the confidence to manage symptoms, avoid emergency room admissions and frequent hospitalization, and remain in familiar and comfortable settings.

Endoscopic retrograde cholangiopancreatography (ERCP): A procedure in which a catheter is introduced through an endoscope into the bile ducts and pancreatic ducts. Injection of contrast materials permits detailed x-ray of these structures. The procedure is used diagnostically as well as therapeutically to relieve obstruction or remove stones.

Endoscopic ultrasound: Specially designed endoscope that incorporates an ultrasound transductor used to obtain detailed images of organs in the chest and abdomen. The endoscope can be passed through the mouth or the anus. When combined with needle biopsy the procedure can assist in diagnosis and staging of cancer.

Enrollment assistance services: A program that provides enrollment assistance for patients who are potentially eligible for public health insurance programs such as Medicaid, State Children's Health Insurance, or local/state indigent care programs. The specific services offered could include explanation of benefits, assist applicants in completing the application and locating all relevant documents, conduct eligibility interviews, and/or forward applications and documentation to state/local social service or health agency.

Equity model: An arrangement that allows established practitioners to become shareholders in a professional corporation in exchange for tangible and intangible assets of their existing practices.

Esophageal impedance study: A test in which a catheter is placed through the nose into the esophagus to measure whether gas or liquids are passing from the stomach into the esophagus and causing symptoms.

Expenses: Includes all expenses for the reporting period including payroll, non-payroll, bad debt, and all nonoperating expenses. *Payroll expenses* include all salaries and wages. *Non-payroll expenses* are all professional fees and those salary expenditures excluded from payroll. *Labor related expenses* are defined as payroll expenses plus employee benefits. *Non-labor related expenses* are all other non-payroll expenses. *Bad debt* has been reclassified from a "reduction in revenue" to an expense in accordance with the revised AICPA Audit Guide. However, for purposes of historical consistency, the expense total that appears throughout *AHA Hospital Statistics does not include "bad debt" as an expense item.* Note: Financial data may not add due to rounding.

Extracorporeal shock wave lithotripter (ESWL): A medical device used for treating stones in the kidney or urethra. The device disintegrates kidney stones noninvasively through the transmission of acoustic shock waves directed at the stones.

Fertility Clinic: A specialized program set in an infertility center that provides counseling and education as well as advanced reproductive techniques such as: injectable therapy, reproductive surgeries, treatment for endometriosis, male factor infertility, tubal reversals, in vitro fertilization (IVF), donor eggs, and other such services to help patients achieve successful pregnancies.

Fitness center: Provides exercise, testing, or evaluation programs and fitness activities to the community and hospital employees.

Foundation: A corporation, organized as a hospital affiliate or subsidiary, that purchases both tangible and intangible assets of one or more medical group practices. Physicians remain in a separate corporate entity but sign a professional services agreement with the foundation.

Freestanding/Satellite Emergency Department: A facility owned an operated by the hospital but physically separate from the hospital for the provision of unscheduled outpatient services to patients whose conditions require immediate care.

Full-field digital mammography (FFDM): Combines the x-ray generators and tubes used in analog screen-film mammography (SFM) with a detector plate that converts the x-rays into a digital signal.

Full time equivalent employees (FTE): Full time personnel on payroll plus one half of the part time personnel on payroll. For purposes of *AHA Hospital Statistics*, full time and part time medical and dental residents/interns and other trainees are excluded from the calculation.

General medical-surgical care: Provides acute care to patients in medical and surgical units on the basis of physicians' orders and approved nursing care plans.

Genetic testing/counseling: A service equipped with adequate laboratory facilities and directed by a qualified physician to advise parents and prospective parents on potential problems in cases of genetic defects. A genetic test is the analysis of human DNA, RNA, chromosomes, proteins, and certain metabolites in order to detect heritable disease-related genotypes, mutations, phenotypes, or karyotypes for clinical purposes. Genetic tests can have diverse purposes, including the diagnosis of genetic diseases in newborns, children, and adults; the identification of future health risks; the prediction of drug responses; and the assessment of risks to future children.

Geriatric services: The branch of medicine dealing with the physiology of aging and the diagnosis and treatment of disease affecting the aged. Services could include: Adult day care; Alzheimer's diagnostic-assessment services; Comprehensive geriatric assessment; Emergency response system; Geriatric acute care unit; and/or Geriatric clinics.

Government, nonfederal, state, local: Controlled by an agency of state, county, or city government.

Gross inpatient revenue: Revenue from services rendered to inpatients at full established rates (also known as "charges").

Gross outpatient revenue: Revenue from services rendered to outpatients at full established rates.

Group practice without walls: In this organization, the hospital sponsors the formation of a physician group or provides capital to physicians to establish one. The group shares administrative expenses, although the physicians remain independent practitioners.

Group Purchasing Organization: An organization whose primary function is to negotiate contracts for the purpose of purchasing for members of the group or has a central supply site for its members.

Health fair: Community health education events that focus on the prevention of disease and promotion of health through such activities as audiovisual exhibits and free diagnostic services.

Health maintenance organization (HMO): A health care organization that acts as both insurer and provider of comprehensive but specified medical services in return for prospective per capita (capitation) payments.

Health Research: Organized hospital research program in any of the following areas: basic research, clinical research, community health research, and/or research on innovative health care delivery.

Health screening: A preliminary procedure such as a test or examination to detect the most characteristic sign or signs of a disorder that may require further investigation.

Heart transplant: See definition for Transplant on page 213.

Hemodialysis: Provision of equipment and personnel for the treatment of renal insufficiency on an inpatient or outpatient basis.

HIV-AIDS services: (could include). *HIV-AIDS unit* – Special unit or team designated and equipped specifically for diagnosis, treatment, continuing care planning, and counseling services for HIV-AIDS patients and their families. *General inpatient care for HIV-AIDS* – Inpatient diagnosis and treatment for human immunodeficiency virus and acquired immunodeficiency syndrome patients, but dedicated unit is not available. *Specialized outpatient program for HIV-AIDS* – Special outpatient program providing diagnostic, treatment, continuing care planning, and counseling for HIV-AIDS patients and their families.

Home health services: Service providing nursing, therapy, and health-related homemaker or social services in the patient's home.

Hospice: A program providing palliative care, chiefly medical relief of pain and supportive services, addressing the emotional, social, financial, and legal needs of terminally ill patients and their families. Care can be provided in a variety of settings, both inpatient and at home.

Hospital unit: The hospital operation, excluding activity pertaining to nursing-home-type unit (as described below), for the following items: Admissions, Beds, FTEs (full-time, part-time, and total), Inpatient Days, Length of Stay, Net Revenue, and Total Expense.

Hospital unit of institutions: A hospital unit that is not open to the public and is contained within a nonhospital unit. An example is an infirmary that is contained within a college.

Hospitals in a network: Hospitals participating in a group that may include other hospitals, physicians, other providers, insurers, and/or community agencies that work together to coordinate and deliver a broad spectrum of services to the community.

Hospitals in a system: Hospitals belonging to a corporate body that owns and/or manages health provider facilities or health-related subsidiaries; the system may also own non-health-related facilities.

Image-guided radiation therapy (IGRT): Automated system for image-guided radiation therapy that enables clinicians to obtain high-resolution x-ray images to pinpoint tumor sites, adjust patient positioning when necessary, and complete a treatment, all within the standard treatment time slot, allowing for more effective cancer treatments.

Immunization program: Program that plans, coordinates and conducts immunization services in the community.

Indemnity fee for service: The traditional type of health insurance, in which the insured is reimbursed for covered expenses without regard to choice of provider. Payment up to a stated limit may be made either to the individual incurring and claiming the expense, or directly to providers.

Independent practice association (IPA): An IPA is a legal entity that holds managed care contracts and contracts with physicians, usually in solo practice, to provide care either on a fee-for-services or capitated basis. The purpose of an IPA is to assist solo physicians in obtaining managed care contracts.

Indigent care clinic: Health care services for uninsured and underinsured persons where care is free of charge or charged on a sliding scale. This would include "free clinics" staffed by volunteer practitioners, but could also be staffed by employees with sponsoring health care organizations subsidizing the cost of service.

Inpatient days: The number of adult and pediatric days of care, excluding newborn days of care, rendered during the entire reporting period.

Inpatient palliative care unit: An inpatient palliative care ward is a physically discreet, inpatient nursing unit where the focus is palliative care. The patient care focus is on symptom relief for complex patients who may be continuing to undergo primary treatment. Care is delivered by palliative medicine specialists.

Inpatient surgeries: Surgical services provided to patients who remain in the hospital overnight.

Insurance product: In tables 3 through 6, insurance product refers to a hospital-owned insurance product.

Integrated salary model: In this arrangement, physicians are salaried by the hospital or other entity of a health system to provide medical services for primary care and specialty care.

Intensity-Modulated Radiation Therapy (IMRT): A type of three-dimensional radiation therapy, which improves the targeting of treatment delivery in a way that is likely to decrease damage to normal tissues and allows varying intensities.

Intermediate nursing care: Provides health-related services (skilled nursing care and social services) to residents with a variety of physical conditions or functional disabilities. These residents do not require the care provided by a hospital or skilled nursing facility, but do need supervision and support services.

Intraoperative magnetic resonance imaging. An integrated surgery system which provides an MRI system in an operating room. The system allows for immediate evaluation of the degree to tumor resection while the patient is undergoing a surgical resection. Intraoperative MRI exists when a MRI (low-field or high-field) is placed in the operating theater and is used during surgical resection without moving the patient from the operating room to the diagnostic imaging suite.

Investor-owned, for-profit: Investor-owned, for-profit hospitals are those controlled on a for-profit basis by an individual, partnership, or profit-making corporation.

Kidney transplant: See definition for Transplant on page 213.

Labor-related expenses: Payroll expenses plus employee benefits. *Non-labor-related expenses refers* to all other nonpayroll expenses, such as interest depreciation, supplies, purchased services, professional fees, and others.

Length of stay (LOS): LOS refers to the average number of days a patient stays at the facility. Short-term hospitals are those where the average LOS is less than 30 days. Long-term hospitals are those where the average LOS is 30 days or more. The figure is derived by dividing the number of inpatient days by the number of admissions.

Note that this publication carries two LOS variables: *total facility length of stay and hospital unit length of stay. Total facility* includes admissions and inpatient days from nursing-home-type units under control of the hospital. In *hospital unit length of stay*, nursing home utilization is subtracted.

Licensed practical nurse (LPN): A nurse who has graduated from an approved school of practical (vocational) nursing and works under the supervision of registered nurses and/or physicians.

Linguistic/Translation services: Services provided by the hospital designed to make health care more accessible to non-English speaking patients and their physicians.

Liver transplant: See definition for Transplant on page 213.

Long-term: Hospitals are classified either short-term or long-term according to the average length of stay (LOS). A long-term hospital is one in which the average LOS is 30 days or more.

Lung transplant: See definition for Transplant on page 213.

Magnetic resonance imaging (MRI): The use of a uniform magnetic field and radio frequencies to study tissue and structure of the body. This procedure enables the visualization of biochemical activity of the cell in vivo without the use of ionizing radiation, radio-isotopic substances, or high-frequency sound.

Managed care: A term covering a broad spectrum of arrangements for health care delivery and financing, including managed indemnity plans (MIP), health maintenance organizations (HMO), preferred provider organizations (PPO), point-of-service plans (POS), and direct contracting arrangements between employers and providers.

Managed care contract: A contract between the hospital and a managed care organization.

Management services organization (MSO): A corporation owned by the hospital or a physician/hospital joint venture that provides management services to one or more medical group practices. As part of a full-service management agreement, the MSO purchases the tangible assets of the practices and leases them back, employs all non-physician staff, and provides all supplies/administrative systems for a fee.

Meals on wheels: A hospital sponsored program which delivers meals to people, usually the elderly, who are unable to prepare their own meals. Low cost, nutritional meals are delivered to individuals' homes on a regular basis.

Medical surgical intensive care: Provides patient care of a more intensive nature than the usual medical and surgical care, on the basis of physicians' orders and approved nursing care plans. These units are staffed with specially trained nursing personnel and contain monitoring and specialized support equipment for patients who, because of shock, trauma, or other life-threatening conditions, require intensified, comprehensive observation and care. Includes mixed intensive care units.

Mobile health services: Vans and other vehicles used to deliver primary care services.

Multi-slice spiral computed tomography (<64 slice CT): A specialized computed tomography procedure that provides three-dimensional processing and allows narrower and multiple slices with increased spatial resolution and faster scanning times as compared to a regular computed tomography scan.

Multi-slice spiral computed tomography (64+ slice CT): Involves the acquisition of volumetric tomographic x-ray absorption data expressed in Hounsfield units using multiple rows of detectors. 64+ systems reconstruct the equivalent of 64 or greater slices to cover the imaged volume.

Neonatal intensive care: A unit that must be separate from the newborn nursery providing intensive care to all sick infants including those with the very lowest birth weights (less than 1500 grams). NICU has potential for providing mechanical ventilation, neonatal surgery, and special care for the sickest infants born in the hospital or transferred from another institution. A full-time neonatologist serves as director of the NICU.

Neonatal intermediate care: A unit that must be separate from the normal newborn nursery and that provides intermediate and/or recovery care and some specialized services, including immediate resuscitation, intravenous therapy, and capacity for prolonged oxygen therapy and monitoring.

Net patient revenue: The estimated net realizable amounts from patients, third-party payers, and others for services rendered. The number includes estimated retroactive adjustments called for by agreements with third-party payers; retroactive adjustments are accrued on an estimated basis in the period the related services are rendered and then adjusted later as final settlements are determined.

Net total revenue: Net patient revenue plus all other revenue, including contributions, endowment revenue, governmental grants, and all other payments not made on behalf of individual patients.

Neurological services: Services provided by the hospital dealing with the operative and nonoperative management of disorders of the central, peripheral, and autonomic nervous system.

Nongovernment, nonprofit: Hospitals that are nongovernment, nonprofit are controlled by not-for-profit organizations, including religious organizations (Catholic hospitals, for example), fraternal societies, and others.

Nursing-home-type unit/facility: A unit/facility that primarily offers the following type of services to a majority of all admissions:

- *Skilled nursing*: The provision of medical and nursing care services, health-related services, and social services under the supervision of a registered nurse on a 24-hour basis.

- *Intermediate care*: The provision, on a regular basis, of health-related care and services to individuals who do not require the degree of care or treatment that a skilled nursing unit is designed to provide.

- *Personal care*: The provision of general supervision and direct personal care services for residents who require assistance in activities of daily living but who do not need nursing services or inpatient care. Medical and nursing services are available as needed.

- *Sheltered/residential care*: The provision of general supervision and protective services for residents who do not need nursing services or continuous personal care services in the conduct of daily life. Medical and nursing services are available as needed.

Nutrition programs: Those services within a health care facility which are designed to provide inexpensive, nutritionally sound meals to patients.

Obstetrics: Levels should be designated: (1) unit provides services for uncomplicated maternity and newborn cases; (2) unit provides services for uncomplicated cases, the majority of complicated problems, and special neonatal services; and (3) unit provides services for all serious illnesses and abnormalities and is supervised by a full-time maternal/fetal specialist.

Occupational health services: Includes services designed to protect the safety of employees from hazards in the work environment.

Oncology services: An organized program for the treatment of cancer by the use of drugs or chemicals.

Open physician hospital organization (Open PHO): A joint venture between the hospital and all members of the medical staff who wish to participate. The open PHO can act as a unified agent in managed care contracting, own a managed care plan, own and operate ambulatory care centers or ancillary services projects, or provide administrative services to physician members.

Optical colonoscopy: An examination of the interior of the colon using a long, flexible, lighted tube with a small built-in camera.

Orthopedic services: Services provided for the prevention or correction of injuries or disorders of the skeletal system and associated muscles, joints and ligaments.

Osteopathic hospitals: Osteopathic medicine is a medical practice based on a theory that diseases are due chiefly to a loss of structural integrity, which can be restored by manipulation of the neuro-muscular and skeletal systems, supplemented by therapeutic measures (such as medicine or surgery).

Other Intensive Care: A distinct intensive care unit that is not one of the following types: medical/surgical, cardiac, pediatric and neonatal.

Other long term care: Provision of long term care other than skilled nursing care or intermediate care. This can include residential care-elderly housing services for those who do not require daily medical or nursing services, but may require some assistance in the activities of daily living, or sheltered care facilities for developmentally disabled.

Other special care: Provides care to patients requiring care more intensive than that provided in the acute area, yet not sufficiently intensive to require admission to an intensive care unit. Patients admitted to this area are usually transferred here from an intensive care unit once their condition has improved. These units are sometimes referred to as definitive observation, step-down, or progressive care units.

Other transplant: See definition for Transplant on page 213.

Outpatient care: Treatment provided to patients who do not remain in the hospital for overnight care. Hospitals may deliver outpatient care on site or through a facility owned and operated by the hospital, but physically separate from the hospital. In addition to treating minor illnesses or injuries, a free-standing center will stabilize seriously ill or injured patients before transporting them to a hospital. Laboratory and radiology services are usually available.

Outpatient care center (Freestanding): A facility owned and operated by the hospital, but physically separate from the hospital, that provides various medical treatments on an outpatient basis only. In addition to treating minor illnesses or injuries, the center will stabilize seriously ill or injured patients before transporting them to a hospital. Laboratory and radiology services are usually available.

Outpatient care center-services (Hospital-based): Organized hospital health care services offered by appointment on an ambulatory basis. Services may include outpatient surgery, examination, diagnosis, and treatment of a variety of medical conditions on a nonemergency basis, and laboratory and other diagnostic testing as ordered by staff or outside physician referral.

Outpatient surgeries: Scheduled surgical services provided to patients who do not remain in the hospital overnight. In the AHA Annual Survey, outpatient surgery may be performed in operating suites also used for inpatient surgery, specially designated surgical suites for outpatient surgery, or procedure rooms within an outpatient care facility.

Outpatient visit: A visit by a patient who is not lodged in the hospital while receiving medical, dental, or other services. Each visit an outpatient makes to a discrete unit constitutes one visit regardless of the number of diagnostic and/or therapeutic treatments that the patient receives. Total outpatient visits should include all clinic visits, referred visits, observation services, outpatient surgeries, and emergency room visits.

Pain management: A hospital wide formalized program that includes staff education for the management of chronic and acute pain based on guidelines and protocols like those developed by the Agency for Health Care Policy Research, etc.

Palliative care program: An organized program providing specialized medical care, drugs or therapies for the management of acute or chronic pain and/or the control of symptoms administered by specially trained physicians and other clinicians; and supportive care services, such as counseling on advanced directives, spiritual care, and social services, to patients with advanced disease and their families.

Patient Controlled Analgesia (PCA). Patient-controlled Analgesia (PCA) is intravenously administered pain medicine under the patient's control. The patient has a button on the end of a cord than can be pushed at will, whenever more pain medicine is desired. This button will only deliver more pain medicine at pre-determined intervals, as programmed by the doctor's order.

Patient education center: Written goals and objectives for the patient and/or family related to therapeutic regimens, medical procedures, and self care.

Patient representative services: Organized hospital services providing personnel through whom patients and staff can seek solutions to institutional problems affecting the delivery of high-quality care and services.

Payroll expenses: Includes all salaries and wages. All professional fees and salary expenditures excluded from payroll, such as employee benefits, are defined as nonpayroll expenses and are included in total expenses.

Pediatric Cardiac Surgery: Includes minimally invasive procedures that include surgery done with only a small incision or no incision at all, such as through a laparoscope or an endoscope and more invasive major surgical procedures that include open chest and open heart surgery.

Pediatric Diagnostic/invasive catheterization: (also called coronary angiography or coronary arteriography) is used to assist in diagnosing complex heart conditions. Cardiac angiography involves the insertion of a tiny catheter into the artery in the groin then carefully threading the catheter up into the aorta where the coronary arteries originate. Once the catheter is in place, a dye is injected which allows the cardiologist to see the size, shape, and distribution of the coronary arteries. These images are used to diagnose heart disease and to determine, among other things, whether or not surgery is indicated.

Pediatric intensive care: Provides care to pediatric patients that is of a more intensive nature than that usually provided to pediatric patients. The unit is staffed with specially trained personnel and contains monitoring and specialized support equipment for treatment of patients who, because of shock, trauma, or other life-threatening conditions, require intensified, comprehensive observation and care.

Pediatric Interventional cardiac catheterization: Non surgical procedure that utilizes the same basic principles as diagnostic catheterization and then uses advanced techniques to improve the heart's function. It can be a less-invasive alternative to heart surgery.

Pediatric medical-surgical care: Provides acute care to pediatric patients on the basis of physicians' orders and approved nursing care plans.

Personnel: Number of persons on the hospital payroll at the end of the reporting period. Personnel are recorded in *Hospital Statistics* as full-time equivalents (FTEs), which are calculated by adding the number of full-time personnel to one half the number of part-time personnel, excluding medical and dental residents, interns, and other trainees. *Per 100 adjusted census* indicates the ratio of personnel to adjusted average daily census, calculated on a per-100 basis.

Physical rehabilitation inpatient care: Provides care encompassing a comprehensive array of restoration services for the disabled and all support services necessary to help patients attain their maximum functional capacity.

Physical rehabilitation outpatient services: Outpatient program providing medical, health-related, therapy, social, and/or vocational services to help disabled persons attain or retain their maximum functional capacity.

Population: Population refers to the residential population of the United States. This includes both civilian and military personnel. Note that population is being used to calculate the values *for community health indicators per 1000 population.*

Positron emission tomography/CT (PET/CT): Provides metabolic functional information for the monitoring of chemotherapy, radiotherapy and surgical planning.

Positron emission tomography scanner (PET): A nuclear medicine imaging technology which uses radioactive (positron emitting) isotopes created in a cyclotron or generator and computers to produce composite pictures of the brain and heart at work. PET scanning produces sectional images depicting metabolic activity or blood flow rather than anatomy.

Preferred provider organization (PPO): A pre-set arrangement in which purchasers and providers agree to furnish specified health services to a group of employees/patients.

Primary care department: A unit or clinic within the hospital that provides primary care services (e.g. general pediatric care, general internal medicine, family practice, gynecology) through hospital-salaried medical and/or nursing staff, focusing on evaluating and diagnosing medical problems and providing medical treatment on an outpatient basis.

Proton beam therapy: A form of radiation therapy which administers proton beams. While producing the same biologic effects as x-ray beams, the energy distribution of protons differs from conventional x-ray beams in that they can be more precisely focused in tissue volumes in a three-dimensional pattern resulting in less surrounding tissue damage than conventional radiation therapy permitting administration of higher doses.

Psychiatric child-adolescent services: Provides care to emotionally disturbed children and adolescents, including those admitted for diagnosis and those admitted for treatment.

Psychiatric consultation-liaison services: Provides organized psychiatric consultation/liaison services to nonpsychiatric hospital staff and/or departments on psychological aspects of medical care that may be generic or specific to individual patients.

Psychiatric education services: Provides psychiatric educational services to community agencies and workers such as schools, police, courts, public health nurses, welfare agencies, clergy, and so forth. The purpose is to expand the mental health knowledge and competence of personnel not working in the mental health field and to promote good mental health through improved understanding, attitudes, and behavioral patterns.

Psychiatric emergency services: Services of facilities available on a 24-hour basis to provide immediate unscheduled out-patient care, diagnosis, evaluation, crisis intervention, and assistance to persons suffering acute emotional or mental distress.

Psychiatric geriatric services: Provides care to emotionally disturbed elderly patients, including those admitted for diagnosis and those admitted for treatment.

Psychiatric inpatient care: Provides acute or long-term care to emotionally disturbed patients, including patients admitted for diagnosis and those admitted for treatment of psychiatric problems, on the basis of physicians' orders and approved nursing care plans. Long-term care may include intensive supervision to the chronically mentally ill, mentally disordered, or other mentally incompetent persons.

Psychiatric outpatient services: Provides medical care, including diagnosis and treatment, of psychiatric outpatients.

Psychiatric partial hospitalization program: Organized hospital services of intensive day/evening outpatient services of three hours of more duration, distinguished from other outpatient visits of one hour.

Radiology, diagnostic: The branch of radiology that deals with the utilization of all modalities of radiant energy in medical diagnoses and therapeutic procedures using radiologic guidance. This includes, but is not restricted to, imaging techniques and methodologies utilizing radiation emitted by x-ray tubes, radionnuclides, and ultrasonographic devices and the radiofrequency electromagnetic radiation emitted by atoms.

Radiology, therapeutic: The branch of medicine concerned with radioactive substances and using various techniques of visualization, with the diagnosis and treatment of disease using any of the various sources of radiant energy. Services could include: megavoltage radiation therapy; radioactive implants; stereotactic radiosurgery; therapeutic radioisotope facility; X-ray radiation therapy.

Registered nurse (RN): A nurse who has graduated from an approved school of nursing and who is currently registered by the state. RNs are responsible for the nature and quality of all nursing care that patients receive. In these tables, the number of RNs does not include those registered nurses more appropriately reported in other occupational categories, such as facility administrators, which are listed under *all other personnel* (Tables 1 and 2).

Rehabilitation services: A wide array of restoration services for disabled and recuperating patients, including all support services necessary to help them attain their maximum functional capacity.

Retirement housing: A facility which provides social activities to senior citizens, usually retired persons, who do not require health care but some

short-term skilled nursing care may be provided. A retirement center may furnish housing and may also have acute hospital and long-term care facilities, or it may arrange for acute and long term care through affiliated institutions.

Robot-assisted walking therapy: A form of physical therapy that uses a robotic device to assist patients who are relearning how to walk.

Robotic surgery: The use of mechanical guidance devices to remotely manipulate surgical instrumentation.

Rural: A rural hospital is located outside a Metropolitan Statistical Area (MSA), as designated by the U.S. Office of Management and Budget (OMB) effective June 6, 2003. An urban area is a geographically defined, integrated social and economic unit with a large population nucleus. Micropolitan areas, which are new to the OMB June 6, 2003 definitions, continue to be classified as rural for purposes of this publication.

Shaped beam radiation system: A precise, non-invasive treatment that involves targeting beams of radiation that mirror the exact size and shape of a tumor at a specific area of a tumor to shrink or destroy cancerous cells. This procedure delivers a therapeutic dose of radiation that conforms precisely to the shape of the tumor, thus minimizing the risk to nearby tissues.

Simulated rehabilitation environment: Rehabilitation focused on retraining functional skills in a contextually appropriate environment (simulated home and community settings) or in a traditional setting (gymnasium) using motor learning principles.

Single photon emission computerized tomography (SPECT): A nuclear medicine imaging technology that combines existing technology of gamma camera imaging with computed tomographic imaging technology to provide a more precise and clear image.

Skilled nursing care: Provides non-acute medical and skilled nursing care services, therapy, and social services under the supervision of a licensed registered nurse on a 24-hour basis.

Sleep Center: Specially equipped and staffed center for the diagnosis and treatment of sleep disorders.

Social work services (could include): Organized services that are properly directed and sufficiently staffed by qualified individuals who provide assistance and counseling to patients and their families in dealing with social, emotional, and environmental problems associated with illness or disability, often in the context of financial or discharge planning coordination.

Sports medicine: Provision of diagnostic screening and assessment and clinical and rehabilitation services for the prevention and treatment of sports-related injuries.

Stereotactic radiosurgery: Stereotactic radiosurgery (SRS) is a radiotherapy modality that delivers a high dosage of radiation to a discrete treatment area in as few as one treatment session. Includes gamma knife, cyberknife, etc.

Support groups: A hospital sponsored program which allows a group of individuals with the same or similar problems who meet periodically to share experiences, problems, and solutions in order to support each other.

Surgical operations: Those surgical operations, whether major or minor, performed in the operating room(s). A surgical operation involving more than one surgical procedure is still considered only one surgical operation.

Swing bed services: A hospital bed that can be used to provide either acute or long-term care depending on community or patient needs. To be eligible a hospital must have a Medicare provider agreement in place, have fewer than 100 beds, be located in a rural area, do not have a 24 hour nursing service waiver in effect, have not been terminated from the program in the prior two years, and meet various service conditions.

Teen outreach services: A program focusing on the teenager which encourages an improved health status and a healthful lifestyle including physical, emotional, mental, social, spiritual and economic health through education, exercise, nutrition and health promotion.

Tissue transplant: See definition for Transplant on page 213.

Tobacco treatment/cessation program: Organized hospital services with the purpose of ending tobacco-use habits of patients addicted to tobacco/nicotine.

Transplant services. The branch of medicine that transfers an organ or tissue from one person to another or from one body part to another to replace a diseased structure or to restore function or to change appearance.

Services could include: Bone marrow transplant program; heart, lung, kidney, intestine, or tissue transplant. The other transplant services include transplant services other than bone marrow, heart, kidney, liver, lung, tissue and heart/lung or other multi-transplant surgeries.

Transportation to health facilities: A long-term care support service designed to assist the mobility of the elderly. Some programs offer improved financial access by offering reduced rates and barrier-free buses or vans with ramps and lifts to assist the elderly or handicapped; others offer subsidies for public transport systems or operate mini-bus services exclusively for use by senior citizens.

Trauma center (certified): A facility to provide emergency and specialized intensive care to critically ill and injured patients. **Level 1:** A regional resource trauma center, which is capable of providing total care for every aspect of injury and plays a leadership role in trauma research and education. **Level 2:** A community trauma center, which is capable of providing trauma care to all but the most severely injured patients who require highly specialized care. **Level 3:** A rural trauma hospital, which is capable of providing care to a large number of injury victims and can resuscitate and stabilize more severely injured patients so that they can be transported to Level 1 or 2 facilities.

Ultrasound: The use of acoustic waves above the range of 20,000 cycles per second to visualize internal body structures.

Urban: An urban hospital is located inside a Metropolitan Statistical Area (MSA), designated by the U.S. Office of Management and Budget effective June 6, 2003. An urban areas is a geographically defined, integrated social and economic unit with a large population base. Micropolitan areas, which are new to the OMB June 6, 2003 definitions, are not considered to be urban for purposes of this publication.

Urgent care center: A facility that provides care and treatment for problems that are not life-threatening but require attention over the short term. These units function like emergency rooms but are separate from hospitals with which they may have backup affiliation arrangements.

Virtual colonoscopy: Noninvasive screening procedure used to visualize, analyze and detect cancerous or potentially cancerous polyps in the colon.

Volunteer services department: An organized hospital department responsible for coordinating the services of volunteers working within the institution.

Women's health center/services: An area set aside for coordinated education and treatment services specifically for and promoted to women as provided by this special unit. Services may or may not include obstetrics but include a range of services other than OB.

Wound Management Services: Services for patients with chronic wounds and nonhealing wounds often resulting from diabetes, poor circulation, improper seating and immunocompromising conditions. The goals are to progress chronic wounds through stages of healing, reduce and eliminate infections, increase physical function to minimize complications from current wounds and prevent future chronic wounds. Wound management services are provided on an inpatient or outpatient basis, depending on the intensity of service needed.

2008 AHA Annual Survey
Health Forum, L.L.C.

Please return to:
AHA Annual Survey
One North Franklin, 29th Floor
Chicago, Illinois 60606

A. REPORTING PERIOD (please refer to the instructions and definitions at the end of this questionnaire)

Report data for a full 12-month period, preferably your last completed fiscal year (**366** days). (Be consistent in using the same reporting period for responses throughout various sections of this survey.)

1. Reporting Period used (beginning and ending date) ...... ___ / ___ / ___ ___ ___   to ___ / ___ / ___ ___ ___
    Month Day Year Month Day Year

2. a. Were you in operation 12 full months
       at the end of your reporting period .... YES ☐   NO ☐   b. Number of days open
                                                                                       during reporting period .... _____

3. Indicate the beginning of your current fiscal year .... ___ / ___ / ___ ___ ___
    Month Day Year

B. ORGANIZATIONAL STRUCTURE

1. CONTROL

Indicate the type of organization that is responsible for establishing policy for overall operation of your hospital. CHECK ONLY ONE:

Government, nonfederal
☐ 12 State
☐ 13 County
☐ 14 City
☐ 15 City-County
☐ 16 Hospital district or authority

Nongovernment, not-for profit (NFP)
☐ 21 Church-operated
☐ 23 Other not-for-profit (including NFP Corporation)

Investor-owned, for-profit
☐ 31 Individual
☐ 32 Partnership
☐ 33 Corporation

Government, federal
☐ 41 Air Force
☐ 42 Army
☐ 43 Navy
☐ 44 Public Health Service

☐ 45 Veterans' Affairs
☐ 46 Federal other than 41-45 or 47-48
☐ 47 PHS Indian Service
☐ 48 Department of Justice

2. SERVICE

Indicate the ONE category that BEST describes your hospital or the type of service it provides to the MAJORITY of **patients**:

☐ 10 General medical and surgical
☐ 11 Hospital unit of an institution (prison hospital, college infirmary)
☐ 12 Hospital unit within an institution for the mentally retarded
☐ 13 Surgical
☐ 22 Psychiatric
☐ 33 Tuberculosis and other respiratory diseases
☐ 41 Cancer
☐ 42 Heart
☐ 44 Obstetrics and gynecology
☐ 45 Eye, ear, nose, and throat

☐ 46 Rehabilitation
☐ 47 Orthopedic
☐ 48 Chronic disease
☐ 62 Institution for the mentally retarded
☐ 80 Acute long-term care hospital
☐ 82 Alcoholism and other chemical dependency
☐ 49 Other-specify treatment area: _____

3. OTHER

a. Does your hospital restrict admissions primarily to children? .... YES ☐   NO ☐

B. ORGANIZATIONAL STRUCTURE (CONTINUED)

b. Does the hospital itself operate subsidiary corporations? .... YES ☐   NO ☐

c. Is the hospital contract managed? If yes, please provide the name, city, and state of the organization .. YES ☐   NO ☐
Name: _____   City: _____   State: _____

d. Is the hospital a participant in a network? If yes, please provide the name, city, state, and telephone number........ YES ☐   NO ☐
of the network. If the hospital participates in more than one network, please provide the name, city, state and telephone number of the network(s) on page 11, under supplemental information.
Name: _____   City: _____   State: _____ Telephone_____

e. Does the hospital participate in a group purchasing arrangement? If yes, please provide the name, city, and state
of the group purchasing organization. If the hospital participates in more than one group purchasing organization,
please provide the name, city, state and telephone number of the group purchasing organization(s) on page 12, under
supplemental information.. YES ☐ NO ☐

Name: _____   City: _____   State: _____

f. Is your hospital owned in whole or in part by physicians or a physician group?........................... YES ☐ NO ☐

g. If you checked 80 Acute long-term care hospital (LTCH) in the Section B2 (Service), please indicate if you are a freestanding LTCH or a LTCH collocated within a general acute care hospital.
☐ Free standing LTCH   ☐ LTCH collocated in a general acute care hospital

If you are collocated in a general acute care hospital, what is your host hospital's name?
Name_____ City_____ State_____

4. NATIONAL PROVIDER IDENTIFIER (NPI)

a. Does your hospital have its new National Provider Identifier (NPI) from the National Plan and Provider Enumeration System?
Yes☐   No☐

If yes, please report the ten digit NPI _ _ _ _ _ _ _ _ _ _

Does your hospital also have a Subpart NPI?   Yes____   No___

If yes, please report the Subpart NPI and provide the relevant taxonomy code to indicate the type of service provided. If you have multiple Subpart NPIs please report them all.

Subpart NPI 1 _ _ _ _ _ _ _ _ _ _   Taxonomy Code _ _

Subpart NPI 2 _ _ _ _ _ _ _ _ _ _   Taxonomy Code_ _

Subpart NPI 3 _ _ _ _ _ _ _ _ _ _   Taxonomy Code_ _

Taxonomy Codes
Ambulatory Health Care Facility   01
Medicare Defined Swing Bed Unit 02
Psychiatric Unit   03
Rehabilitation Unit   04
Rehabilitation, Substance Use Disorder Unit 05
Laboratory 06
Nursing and Custodial Care Facility 07
Residential Treatment Facility 08
Respite Care Facility 09
Other 10

C. FACILITIES AND SERVICES

For each service or facility listed below, please check all the categories that describe how each item is provided **as of the last day of the reporting period**. Check all categories that apply for an item. Leave all categories blank for a facility or service that is not provided. Column 3 refers to the networks that were identified in section B, question 3d. If you checked column (1) C1-19, please include the number of beds. *The sum of the beds reported in 1-19 should equal Section D(1b), beds set up and staffed on page 8.*

	(1) Owned or provided by my hospital or its subsidiary	(2) Provided by my Health System (in my local community)	(3) Provided by my network (in my local community)	(4) Provided through a formal contractual arrangement or joint venture with another provider that is not in my system or network
1. General medical-surgical care.........................(# Beds: _____)	☐	☐	☐	☐
2. Pediatric medical-surgical care .... (# Beds: _____)	☐	☐	☐	☐
3. Obstetrics [Level of unit (1-3): (___).................(# Beds: _____)	☐	☐	☐	☐
4. Medical surgical intensive care...................... (# Beds: _____)	☐	☐	☐	☐
5. Cardiac Intensive care................................ (# Beds: _____)	☐	☐	☐	☐
6. Neonatal intensive care............................... (# Beds: _____)	☐	☐	☐	☐
7. Neonatal intermediate care............................(# Beds: _____)	☐	☐	☐	☐
8. Pediatric intensive care................................ (# Beds:_____)	☐	☐	☐	☐
9. Burn care................................ (# Beds: _____)	☐	☐	☐	☐
10. Other special care _____..... (# Beds: _____)	☐	☐	☐	☐
11. Other intensive care_____......(# Beds: _____)	☐	☐	☐	☐
12. Physical rehabilitation................................ (# Beds: _____)	☐	☐	☐	☐
13. Alcoholism-drug abuse or dependency care...... (# Beds: _____)	☐	☐	☐	☐
14. Psychiatric care....................................... (# Beds: _____)	☐	☐	☐	☐
15. Skilled nursing care................................... (# Beds: _____)	☐	☐	☐	☐
16. Intermediate nursing care............................(# Beds: _____)	☐	☐	☐	☐
17. Acute long-term care................................ (# Beds: _____)	☐	☐	☐	☐
18. Other long term care................................. (# Beds: _____)	☐	☐	☐	☐
19. Other care (specify): _____...... (# Beds: _____)	☐	☐	☐	☐
20. Adult day care program..	☐	☐	☐	☐
21. Airborne infection isolation room (# rooms _____)....................	☐	☐	☐	☐
22. Alcoholism-drug abuse or dependency outpatient services..........	☐	☐	☐	☐
23. Alzheimer Center..	☐	☐	☐	☐
24. Ambulance services...	☐	☐	☐	☐
25. Ambulatory surgery center.......................................	☐	☐	☐	☐
26. Arthritis treatment center..	☐	☐	☐	☐
27. Assisted living..	☐	☐	☐	☐
28. Auxiliary..	☐	☐	☐	☐
29. Bariatric/weight control services................................	☐	☐	☐	☐
30. Birthing room-LDR room – LDRP room................................	☐	☐	☐	☐
31. Blood Donor Center...	☐	☐	☐	☐
32. Breast cancer screening/mammograms.............................	☐	☐	☐	☐

C. FACILITIES AND SERVICES (continued)

	(1) Owned or provided by my hospital or its subsidiary	(2) Provided by my Health System (in my local community)	(3) Provided by my network (in my local community)	(4) Provided through a formal contractual arrangement or joint venture with another provider that is not in my system or network (in local community)
33. Cardiology and cardiac surgery services				
a. Adult diagnostic catheterization	☐	☐	☐	☐
b. Pediatric diagnostic catheterization	☐	☐	☐	☐
c. Adult interventional cardiac catheterization	☐	☐	☐	☐
d. Pediatric interventional cardiac catheterization	☐	☐	☐	☐
e. Adult cardiac surgery	☐	☐	☐	☐
f. Pediatric cardiac surgery	☐	☐	☐	☐
g. Adult cardiac electrophysiology	☐	☐	☐	☐
h. Pediatric cardiac electrophysiology	☐	☐	☐	☐
i. Cardiac rehabilitation	☐	☐	☐	☐
34. Case management	☐	☐	☐	☐
35. Chaplaincy/pastoral care services	☐	☐	☐	☐
36. Chemotherapy	☐	☐	☐	☐
37. Children's wellness program	☐	☐	☐	☐
38. Chiropractic services	☐	☐	☐	☐
39. Community outreach	☐	☐	☐	☐
40. Complementary **and alternative** medicine services	☐	☐	☐	☐
41. Computer assisted orthopedic surgery (CAOS)	☐	☐	☐	☐
42. Crisis prevention	☐	☐	☐	☐
43. Dental services	☐	☐	☐	☐
44. Emergency services				
a. Emergency department	☐	☐	☐	☐
b. Satellite Emergency Department	☐	☐	☐	☐
c. If you checked column 1 (44b), is the department open 24 hours a day, 7 days a week?	Yes ☐	No ☐		
d. Trauma center (certified) [Level of unit (1-3)]____	☐	☐	☐	☐
45. Enabling services	☐	☐	☐	☐
46. End of life service				
a. Hospice program	☐	☐	☐	☐
b. Pain management	☐	☐	☐	☐
c. Palliative care program	☐	☐	☐	☐
d. Inpatient palliative care unit	☐	☐	☐	☐
47. Endoscopic services				
a. **Optical colonoscopy**	☐	☐	☐	☐
b. Endoscopic ultrasound	☐	☐	☐	☐
c. Ablation of Barrett's esophagus	☐	☐	☐	☐
d. Esophageal impedance study	☐	☐	☐	☐
e. Endoscopic retrograde cholangiopancreatography (ERCP)	☐	☐	☐	☐
48. Enrollment assistance services	☐	☐	☐	☐
49. Extracorporeal shock wave lithotripter (ESWL)	☐	☐	☐	☐
50. Fitness center	☐	☐	☐	☐
51. Freestanding outpatient care center	☐	☐	☐	☐
52. Geriatric services	☐	☐	☐	☐
53. Health fair	☐	☐	☐	☐

C. FACILITIES AND SERVICES (continued)

	(1) Owned or provided by my hospital or its subsidiary	(2) Provided by my Health System (in my local community)	(3) Provided by my network (in my local community)	(4) Provided through a formal contractual arrangement or joint venture with another provider that is not in my system or network (in local community)
54. Community health education..	☐	☐	☐	☐
55. Health screenings..	☐	☐	☐	☐
56. Health research...	☐	☐	☐	☐
57. Hemodialysis...	☐	☐	☐	☐
58. HIV/AIDS services...	☐	☐	☐	☐
59. Home health services..	☐	☐	☐	☐
60. Hospital-based outpatient care center services.....................	☐	☐	☐	☐
61. Immunization program...	☐	☐	☐	☐
62. Indigent care clinic..	☐	☐	☐	☐
63. Linguistic/translation services..	☐	☐	☐	☐
64. Meal on wheels...	☐	☐	☐	☐
65. Mobile health services..	☐	☐	☐	☐
66. Neurological services...	☐	☐	☐	☐
67. Nutrition program..	☐	☐	☐	☐
68. Occupational health services..	☐	☐	☐	☐
69. Oncology services...	☐	☐	☐	☐
70. Orthopedic services...	☐	☐	☐	☐
71. Outpatient surgery...	☐	☐	☐	☐
72. Patient controlled analgesia (PCA).................................	☐	☐	☐	☐
73. Patient education center...	☐	☐	☐	☐
74. Patient representative services..	☐	☐	☐	☐
75. Physical rehabilitation services				
a. Physical rehabilitation outpatient services	☐	☐	☐	☐
b. Robot-assisted walking therapy	☐	☐	☐	☐
c. Simulated rehabilitation environment	☐	☐	☐	☐
76. Primary care department..	☐	☐	☐	☐
77. Psychiatric services				
a. Psychiatric child-adolescent services........................	☐	☐	☐	☐
b. Psychiatric consultation-liaison services.....................	☐	☐	☐	☐
c. Psychiatric education services..................................	☐	☐	☐	☐
d. Psychiatric emergency services...............................	☐	☐	☐	☐
e. Psychiatric geriatric services...................................	☐	☐	☐	☐
f. Psychiatric outpatient services.................................	☐	☐	☐	☐
g. Psychiatric partial hospitalization services..................	☐	☐	☐	☐
78. Radiology, diagnostic				
a. CT Scanner...	☐	☐	☐	☐
b. Diagnostic radioisotope facility	☐	☐	☐	☐
c. Electron beam computed tomography (EBCT)............	☐	☐	☐	☐
d. Full-field digital mammography (FFDM)...................	☐	☐	☐	☐
e. Magnetic resonance imaging (MRI).........................	☐	☐	☐	☐
f. Intraoperative magnetic resonance imaging................	☐	☐	☐	☐
g. Multi-slice spiral computed tomography (<64+ slice CT).........	☐	☐	☐	☐
h. Multi-slice spiral computed tomography (64+ slice CT)...........	☐	☐	☐	☐

C. FACILITIES AND SERVICES (continued)

	(1) Owned or provided by my hospital or its subsidiary	(2) Provided by my Health System (in my local community)	(3) Provided by my network (in my local community)	(4) Provided through a formal contractual arrangement or joint venture with another provider that is not in my system or network (in local community)
i. Positron emission tomography (PET)....................................	☐	☐	☐	☐
j. Positron emission tomography/CT (PET/CT)......................	☐	☐	☐	☐
k. Single photon emission computerized tomography (SPECT)...	☐	☐	☐	☐
l. Ultrasound...	☐	☐	☐	☐
79. Radiology, therapeutic				
a. Image-guided radiation therapy (IGRT)............................	☐	☐	☐	☐
b. Intensity-modulated radiation therapy (IMRT).....................	☐	☐	☐	☐
c. Proton beam therapy..	☐	☐	☐	☐
d. Shaped beam radiation system.....................................	☐	☐	☐	☐
e. Stereotactic radiosurgery..	☐	☐	☐	☐
80. Reproductive health				
a. Fertility clinic..	☐	☐	☐	☐
b. Genetic testing/counseling...	☐	☐	☐	☐
81. Retirement housing..	☐	☐	☐	☐
82. Robotic surgery...	☐	☐	☐	☐
83. Sleep center..	☐	☐	☐	☐
84. Social work services...	☐	☐	☐	☐
85. Sports medicine..	☐	☐	☐	☐
86. Support groups...	☐	☐	☐	☐
87. Swing bed services...	☐	☐	☐	☐
88. Teen outreach services..	☐	☐	☐	☐
89. Tobacco treatment/cessation program.......................	☐	☐	☐	☐
90. Transplant services				
a. Bone marrow transplant services...................................	☐	☐	☐	☐
b. Heart..	☐	☐	☐	☐
c. Kidney...	☐	☐	☐	☐
d. Liver...	☐	☐	☐	☐
e. Lung...	☐	☐	☐	☐
f. Tissue...	☐	☐	☐	☐
g. Other..	☐	☐	☐	☐
91. Transportation to health services.............................	☐	☐	☐	☐
92. Urgent care center..	☐	☐	☐	☐
93. Virtual colonoscopy...	☐	☐	☐	☐
94. Volunteer services department.................................	☐	☐	☐	☐
95. Women's health center/services...............................	☐	☐	☐	☐
96. Wound management services...................................	☐	☐	☐	☐

97. In which of the following physician arrangements does your hospital or system/network participate? Column 3 refers to the networks that were identified in section B, question 3d. For hospital level physician arrangements that are reported in column 1, please report the number of physicians involved.

	(1) My Hospital		(2) My Health System	(3) My Health Network
a. Independent Practice Association	☐	(# of physicians _____)	☐	☐
b. Group practice without walls	☐	(# of physicians _____)	☐	☐
c. Open Physician-Hospital Organization (PHO)	☐	(# of physicians _____)	☐	☐

C. FACILITIES AND SERVICES (continued)

		(1) My Hospital		(2) My Health System	(3) My Health Network
d.	Closed Physician-Hospital Organization (PHO)	☐	(# of physicians _____)	☐	☐
e.	Management Service Organization (MSO)	☐	(# of physicians _____)	☐	☐
f.	Integrated Salary Model	☐	(# of physicians _____)	☐	☐
g.	Equity Model	☐	(# of physicians _____)	☐	☐
h.	Foundation..	☐	(# of physicians _____)	☐	☐

98a. Does your hospital participate in any joint venture arrangements with physicians or physician groups?　　　YES ☐　　NO ☐

98b. If your hospital participates in any joint ventures with physicians or physician groups, please indicate which types of services are involved in those joint ventures (Check all that apply)

- a. ☐ Limited service hospital
- b. ☐ Ambulatory surgical centers
- c. ☐ Imaging centers
- d. ☐ Other _____

98c. If you selected 'a. Limited Service Hospital', please tell us what type(s) of services are provided. (Check all that apply.)

- a. ☐ Cardiac
- b. ☐ Orthopedic
- c. ☐ Surgical
- d. ☐ Other _____

98d. Does your hospital participate in joint venture arrangements with organizations other than physician groups?　　　YES ☐　NO ☐

99. Does your hospital, health system or health network have an equity interest in any of the following insurance products? (Check all that apply) Contractual relationships with HMOs and PPOs should not be reported here but in Question 100. Column 3 refers to the networks that were identified in section B, question 3d.

	(1) My Hospital	(2) My Health System	(3) My Health Network	(4) Joint Venture With Insurer
a. Health Maintenance Organization....................................☐		☐	☐	☐
b. Preferred Provider Organization.......................................☐		☐	☐	☐
c. Indemnity Fee For Service Plan.......................................☐		☐	☐	☐

100. Does your hospital have a formal written contract that specifies the obligations of each party with:

a. Health maintenance organization (HMO) .... YES ☐　　NO ☐　　b. If YES, how many contracts?　_____

c. Preferred provider organization (PPO) .... YES ☐　　NO ☐　　d. If YES, how many contracts?　_____

101a. What percentage of the hospital's net patient revenue is paid on a capitated basis?
If the hospital does not participate in capitated arrangements, please enter "0")　_____ %

101b. What percentage of the hospital's net patient revenue is paid on a shared risk basis?　_____ %

102. Does your hospital contract directly with employers or a coalition of employers to provide
care on a capitated, predetermined, or shared risk basis? ....YES ☐　NO ☐

103. If your hospital has arrangements to care for a specific group of enrollees in exchange for a capitated payment, how many lives are covered?　_____

D. TOTAL FACILITY BEDS, UTILIZATION, FINANCES, AND STAFFING

Please report beds, utilization, financial, and staffing data for a 12-month period that is consistent with the period reported on page 1. Report financial data for reporting period only. Include within your operations all activities that are wholly owned by the hospital, including subsidiary corporations regardless of where the activity is physically located. Please do not include within your operations distinct and separate divisions that may be owned by your hospital's parent corporation. If final figures are not available, please estimate. Round to the nearest dollar. Report all personnel who were on the payroll and whose payroll expenses are reported in D3f. (Please refer to specific definitions on pages **20-22**.)

	(1) Total Facility	(2) Nursing Home Unit/Facility
Fill out column (2) if hospital owns and operates a nursing home type unit/facility. Column (1) should be the combined total of hospital plus Nursing Home Unit/Facility.		

1. BEDS AND UTILIZATION

a. Total licensed beds.. _____ _____

b. Beds set up and staffed for use at the end of the reporting period .... _____ _____

c. Bassinets set up and staffed for use at the end of the reporting period .... _____

d. Births (exclude fetal deaths) .... _____

e. Admissions (exclude newborns, include neonatal & swing admissions) .... _____ _____

f. Inpatient days (exclude newborns, include neonatal & swing days) .... _____ _____

g. Emergency department visits .... _____

h. Total outpatient visits (include emergency department visits & outpatient surgeries) .. _____

i. Inpatient surgical operations .... _____

j. Number of operating rooms .... _____

k. Outpatient surgical operations... _____

2. MEDICARE/MEDICAID UTILIZATION (exclude newborns, include neonatal & swing days and deaths)

a1. Total Medicare (Title XVIII) inpatient discharges (including Medicare Managed Care) .... _____ _____

a2. How many Medicare inpatient discharges were Medicare Managed Care .... _____ _____

b1. Total Medicare (Title XVIII) inpatient days (including Medicare Managed Care) .... _____ _____

b2. How many Medicare inpatient days were Medicare Managed Care .... _____ _____

c1. Total Medicaid (Title XIX) inpatient discharges (including Medicaid Managed Care) .... _____ _____

c2. How many Medicaid inpatient discharges were Medicaid Managed Care .... _____ _____

d1. Total Medicaid (Title XIX) inpatient days (including Medicaid Managed Care) .... _____ _____

d2. How many Medicaid inpatient days were Medicaid Managed Care .... _____ _____

3. FINANCIAL

*a. Net patient revenue .... _____.00 _____.00

*b. Tax appropriations .... _____.00

*c. Other operating revenue .... _____.00

*d. Nonoperating revenue .... _____.00

*e. TOTAL REVENUE (add 3a thru 3d) .... _____.00 _____.00

f. PAYROLL EXPENSES (only) .... _____.00 _____.00

g. Employee benefits .... _____.00 _____.00

h. Depreciation expense (for reporting period only) .... _____.00

i. Interest expense .... _____.00

j. TOTAL EXPENSES (Payroll plus all non-payroll expenses, including bad debt) _____.00 _____.00

k. **Due to differing accounting standards in use, please indicate whether or not bad debt is included in:**

Total Expenses	YES ☐	NO ☐
Net Patient Revenue	YES ☐	NO ☐

4. REVENUE BY TYPE

a. Total gross inpatient revenue... _____.00

b. Total gross outpatient revenue .... _____.00

c. Total gross patient revenue .... _____.00

D. TOTAL FACILITY BEDS, UTILIZATION, FINANCES, AND STAFFING (continued)

*5. UNCOMPENSATED CARE

a. Bad debt expense .... _____.00

b. Charity (Revenue forgone at full-established rates. Include in gross revenue.)......... _____.00

c. Is your bad debt reported here (5a.1) reported on the basis of full charges?   YES ☐   NO ☐

*6. REVENUE BY PAYOR (report total facility gross and net figures)
(E.6a(2a) should include Medicaid disproportionate payments in the net column (2)

			(1) Gross	(2) Net
*a. GOVERNMENT	(1) Medicare:			
		a) Routine patient revenue	_____.00	_____.00
		b) Managed care revenue	_____.00	_____.00
		c) **Total (a + b)**	_____.00	_____.00
	(2) Medicaid:			
		a) Routine patient revenue	_____.00	_____.00
		b) Managed care revenue	_____.00	_____.00
		c) **Total (a + b)**	_____.00	_____.00
	(3) Other government:		_____.00	_____.00
*b. NONGOVERNMENT	(1) Self-pay		_____.00	_____.00
	(2) Third-party payors:			
		a) Managed care (includes HMO and PPO)	_____.00	_____.00
		b) Other third-party payors	_____.00	_____.00
		c) **Total third-party payors (a + b)**	_____.00	_____.00
	(3) All Other nongovernment:		_____.00	_____.00
*c. **TOTAL**			_____.00	_____.00

(Total gross should equal 4c on page 8. Total net should equal 3a on page 8.)

Are the financial data on pages 8 and 9 from your audited financial statement? .... YES ☐   No ☐

---

*These data will be treated as confidential and not released without written permission. AHA will, however, share these data with your respective state hospital association and, if requested, with your appropriate metropolitan/regional association.

For members of the Catholic Health Association of the United States (CHA), AHA will also share these data with CHA unless there are objections expressed by checking this box ☐. The state/metropolitan/regional association and CHA may not release these data without written permission from the hospital.

7. FIXED ASSETS

---

a. Property, plant and equipment at cost .... _____.00

b. Accumulated depreciation .... _____.00

c. Net property, plant and equipment (a-b) .... _____.00

d. Total gross square feet of your physical plant used for or in support of your
healthcare activities .... _____

8. TOTAL CAPITAL EXPENSES

Include all expenses used to acquire assets, including buildings, remodeling projects, equipment, or property. _____.00

9. ENERGY CONSUMPTION

a. Total energy usage (in MMBTU) for total gross square footage identified in 7 (d) _____ (MMBTU)

b. If you have obtained an Energy Star rating from the EPA, what is your rating? _____

10. INFORMATION TECHNOLOGY

*a. IT operating expense.._____.00

*b. IT Capital expense.._____.00

*c. Number of employed IT staff (in FTEs) ...._____

*d. Number of outsourced IT staff (in FTEs).._____

e. Does your hospital have an electronic health record (see definition)?

☐ Yes, fully implemented   ☐ Yes, partially implemented   ☐ No (If no, please skip to Question g)

	Yes, fully implemented	Yes, partially implemented	No	
f. Does your electronic health record include:				
1. Patient-level health information and data (such as medications, orders, and clinical notes)?	☐	☐	☐	
2. Results management (such as results from laboratory tests, radiology studies, and other tests)?	☐	☐	☐	
3. Order entry management (such as orders for laboratory tests, radiology studies, and other tests)?	☐	☐	☐	
4. Decision support (such as knowledge sources, drug alerts, reminders, and clinical guidelines and pathways)?	☐	☐	☐	

	0%	1-24%	25-49%	50-74%	75-100%
g. What percentage of treating physicians in your hospital:					
1. Routinely order medications electronically?	☐	☐	☐	☐	☐
2. Routinely order laboratory or other tests electronically?	☐	☐	☐	☐	☐

*These data will be treated as confidential and not released without written permission. AHA will, however, share these data with your respective state hospital association and, if requested, with your appropriate metropolitan/regional association.

For members of the Catholic Health Association of the United States (CHA), AHA will also share these data with CHA unless there are objections expressed by checking this box ☐. The state/metropolitan/regional association and CHA may not release these data without written permission from the hospital.

D. TOTAL FACILITY BEDS, UTILIZATION, FINANCES, AND STAFFING (continued)

11. **STAFFING** Report full-time (35 hours or more) and part-time (less than 35 hours) personnel who were on the hospital/facility **payroll at the end of your reporting period.** Include members of religious orders for whom dollar equivalents were reported. Exclude private-duty nurses, volunteers, and all personnel whose salary is financed entirely by outside research grants. Exclude physicians and dentists who are paid on a fee basis. FTE is the total number of hours worked by all employees over the full (12 month) reporting period divided by the normal number of hours worked by a full-time employee for that same time period. For example, if your hospital considers a normal workweek for a full-time employee to be 40 hours, a total of 2,080 would be worked over a full year (52 weeks). If the total number of hours worked by all employees on the payroll is 208,000, then the number of Full-Time Equivalents (FTE) is 100 (employees). The FTE calculation for a specific occupational category such as Registered nurses is exactly the same. The calculation for each occupational category should be based on the number of hours worked by staff employed in that specific category.

	(1) Full-Time (35 hr/wk or more) On Payroll	(2) Part-Time (Less than 35hr/wk) On Payroll	(3) FTE
a. Physicians and dentists...			
b. Medical and dental residents/interns......................................			
c. Other trainees..			
d. Registered nurses..			
e. Licensed practical (vocational) nurses..................................			
f. Nursing assistive personnel..			
g. Radiology technicians..			
h. Laboratory technicians..			
i. Pharmacists, licensed...			
j. Pharmacy technicians..			
k. Respiratory therapists...			
l. All other personnel..			
m. Total facility personnel (add 11a through 11l)........................			

(Total facility personnel should include hospital plus nursing home type unit/facility personnel reported in 11n and 11o.)

n. Nursing home type unit/facility Registered Nurses.................			
o. Total nursing home type unit/facility personnel......................			

12. **HOSPITALISTS**

a. Do hospitalists provide care for patients in your hospital?......................... **YES** ☐   **NO** ☐   (if no, please skip to 13.)

b. If yes, please report the number of full time, part time and FTE hospitalists. _____Full-time _____Part-time _____FTE

c. If yes, please select the category below that best describes the employment model for your hospitalists.
   - ☐ Independent provider group   ☐ Employed by your hospital
   - ☐ Employed by a physician group   ☐ Employed by a university or school program   ☐ Other

13. **INTENSIVISTS**

a. Do intensivists provide care for patients in your hospital? If no, please skip to 14.)   **YES** ☐   **NO** ☐

b. If yes, please report the total number of full-time, part-time and FTE intensivists and assign them to the following areas.

	Full-time	Part-time	FTE
1. Medical-surgical intensive care			
2. Cardiac intensive care			
3. Neonatal intensive care			
4. Pediatric intensive care			
5. Other intensive care			
6. **Total**			

14. **FOREIGN EDUCATED NURSES**

a. Did your facility hire more foreign-educated nurses (including contract or agency nurses) to help fill RN vacancies in 2008 vs. 2007?

     More ☐   Less ☐   Same ☐   Did not hire foreign nurses ☐

b. From which countries/continents are you recruiting foreign-educated nurses? CHECK ALL THAT APPLY

     Africa ☐   Korea ☐   Canada ☐   Philippines ☐   China ☐   India ☐   Other ☐

SECTION E. SUPPLEMENTAL INFORMATION

1. COMMUNITY BENEFIT
                                                                                            YES   NO

a. Does your hospital's mission statement include a focus on community benefit?   ☐   ☐

b. Does your hospital have long-term plan for improving the health of its community?   ☐   ☐

c. Does your hospital have a specific budget for its community benefit activities?   ☐   ☐

d. Does your hospital have dedicated staff to manage community benefit activities?   ☐   ☐

e. Does your hospital provide support for community building activities (e.g. economic development, housing, environmental improvements, coalition building)?   ☐   ☐

f. Does your hospital make financial contributions (grants, donations, scholarships), provide in-kind support or participate in fundraising for community programs not directly affiliated with the hospital?   ☐   ☐

g. Does your hospital partner with your local school system to offer health or wellness programs to help your community?   ☐   ☐

h. Does your hospital work with other providers, public agencies, or community representatives to conduct a health status assessment of the community?   ☐   ☐

i. Does your hospital use health status indicators (such as rates of health problems or surveys of self reported health for defined populations) to design new services or modify existing services?   ☐   ☐

j1. Does your hospital work with other local providers, public agencies, or community representatives to develop a written assessment of the appropriate capacity for health services in the community?   ☐   ☐

j2. If yes, have you used the assessment to identify unmet health needs, excess capacity, or duplicative services in the community?   ☐   ☐

k. Does your hospital work with other providers to collect, track and communicate clinical and health information across cooperating organizations?   ☐   ☐

l. Does your hospital either by itself or in conjunction with others disseminate reports to the community on the quality and costs of health care services?   ☐   ☐

2. DIVERSITY, LANGUAGE AND LEADERSHIP
                                                                                            YES   NO

a. Does your hospital gather information on a patient's race/ethnicity at any point during their stay?   ☐   ☐

b. Does your hospital gather information on a patient's primary language at any point during their stay?   ☐   ☐

c. Does your hospital or health system currently have or plan to develop, implement, or evaluate a leadership development program?   ☐   ☐

d. Does your hospital or health system currently have or plan to develop, execute, or evaluate a diversity strategy or plan?   ☐   ☐

e. Does your hospital or health system engage in leadership succession planning?   ☐   ☐

f. Does your hospital or health system currently provide career development resources to administrators?   ☐   ☐

3. OTHER

a. Does your hospital provide services through one or more satellite facilities?   YES ☐   NO ☐

b. Use this space to describe your community benefit activities as well as any partners you are currently working with on such activities. Also use this space or additional sheets if more space is required for comments or to elaborate on any information supplied on this survey. Refer to the response by page, section and item name.

_____

_____

_____

_____

_____

As declared previously, hospital specific revenue data are treated as confidential. AHA's policy is not to release these data without written permission from your institution. The AHA will however, share these data with your respective state hospital association and if requested with your appropriate metropolitan/regional association.

On occasion, the AHA is asked to provide these data to external organizations, both public and private, for their use in analyzing crucial health care policy or research issues. The AHA is requesting your permission to allow us to release your confidential data to those requests that we consider legitimate and worthwhile. In every instance of disclosure, the receiving organization will be prohibited from releasing hospital specific information.

Please indicate below whether or not you agree to these types of disclosure:

[ ] I hereby grant AHA permission to release my hospital's revenue data to external users that the AHA determines have a legitimate and worthwhile need to gain access to these data subject to the user's agreement with the AHA not to release hospital specific information.

_____
Chief Executive Officer   Date

[ ] I do not grant AHA permission to release my confidential data.

_____
Chief Executive Officer   Date

Does your hospital or health system have an Internet or Homepage address?   Yes ☐ No ☐

If yes, please provide the address: http:// _____

Thank you for your cooperation in completing this survey. If there are any questions about your responses to this survey, who should be contacted?

_____
Name (please print)   Title   (Area Code) Telephone Number

____/____/____   _____   (___)_____
Date of Completion   Chief Executive Officer   Hospital's Main Fax Number

NOTE: PLEASE PHOTOCOPY THE INFORMATION FOR YOUR HOSPITAL FILE BEFORE RETURNING THE ORIGINAL FORM TO THE AMERICAN HOSPITAL ASSOCIATION. ALSO, PLEASE FORWARD A PHOTOCOPY OF THE COMPLETED QUESTIONNAIRE TO YOUR STATE HOSPITAL ASSOCIATION.

THANK YOU

SECTION A

REPORTING PERIOD
Instructions

INSTRUCTIONS AND DEFINITIONS FOR THE 2008 ANNUAL SURVEY

HOSPITAL. For purposes of this survey, a hospital is defined as the organization or corporate entity licensed or registered as a hospital by a state to provide diagnostic and therapeutic patient services for a variety of medical conditions, both surgical and nonsurgical.

1. **Reporting period used (beginning and ending date):** Record the beginning and ending dates of the reporting period in an eight-digit number: for example, **January 1, 2008** should be shown as **01/01/2008**. Number of days should equal the time span between the two dates that the hospital was open. If you are reporting for less than **366** days, utilization and finances should be presented for days reported only.

2. **Were you in operation 12 full months at the end of your reporting period?** If you are reporting for less than **366** days, utilization and finances should be presented for days reported only.

3. **Number of days open during reporting period:** Number of days should equal the time span between the two dates that the hospital was open.

SECTION B
ORGANIZATIONAL STRUCTURE
Instructions and Definitions

1. **CONTROL**
   Check the box to the left of the type of organization that is responsible for establishing policy for overall operation of the hospital.
   Government, nonfederal.
   State. Controlled by an agency of state government.
   County. Controlled by an agency of county government.
   City. Controlled by an agency of municipal government.
   City-County. Controlled jointly by agencies of municipal and county governments.
   Hospital district or authority. Controlled by a political subdivision of a state, county, or city created solely for the purpose of establishing and maintaining medical care or health-related care institutions.
   Nongovernment, not for profit. Controlled by not-for-profit organizations, including religious organizations (Catholic hospitals, for example), community hospitals, cooperative hospitals, hospitals operated by fraternal societies, and so forth.
   Investor owned, for profit. Controlled on a for profit basis by an individual, partnership, or a profit making corporation.
   Government, federal. Controlled by an agency or department of the federal government.

2. **SERVICE**
   Indicate the ONE category that best describes the type of service that your hospital provides to the majority of patients.
   General medical and surgical. Provides diagnostic and therapeutic services to patients for a variety of medical conditions, both surgical and nonsurgical.
   Hospital unit of an institution. Provides diagnostic and therapeutic services to patients in an institution.
   Hospital unit within an institution for the mentally retarded. Provides diagnostic and therapeutic services to patients in an institution for the mentally retarded.
   Surgical. An acute care specialty hospitals where 2/3 or more of its inpatient claims are for surgical/diagnosis related groups.
   Psychiatric. Provides diagnostic and therapeutic services to patients with mental or emotional disorders.
   Tuberculosis and other respiratory diseases. Provides medical care and rehabilitative services to patients for whom the primary diagnosis is tuberculosis or other respiratory diseases.
   Cancer. Provides medical care to patients for whom the primary diagnosis is cancer.
   Heart. Provides diagnosis and treatment of heart disease.
   Obstetrics and gynecology. Provides medical and surgical treatment to pregnant women and to mothers following delivery. Also provides diagnostic and therapeutic services to women with diseases or disorders of the reproductive organs.
   Eye, ear, nose, and throat. Provides diagnosis and treatment of diseases and injuries of the eyes, ears, nose, and throat.
   Rehabilitation. Provides a comprehensive array of restoration services for the disabled and all support services necessary to help them attain their maximum functional capacity.
   Orthopedic. Provides corrective treatment of deformities, diseases, and ailments of the locomotive apparatus, especially affecting the limbs, bones, muscles, and joints.
   Chronic disease. Provides medical and skilled nursing services to patients with long-term illnesses who are not in an acute phase, but who require an intensity of services not available in nursing homes.
   Institution for the mentally retarded. Provides health-related care on a regular basis to patients with psychiatric or developmental impairment who cannot be treated in a skilled nursing unit.
   Acute long term care hospital. Provides high acuity interdisciplinary services to medically complex patients that require more intensive recuperation and care than can be provided in a typical nursing facility.
   Alcoholism and other chemical dependency. Provides diagnostic and therapeutic services to patients with alcoholism or other drug dependencies.

3. **OTHER**
   a. **Children admissions.** A hospital whose primary focus is the health and treatment of children and adolescents.
   b. **Subsidiary.** A company that is wholly controlled by another or one that is more than 50% owned by another organization.
   c. **Contract managed.** General day-to-day management of an entire organization by another organization under a formal contract. Managing organization reports directly to the board of trustees or owners of the managed organization; managed organization retains total legal responsibility and ownership of the facility's assets and liabilities.
   d. **Network.** A group of hospitals, physicians, other providers, insurers and/or community agencies that voluntarily work together to coordinate and deliver health services
   e. **Group Purchasing Organization.** An organization whose primary function is to negotiate contracts for the purpose of purchasing for members of the group or has a central supply site for its members.

SECTION C
FACILITIES AND SERVICES
Definitions

Owned/provided by the hospital or its subsidiary. All patient revenues, expenses and utilization related to the provision of the service are reflected in the hospital's statistics reported elsewhere in this survey.

Provided by my Health System (in my local community). Another health care provider in the same system as your hospital provides the service and patient revenue, expenses, and utilization related to the provision of the service are recorded at the point where the service was provided and would not be reflected in your hospital's statistics reported elsewhere in this survey.

Provided by my network (in my local community). Another health care provider in the same network as your hospital provides the service and patient revenue, expenses and utilization related to the provision of the service are recorded at the point where the service was provided and would not be reflected in your hospital's statistics reported elsewhere in this survey.

Provided through a formal contractual arrangement or joint venture with another provider that is not in my system or network. All patient revenues and utilization related to the provision of the service are recorded at the site where the service was provided and would not be reflected in your hospital statistics reported elsewhere in this survey.

1. **General medical-surgical care.** Provides acute care to patients in medical and surgical units on the basis of physicians' orders and approved nursing care plans.
2. **Pediatric medical-surgical care.** Provides acute care to pediatric patients on the basis of physicians' orders and approved nursing care plans.
3. **Obstetrics.** Levels should be designated: (1) unit provides services for uncomplicated maternity and newborn cases; (2) unit provides services for uncomplicated cases, the majority of complicated problems, and special neonatal services; and (3) unit provides services for all serious illnesses and abnormalities and is supervised by a full-time maternal/fetal specialist.
4. **Medical surgical intensive care.** Provides patient care of a more intensive nature than the usual medical and surgical care, on the basis of physicians' orders and approved nursing care plans. These units are staffed with specially trained nursing personnel and contain monitoring and specialized support equipment for patients who because of shock, trauma or other life-threatening conditions require intensified comprehensive observation and care. Includes mixed intensive care units.
5. **Cardiac intensive care.** Provides patient care of a more specialized nature than the usual medical and surgical care, on the basis of physicians' orders and approved nursing care plans. The unit is staffed with specially trained nursing personnel and contains monitoring and specialized support or treatment equipment for patients who, because of heart seizure, open-heart surgery, or other life-threatening conditions, require intensified, comprehensive observation and care. May include myocardial infarction, pulmonary care, and heart transplant units.
6. **Neonatal intensive care.** A unit that must be separate from the newborn nursery providing intensive care to all sick infants including those with the very lowest birth weights (less than 1500 grams). NICU has potential for providing mechanical ventilation, neonatal surgery, and special care for the sickest infants born in the hospital or transferred from another institution. A full-time neonatologist serves as director of the NICU.
7. **Neonatal Intermediate care.** A unit that must be separate from the normal newborn nursery and that provides intermediate and/or recovery care and some specialized services, including immediate resuscitation, intravenous therapy, and capacity for prolonged oxygen therapy and monitoring.
8. **Pediatric intensive care.** Provides care to pediatric patients that is of a more intensive nature than that usually provided to pediatric patients. The unit is staffed with specially trained personnel and contains monitoring and specialized support equipment for treatment of patients who, because of shock, trauma, or other life-threatening conditions, require intensified, comprehensive observation and care.
9. **Burn care.** Provides care to severely burned patients. Severely burned patients are those with any of the following: (1) second-degree burns of more than 25% total body surface area for adults or 20% total body surface area for children; (2) third-degree burns of more than 10% total body surface area; (3) any severe burns of the hands, face, eyes, ears, or feet; or (4) all inhalation injuries, electrical burns, complicated burn injuries involving fractures and other major traumas, and all other poor risk factors.
10. **Other special care.** Provides care to patients requiring care more intensive than that provided in the acute area, yet not sufficiently intensive to require admission to an Intensive care unit. Patients admitted to this area are usually transferred here from an intensive care unit once their condition has improved. These units are sometimes referred to as definitive observation, step-down or progressive care units.
11. **Other intensive care.** A specially staffed, specialty equipped, separate section of a hospital dedicated to the observation, care, and treatment of patients with life threatening illnesses, injuries, or complications from which recovery is possible. It provides special expertise and facilities for the support of vital function and utilizes the skill of medical nursing and other staff experienced in the management of these problems.
12. **Physical rehabilitation.** Provides care encompassing a comprehensive array of restoration services for the disabled and all support services necessary to help patients attain their maximum functional capacity.
13. **Alcoholism-drug abuse or dependency care.** Provides diagnosis and therapeutic services to patients with alcoholism or other drug dependencies. Includes care for inpatient/residential treatment for patients whose course of treatment involves more intensive care than provided in an outpatient setting or where patient requires supervised withdrawal.
14. **Psychiatric care.** Provides acute or long-term care to emotionally disturbed patients, including patients admitted for diagnosis and those admitted for treatment of psychiatric problems, on the basis of physicians' orders and approved nursing care plans. Long-term care may include intensive supervision to the chronically mentally ill, mentally disordered, or other mentally incompetent persons.
15. **Skilled nursing care.** Provides non-acute medical and skilled nursing care services, therapy, and social services under the supervision of a licensed registered nurse on a 24-hour basis.
16. **Intermediate nursing care.** Provides health-related services (skilled nursing care and social services) to residents with a variety of physical conditions or functional disabilities. These residents do not require the care provided by a hospital or skilled nursing facility, but do need supervision and support services.
17. **Acute long-term care.** Provides specialized acute hospital care to medically complex patients who are critically ill, have multisystem complications and/or failure, and require hospitalization averaging 25 days, in a facility offering specialized treatment programs and therapeutic intervention on a 24-hour/7 day a week basis.
18. **Other long-term care.** Provision of long term care other than skilled nursing care or intermediate care. This can include residential care-elderly housing services for those who do not require daily medical or nursing services, but may require some assistance in the activities of daily living, or sheltered care facilities for developmentally disabled.
19. **Other care.** (specify) Any type of care other than those listed above.
    The sum of the beds reported in 1-19 should equal what you have reported in Section D(1b) for beds set up and staffed.
20. **Adult day care program.** Program providing supervision, medical and psychological care, and social activities for older adults who live at home or in another family setting, but cannot be alone or prefer to be with others during the day. May include intake assessment, health monitoring, occupational therapy, personal care, noon meal, and transportation services.
21. **Airborne infection isolation room.** A single-occupancy room for patient care where environmental factors are controlled in an effort to minimize the transmission of those infectious agents, usually spread person to person by droplet nuclei associated with coughing and inhalation. Such rooms typically have specific ventilation requirements for controlled ventilation, air pressure and filtration.

22. **Alcoholism-drug abuse or dependency outpatient services.** Organized hospital services that provide medical care and/or rehabilitative treatment services to outpatients for whom the primary diagnosis is alcoholism or other chemical dependency.

23. **Alzheimer Center.** Facility that offers care to persons with Alzheimer's disease and their families through an integrated program of clinical services, research, and education.

24. **Ambulance services.** Provision of ambulance service to the ill and injured who require medical attention on a scheduled and unscheduled basis.

25. **Ambulatory Surgery Center.** Facility that provides care to patients requiring surgery who are admitted and discharged on the same day. Ambulatory surgery centers are distinct from same day surgical units within the hospital outpatient departments for purposes of Medicare payment.

26. **Arthritis treatment center.** Specifically equipped and staffed center for the diagnosis and treatment of arthritis and other joint disorders.

27. **Assisted living.** A special combination of housing, supportive services, personalized assistance and health care designed to respond to the individual needs of those who need help in activities of daily living and instrumental activities of daily living. Supportive services are available, 24 hours a day, to meet scheduled and unscheduled needs, in a way that promotes maximum independence an dignity for each resident and encourages the involvement of a resident's family, neighbor and friends.

28. **Auxiliary.** A volunteer community organization formed to assist the hospital in carrying out its purpose and to serve as a link between the institution and the community.

29. **Bariatric/weight control services.** Bariatrics is the medical practice of weight reduction.

30. **Birthing room/LDR room/LDRP room.** A single-room type of maternity care with a more homelike setting for families than the traditional three-room unit (labor/delivery/recovery) with a separate postpartum area. A birthing room combines labor and delivery in one room. An LDR room accommodates three stages in the birthing process--labor, delivery, and recovery. An LDRP room accommodates all four stages of the birth process--labor, delivery, recovery, and postpartum.

31. **Blood Donor Center.** A facility that performs, or is responsible for the collection, processing, testing or distribution of blood and components.

32. **Breast cancer screening/mammograms.** Mammography screening - The use of breast x-ray to detect unsuspected breast cancer in asymptomatic women. Diagnostic mammography - The x-ray imaging of breast tissue in symptomatic women who are considered to have a substantial likelihood of having breast cancer already.

33. **Cardiology and cardiac surgery services.** Services which include the diagnosis and treatment of diseases and disorders involving the heart and circulatory system.

    a-b. Diagnostic catheterization. (also called coronary angiography or coronary arteriography) is used to assist in diagnosing complex heart conditions. Cardiac angiography involves the insertion of a tiny catheter into the artery in the groin then carefully threading the catheter up into the aorta where the coronary arteries originate. Once the catheter is in place, a dye is injected which allows the cardiologist to see the size, shape, and distribution of the coronary arteries. These images are used to diagnose heart disease and to determine, among other things, whether or not surgery is indicated.

    c-d. Interventional cardiac catheterization. Nonsurgical procedure that utilizes the same basic principles as diagnostic catheterization and then uses advanced techniques to improve the heart's function. It can be a less-invasive alternative to heart surgery.

    e-f. Cardiac surgery. Includes minimally invasive procedures that include surgery done with only a small incision or no incision at all, such as through a laparoscope or an endoscope and more invasive major surgical procedures that include open chest and open heart surgery.

    g-h. Cardiac electrophysiology. Evaluation and management of patients with complex rhythm or conduction abnormalities, including diagnostic testing, treatment of arrhythmias by catheter ablation or drug therapy, and pacemaker/defibrillator implantation and follow-up.

    i. Cardiac rehabilitation. A medically supervised program to help heart patients recover quickly and improve their overall physical and mental functioning. The goal is to reduce risk of another cardiac event or to keep an already present heart condition from getting worse. Cardiac rehabilitation programs include: counseling to patients, an exercise program, helping patients modify risk factors such as smoking and high blood pressure, providing vocational guidance to enable the patient to return to work, supplying information on physical limitations and lending emotional support.

34. **Case management.** A system of assessment, treatment planning, referral and follow-up that ensures the provision of comprehensive and continuous services and the coordination of payment and reimbursement for care.

35. **Chaplaincy/pastoral care services.** A service ministering religious activities and providing pastoral counseling to patients, their families, and staff of a health care organization.

36. **Chemotherapy.** An organized program for the treatment of cancer by the use of drugs or chemicals.

37. **Children's wellness program.** A program that encourages improved health status and a healthful lifestyle of children through health education, exercise, nutrition and health promotion.

38. **Chiropractic services.** An organized clinical service including spinal manipulation or adjustment and related diagnostic and therapeutic services.

39. **Community outreach.** A program that systematically interacts with the community to identify those in need of services, alerting persons and their families to the availability of services, locating needed services, and enabling persons to enter the service delivery system.

40. **Complementary and alternative medicine services.** Organized hospital services or formal arrangements to providers that provide care or treatment not based solely on traditional western allopathic medical teachings as instructed in most U.S. medical schools. Includes any of the following: acupuncture, chiropractic, homeopathy, osteopathy, diet and lifestyle changes, herbal medicine, massage therapy, etc.

41. **Computer assisted orthopedic surgery (CAOS).** Orthopedic surgery using computer technology, enabling three-dimensional graphic models to visualize a patient's anatomy.

42. **Crisis prevention.** Services provided in order to promote physical and mental well being and the early identification of disease and ill health prior to the onset and recognition of symptoms so as to permit early treatment.

43. **Dental Services.** An organized dental service or dentists on staff, not necessarily involving special facilities, providing dental or oral services to inpatients or outpatients.

44. **Emergency services.** Health services that are provided after the onset of a medical condition that manifests itself by symptoms of sufficient severity, including severe pain, that the absence of immediate medical attention could reasonably be expected by a prudent layperson, who possesses an average knowledge of health and medicine, to result in placing the patient's health in serious jeopardy.

    a. Emergency department. Hospital facilities for the provision of unscheduled outpatient services to patients whose conditions require immediate care.

    b. Satellite Emergency Department. A facility owned and operated by the hospital but physically separate from the hospital for the provision of unscheduled outpatient services to patients whose conditions require immediate care. A freestanding ED is not physically connected to a hospital, but has all necessary emergency staffing and equipment on-site.

    d. Trauma center (certified). A facility to provide emergency and specialized intensive care to critically ill and injured patients. Level 1: A regional resource trauma center, which is capable of providing total care for every aspect of injury and plays a leadership role in trauma research and education. Level 2: A community trauma center, which is capable of providing trauma care to all but the most severely injured patients who require highly specialized care. Level 3: A rural trauma hospital, which is capable of providing care to a large number of injury victims and can resuscitate and stabilize more severely injured patients so that they can be transported to level 1 or 2 facilities. Please provide explanation on page 12 if necessary.

45. **Enabling services.** A program that is designed to help the patient access health care services by offering any of the following: transportation services and/or referrals to local social services agencies.

46. **End of life services.** Services offered to patients suffering from chronic, severe, and life-threatening diseases including comprehensive services that give patients and caregivers the resources and the confidence to manage symptoms, avoid emergency department admissions and frequent hospitalization, and remain in familiar and comfortable settings.

   a. **Hospice Program.** A recognized clinical program with specific eligibility criteria that provides palliative medical care focused on relief of pain and symptom control and other services that address the emotional, social, financial and spiritual needs of terminally ill patients and their families. Hospice care can be provided either at home, in a hospital setting, or a freestanding facility.

   b. **Pain management program.** A recognized clinical service or program providing specialized medical care, drugs or therapies for the management of acute or chronic pain and other distressing symptoms, administered by specially trained physicians and other clinicians, to patients suffering from an acute illness of diverse causes.

   c. **Palliative care program.** An organized program providing specialized medical care, drugs or therapies for the management of acute or chronic pain and/or the control of symptoms administered by specially trained physicians and other clinicians; and supportive care services, such as counseling on advanced directives, spiritual care, and social services, to patients with advanced disease and their families.

   d. **Inpatient palliative care unit.** An inpatient palliative care ward is a physically discreet, inpatient nursing unit where the focus is palliative care. The patient care focus is on symptom relief for complex patients who may be continuing to undergo primary treatment. Care is delivered by palliative medicine specialists.

47. **Endoscopic services.**

   a. **Optical colonoscopy.** An examination of the interior of the colon using a long, flexible, lighted tube with a small built-in camera.

   b. **Endoscopic ultrasound.** Specially designed endoscope that incorporates an ultrasound transducer used to obtain detailed images of organs in the chest and abdomen. The endoscope can be passed through the mouth or the anus. When combined with needle biopsy the procedure can assist in diagnosis of disease and staging of cancer.

   c. **Ablation of Barrett's esophagus.** Premalignant condition that can lead to adenocarcinoma of the esophagus. The nonsurgical ablation of premalignant tissue in Barrett's esophagus by the application of thermal energy or light through an endoscope passed from the mouth into the esophagus.

   d. **Esophageal impedance study.** A test in which a catheter is placed through the nose into the esophagus to measure whether gas or liquids are passing from the stomach into the esophagus and causing symptoms.

   e. **Endosopic retrograde cholangiopancreatography (ERCP).** A procedure in which a catheter is introduced through an endoscope into the bile ducts and pancreatic ducts. Injection of contrast material permits detailed x-ray of these structures. The procedure is used diagnostically as well as therapeutically to relieve obstruction or remove stones.

48. **Enrollment assistance services.** A program that provides enrollment assistance for patients who are potentially eligible for public health insurance programs such as Medicaid, State Children's Health Insurance, or local/state indigent care programs. The specific services offered could include explanation of benefits, assist applicants in completing the application and locating all relevant documents, conduct eligibility interviews, and/or forward applications and documentation to state/local social service or health agency.

49. **Extracorporeal shock wave lithotripter (ESWL).** A medical device used for treating stones in the kidney or urethra. The device disintegrates kidney stones noninvasively through the transmission of acoustic shock waves directed at the stones.

50. **Fitness center.** Provides exercise, testing, or evaluation programs and fitness activities to the community and hospital employees.

51. **Freestanding outpatient care center.** A facility owned and operated by the hospital, that is physically separate from the hospital and provides various medical treatments and diagnostic services on an outpatient basis only. Laboratory and radiology services are usually available.

52. **Geriatric services.** The branch of medicine dealing with the physiology of aging and the diagnosis and treatment of disease affecting the aged. Services could include: Adult day care; Alzheimer's diagnostic-assessment services, Comprehensive geriatric assessment; Emergency response system; Geriatric acute care unit; and/or Geriatric clinics.

53. **Health fair.** Community health education events that focus on the prevention of disease and promotion of health through such activities as audiovisual exhibits and free diagnostic services.

54. **Community health education.** Education that provides health information to individuals and populations as well as support for personal, family and community health decisions with the objective of improving health status.

55. **Health screening.** A preliminary procedure such as a test or examination to detect the most characteristic sign or signs of a disorder that may require further investigation.

56. **Health research.** Organized hospital research program in any of the following areas: basic research, clinical research, community health research, and/or research on innovative health care delivery.

57. **Hemodialysis.** Provision of equipment and personnel for the treatment of renal insufficiency on an inpatient or outpatient basis.

58. **HIV-AIDS services.** Could include: HIV-AIDS unit-Special unit or team designated and equipped specifically for diagnosis, treatment, continuing care planning, and counseling services for HIV-AIDS patients and their families. General inpatient care for HIV-AIDS-Inpatient diagnosis and treatment for human immunodeficiency virus and acquired immunodeficiency syndrome patients, but dedicated unit is not available. Specialized outpatient program for HIV-AIDS-Special outpatient program providing diagnostic, treatment, continuing care planning, and counseling for HIV-AIDS patients and their families.

59. **Home health services.** Service providing nursing, therapy, and health-related homemaker or social services in the patient's home.

60. **Hospital-based outpatient care center-services.** Organized hospital health care services offered by appointment on an ambulatory basis. Services may include outpatient surgery, examination, diagnosis, and treatment of a variety of medical conditions on a nonemergency basis, and laboratory and other diagnostic testing as ordered by staff or outside physician referral.

61. **Immunization program.** Program that plans, coordinates and conducts immunization services in the community.

62. **Indigent care clinic.** Health care services for uninsured and underinsured persons where care is free of charge or charged on a sliding scale. This would include "free clinics" staffed by volunteer practitioners, but could also be staffed by employees with the sponsoring health care organization subsidizing the cost of service.

63. **Linguistic/translation services.** Services provided by the hospital designed to make health care more accessible to non-English speaking patients and their physicians.

64. **Meals on wheels.** A hospital sponsored program which delivers meals to people, usually the elderly, who are unable to prepare their own meals. Low cost, nutritional meals are delivered to individuals' homes on a regular basis.

65. **Mobile health services.** Vans and other vehicles used to delivery primary care services.

66. **Neurological services.** Services provided by the hospital dealing with the operative and nonoperative management of disorders of the central, peripheral, and autonomic nervous system.

67. **Nutrition programs.** Those services within a health care facility which are designed to provide inexpensive, nutritionally sound meals to patients.

68. **Occupational health services.** Includes services designed to protect the safety of employees from hazards in the work environment.

69. **Oncology services.** Inpatient and outpatient services for patients with cancer, including comprehensive care, support and guidance in addition to patient education and prevention, chemotherapy, counseling and other treatment methods.

70. **Orthopedic services.** Services provided for the prevention or correction of injuries or disorders of the skeletal system and associated muscles, joints and ligaments.

71. **Outpatient surgery.** Scheduled surgical services provided to patients who do not remain in the hospital overnight. The surgery may be performed in operating suites also used for inpatient surgery, specially designated surgical suites for outpatient surgery, or procedure rooms within an outpatient care facility.

72. **Patient controlled analgesia (PCA).** Patient-controlled analgesia (PCA) is intravenously administered pain medicine under the patient's control. The patient has a button on the end of a cord than can be pushed at will, whenever more pain medicine is desired. This button will only deliver more pain medicine at pre-determined intervals, as programmed by the doctor's order.

73. **Patient education center.** Written goals and objectives for the patient and/or family related to therapeutic regimens, medical procedures, and self care.

74. **Patient representative services.** Organized hospital services providing personnel through whom patients and staff can seek solutions to institutional problems affecting the delivery of high quality care and services.

75. **Physical rehabilitation services.** Program providing medical, health-related, therapy, social, and/or vocational services to help disabled persons attain or retain their maximum functional capacity.
    a. **Physical rehabilitation outpatient services.** Outpatient program providing medical, health-related, therapy, social, and/or vocational services to help disabled persons attain or retain their maximum functional capacity.
    b. **Robot-assisted walking therapy.** A form of physical therapy that uses a robotic device to assist patients who are relearning how to walk.
    c. **Simulated rehabilitation environment.** Rehabilitation focused on retraining functional skills in a contextually appropriate environment (simulated home and community settings) or in a traditional setting (gymnasium) using motor learning principles.

76. **Primary care department.** A unit or clinic within the hospital that provides primary care services (e.g. general pediatric care, general internal medicine, family practice, gynecology) through hospital-salaried medical and/or nursing staff, focusing on evaluating and diagnosing medical problems and providing medical treatment on an outpatient basis.

77. **Psychiatric services.** Services provided by the hospital that offer immediate initial evaluation and treatment to patients with mental or emotional disorders.
    a. **Psychiatric child-adolescent services.** Provides care to emotionally disturbed children and adolescents, including those admitted for diagnosis and those admitted for treatment.
    b. **Psychiatric consultation-liaison services.** Provides organized psychiatric consultation/liaison services to nonpsychiatric hospital staff and/or departments on psychological aspects of medical care that may be generic or specific to individual patients.
    c. **Psychiatric education services.** Provides psychiatric educational services to community agencies and workers such as schools, police, courts, public health nurses, welfare agencies, clergy, and so forth. The purpose is to expand the mental health knowledge and competence of personnel not working in the mental health field and to promote good mental health through improved understanding, attitudes, and behavioral patterns.
    d. **Psychiatric emergency services.** Services of facilities available on a 24-hour basis to provide immediate unscheduled out-patient care, diagnosis, evaluation, crisis intervention, and assistance to persons suffering acute emotional or mental distress.
    e. **Psychiatric geriatric services.** Provides care to emotionally disturbed elderly patients, including those admitted for diagnosis and those admitted for treatment.
    f. **Psychiatric outpatient services.** Provides medical care, including diagnosis and treatment, of psychiatric outpatients.
    g. **Psychiatric partial hospitalization program.** Organized hospital services of intensive day/evening outpatient services of three hours or more duration, distinguished from other outpatient visits of one hour.

78. **Radiology, diagnostic.** The branch of radiology that deals with the utilization of all modalities of radiant energy in medical diagnoses and therapeutic procedures using radiologic guidance. This includes, but is not restricted to, imaging techniques and methodologies utilizing radiation emitted by x-ray tubes, radionuclides, and ultrasonographic devices and the radiofrequency electromagnetic radiation emitted by atoms.
    a. **CT scanner.** Computed tomographic scanner for head or whole body scans.
    b. **Diagnostic radioisotope facility.** The use of radioactive isotopes (Radiopharmaceuticals) as tracers or indicators to detect an abnormal condition or disease.
    c. **Electron beam computed tomography (EBCT).** A high tech computed tomography scan used to detect coronary artery disease by measuring coronary calcifications. This imaging procedure uses electron beams which are magnetically steered to produce a visual of the coronary artery and the images are produced faster than conventional CT scans.
    d. **Full-field digital mammography (FFDM).** Combines the x-ray generators and tubes used in analog screen-film mammography (SFM) with a detector plate that converts the x-rays into a digital signal.
    e. **Magnetic resonance imaging (MRI).** The use of a uniform magnetic field and radio frequencies to study tissue and structure of the body. This procedure enables the visualization of biochemical activity of the cell in vivo without the use of ionizing radiation, radioisotopic substances or high-frequency sound.
    f. **Intraoperative magnetic resonance imaging.** An integrated surgery system which provides an MRI system in an operating room. The system allows for immediate evaluation of the degree to tumor resection while the patient is undergoing a surgical resection. Intraoperative MRI exists when a MRI (low-field or high-field) is placed in the operating theater and is used during surgical resection without moving the patient from the operating room to the diagnostic imaging suite.
    g. **Multi-slice spiral computed tomography (<64+slice CT).** A specialized computed tomography procedure that provides three-dimensional processing and allows narrower and multiple slices with increased spatial resolution and faster scanning times as compared to a regular computed tomography scan.
    h. **Multi-slice spiral computed tomography (64+ slice CT).** Involves the acquisition of volumetric tomographic x-ray absorption data expressed in Hounsfield units using multiple rows of detectors. 64+ systems reconstruct the equivalent of 64 or greater slices to cover the imaged volume.
    i. **Positron emission tomography (PET).** A nuclear medicine imaging technology which uses radioactive (positron emitting) isotopes created in a cyclotron or generator and computers to produce composite pictures of the brain and heart at work. PET scanning produces sectional images depicting metabolic activity or blood flow rather than anatomy.
    j. **Positron emission tomography/CT (PET/CT).** Provides metabolic functional information for the monitoring of chemotherapy, radiotherapy and surgical planning.
    k. **Single photon emission computerized tomography (SPECT).** Single photon emission computerized tomography is a nuclear medicine imaging technology that combines existing technology of gamma camera imaging with computed tomographic imaging technology to provide a more precise and clear image.
    l. **Ultrasound.** The use of acoustic waves above the range of 20,000 cycles per second to visualize internal body structures.

79. **Radiology, therapeutic.** The branch of medicine concerned with radioactive substances and using various techniques of visualization, with the diagnosis and treatment of disease using any of the various sources of radiant energy. Services could include: megavoltage radiation therapy; radioactive implants; stereotactic radiosurgery; therapeutic radioisotope facility; X-ray radiation therapy.
    a. **Image-guided radiation therapy (IGRT).** Automated system for image-guided radiation therapy that enables clinicians to obtain high-resolution x- ray images to pinpoint tumor sites, adjust patient positioning when necessary, and complete a treatment, all within the standard treatment time slot, allowing for more effective cancer treatments.
    b. **Intensity-Modulated Radiation Therapy (IMRT).** A type of three-dimensional radiation therapy, which improves the targeting of treatment

delivery in a way that is likely to decrease damage to normal tissues and allows varying intensities.

 c. **Proton beam therapy.** A form of radiation therapy which administers proton beams. While producing the same biologic effects as x-ray beams, the energy distribution of protons differs from conventional x-ray beams in that they can be more precisely focused in tissue volumes in a three-dimensional pattern resulting in less surrounding tissue damage than conventional radiation therapy permitting administration of higher doses.

 d. **Shaped beam radiation system.** A precise, non-invasive treatment that involves targeting beams of radiation that mirrors the exact size and shape of a tumor at a specific area of a tumor to shrink or destroy cancerous cells. This procedure delivers a therapeutic dose of radiation that conforms precisely to the shape of the tumor, thus minimizing the risk to nearby tissues.

 e. **Stereotactic radiosurgery.** Stereotactic radiosurgery (SRS) is a radiotherapy modality that delivers a high dosage of radiation to a discrete treatment area in as few as one treatment session. Includes gamma knife, cyberknife, etc.

80. **Reproductive health.**

 a. **Fertility clinic.** A specialized program set in an infertility center that provides counseling and education as well as advanced reproductive techniques such as: injectable therapy, reproductive surgeries, treatment for endometriosis, male factor infertility, tubal reversals, in vitro fertilization (IVF), donor eggs, and other such services to help patients achieve successful pregnancies.

 b. **Genetic testing/counseling.** A service equipped with adequate laboratory facilities and directed by a qualified physician to advise parents and prospective parents on potential problems in cases of genetic defects. A genetic test is the analysis of human DNA, RNA, chromosomes, proteins, and certain metabolites in order to detect heritable disease-related genotypes, mutations, phenotypes, or karyotypes for clinical purposes. Genetic tests can have diverse purposes, including the diagnosis of genetic diseases in newborns, children, and adults; the identification of future health risks; the prediction of drug responses; and the assessment of risks to future children.

81. **Retirement housing.** A facility that provides social activities to senior citizens, usually retired persons, who do not require health care but some short-term skilled nursing care may be provided. A retirement center may furnish housing and may also have acute hospital and long-term care facilities, or it may arrange for acute and long-term care through affiliated institutions.

82. **Robotic surgery.** The use of mechanical guidance devices to remotely manipulate surgical instrumentation.

83. **Sleep center.** Specially equipped and staffed center for the diagnosis and treatment of sleep disorders.

84. **Social work services**. Could include: organized services that are properly directed and sufficiently staffed by qualified individuals who provide assistance and counseling to patients and their families in dealing with social, emotional, and environmental problems associated with illness or disability, often in the context of financial or discharge planning coordination.

85. **Sports medicine.** Provision of diagnostic screening and assessment and clinical and rehabilitation services for the prevention and treatment of sports-related injuries.

86. **Support groups.** A hospital sponsored program that allows a group of individuals with the same or similar problems who meet periodically to share experiences, problems, and solutions in order to support each other.

87. **Swing bed services.** A hospital bed that can be used to provide either acute or long-term care depending on community or patient needs. To be eligible a hospital must have a Medicare provider agreement in place, have fewer than 100 beds, be located in a rural area, do not have a 24 hour nursing service waiver in effect, have not been terminated from the program in the prior two years, and meet various service conditions.

88. **Teen outreach services.** A program focusing on the teenager which encourages an improved health status and a healthful lifestyle including physical, emotional, mental, social, spiritual and economic health through education, exercise, nutrition and health promotion.

89. **Tobacco treatment/cessation program.** Organized hospital services with the purpose of ending tobacco-use habits of patients addicted to tobacco/nicotine.

90. **Transplant services.** The branch of medicine that transfers an organ or tissue from one person to another or from one body part to another to replace a diseased structure or to restore function or to change appearance. Services could include: Bone marrow transplant program; heart, lung, kidney, intestine, or tissue transplant. Please include heart/lung or other multi-transplant surgeries in 'other'.

91. **Transportation to health facilities.** A long-term care support service designed to assist the mobility of the elderly. Some programs offer improved financial access by offering reduced rates and barrier-free buses or vans with ramps and lifts to assist the elderly or handicapped; others offer subsidies for public transport systems or operate mini-bus services exclusively for use by senior citizens.

92. **Urgent care center.** A facility that provides care and treatment for problems that are not life threatening but require attention over the short term.

93. **Virtual colonoscopy.** Noninvasive screening procedure used to visualize, analyze and detect cancerous or potentially cancerous polyps in the colon.

94. **Volunteer services department.** An organized hospital department responsible for coordinating the services of volunteers working within the institution.

95. **Women's health center/services.** An area set aside for coordinated education and treatment services specifically for and promoted to women as provided by this special unit. Services may or may not include obstetrics but include a range of services other than OB.

96. **Wound management Services**. Services for patients with chronic wounds and nonhealing wounds often resulting from diabetes, poor circulation, improper seating and immunocompromising conditions. The goals are to progress chronic wounds through stages of healing, reduce and eliminate infections, increase physical function to minimize complications from current wounds and prevent future chronic wounds. Wound management services are provided on an inpatient or outpatient basis, depending on the intensity of service needed.

97. **Physician arrangements.** An integrated healthcare delivery program implementing physician compensation and incentive systems for managed care services.

 a. **Independent practice association (IPA).** AN IPA is a legal entity that holds managed care contracts. The IPA then contracts with physicians, usually in solo practice, to provide care either on a fee-for-services or capitated basis. The purpose of an IPA is to assist solo physicians in obtaining managed care contracts.

 b. **Group practice without walls.** Hospital sponsors the formation of, or provides capital to physicians to establish, a "quasi" group to share administrative expenses while remaining independent practitioners.

 c. **Open physician-hospital organization (PHO).** A joint venture between the hospital and all members of the medical staff who wish to participate. The PHO can act as a unified agent in managed care contracting, own a managed care plan, own and operate ambulatory care centers or ancillary services projects, or provide administrative services to physician members.

 d. **Closed physician-hospital organization (PHO).** A PHO that restricts physician membership to those practitioners who meet criteria for cost effectiveness and/or high quality.

 e. **Management services organization (MSO).** A corporation, owned by the hospital or a physician/hospital joint venture, that provides management services to one or more medical group practices. The MSO purchases the tangible assets of the practices and leases them back as part of a full-service management agreement, under which the MSO employs all non-physician staff and provides all supplies/administrative systems for a fee.

 f. **Integrated salary model.** Physicians are salaried by the hospital or another entity of a health system to provide medical services for primary care and specialty care.

 g. **Equity model.** Allows established practitioners to become shareholders in a professional corporation in exchange for tangible and intangible assets of their existing practices.

h. **Foundation.** A corporation, organized either as a hospital affiliate or subsidiary, which purchases both the tangible and intangible assets of one or more medical group practices. Physicians remain in a separate corporate entity but sign a professional services agreement with the foundation.

98. **Joint venture.** A contractual arrangement between two or more parties forming an unincorporated business. The participants in the arrangement remain independent and separate outside of the ventures purpose.

101. **Percentage of hospital's net patient revenue.**

a. **Capitation.** An at-risk payment arrangement in which an organization receives a fixed prearranged payment and in turn guarantees to deliver or arrange all medically necessary care required by enrollers in the capitated plan. The fixed amount is specified within contractual agreements between the payor and the involved organization. The fixed payment amount is based on an actuarial assessment of the services required by enrollees and the costs of providing these services, recognizing enrollees' adjustment factors such as age, sex, and family size.

b. **Shared risk payments.** A payment arrangement in which a hospital and a managed care organization share the risk of adverse claims experience. Methods for sharing risk could include: capitation with partial refunds or supplements if billed hospital charges or costs differ from capitated payments, and service or discharge-based payments with withholds and bonus payouts that depend on expenditure targets.

SECTION D
TOTAL FACILITY BEDS, UTILIZATION, FINANCES, AND STAFFING

Instructions and Definitions

For the purposes of this survey, nursing home type unit/facility provides care for the elderly and chronic care in a non-acute setting in any of the following categories: *Skilled nursing care *Intermediate care *Other Long-term Care (*see page 15 definitions)The nursing home type units/facilities are to be owned and operated by the hospital. Only one legal entity may be vested with title to the physical property or operate under the authority of a duly executed lease of the physical property.

1a. **Total licensed beds** is the total number of beds authorized by the state licensing (certifying agency).

b. Report the number of **beds** regularly available (those **set up and staffed for use**) at the end of the reporting period. Report only operating beds, not constructed bed capacity. Include all bed facilities that are set up and staffed for use by inpatients that have no other bed facilities, such as pediatric bassinets, isolation units, quiet rooms, and reception and observation units assigned to or reserved for them. Exclude newborn bassinets and bed facilities for patients receiving special procedures for a portion of their stay and who have other bed facilities assigned to or reserved for them. Exclude, for example, labor room, post anesthesia, or postoperative recovery room beds, psychiatric holding beds, and beds that are used only as holding facilities for patients prior to their transfer to another hospital.

c. Report the number of normal newborn **bassinets**. Do not include neonatal intensive care or intermediate care bassinets. These should be reported on page 2, C6 and C7.

d. Total **births** should exclude fetal deaths.

e. Include the number of adult and pediatric **admissions** only (exclude births). This figure should include all patients admitted during the reporting period, including neonatal and swing admissions.

f. Report the number of adult and pediatric **days of care** rendered during the entire reporting period. Do not include days of care rendered for normal infants born in the hospital, but do include those for their mothers. Include days of care for infants born in the hospital and transferred into a neonatal care unit. Also include swing bed inpatient days. **Inpatient day** of care (also commonly referred to as a **patient day** or a **census day**, or by some federal hospitals as an **occupied bed day**) is a period of service between the census-taking hours on two successive calendar days, the day of discharge being counted only when the patient was admitted the same day.

g. **Emergency department visits** should reflect the number of visits to the emergency unit. Emergency outpatients can be admitted to the inpatient areas of the hospital, but they are still counted as emergency visits and subsequently as inpatient admissions.

h. An **Outpatient visit** is a visit by a patient who is not lodged in the hospital while receiving medical, dental, or other services. Each appearance of an outpatient in each unit constitutes one visit regardless of the number of diagnostic and/or therapeutic treatments that the patient receives. Total outpatient visits should include all clinic visits, referred visits, observation services, outpatient surgeries (also reported on line D1J), home health service visits, and emergency department visits (also reported on line D1g).

Clinic visits should reflect total number of visits to each specialized medical unit that is responsible for the diagnosis and treatment of patients on an outpatient, nonemergency basis (i.e., alcoholism, dental, gynecology, etc.). Visits to the satellite clinics and primary group practices should be included if revenue is received by the hospital.

Referred visits should reflect total number of outpatient ancillary visits to each specialty unit of the hospital established for providing technical aid used in the diagnosis and treatment of patients. Examples of such units are diagnostic radiology, EKG, pharmacy, etc.

Observation services are those services furnished on a hospital's premises, including use of a bed and periodic monitoring by a hospital's nursing or other staff, which are reasonable and necessary to evaluate an outpatient's condition or determine the need for a possible admission to the hospital as an inpatient. Observation services usually do not exceed 24 hours. However, there is no hourly limit on the extent to which they may be used.

Home health service visits are visits by home health personnel to a patient's residence.

i. **Inpatient surgical operation.** Count each patient undergoing surgery as one surgical operation regardless of the number of surgical procedures that were performed while the patient was in the operating or procedure room.

j. **Operating room.** A unit/room of a hospital or other health care facility in which surgical procedures requiring anesthesia are performed.

k. **Outpatient surgical operation.** For outpatient surgical operations, please record operations performed on patients who do not remain in the hospital overnight. Include all operations whether performed in the inpatient operating rooms or in procedure rooms located in an outpatient facility. Include an endoscopy only when used as an operative tool and not when used for diagnosis alone.Count each patient undergoing surgery as one surgical operation regardless of the number of surgical procedures that were performed while the patient was in the operating or procedure room.

2a2. **Managed Care Medicare Discharges.** A discharge day where a Medicare Managed Care Plan is the source of payment.
2b2. **Managed Care Medicare Inpatient Days.** An inpatient day where a Medicare Managed Care Plan is the source of payment.
2c2. **Managed Care Medicaid Discharges.** A discharge day where a Medicaid Managed Care Plan is the source of payment.
2d2. **Managed Care Medicaid Inpatient Days.** An inpatient day where a Medicaid Managed Care Plan is the source of payment.
3a. **Net patient revenue.** Reported at the estimated net realizable amounts from patients, third-party payors, and others for services rendered, including estimated retroactive adjustments under reimbursement agreements with third-party payors. Retroactive adjustments are accrued on an estimated basis in the period the related services are rendered and adjusted in future periods, as final settlements are determined.
3b. **Tax appropriations.** A predetermined amount set aside by the government from its taxing authority to support the operation of the hospital.
c. **Other operating revenue.** Revenue from services other than health care provided to patients, as well as sales and services to nonpatients. Revenue that arises from the normal day-to-day operations from services other than health care provided to patients. Includes sales and services to nonpatients, and revenue from miscellaneous sources (rental of hospital space, sale of cafeteria meals, gift shop sales). Also include operating gains in this category.

d. **Nonoperating revenue.** Includes investment income, extraordinary gains and other nonoperating gains.

e. **Total revenue.** Add net patient revenue, tax appropriations, other operating revenue and nonoperating revenue.

f. **Payroll expenses.** Include payroll for all personnel including medical and dental residents/interns and trainees.

g. **Employee benefits.** Includes social security, group insurance, retirement benefits, workman's compensation, unemployment insurance, etc.

h. **Depreciation expense (for reporting period only)** report only the depreciation expense applicable to the reporting period. The amount also Should be included in accumulated depreciation(D7b).

i. **Interest expense.** Report interest expense for the reporting period only.

j. **Total expenses.** Includes all payroll and non-payroll expenses (including bad debt) as well as any nonoperating losses (including extraordinary losses).

4a. **Total gross inpatient revenue.** The hospitals full-established rates(charges) for all services rendered to inpatients.

4b. **Total gross outpatient revenue.** The hospitals full-established rates(charges) for all services rendered to outpatients.

4c. **Total gross patient revenue.** Total gross patient revenue (add total gross inpatient revenue and total gross outpatient revenue).

5. **Uncompensated care.** Care for which no payment is expected or no charge is made. It is the sum of bad debt and charity care absorbed by a hospital or other health care organization in providing medical care for patients who are uninsured or are unable to pay.

5a. **Bad debt expense.** The provision for actual or expected uncollectibles resulting from the extension of credit. Because bad debts are reported as an expense and not a deduction from revenue, the gross charges that result in bad debts will remain in net revenue (D3a).

5b. **Charity care.** Health services that were never expected to result in cash inflows. Charity care results from a provider's policy to provide health care services free of charge to individuals who meet certain financial criteria. For purposes of this survey, charity care is measured on the basis of revenue forgone, at full-established rates.

6a1 **Medicare.** Should agree with the Medicare utilization reported in questions D2a1-Db2.

6a1a **Routine patient revenue.** Include traditional Medicare fee-for-service.

6a1c.**Total.** Medicare revenue (add Medicare routine patient revenue and Medicare managed care revenue).

6a2. **Medicaid.** Should agree with Medicaid utilization reported in questions D2c1-D2d2.

6a2a.**Routine patient revenue.** Include Medicaid disproportionate payments under Medicaid routine patient care (2a), in the net column (2).

6a2c.**Total** Medicaid revenue (add Medicaid routine Patient revenue and Medicaid managed care revenue).

6c. **Total** revenue (gross should equal D4c and net should equal D3a).

7. **Fixed Assets.** Represent land and physical properties that are consumed or used in the creation of economic activity by the health care entity. The historical or acquisition costs are used in recording fixed assets. Net plant, property, and equipment represent the original costs of these items less accumulated depreciation and amortization.

7d. **Gross Square Footage:** Include all inpatient, outpatient, office, and support space used for or in support of your health care activities. Exclude exterior, roof, and garage space in the figure.

8. **Capital Expenses.** Expenses used to acquire assets, including buildings, remodeling projects, equipment, or property.

9. **Energy Consumption.**

   a. **Total energy usage includes electricity, natural gas, fuel oil, district stream, district chilled water, diesel (no. 2) and coal. Total energy usage is the sum of all MMBTUs.**

CONVERSION CHART TO MMBTU:

Electric	Number of kW h x .0034 = Number of MMBTU
Natural Gas	Number of Therms x .1 = Number of MMBTU
	or
	Number of MCF x 1.03 = Number of MMBTU

   b. **Energy Star rating is a** national energy performance rating system, which utilizes a 1-100 scale to give meaning to the energy usage. To qualify, each building must meet specific guidelines in four areas: energy performance; thermal comfort; indoor air quality; illumination levels.

10. **Information Technology.**

   i. **IT Operating expense.** Exclude department depreciation and operating dollars paid against capital leases.

   j. **IT Capital expense.** Include IT capital expense for the current year only. Any capital expense that is carried forward from the previous year should be excluded from this figure. Include IT related capital included in the budget of other departments. (i.e. lab, radiology, etc., if known or can be reasonably estimated.) Include the total value of capital leases to be signed in the current year.

   k. **Number of Employed IT staff (in FTEs).** Number of full-time equivalent (FTE) staff employed in the IT department/organization and on the hospital payroll.

   l. **Total number of outsourced IT staff.** (i.e. contracted staff).

   m. **Electronic Health Record.** An electronic health record (EHR) integrates electronically originated and maintained patient-level clinical health information, derived from multiple sources, into one point of access. An EHR replaces the paper medical record as the primary source of patient information.

STAFFING

11. **Full-Time Equivalent (FTE)** is the total number of hours worked by all employees over the full (12 month) reporting period divided by the normal number of hours worked by a full-time employee for that same time period. For example, if your hospital considers a normal workweek for a full-time employee to be 40 hours, a total of 2,080 would be worked over a full year (52 weeks). If the total number of hours worked by all employees on the payroll is 208,000, then the number of Full-Time Equivalents (FTE) is 100 (employees). The FTE calculation for a specific occupational category such as Registered nurses is exactly the same. The calculation for each occupational category should be based on the number of hours worked by staff employed in that specific category.

   a. **Physicians and dentists.** Include only those physicians and dentists engaged in clinical practice and on the payroll. Those who hold administrative positions should be reported in "All other personnel."

   c. **Other trainees.** A trainee is a person who has not completed the necessary requirements for certification or met the qualifications required for full salary under a related occupational category. Exclude medical and dental residents/interns who should be reported on line 7b.

   d. **Registered nurses.** Nurses who have graduated from approved schools of nursing and who are currently registered by the state. They are responsible for the nature and quality of all nursing care that patients receive. Do not include any registered nurses more appropriately reported in other occupational categories, such as facility administrators, and therefore listed under "All other personnel."

   e. **Licensed practical (vocational) nurses.** Nurses who have graduated from an approved school of practical (vocational) nursing who work under the supervision of registered nurses and/or physicians.

   f. **Nursing assistive personnel.** Certified nursing assistant or equivalent unlicensed staff assigned to patient care units and reporting to nursing.

   g. **Radiology Technicians.** Technical positions in imaging fields, including, but not limited to, radiology, sonography, nuclear medicine, radiation therapy, CT, MRI.

   h. **Laboratory professional/technical.** Professional and technical positions in all areas of the laboratory, including, but not limited to, histology, phlebotomy, microbiology, pathology, chemistry, etc.

   i. **Pharmacists, licensed.** Persons licensed within the state who are concerned with the preparation and distribution of medicinal products.

   j. **Pharmacy technicians.** Persons who assist the pharmacist with selected activities, including medication profile reviews for drug incompatibilities, typing labels and prescription packaging, handling of purchase records and inventory control.

   l. **All other personnel.** This should include all other personnel not already accounted for in other categories.

   m. **Total facility personnel.** This line is to include the total facility personnel - hospital plus nursing home type unit/facility personnel (for those hospitals that own and operate a nursing home type unit/facility).

   n. **Nursing home type unit/facility personnel.** This line should be filled out only by hospitals that own and operate a nursing home type unit/facility, where only one legal entity is vested with title to the physical property or operates under the authority of a duly executed lease of the physical property. If nursing home type unit/facility personnel are reported on the total facility personnel line, but cannot be broken out, please write "cannot break out" on this line.

12a. **Hospitalist.** Physician whose primary professional focus is the care of hospitalized medical patients (through clinical, education, administrative and research activity).

   c. **Independent provider group.** A private practitioner or hospitalist only or a hospitalist management company.
   Employed by your hospital. Either as direct hospital employees or as employees of a hospital subsidiary corporation.
   Employed by a physician group. A multi-specialty group, a primary care group, an emergency physician group, or an IPA.
   Employed by a university or school program. Either as a university/medical school employee or as an employee of a university-based group practice.
   Other. e.g., an insurance company, HMO.

13a. **Intensivists.** Board-certified physicians who are additionally certified in the subspecialty of critical care medicine; or physicians board-certified in emergency medicine who have completed a critical care fellowship in an ACGME accredited program; or physicians board-certified in Medicine, Anesthesiology, Pediatrics or Surgery who completed training prior to the availability of subspecialty certification in critical care and who have provided at least six weeks of full-time ICU care annually since 1987.

14a. **Foreign-educated nurses.** Individuals who are foreign born and received basic nursing education in a foreign country. In general many of these nurses come to the US on employment-based visas which allow them to obtain a green card.

SECTION E. SUPPLEMENTAL INFORMATION
DEFINITIONS

1a. **Mission statement.** A general statement that describes a company's reason for existence, its vision and direction, its areas of expertise and its goals.

1h. **Self-assessment.** An evaluation of an organization's management system through achievements in areas such as: leadership, strategic planning, human resource management, information management, process management, customer focus and satisfaction, and business results.

1i. **Health status indicators.** Measures used to quantify various aspects of a populations health status.

2c. **Leadership development program.** A program that is designed to increase the leadership skills of manager level personnel for eventual placement in a more senior level position. This program focuses on two classes of personnel. Of greatest importance is the Mid-careerist that has been working in a hospital setting for 7-12 years and is stuck at the Manger level. The other category of a good Leadership Development program focuses on increasing the number of minorities at the Senior Executive level. This would include all titles *above* Department Director, including Administrator, Associate Administrator, and the various levels of Vice President.

2d. **Diversity plan.** A set of goals and objectives that are linked to the organization's Strategic Plan to promote the elimination of disparities and identify strategies to ensure the ethnic and racial composition of the workforce better reflects the composition of the communities being served.

2e. **Leadership Succession planning.** The deliberate use of mentoring, coaching and grooming of individuals inside the organization that have been identified as having the potential to advance when vacancies occur at the senior executive level.

2f. **Career development resources.** Tools, training programs, financial aid, executive coaching and other resources that can be used to prepare individuals to compete for advancement opportunities in an organization.

3a. **Satellite facility(s).** Satellite Services are available at a facility geographically remote from the hospital campus.